FUNDAMENTALS OF CHEMICAL ENGINEERING

CHARLES M. THATCHER

Professor of Chemical Engineering
and Chairman of the Department,
Pratt Institute — Brooklyn, New York

CHARLES E. MERRILL BOOKS, INC.

Columbus, Ohio

To J. C. Brier

for many years of encouragement and friendship

Photograph and color separation,
courtesy of Petrochemicals Department,
Gulf Oil Corporation

William E. Frost, *jacket and cover design*

Library of Congress Catalog Card Number: 62-9237*

Printed in the United States of America

PREFACE

This book presents the fundamentals of chemical engineering in an introductory but quantitative manner. Its purpose is to provide the prospective chemical engineer with a firm foundation for further development in his chosen field by making him aware of *all* its aspects, so as to leave him both better prepared and better motivated for a meaningful learning experience. It is also intended to initiate the development of those skills which are so essential to his immediate and ultimate success: the ability to reason logically and independently, to make quantitative calculations, and to exercise engineering judgment.

Just as the practicing engineer is often called upon to submit a quick, approximate solution to a comprehensive problem, so this book is a first approximation to the study of chemical engineering. Its scope is wholly consistent with this role, depth of treatment having been made subordinate to breadth. This is not to say that the treatment is superficial. The development of basic principles—the mass balance, first and second law thermodynamics, the rate concept, and economic considerations—is rigorous and complete, and the quantitative application of these principles in the solution of practical problems is repeatedly exemplified. But, like all engineering approximations, the book leaves many details for subsequent consideration.

The first four chapters identify the types of problems the chemical engineer is expected to solve, the nature of the specialized knowledge he applies in solving such problems, and the qualitative and quantitative methods he utilizes in effecting their solution. The basic principles listed above are successively emphasized in the middle chapters, which also include a discussion of properties and property relationships. In the concluding chapters the analysis and solution of comprehensive problems pertaining to various unit operations and complex chemical processes are given primary attention.

The author is deeply indebted to Prof. H. Y. Krinsky for his painstaking review of the manuscript and for the many valuable suggestions which resulted. Gratitude is also due the students in the chemical engineering classes of 1962 and 1963 at Pratt Institute. Their reaction to the use of the book as a classroom text in note form led to many significant improvements.

C. M. Thatcher

CONTENTS

v

PART II
Properties and Property Relationships   101

PART III

Chemical Engineering Design and Analysis   217

PART I

Introduction to Chemical Engineering

Most readers of this text have already decided upon chemical engineering as a career. Unfortunately, the choice of any career is all too frequently based on inaccurate or incomplete information. Even those who consider themselves to be well informed may actually have little more than a very vague idea of what a chemical engineer is and does. Therefore, this introductory examination of the profession will insure that all readers are equally well prepared for the more advanced material which follows.

A chemical engineer can be characterized by the type of problems he is expected to solve, by the specialized knowledge he applies in solving such problems, and, in common with other branches of engineering, by the method he uses in effecting their solution. The first three chapters of this book detail each of these characteristic features in turn. The fourth chapter considers the adroit use of quantitative numerical calculations in chemical engineering.

1

CHAPTER 1

Definition of Chemical Engineering

Chemical engineering is closely related to the field of pure chemistry on the one hand, and to its sister branches of engineering on the other. The latter relationship properly deserves initial attention, for the chemical engineer is first and foremost an engineer. It will accordingly be advantageous to characterize the profession of engineering in general before prefixing the adjective "chemical." With the chemical engineer's identity as an engineer well established, we can then examine his role as a chemical specialist within the field of engineering.

1.1 The Engineering Profession

Even engineers themselves are not in complete agreement as to the proper definition of engineering. Fortunately, an official definition has recently been proposed by the Engineers' Council for Professional Development:*

"Engineering is the Profession in which a knowledge of the mathematical and natural sciences gained by study, experience and practice is applied with judgment to develop ways to utilize, economically, the materials and forces of nature for the progressive well being of mankind."

---

* Engineers' Council for Professional Development, "26th Annual Report for the Year Ending September 30, 1958" (report of the Recognition Committee).

A paraphrase of this carefully worded statement is inadvisable, but it is convenient to examine certain aspects of the definition separately and at greater length in the development which follows, thereby providing some amplification of this basic definition of engineering. In the meantime it is suggested that the definition itself be reread carefully and thoughtfully.

It is helpful to identify more specifically the sciences referred to in the above definition. Mathematics, physics, and chemistry head the list of *basic* sciences. Less obvious (in terms of their importance to engineering) are such fields as geology, astronomy, and biology, but they are also included. Indeed, a knowledge of one or more of these secondary sciences is of critical importance in many specialized areas of engineering activity.

Attendant on the basic sciences is the field of *engineering* science, considered to be of fundamental importance even though it generally involves the *application* of basic concepts. An evaluation of engineering education by a committee of the American Society for Engineering Education resulted in a suggested breakdown of engineering science into six rather broad areas of subject matter:*

1) Mechanics of solids (statics, dynamics, and strength of materials).
2) Fluid mechanics.
3) Thermodynamics.
4) Transfer and rate mechanisms or processes (heat, mass, and momentum transfer).
5) Electrical theory (fields, circuits, electronics).
6) Nature and properties of materials (relating atomic, particle, and aggregate structure to properties).

It is patently impossible for any one person to assimilate a depth of knowledge in all areas of basic and engineering science. The obvious alternative is to specialize, and it is this practice which accounts for the existence of the various branches of engineering. Thus the electrical engineer is primarily concerned with electrical theory; the mechanical engineer with mechanics, thermodynamics, and heat transfer; the aeronautical engineer with fluid mechanics and thermodynamics; and so on.

The utilization of engineers in industry follows the same pattern, for the birth and growth of each of the major branches of engineering is a direct consequence of industry's need for a particular type of engineering specialist. In summary, then, each branch of engineering can be identified by those areas of science with which it is primarily concerned, and also by the corresponding areas of industry in which this specialized knowledge is applied.

---

* American Society for Engineering Education, "Report on Evaluation of Engineering Education," June 15, 1955.

1.2 The Chemical Branch of Engineering

Chemical change in industrial processes has increased prodigiously in importance since the turn of the century. This development is perhaps most readily associated with the so-called chemical process industries; but the petroleum, food, paper, rubber, drug, and primary metals industries are typical examples of major industries which have also been affected. Even the automotive industry, generally considered to be the domain of mechanical and automotive engineers, depends on chemical processes for: tires, glass, lightweight metals, plastic materials, fuels and lubricants, paints and lacquers, and chemical specialties such as rust inhibitors and permanent anti-freeze.

Although all branches of engineering are firmly based on the underlying sciences of mathematics and physics, chemical engineering is unique because of its equally strong dependence on the science of chemistry. In the areas of engineering science, the chemical engineer gives special attention to fluid mechanics, thermodynamics, transfer processes, and the nature and properties of materials. This broad background makes him particularly well suited to handle not only those engineering problems specifically pertaining to chemistry, but all related non-chemical problems as well.

To substantiate this assertion, we need only note the dependence upon chemical engineering characterizing all industrial manufacturing processes in which chemical changes are involved: the development and operation of all phases, physical as well as chemical, of such processes are for the most part the responsibility of the chemical engineer. Since chemical change is involved in the manufacture of almost all products of importance, the tremendous potential of chemical engineering is clearly indicated.

1.3 The Realm of the Chemist

Sketchy though it be, the foregoing development should suffice to give an adequate understanding, for the present at least, of what chemical engineering is and how it differs from its sister branches of engineering. Let us now examine the other side of the family tree, i.e., the relationship between chemical engineering and chemistry. It will then be possible to present a more detailed job description for the chemical engineer.

At first glance, the definition of engineering presented earlier would seem to include chemistry as well. Careful scrutiny discloses ample grounds for excluding it, but it is indeed true that there is a close kinship between chemistry and chemical engineering. As a matter of fact, chemical engineers were originally known as industrial chemists, and this term still persists to some extent outside the United States.

The implication that chemical engineering is merely a specialty within the field of chemistry—as are physical and organic chemistry, for example—is most unfortunate. The chemical engineer is first and foremost an engineer and only secondarily a chemical specialist. The chemist, on the other hand, is not an engineer at all. The distinction can best be emphasized by means of a hypothetical example.

Consider a chemist carrying out a typical organic synthesis in an industrial laboratory: He pours liquid A into a flask and sets the flask over a burner to heat it. When conditions are right, he bubbles gas B through the liquid until the resulting reaction stops and then sets the flask aside to cool. His next step is to add a second liquid, C, while vigorously agitating the contents of the flask, thereupon obtaining a precipitate. The contents of the flask are next emptied into a filtering funnel, after which the wet solid residue is scraped off the filter paper onto a watch glass and evaporated to dryness. The yield is approximately one gram of final product D.*

When the chemist makes tests to determine the properties of compound D, his findings indicate that the compound has potential applications as a pharmaceutical. After a market study, the company decides to put the compound into commercial production at a rate of one ton per day. (This rate, while not unrealistic for a pharmaceutical, is actually quite low when compared to typical rates of production in other industries. Rates upwards of 50 tons per day are typical for many chemical intermediates, and plants which turn out hundreds of tons per day of heavy inorganic chemicals are not uncommon.)

A simple calculation will show that the proposed rate represents the scale-up of the chemist's original one-gram batch by a factor of more than 900,000. Even assuming that the chemist and his colleagues might turn out as many as 1,000 batches in a 24-hour day, it would be necessary for them to increase the size of their flasks, burners, filtering funnels, etc., by a factor of more than 900. The conclusion is inescapable: the bench-scale techniques of the chemist, however effective they may be in making original and exploratory investigations, are entirely unsuited for large-scale production.

---

* The process described is for the most part coincident with that used to prepare 2,4,6-tripropyl-*s*-trithiane-trisulfone from butyraldehyde, hydrogen sulfide, and aqueous hydrogen peroxide. The specific identification of these compounds is not essential, and could actually detract from clarity and simplicity to the extent that it would require the repeated use of complex and unfamiliar organic nomenclature. Hypothetical reactions are used freely in this text because they can be carefully tailored to illustrate specific points. Equivalent reactions do almost invariably exist in fact.

1.4 Chemical Engineering vs. Chemistry

The foregoing correctly implies that the problems involved in producing a chemical compound on a commercial scale lie beyond the knowledge and skill of the laboratory chemist. The engineering background of the chemical engineer, on the other hand, is a significant additional qualification. It therefore falls to him to convert the chemist's laboratory-scale synthesis into full-scale production.

Mere scale-up is not the only challenge to be faced, however. The company's—and hence the engineer's—ultimate objective is not to make compound D but rather to make a profit. This motive is hardly as materialistic as it may sound, for it is a basic tenet in our system of free enterprise. In any event the chemical engineer must devise a process which will produce large quantities of compound D *economically*. Recall that this word appears in the definition of engineering, and that it automatically excludes the chemist: his sole objective is to make compound D, not money.

The difference between laboratory-scale and plant-scale production, even when coupled with the fact that the chemical engineer must satisfy economic restrictions not imposed on the chemist, may appear to be a trivial distinction between the fields of chemistry and chemical engineering. Actually, the detailed process ultimately specified by the chemical engineer may differ radically from that originally used by the chemist. Each point of departure introduces problems which are, for the most part, totally different from those faced by the chemist. It is this difference which justifies the existence of chemical engineering as a separate profession.

1.5 Design of a Production Process

By way of preparation for an analysis of the chemical engineering problems involved in the design of a plant for the large-scale, economical production of compound D, let us summarize the procedure followed by the chemist. The *schematic flow diagram* shown in Fig. 1.1 serves this purpose.

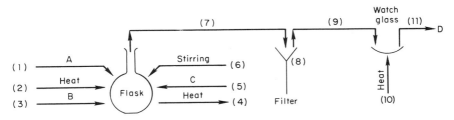

Fig. 1.1 Schematic flow diagram for the laboratory synthesis of product D from reactants A, B, and C.

The numbers in the figure denote the order in which the chemist performed the various steps. The flask is heated in step (2), for example, while the cooling operation which followed the initial chemical reaction is shown as the removal of heat in step (4).

The basis for the chemical engineer's responsibility for physical as well as chemical operations is readily apparent in Fig. 1.1. Even if we argue that the first six steps are intimately associated with chemical reactions, we see that no chemistry whatsoever is involved once the second reaction in the flask is completed. Since purely physical operations are clearly an integral part of the entire chemical synthesis, it is not surprising that a significant portion of the chemical engineer's time is devoted to what can properly be called non-chemical problems.

The continuous process. One of the major economic considerations in planning any production facility is the cost of labor. The *batch* techniques of the chemist are particularly disadvantageous in this respect. Even though a plant can be equipped with automatic timing devices to open and close valves and for other similar purposes, considerable human supervision is necessary to insure satisfactory operation. As a consequence, batch processing is largely restricted to small-scale operations or to situations in which extremely careful control is essential. Most modern chemical processing plants are designed for *continuous* rather than batch operation.

The basic features of a continuous or *flow* process can best be identified by illustration: Suppose that two liquids react when mixed together and that the reaction is complete in ten seconds. If the liquids enter one end of a 10-foot length of pipe and flow through the pipe at a rate of one foot per second, we might expect the reaction to be complete when the mixture emerged at the other end of the pipe ten seconds later. In actual operation, then, we might continuously feed the reactants into one end of the pipe and obtain a continuous product stream at the other.

This illustration might also include a description of other types of continuous reactors, but at this point it is only necessary to point out that carrying out a chemical reaction on a continuous basis is entirely practicable. In passing, note that the *quantity* of material to be reacted will provide the basis for selecting the proper pipe diameter in the example cited.

It should be emphasized that the ultimate bases for deciding between a batch and a continuous process are the comparative costs for the complete operation, i.e., the cost of equipment, labor, utilities, etc. In practice it may be necessary to investigate both types of process before a final decision can be made. For purposes of our illustration, we will assume that a continuous process has been decided upon, since this will introduce typical problems which might otherwise be avoided.

Preliminary design. A flow diagram for the continuous production of compound D is shown in Fig. 1.2. Note that it is equivalent in every respect to the corresponding diagram for the chemist's batch process. Simple rectangles, appropriately labeled, have been used to represent most of the

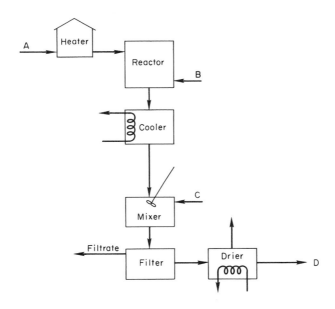

Fig. 1.2   Preliminary flow diagram for the continuous production of compound *D*.

major elements of the process. A more detailed representation is impracticable, for we are not yet prepared to specify either particular types or sizes of equipment.

On the other hand, some symbolism is conventionally used in flow diagrams even in the preliminary stages of the design. Three common symbols—the house representing a heater of the furnace type, the coil symbolizing heat removal or addition, and the propeller denoting agitation—appear in Fig. 1.2. Their use indicates the need for heating, cooling, and agitating equipment of whatever design and does not imply any particular type of device.

A feasible method for carrying out a chemical reaction on a continuous basis has already been described, and the student should be able to envision suitable methods for continuous heating, cooling, and mixing. Continuous filtration and drying provide a greater challenge to ingenuity. The design of special equipment for such purposes is another responsibility of the chemical engineer and will be considered at greater length later in this chapter.

Design modifications. The chemist's batch synthesis has now been replaced with a continuous process, but the design is still far from complete. In his efforts to produce compound D as economically as possible, the chemical engineer must strive for maximum economy in three separate but related areas: materials, energy, and manpower. Let us consider each of these in turn.

When the chemist bubbled gas B through the liquid in his flask, he paid little attention to the unreacted gas which escaped to the laboratory hood. Multiply this gas loss by the scale-up factor of 900,000 and it is easy to see why the chemical engineer cannot afford to be so unconcerned. Accordingly, he modifies the process to provide for the recovery of the unreacted gas so that it may be recycled back into the reactor feed stream.

The chemist also casually discarded his filtrate, little caring that it contained some unreacted A. Not so the chemical engineer. Again he takes cognizance of the scale-up factor and decides that the recovery and reuse of unreacted A is necessary. The resulting process modification presumably must include additional processing equipment to remove undesirable by-products of the reactions before the unreacted A can be recycled.

Turning to a consideration of energy, the chemical engineer notes that both heating and cooling are involved in the process. The cooling can be accomplished by circulating cold water through the coils (or their equivalent), but cold A might be equally satisfactory. If so, there is little point in spending extra money for water. Further, less fuel will be needed for the heater since the entering A will already have been heated to some extent by the heat picked up in the cooler. The engineer accordingly provides for *heat exchange* between the stream leaving the reactor and the feed stream of cold A en route to the heater.

In all but the simplest of processes there are usually numerous opportunities to specify heat exchange as a means of reducing utilities costs. The chemical engineer must consider all of them if he is to attain his goal of production at minimum cost. This is not to say that heat exchange is prescribed in every possible case. It can be justified only when there is a net reduction in cost. In our illustration, heat might be recovered from the vapor stream leaving the drier, but the amount would be small. It is unlikely that the cost of installing and maintaining an additional heat exchanger could be recovered.

As for economy of manpower, the use of continuous rather than batch processing has already effected a considerable saving. The extensive use of automatic instrumentation reduces labor costs even further, and it logically follows that the specification of the necessary instruments, their locations, and their tie-in with the process is also the responsibility of the chemical engineer.

Miscellaneous considerations. Although the end is now in sight, the chemical engineer still has work to do before he can consider the process design to be completed. Let us first take up what might be termed an optional problem and then finish with three others which are generally essential:

1) The chemist started his synthesis by reaching for a bottle of reagent-grade *A* sitting on the laboratory shelf, but the chemical engineer needs *A* in tank-car lots. Even though some other company is willing to supply it—thereby making its own profit, of course—it may be more economical to start with *A* of some lesser purity and include purification facilities in the plant design. In any event, it is frequently necessary to start with raw materials which do not meet all of the required specifications, and pre-treating facilities must be provided.

To carry this consideration one step further, it may even be advisable to eliminate *A* as a raw material and to seek instead other materials from which *A* itself can be synthesized. How far back the chemical engineer goes to reach a suitable starting point for the entire process generally depends on such considerations as the nature and extent of the company's other operations, the availability of investment capital, and the dependability of outside sources of supply. In our illustration, the chemist's original laboratory research might well have been prompted by the fact that the company's other operations were already producing *A* for direct sale, and the company anticipated an unfavorable change in the market.

2) In any continuous process the breakdown of some minor piece of equipment might conceivably force the shutdown of the entire plant. To guard against such eventualities, the chemical engineer provides for storage facilities at key points in the process. For example, were a storage tank to be inserted between the cooler and the mixer shown in Fig. 1.2, the filter, mixer, or drier could be shut down for repairs without affecting the operation of the reactor, for the reactor effluent could be sent to temporary storage. Similarly, a reserve stock in the storage tank would permit continued operation of the mixer, filter, and drier in the event of a reactor breakdown or upset.

The operation of the plant is just as vulnerable to interruptions in the supply of raw materials, and storage facilities for an adequate supply of *A*, *B*, and *C* are also necessary. Finally, batch rather than continuous processing may be advisable in some parts of the plant, and the need for storage both before and after any batch operations should be obvious. This might be the case in reprocessing the filtrate in our illustration, if the quantity of filtrate is not sufficient to make continuous processing economical.

3) Provision for the movement of materials from one part of the plant to another is also the responsibility of the chemical engineer. Even when full use is made of gravity flow or supply pressure (for the flow of cooling

water or fuel to the furnace, for example), it is necessary to specify numerous pumps for liquid flow, compressors or blowers for gas flow, and conveyors of various types for solids handling.

The fact that such mechanical devices are specified by the chemical engineer requires explanation. The mechanical engineer is eventually called in to design the actual equipment; but it is up to the chemical engineer to decide what units are needed, where they are to be located, the required capacity, and the quantities of electricity or steam which are needed to drive them.

4) In our illustration it is necessary to arrange for natural gas or fuel oil for the furnace, electricity for pump motors, steam or hot gas for the drier, water for cooling and fire fighting, and even a sewer system for the disposal of waste material. Even though these auxiliary facilities do not normally appear on the basic flow diagram for the process, they cannot be overlooked. Their design and specification logically fall to the chemical engineer.

In times past waste disposal might have meant dumping waste into a nearby river, or perhaps discharging gaseous waste directly to the atmosphere. For modern plants, anti-pollution legislation usually prohibits such a simple solution to the problem. The chemical engineer may therefore find it necessary to provide extensive waste-treating facilities to render the material ultimately discharged by the plant non-objectionable.

Secondary streams produced in the course of manufacturing a primary product often contain valuable components, and the further processing of such streams for the recovery of by-products may be considered to be an integral part of the primary process. Potential waste streams are always examined from this viewpoint. If extra processing yields a product which can be recovered and sold or put to good use in some way, so much the better.

Summary. We have come a long way from the original flow diagram shown in Fig.1.2, and it is helpful at this point to summarize the many modifications and additions which were found to be necessary:

1) Unreacted B is to be recovered and recycled.

2) The filtrate leaving the filter is to be processed to recover unreacted A, which will also be recycled.

3) Heat is to be exchanged between the stream leaving the reactor and the stream of A being fed to the heater.

4) Extensive automatic instrumentation is to be provided, although this does not ordinarily appear on the primary flow diagram.

5) We assume that facilities for the pre-treatment of raw material A are necessary.

6) Intermediate storage facilities are to be provided between the cooler and the mixer. Feed storage tanks for A, B, and C are also needed.

7) Assuming batch processing of the filtrate stream, a hold-up tank must be provided.

8) All necessary pumps, compressors, blowers, and conveyors are to be specified.

9) Provision is to be made for waste disposal or by-product recovery facilities.

10) Other auxiliary facilities may be required.

Needless to say, the flow diagram of Fig. 1.2 is no longer adequate. The modified process is shown in Fig.1.3, in which the scale and general orientation of Fig. 1.2 has been retained to facilitate comparison. It can be seen at

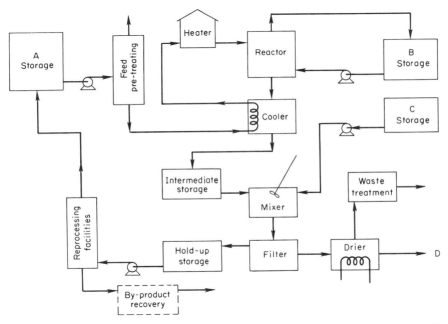

Fig. 1.3 Revised flow diagram for the continuous production of compound *D*.

a glance that the chemical engineer has been a very busy individual indeed. Comparison with Fig. 1.1 is equally informative: is there yet any question as to how the chemical engineer differs from the chemist?

Flow sheet analysis. Many beginning chemical engineers become alarmed at the prospect of analyzing a complex flow diagram. The problem becomes a simple one if it is recognized that the chemical reaction is the key to the entire process. Once the reaction vessel has been identified, the functions of

other process units can be readily deduced. Process units upstream of the
reactor bring the reactor feed to the proper chemical composition, pressure,
temperature, phase, etc., for the reaction. Units following the reactor effect
the separation of the desired product from by-products, waste products, or
unreacted feed.

Branches off the main line of process flow generally lead to facilities for
by-product recovery or waste treatment. These are readily identifiable once
the flow of the primary product has been traced. Recycle of unreacted feed
material is indicated when a "product" stream is returned to the process
ahead of the reactor. Should more than one reaction be involved—as was
the case in our example—the problem can be broken apart and each reaction
considered separately.

The scheme of analysis outlined above will generally make it possible to
deduce the function of the major pieces of equipment shown in a process
flow diagram even if the nomenclature on the diagram is unfamiliar or

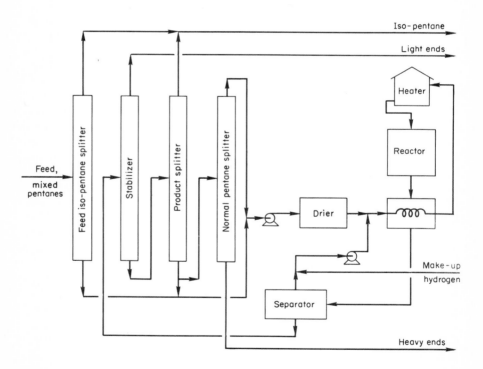

Fig. 1.4 Schematic flow diagram for the production of iso-pentane from mixed
pentanes (iso- plus normal) by isomerization in the presence of hydrogen.

incomplete. The pentane isomerization process depicted in Fig. 1.4 is presented as an exercise in flowsheet analysis. The primary reaction is

$$CH_3—CH_2—CH_2—CH_2—CH_3 \longrightarrow CH_3—CH_2—CH \overset{CH_3}{\underset{CH_3}{}}$$

(normal pentane)   (iso-pentane)

and is carried out in a hydrogen atmosphere. It will be noted that the feed stream entering the plant already contains some iso-pentane.

1.6 Specialization within Chemical Engineering

At this point the prospective chemical engineer may well find himself somewhat overwhelmed by the tremendous scope of his chosen field. If so, he can draw reassurance from the fact that it will not be necessary for him to be an expert in all of the many areas of chemical engineering. The field is characterized by extensive specialization, both with respect to subject matter and with respect to function.

Even the newcomer to chemical engineering should be able to visualize a number of possible areas of specialization by subject matter. In the course of designing our hypothetical plant we found ourselves concerned with chemical reactions, heat exchange, mixing, filtration, drying, instrumentation, and waste disposal, to mention but a few. Every chemical engineer should be familiar with the fundamental principles underlying these and similar operations, but each individual has his choice of one or more in which to become particularly proficient.

The breakdown of chemical engineering into functional fields is presumably less obvious and will be considered at greater length. Even though the beginning student has a few years in which to decide upon a field of major interest, he should be fully aware of the various choices which are open to him. He can then investigate further those which sound most interesting before he must make a final decision.

Process design. The chemical engineer who enters the process design field finds himself specifying sequences of operations for the conversion of given raw materials into desired products much as we have done in the preceding section. Where we made numerous simplifying assumptions, however, the process designer must make detailed calculations to insure that his final design is an economic optimum. His full responsibilities thus extend far beyond the development of a qualitative process flow diagram such as is shown in Fig. 1.3.

As part of his economic evaluation, the process designer must prepare a reasonably accurate estimate of the total capital investment which will be needed to build the plant. This makes it necessary for him to select a specific type of equipment for each operation and to determine the required size or capacity. Eventually he arrives at estimates of the purchased cost of the major pieces of equipment as well as such considerations as the cost of installation, piping, insulation, structural framework, buildings, land purchase and preparation, contractors' fees, and many other pertinent costs.

Operating costs are equally important. In addition to the cost of raw materials, utilities, and labor, the process designer must consider such items as interest on the required capital investment, taxes, insurance, royalties, depreciation, maintenance, and administrative overhead. The total cost of production then provides the basis for estimating the price at which the product must be sold to make the entire venture worthwhile.

It should be apparent that the process designer must be familiar not only with the technical aspects of engineering but with economic principles as well. Versatility is the key to success in the process design field. The chemical engineer who specializes therein need not be a full-fledged economist, but he must definitely be prepared to give the dollar sign full status as an engineering symbol.

Equipment design. Only rarely is the chemical engineer able to make expedient use of large-scale equipment similar to that used by the chemist. The chemist's flask might be replaced by a large tank, for example, but what of the burner, the stirring rod, the filtering funnel and filter paper, the spatula, or the watch glass? Obviously equipment of special design is

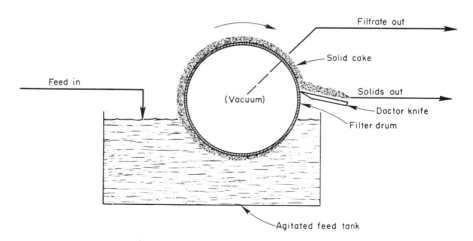

Fig. 1.5 Schematic diagram of a rotary vacuum filter.

required for many operations. The design of large-scale processing equipment therefore becomes a major area of chemical engineering activity.

The continuous rotary vacuum filter shown schematically in Fig. 1.5 is a typical product of the chemical engineer's ingenuity in the field of equipment design. The cylindrical face of the drum is covered with screen or heavy cloth which, like the filter paper used by the chemist, blocks the passage of solid material. With the drum partially submerged in the liquid-solid mixture to be processed, a vacuum is applied inside the drum. This pulls liquid through the filter medium and a cake of solid material builds up on the outside surface of the drum. Rotation of the drum brings the accumulated solids into contact with a *doctor knife* which pares off a layer of the cake, thereby permitting continuous operation.

The ability to design a piece of equipment such as the above-described continuous filter clearly requires a working knowledge of pertinent scientific principles. The importance of mechanical details suggests that the equipment designer should also possess some mechanical aptitude, even though such details may ultimately become the responsibility of the mechanical engineer. Finally, the equipment designer must have an inventive imagination coupled with the ability to recognize those ideas which are most likely to be practicable.

Research. Many chemical engineers are needed in the research field to supplement as well as to complement the efforts of the theoretical scientist. It is natural for the chemical engineer to be active in research pertaining to new processes and processing techniques and equipment, but the pursuit of the unknown often leads him far afield. The research engineer not only joins the quest for new knowledge when the need arises but is quick to identify and follow promising paths of investigation on his own initiative.

The scope of the research field in chemical engineering is circumscribed only by the limits of the researcher's imagination and curiosity. Consider such problems as: the utilization of solar energy, maintaining life in outer space, developing better and more complete methods of automation, replacing organs of the body with artificial substitutes, or even making dentistry truly painless. Obscure as the relationship may be, chemical engineers are making, and will continue to make, significant contributions to the solution of these problems (and others equally diverse). At the same time, problems more directly associated with chemical engineering are no less challenging.

New knowledge is the lifeblood of technological progress, and the importance of systematic research in chemical engineering cannot be overemphasized. Even though many important research accomplishments might be traced to a lucky guess or a flash of inspiration, most advances are attributable to a thorough knowledge of pertinent scientific and engineering principles. Graduate study leading to a doctorate is almost prerequisite to a research career. In addition, the successful research engineer must have patience, perseverance, and the aforementioned characteristics of imagination and curiosity.

Development. The jump from laboratory research to full-scale plant operation is a long one, and no soundly managed company would authorize the expenditure of several million dollars for a new plant solely on the basis of a chemist's success in the laboratory. Instead, the chemist's findings will usually be turned over to one or more chemical engineers for intermediate development. This practice provides for the investigation of aspects of the proposed process which do not logically fall within the scope of chemical laboratory research.

Consider, for example, the fact that the chemist carries out his reactions in spotless glassware. Will the reaction or product purity be affected by the use of a steel reaction vessel? Will corrosion be a problem? Will the change from batch to continuous operation affect the outcome of the reaction? Are the conditions used by the chemist such as pressure, temperature, and concentration equally suited to continuous production? Is it possible to maintain the same temperature uniformity in a large vessel as was achieved by the chemist in his small flask? If not, how will the reaction be affected?

These are but a few of the questions that must be answered by the development engineer. Many problems he cannot foresee, and they become evident only as his work progresses. To insure that no major problems go undetected, the development engineer often builds and operates a small-scale pilot plant in which each step in the proposed production process is carefully reproduced. Any unforeseen difficulties can then be eliminated with only moderate expense, while experimentation will establish the optimum operating conditions for the larger plant to come later.

Since development serves as a bridge between research and process (or equipment) design, the development engineer must have cognizance of both of these areas. The ability to work harmoniously with others is also an important qualification, for development work will generally be a cooperative venture involving engineers, laboratory technicians, and both skilled and unskilled laborers.

Production. Even though the daily operation of a plant is the direct responsibility of skilled and semi-skilled operators, some engineering supervision is essential. This is usually provided by one or two engineers assigned to each major operating unit on a full-time basis. The operation of a complex production facility is never entirely routine, and the production engineer is called upon to solve a wide variety of problems in the course of maintaining an efficient operation. Since these problems may be personal as well as technical, the production engineer must be prepared to exercise leadership and good social judgment along with his technical knowledge.

The production engineer requires additional engineering assistance when major difficulties are encountered. This is a function of the *technical service* group, which constitutes a mobile reserve of technical trouble-shooters. When normal conditions prevail, the technical service engineer generally studies and analyzes the technical aspects of plant operation, seeking improvement in such areas as efficiency of operation and product quality. In this respect he is akin to the development engineer, with data from actual production facilities replacing that obtained from the pilot plant.

Project engineering. Strict adherence to the functional divisions enumerated so far would require that a new process originating with the research group be passed along through the development and process design groups until it finally reached the production stage. Many companies find it advisable to provide for continuity of supervision along the way, and therefore assign one or more project engineers to the process in the early stages of development. The project engineer then follows the project through development, process design, and even plant construction and initial operation, at which point he is available for reassignment to a new project at the developmental level.

Engineering sales. Like his colleagues in research, development, design, and production, the sales engineer is a problem-solver, the distinction being that the problems he solves are those of his customers. The successful sales engineer seeks out problems whose solution will involve the use of his company's product, but he will unhesitatingly recommend an alternative solution when the occasion warrants. In this respect the term *customer service* is perhaps preferable to sales. In the engineering sales field, building customer satisfaction and confidence is far more important than the "hard sell."

The salesman's contacts are, for the most part, technical people like himself. Accordingly, he must have a firm engineering background in those areas related to the use of his product or products, along with such attributes as social charm, personality and tact.

Consulting. Although most chemical engineers work on a salary in industry, many prefer to enter private practice as consultants. Their services are made available on a fee basis to those companies needing them. The establishment of a profitable consulting practice is not easy, and considerable prior experience in industry is usually advisable. If the would-be consultant can make his reputation in some particular field of chemical engineering before setting out on his own, he can look forward to a career which is rewarding financially as well as personally.

Education. The gibe, "Those who can, do; those who can't, teach," has little basis in fact, for probably no field of engineering endeavor is as demanding as teaching. Teaching salaries tend to be lower than those in other fields, but there are compensating advantages. Among other things, the engineering teacher can often supplement his income by engaging in outside consulting activity. More important to most teachers is the feeling of personal satisfaction which the teaching profession affords.

A doctorate is almost a prerequisite to a career in teaching, but it is often possible to begin teaching with a lesser degree and take graduate work while on the job. The availability of teaching assistantships also makes it possible for a student to obtain first-hand confirmation of his interest in and aptitude for teaching. A teaching career deserves the same careful consideration given to other opportunities in chemical engineering, for engineering education must compete with the other fields of specialization for engineering talent.

Other opportunities. Many people with chemical engineering degrees are currently working as nuclear engineers, maintenance engineers, construction engineers, safety engineers, and patent lawyers. All of these fields can make excellent use of a man with a background in chemical engineering. Many important executive positions in industry are also filled by former chemical engineers, indicating that chemical engineering can be a firm stepping-stone to industrial administration and management. The chemical engineer's experience with the overall aspects of processing is particularly advantageous in this respect.

For what it's worth, we will conclude this resume of the many opportunities open to chemical engineers by recalling a national survey, made some years ago, which resulted in the conclusion that chemical engineers make the best husbands. Sic transit gloria!

1.7 Summary

We set out to define chemical engineering and have done so indirectly by citing numerous examples of what the chemical engineer does. In a sense we have been holding out, for a good, one-sentence definition of chemical engineering has been available all along. We trust that the definition is more meaningful at this point than it would have been at the beginning of the chapter.

According to the American Institute of Chemical Engineers,* "Chemical Engineering is defined as the application of the principles of the physical sciences, together with the principles of economics and human relations, to fields that pertain directly to processes and process equipment in which material is treated to effect a change in state, energy content, or composition."

---

* American Institute of Chemical Engineers, Constitution of the Institute.

The use in the definition of the phrase "to effect a change" is particularly noteworthy. Throughout the illustrative example used in this chapter we found ourselves concerned with change: change of chemical composition in the reactor, change of physical composition in the filter and drier, change of temperature, change of pressure, and even change of location (the practical result of pumping). In short, perhaps the most significant characteristic of the chemical engineer is his concern with *change*. It is this concern which provides the basis for the next chapter.

REVIEW, STUDY, AND DISCUSSION

1-1. Define engineering, basic science, engineering science, schematic flow diagram, batch operation, continuous or flow operation, heat exchange, auxiliary facilities, process design, research, development, technical service, project engineering, customer service, chemical engineering.

1-2. What major distinctions separate the fields of chemical engineering and pure chemistry?

1-3. Identify and describe the function of each of the process units shown in Fig. 1.4.

1-4. Describe one or more possible methods for drying a crystalline solid on a continuous basis. What considerations might dictate the use of a specific method?

1-5. List the functional fields of specialization in chemical engineering. Which field is most attractive to you at the present time? Why?

CHAPTER 2

The Engineering Aspects of Change

The word *change* has many different meanings, but one dictionary listing stands out as being particularly applicable to change as it concerns the chemical engineer: ". . . the passing from one place, state, form, or phase to another." Such a qualitative definition, however appropriate, leaves many questions unanswered. If he is to put change to practical use, the chemical engineer must also determine or specify

What changes
How much changes
Which way the change goes
How far it goes
How fast it takes place
How it is or can be effected
How to measure the extent of change
How to control the extent and rate of change
The cost of effecting the change

These, then, are the *engineering* aspects of change, and the competence of the chemical engineer can be measured directly by his ability to deal with them. It is the purpose of this chapter to give quantitative meaning to each of these aspects, thereby preparing the chemical engineering student for detailed analysis and application in his subsequent studies.

WHAT CHANGES

Several examples of *what* can be changed were presented in Chap. 1: chemical composition, physical composition, temperature, pressure, and location. This brief listing might readily be extended to include a substantial number of other properties, such as phase, size, density, or surface tension, but let us first recognize an alternative interpretation to the "what" question:

Consider a gas under pressure in one vessel, connected by suitable piping to a second vessel that is initially evacuated. If gas is permitted to flow from the first vessel into the second, it should be apparent that the *pressure* will change. It is equally apparent, however, that the *gas* will undergo a change. We can therefore make a distinction between the *property* (pressure) which changes and the *system* (the gas) involved in the change.

The terms *system* and *property* are so frequently encountered in chemical engineering that it is advisable to define them formally at this point, in order to avoid any misunderstanding. (A few supplementary definitions will also be helpful.)

2.1 Fundamental Definitions

System. A *system* is "that portion of the universe specifically being considered." Changes of one sort or another are continually occurring in all parts of the universe, but our concern in any particular problem is with specific changes affecting only a limited part of the universe. To eliminate all extraneous considerations, we focus our attention on a particular system, thus facilitating the analysis and solution of the problem.

The remainder of the universe external to the system is referred to as *the surroundings*, and the surroundings are separated from the system by a *boundary*. It should be apparent that the engineer's concern for the surroundings will, for practical purposes, be limited to those which are immediately adjacent to the system.

The deliberate selection of the system upon which calculations will be based is essential in approaching problems involving change. Only rarely will the system be defined automatically by the nature of the problem. The simple gas-flow example cited above illustrates this important point: Taking the gas itself as the system is perhaps an obvious choice; we are equally free to choose the first vessel and its contents, the second vessel and its contents, both vessels plus the gas, that portion of the gas which passes into the second vessel, or that portion of the gas which remains in the first vessel when flow ceases. Clearly the particular system of interest must be specifically defined at the outset of any consideration of change.

A number of adjectives are commonly applied to the term *system* to fit special cases. If no matter enters or leaves the system during the period it is under consideration, we have what is known as a *closed* system. Conversely, if matter does enter or leave, we have an *open* system. Neither matter nor energy cross the boundary of an *isolated* system. Finally, a *homogeneous* system is one in which all properties are everywhere the same, while a *steady-state* system is one in which the properties at any point do not change with time.

An analysis of the operation of a heat exchanger may help to clarify some of these concepts. Let us first take as the system one pound of cooling water flowing through the exchanger: With attention focused on the same pound at all times, the system is clearly closed. It is not isolated, however, for it will receive energy from the surroundings. In view of the resultant temperature rise, it will definitely not be a steady-state system. It will probably not be absolutely homogeneous either, although it may be necessary to assume homogeneity for practical purposes.

The exchanger itself might also be taken as the system, and would constitute an open system. Under normal operation it would also be steady-state, for conditions *at any point in the exchanger* do not change with time, even though the water undergoes change as it flows from point to point. It is necessary to specify normal operation in the foregoing because unsteady-state conditions are obviously encountered when the exchanger is being started up or shut down.

It is suggested that the student decide for himself which of the several systems cited for the gas-flow example are open, closed, isolated, homogeneous, or steady-state. Such considerations are frequently helpful in deciding which system should be selected as a basis for the solution of a given problem.

Property. With the definition and concept of a system firmly in mind, a *property* may be defined as "a distinctive attribute, quality, or observable characteristic of a system." The sum of all the properties of a system then establishes what is referred to as the *state* of the system, defined formally as "the condition or position of a system, referring to and identified through the properties of the system."

Three corollaries of the relationship between properties and state may promote an understanding of these two concepts: (1) All properties are identical for identical states. (2) Any quantity which is fixed by the state alone is a property. (3) Conversely, properties are fixed by the state alone and are therefore not dependent on past history, that is, on the path or process by which the state was established.

It will be convenient to differentiate between properties which depend on the mass or *extent* of the system and those which do not. The former are called *extensive* properties, in contradistinction to *intensive* properties which are *in*dependent of the size or extent of the system. The italicized prefixes call attention to a simple mnemonic scheme for remembering which are which.

Pressure and temperature are typical examples of intensive properties, whereas volume is clearly an extensive property. Note, however, that extensive properties become intensive when they are expressed on a unit-mass basis. Thus *specific* volume, or volume per unit mass, is an intensive property, even though volume (i.e., total volume) itself is extensive. The student can easily reach these conclusions himself by envisioning a quantity of gas and noting which properties differ when a system which includes all the gas is compared with one which includes only half of it.

Process. The term *process* was freely used in Chap. 1, with the assumption that its general meaning was clear. It may now be defined formally as "the mechanism, method, or path by which a system changes from one state to another." As was the case with a system, various adjectives are used to describe particular features:

A *flow* process has to do with an open system, while a *batch* or *unsteady-state* process pertains to a closed system. A *steady-state* process is one which is unchanged with respect to time. An *adiabatic* process is one which occurs without the transfer of heat. Many other types of processes—e.g., cyclic, throttling, isothermal—will be encountered and defined in due course.

Property relationships. Returning to the original question of what can be changed, we might conclude that a proper answer would be, "the properties or states of systems." Equally important, however, are the interrelationships among properties. It is well known, for example, that the temperature of a fixed volume of gas cannot be raised without also causing an increase in pressure. Thus a change in one property may be accompanied by an unavoidable change in another. The latter may have considerable bearing on the acceptability of a solution to any given change problem.

Some rudimentary principles of the relationships among properties will be presented in Chap. 5 to provide a background for the solution of introductory problems. For the most part, however, we must await subsequent courses in physical chemistry and thermodynamics for an adequate treatment of the relation between the physical properties of substances and their chemical composition and transformation.

HOW MUCH CHANGES

At first glance it would seem that the answer to the "how much" question is an integral part of the problem statement. For example, the chemical engineer was specifically told how much compound D was to be produced by the plant he was asked to design in Chap. 1. But does this immediately tell him how much A, B, and C will be required? Does it directly prescribe the amount of moisture to be removed in the drier, or the quantity of fuel to be supplied to the heater?

The answer to these questions is obviously "No." Yet quantitative answers to these and similar questions must be determined before the detailed design of the plant can proceed very far. Indeed, it can be asserted that the first step beyond a qualitative design such as that presented in the first chapter will almost invariably be the consideration of the "how much" question. It should also be noted that the question cannot be restricted to mass or materials but must also take energy into account.

2.2 The Principle of Conservation

Determination of the quantities of matter and energy which are involved in any given change requires only the judicious application of the familiar laws of conservation of matter and energy. Historically, these laws have always been considered to be independent and have been stated separately: "Matter can neither be created nor destroyed" and "Energy can neither be created nor destroyed".

With the advent of nuclear fission, it became apparent that matter could in fact be destroyed while energy could be created. But the destruction of matter is always accompanied by the creation of an equivalent quantity of energy. The quantitative relationship is given by the Einstein equation,

$$E = Mc^2 \qquad (2.1)$$

in which E is the energy created, M is the mass destroyed, and c is the velocity of light. This relationship makes it possible to salvage the principle of conservation by utilizing a single law which embraces both matter and energy: "Matter-energy cannot be created or destroyed."

Despite the foregoing, it is usually convenient to consider mass and energy separately in applying the principle of conservation, with an exception being made only for problems involving nuclear reactions. Let us therefore develop the principle as it applies to mass or matter first, after which we can extend it to energy by analogy.

2.3 The Mass Balance

Consider an open system having an initial mass M_1. In the completely general case, mass might flow into this system from any number of sources during a given period of observation. Let the total quantity of mass entering the system from all sources be denoted by M_i. Similarly, let M_o be the total quantity of mass flowing out of the system during the same period; let M_e denote any mass converted to energy within the system and thereby destroyed; and let M_2 be the mass remaining in the system at the end of the period of observation. The significance of each of these terms is shown schematically in Fig. 2.1.

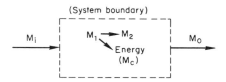

Fig. 2.1   Schematic representation of mass quantities associated with an unsteady-state, open system.

The conservation principle requires that
$$M_2 = M_1 + M_i - M_o - M_e$$
It will be advantageous to rearrange this expression to separate those terms referring to changes *within* the system from those which pertain to flow across the system boundary. Fig. 2.1 shows the desired arrangement to be
$$M_i - M_o = M_2 - M_1 + M_c \qquad (2.2)$$
Thus all flow (open system) terms are now grouped on the left and all unsteady-state (closed system) terms appear on the right.

Eq. (2.2), constituting a mathematical statement of the law of conservation of matter, is commonly referred to as a materials or *mass balance* equation. Its importance to chemical engineering can hardly be over-emphasized, for it is both necessary and sufficient for the determination of "how much," insofar as materials are concerned.

Specific applications. Two extremely important considerations appear in Eq. (2.2) only by implication: First, the mass balance applies to a specific system, and the system of interest must be clearly identified before the equation is applied. Second, the balance must be made over some fixed interval of time. This interval may coincide with the duration of a particular process being investigated or, on many occasions, may be selected arbitrarily. In either case the time interval or *basis* for the application should be settled upon before Eq. (2.2) is used.

Once a system and basis have been established, the first step in applying Eq. (2.2) to any particular problem will normally be the elimination of those terms which are not pertinent. The M_e term drops out immediately in all applications which do not involve nuclear reaction. More significant is the fact that the entire left-hand side of the equation goes to zero for any closed system. Conversely, the entire right-hand side vanishes for any steady-state system.

It may appear that the foregoing can reduce the mass balance to the point of absurd simplicity. For any steady-state system, for example, Eq. (2.2) reduces to $M_i = M_o$. Even this simple equality has far-reaching significance in a wide variety of problems, and should not be viewed disdainfully. The mass-balance applications in Chaps. 12–14 will provide ample proof of its importance.

Multi-component processes. Much of the utility of Eq. (2.2) springs from the fact that it can be applied not only to total mass but also to components. This is true even when there is a change of composition within the system. Thus, were a salt solution to be concentrated in an evaporator, separate mass balances might be written for the salt, for the water, and for the total mass being processed. In addition to specifying a system and a basis, we accordingly have another obligation before undertaking a problem: We must specify the component or combination of components being considered.

In the absence of nuclear reaction, Eq. (2.2) also applies to changes in chemical composition, provided that *only elements* (rather than compounds) are considered to be components. In the combustion of methane,

$$CH_4 + 2O_2 \longrightarrow CO_2 + 2H_2O$$

the carbon is conserved, despite the fact that it enters the reaction in combination with hydrogen and leaves in combination with oxygen. On the other hand, it is immediately obvious that methane is not conserved.

2.4 The Energy Balance

In view of the similarity between the conservation laws for matter and energy, it should be immediately apparent that the relationship

$$E_i - E_o = E_2 - E_1 - E_c \qquad (2.3)$$

constitutes a mathematical statement of the law of conservation of energy or, as it is more commonly known in engineering, the *first law of thermodynamics*. At this point it will be advisable to pause for a few more definitions, since we will be using some terms definitively for the first time.

Energy. There are several possible definitions of energy, one or more of which may already be familiar to the student. We prefer one which is somewhat qualitative but nonetheless completely correct and, as it happens, ideally suited for introductory use: *Energy* is "an intangible concept invented to account for the external manifestations of heat and work." In other words, when a system provides work or heat in the absence of other external effects, we surmise that something must be "running down" inside the system, and we elect to call that something energy.

It will be convenient to consider total energy, E, to be equal to the sum of three more specific forms of energy: *kinetic* energy, which is that energy associated with motion or velocity; *potential* energy, which is associated with position in a gravitational or equivalent force field; and *internal* energy, any form of energy other than kinetic or potential. Thus mechanical, thermal, chemical, surface, and magnetic energy, etc., are all forms of internal energy as here defined.

Heat and Work. It is with some embarrassment that we now define heat and work in terms of energy, having already used these concepts in the definition of energy. But whereas a qualitative concept of heat and work was sufficient to define energy, we now need quantitative definitions. Accordingly, we shall define *heat* as "energy in transit between the system and the surroundings under the influence of a temperature difference," while *work* is "energy in transit between the system and the surroundings under the influence of any potential other than temperature."

Note that heat and work cannot be properties, for they denote only the transfer of energy and not its possession by a system. In accordance with the concept of a property, then, both must depend on the process or path followed in changing a system from one state to another. Note, too, that the specification of a system is prerequisite to any consideration of heat and work, for both are restricted to energy in transit "between the system and the surroundings."

Heat and work may refer to energy flow either to or from a system, but some indication of direction is essential in quantitative calculations. It is customary to let Q represent the *heat absorbed* by a system from its surroundings, it being tacitly agreed that a negative value will be substituted if the system is in fact liberating rather than absorbing heat. Similarly, W represents *work done by* a system.

Energy accompanying mass. Taken together, the definitions of heat and work would appear to rule out any other means of transferring energy between a system and its surroundings. This is true for closed systems; with an open system, energy can also enter or leave in the company of mass, for any mass entering or leaving the system will have some kinetic, potential, or internal energy associated with it.

The distinction between such mass-energy streams and pure energy in the form of heat and work can be emphasized by utilizing the concept of *specific energy*, or energy per unit mass. We shall use an underline to indicate properties which are expressed on a unit mass basis. Thus $\underline{E}$ denotes energy per unit mass, $\underline{V}$ denotes volume per unit mass, etc. The total energy E associated with a mass M is accordingly equal to the product $\underline{E}M$.

The use of the foregoing notation together with the definitions of Q and W makes it possible to rewrite Eq. (2.3) in the form

$$[(\underline{EM})_i + Q] - [(\underline{EM})_o + W] = (\underline{EM})_2 - (\underline{EM})_1 - E_c \qquad (2.4)$$

Note that Q appears as a positive or input quantity and W represents outgoing energy. This usage is entirely consistent with the definitions of these two symbols, and we merely reserve the option of substituting negative values should the actual heat flow be out or the work flow in for any particular problem.

PV energy. In view of the definitions of kinetic, potential, and internal energy, it should be possible to replace each of the $\underline{E}$ terms in Eq. (2.4) with the combination $\underline{U} + \underline{KE} + \underline{PE}$, these symbols denoting internal, kinetic, and potential energy, respectively. Such a substitution is correct for the static terms on the right-hand side of the equation, but it will be necessary to include an additional term when replacing the flow terms on the left-hand side. Without attempting a formal proof, we can justify this modification as follows:

Consider a mass M_i in a position just outside the boundary of a system and having a total energy $[(\underline{U} + \underline{KE} + \underline{PE})M]_i$. If the mass is to be moved from the surroundings into the system, it must be pushed in, so to speak, and it might be deduced that the mass will receive additional energy by virtue of the push. A thermodynamic analysis of this operation will show that the additional energy so received is equal to the product of the pressure acting on the mass times the volume of the mass,* or $(P\underline{V}M)_i$. Thus the energy actually carried into the system by the mass will be equal to $[(\underline{U} + P\underline{V} + \underline{KE} + \underline{PE})M]_i$.

Similarly, when mass pushes its way out of a system, it is accompanied by a quantity of energy $[(\underline{U} + P\underline{V} + \underline{KE} + \underline{PE})M]_o$. It may therefore be concluded that PV energy always accompanies mass entering or leaving a system. The proof for this statement comes in more advanced thermodynamics study.

Enthalpy. Because of the frequent use of the $U + PV$ combination in dealing with problems involving energy, a new variable is often defined for convenience. This variable, defined by $H = U + PV$ (or $\underline{H} = \underline{U} + P\underline{V}$), is called enthalpy. Thus *enthalpy*, H, is "a property defined for mathematical convenience, equal to $U + PV$."

With the introduction of the new variable, Eq. (2.4) can be expanded to

$$[(\underline{H} + \underline{KE} + \underline{PE})M]_i - [(\underline{H} + \underline{KE} + \underline{PE})M]_o + Q - W$$
$$= [(\underline{U} + \underline{KE} + \underline{PE})M]_2 - [(\underline{U} + \underline{KE} + \underline{PE})M]_1 - E_c \qquad (2.5)$$

---

* This relationship, while valid in a great majority of chemical engineering applications, is not strictly true under all possible circumstances. The exceptions are beyond the scope of the present treatment.

Note particularly that $\underline{H}$ appears only in the flow terms on the left-hand side of the expanded equation, whereas $\underline{U}$ remains unchanged in the static terms on the right-hand side. The significance of the various terms in Eq. (2.5) is shown schematically in Fig. 2.2.

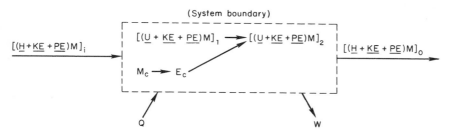

Fig. 2.2 Schematic representation of energy quantities associated with an unsteady-state, open system.

The difference symbol. The repetitious use of identical groups in Eq. (2.5) is frequently avoided by introducing another convenience symbol, Δ, to denote a finite difference. By definition, $\Delta\Gamma = \Gamma_2 - \Gamma_1$ or $\Gamma_o - \Gamma_i$, where Γ is any property whatsoever. Like Q and W, Δ is directional, and should be used consistently to indicate either one of two sets of conditions: final minus initial or outlet minus inlet. The reverse differences are denoted by $-\Delta$.

With due attention to the proper sign to be used with Δ, Eq. (2.5) can be shortened to

$$-\Delta_{oi}[(\underline{H} + \underline{KE} + \underline{PE})M] + Q - W$$
$$= \Delta_{21}[(\underline{U} + \underline{KE} + \underline{PE})M] - E_c \qquad (2.6)$$

where the subscripts serve to remind us that the first Δ signifies outlet minus inlet; the second Δ denotes final minus initial.

Application of the energy balance. Properly used, the *energy balance* as given by Eq. (2.5) or (2.6) can be of great aid in solving a wide variety of chemical engineering problems. Its application requires the prior selection of a system and a basis, as was the case with the mass balance. The next step is to eliminate those terms which are not pertinent to the problem at hand. E_c will be zero unless the process under study involves nuclear reactions. The Δ_{21} term in Eq. (2.6) is equal to zero for any steady-state process. Alternately, the entire left-hand side of the energy balance vanishes for any isolated system.

Either of the Δ terms in Eq. (2.6) can be expanded by applying the difference symbol to each of the affected variables separately. Thus

$$-\Delta_{oi}[(\underline{H} + \underline{KE} + \underline{PE})M] = -\Delta(\underline{H}M) - \Delta(\underline{KE}M) - \Delta(\underline{PE}M) \qquad (2.7)$$
$$\Delta_{21}[(\underline{U} + \underline{KE} + \underline{PE})M] = \Delta(\underline{U}M) + \Delta(\underline{KE}M) + \Delta(\underline{PE}M) \qquad (2.8)$$

This form makes it clear that a negligible *change* in $\underline{H}$, $\underline{U}$, $\underline{KE}$ or $\underline{PE}$ permits the elimination of the corresponding Δ term, even though the inlet, outlet, final, or initial values of the eliminated variable are not individually negligible. This observation is particularly pertinent insofar as kinetic and potential energy are concerned: Changes in these forms of energy will frequently be negligibly small compared to the other energy quantities of interest.

A simultaneous consideration of the mass balance will generally permit further simplification of the energy balance. For a steady-state process, $M_i = M_o$ and

$$-\Delta_{oi}[(H + \underline{KE} + \underline{PE})M] = -M_{oi}(\Delta\underline{H} + \Delta\underline{KE} + \Delta\underline{PE}) \qquad (2.9)$$

Similarly, $M_2 = M_1$ for a closed system and

$$\Delta_{21}[(U + \underline{KE} + \underline{PE})M] = M_{21}(\Delta\underline{U} + \Delta\underline{KE} + \Delta\underline{PE}) \qquad (2.10)$$

The definition of heat correctly implies that Q will be zero if there is no temperature difference at the boundary of the system. The Q term may also be eliminated if the system is well insulated. If neither of these conditions is met, heat effects may still be negligibly small compared to other effects. This situation is most frequently encountered when the system is small, and provides little surface area for the transfer of heat.

In the majority of applications of interest to chemical engineers, only two types of work need be considered. *Work of expansion* occurs when *the system* expands (or is compressed) against a resisting force or pressure. Alternately, work may be transmitted to or from the surroundings through a rotating driveshaft, a spring, or some other mechanical linkage which crosses the boundary of the system. Such work is commonly called *shaft work*. The presence or absence of either type of work can often be established by temporarily concentrating on the surroundings rather than on the system: If the system does work, the effects of this work must show up in the surroundings. Thus a gas expanding into a vacuum does no work because nothing in the surroundings is compressed. In the absence of both shaft work and work of expansion, the W term drops out of the energy balance.

As an example of the reduction of the general energy balance to a simplified form more suitable for a specific application, consider a gas flowing through a valve under steady-state conditions. Let the system be the valve and the basis be any arbitrary time interval. First, the right-hand side of Eq. (2.6) may be eliminated, in view of the steady-state stipulation. Second, changes in kinetic and potential energy will generally be negligible for a process of this type. Thus Eq. (2.6) reduces to

$$-M_{oi}(\Delta\underline{H}) + Q - W = 0 \qquad (2.11)$$

The valve being small, it is not unreasonable to assume that Q is negligible. And, finally, W is zero because the valve (the system) does not expand and there is no shaft or other mechanical linkage to transmit work. Accordingly,

$$-M_{oi}(\Delta \underline{H}) = 0 \qquad \text{or} \qquad \underline{H}_i = \underline{H}_o \qquad (2.12)$$

Although it may appear that the energy balance has now been pared down to the point where there is nothing of consequence left, Eq. (2.12) actually has considerable significance. This will be demonstrated when energy is studied more intensively in Chap. 6.

It should be remembered that M_i and M_o (and, by analogy, E_i and E_o) represent total inlet and outlet quantities from all sources. This is an important aspect when more than one stream enters or leaves a system, as is the case for the heat exchanger shown in Fig. 2.3. Assuming the exchanger

Fig. 2.3   Schematic flow diagram for a heat exchanger (no mixing of streams A and B).

to be well insulated, that steady-state conditions prevail, and that changes in kinetic and potential energy are negligible, the general energy balance can be reduced to

$$\Delta(\underline{H}M) = 0 \qquad \text{or} \qquad (\underline{H}M)_i = (\underline{H}M)_o \qquad (2.13)$$

But $(\underline{H}M)_i = (\underline{H}_A M_A)_i + (\underline{H}_B M_B)_i$ and $(\underline{H}M)_o = (\underline{H}_A M_A)_o + (\underline{H}_B M_B)_o$. Substituting these equalities into Eq. (2.13), recognizing that $M_i = M_o$ for both streams, and rearranging terms,

$$(\underline{H}_i - \underline{H}_o)_A M_A = -(\underline{H}_i - \underline{H}_o)_B M_B \qquad (2.14)$$

Thus the enthalpy changes for the two streams are shown to be equal but opposite in sign. The significance of this conclusion will also be investigated in Chap. 6.

It is suggested that the student satisfy himself that Eq. (2.6) reduces to $\Delta U = Q - W$ for any closed system for which changes in kinetic and potential energy may be neglected. Additional exercises of this kind will be found at the end of the chapter.

For the most part, the determination of the numerical values to be substituted into Eq. (2.6) or one of its many reduced forms is taken up in more advanced work in *thermodynamics*, "the science of the relationship between heat, work, and the properties of systems." Once this last step has been mastered, the energy balance, together with the simpler mass balance, provides a practical means for determining "how much" is involved in both physical and chemical change.

WHICH WAY THE CHANGE GOES

Literally interpreted, the "which way" question gives rise to an immediate and unassailable answer: The change should go the way the chemical engineer wants it to. But Nature has her own ideas about which way things should go, and the real problem is to determine whether Nature and the engineer are allies or enemies.

Consider two adjacent mountain lakes at different elevations: If the engineer wishes to transfer water from Lake High to Lake Low, he need only provide a suitable pipeline or ditch between the two and let gravity do the rest. Indeed, he might even install a water turbine and obtain some useful work as a by-product of the operation. To transfer water in the reverse direction, however, he must provide a pump, which means that he can no longer obtain work but will have to expend it instead. Therein lies the significance of the "which way" question.

The same consideration can be readily applied to the transfer of energy. Given two solid objects, one hot and the other cold, the engineer need only place them together to get heat to flow from hot to cold. And, as we shall learn later in thermodynamics, he might even install a "heat engine" and obtain useful work just as he did in the water flow problem. But again, should it become desirable to reverse the flow, the engineer will be forced to expend work instead of obtaining it from the process.

2.5 The Second Law of Thermodynamics

Many other examples of the uni-directional nature of spontaneous change could be cited. All such phenomena can be summed up by stating that "it is impossible for energy to move unaided from a given potential to a higher one." Hopefully, the student will accept this generalization as being perfectly logical and perhaps even obvious, because its validity cannot be proven in the usual sense of the word. On the other hand, since no one has ever succeeded in disproving it, it is universally accepted and is, in fact, a statement of the *second law of thermodynamics*.

Lest there be concern over the absence of formal proof for the second law, it should be pointed out that this situation pertains to the first law as well. Countless experiments attest to the validity of these laws; none have yet been found to refute them. They are consequently accepted as laws even though neither one can be formally proven.

The applicability of any purely qualitative concept is limited, and the second law statement given above leaves much to be desired in this respect. The original qualitative statement of the first law led to the quantitative energy balance given by Eq. (2.6), however, and we might anticipate that a mathematical expression for the second law can also be developed.

Lost work. Let us return momentarily to the transfer of water from Lake High to Lake Low, where the engineer may or may not install a water turbine to recover useful work. In either case, water originally in Lake High, where it has considerable potential for doing work, finally reaches Lake Low, where its potential for doing work is definitely reduced. Thus work is available in both cases, but is recovered only when the turbine is installed. In the absence of a turbine or other similar device, this available potential for doing work is lost.

Lost work, denoting work which could have been done but wasn't, is clearly a uni-directional concept, for it would be patently absurd to speak of work which could not have been done but was. This restriction leads to an alternative statement of the second law: "There exists in nature a quantity which changes always in the same sense for all natural processes."

Entropy. As it happens, the quantity referred to in the foregoing statement is not lost work, for in any completely general case heat effects must also be considered. We therefore need some quantity which embraces both lost work and heat effects. Since this specification is not met by any of the quantities with which we are already familiar, it will be necessary to invent a new one. If this seems improper or arbitrary, remember that we have already accepted one invented concept, energy, to account for the external manifestations of heat and work. Why not a second to account for the uni-directional nature of spontaneous change? As a matter of fact, just such a quantity was "invented" by the German physicist Clausius in the mid-nineteenth century, and he proposed that it be called *entropy*.

Entropy can be shown to be a true property, just as are temperature, pressure, internal energy, and other more familiar concepts. It is conventionally denoted by the symbol S. Since the second law is concerned with the *change* of entropy rather than with absolute values (which are the basis for the third law), we shall not attempt to define entropy itself in mathematical terms. Instead, it will suffice to present a quantitative relationship that, for practical purposes, defines *change* of entropy in terms of heat, lost work, and absolute temperature:

$$dS = \frac{\delta Q + \delta \mathrm{lw}}{T} \tag{2.15}$$

The symbol δ indicates an infinitesimal *quantity*, and should not be confused with the differential operator *d*, which represents an infinitesimal *change*. The symbol lw, of course, denotes *lost work*.

Actually, Eq. (2.15) should be placed under restriction in view of the fact that entropy, being a property, can enter or leave a system in the company of mass in the same way that energy can. A more general entropy balance, analogous to the energy balance given by Eq. (2.6), is

$$-dS_{oi} + \frac{\delta Q}{T} + \frac{\delta lw}{T} = dS_{21} \tag{2.16}$$

In most practical applications, one or the other of the two *dS* terms in this equation will drop out, whereupon the expression reduces to that given in Eq. (2.15).

The integral form of Eq. (2.15) is

$$\int T dS = Q + lw \tag{2.17}$$

and it is now possible to see exactly what happens when any system undergoes a spontaneous change: If work could have been done but wasn't, the lw term in Eq. (2.17) will be finite and positive. Where does this lost work go? Part of it, because of frictional effects, will almost invariably be dissipated to the surroundings in the form of heat. The remainder, in accordance with Eq. (2.17), must result in an increase in the entropy of the system.

Since lw must always be positive or, in the limit, zero, Eq. (2.15) might also be written

$$dS \geq \frac{\delta Q}{T} \tag{2.18}$$

and this form corresponds to still another alternative statement of the second law: "The entropy of an isolated system always increases or, in the limit, remains constant," since $Q = 0$ for an isolated system.

Eqs. (2.15) through (2.18) correctly imply that the concept of entropy will be extremely useful in evaluating the *efficiency* of a process or path used to change a system from one state to another. In this regard Eq. (2.18) merits special attention because it relates a change in S (a property depending only on the initial and final states of the system) to Q, which depends on the path or process connecting these states. The nature of the process for which dS will be identically equal to $\delta Q/T$ is therefore of particular interest, for it will provide an absolute standard against which the efficiency of other processes can be measured.

Reversibility. It can be shown that any process which satisfies the equality mentioned above must be *reversible*. A reversible process is defined as one that is "capable of being reversed in direction by an infinitesimal change in potential." The significance of this definition will be clearer if we first identify a process which is obviously irreversible and then alter conditions so as to establish reversibility:

If heat flows from a body at 400°F to another at 100°F, the potential or driving force responsible for heat flow is the difference in the two temperatures, 300°. Clearly, the direction of flow will not be reversed if this potential is changed only infinitesimally, and we therefore conclude that this is an irreversible process.

We may deduce from the foregoing that any change occuring under the influence of a *finite* potential or driving force must be irreversible, and this is indeed the case. Suppose, though, that one body is at a temperature T and the other is at an infinitesimally higher temperature $T + \delta T$. Here again heat can flow because of the driving force δT. But now an infinitesimal change in the driving force from δT to $-\delta T$ will clearly reverse the flow, and the process may therefore be considered to be reversible.

All real processes are inherently irreversible, but the concept of reversibility is an extremely useful supplement to the concept of entropy in thermodynamic analysis. As was suggested earlier, the two concepts can be shown to be directly related by the expression

$$dS = \frac{\delta Q_R}{T} \tag{2.19}$$

where the subscript R reminds us that this equality is true only for a reversible process. Should the process also be adiabatic,

$$dS = 0 \tag{2.20}$$

This equation, stating that entropy remains constant *for an adiabatic, reversible process*, will be used extensively in many practical applications.

Eqs. (2.15) through (2.20), with their associated restrictions, may all be considered to constitute alternative mathematical statements of the second law of thermodynamics.

Whereas the first law deals with the *quantity* of energy associated with change, the second law indicates that energy also has *quality*. For example, a gas may undergo a free expansion from a high to a low pressure without doing work or liberating heat and, in accordance with the energy balance, its total energy will be unchanged. Not so its entropy, however; the increase in this property signifies that the energy, although unchanged in amount, has lost some of its potential usefulness. It is therefore of lower quality, so to speak.

The consequences of the second law as it affects the conversion of heat into work are particularly far-reaching. Little has been said about this aspect in the present development, the primary objective being to investigate the directional nature of change. In more advanced study of thermodynamics these consequences are given detailed attention.

In summary, it is important to recognize that all spontaneous changes are uni-directional in nature and that all actual change is inherently irreversible. The degree of irreversibility can be related to a change in a property called entropy. These concepts provide a basis for evaluating the efficiency with which the engineer derives the maximum benefit from the forces of nature or, conversely, expends energy to oppose them.

HOW FAR THE CHANGE GOES

Like the direction of change discussed in the preceding section, the *extent* of change is in many cases specified by the engineer without his encountering any restrictions pertaining to his decision. But this is not always the case, as may be readily demonstrated by reconsidering the two transfer examples introduced previously:

What is to prevent the engineer from arbitrarily raising the level of Lake Low one inch, two inches, or ten inches by transferring water from Lake High? One limitation is the amount of water available in Lake High. But there is another limitation which may be encountered first: Unless the engineer is prepared to expend work for pumping to continue it, the transfer process will also come to an end when the levels in both lakes become the same.

Similarly, heat will flow spontaneously from a hot to a cold body only until the temperatures become equal. Again, if the engineer wishes to continue the process beyond this point he will be able to do so only by supplying energy to a "heat pump" which can pump heat from one temperature level to a higher one. If this sounds like an impracticable idea, note that this is precisely what is accomplished in any refrigeration process.

2.6 The Equilibrium Concept

When a change of any sort comes to a halt because there is no longer any driving force or potential acting on the system, the system is said to be at *equilibrium*, for there is no longer any tendency toward change. Strictly speaking, the condition of equilibrium requires that *all* potentials be zero. Thus even when our two lakes reach the same level, they may not be in complete equilibrium. The temperature of the water in one lake might be different from that in the other, and this would constitute a tendency toward the flow of heat.

The ability to recognize an approach to equilibrium is important in chemical engineering, as can be seen from the examples above. More important is the fact that, under many circumstances, the equilibrium condition constitutes a practical limit to the extent of change, for the use of a pump or its equivalent will not always be feasible. As a case in point, consider the reversible chemical reaction

$$CO + H_2O(g) \rightleftharpoons CO_2 + H_2$$

the (g) indicating that the water is in the gaseous state.

If, under suitable conditions of pressure and temperature, equal volumes of carbon monoxide and water vapor are brought together, they will react to yield an equilibrium mixture of carbon dioxide, hydrogen, and unreacted carbon monoxide and water vapor. An identical equilibrium mixture can be obtained by bringing together the same equal volumes of carbon dioxide and hydrogen at the same pressure and temperature. This raises an interesting "which way" situation, for it can be seen that the direction of the reaction depends entirely on the starting point with respect to the equilibrium condition.

Suppose that the chemical engineer, starting with a gas mixture on one side of the equilibrium point, wants the reaction to pass through that point to yield a mixture on the other side. From the analogy to the water and heat flow problems, we can conclude that he will have to supply energy to a suitable "chemical reaction pump." Such a pump might take the form of an electrochemical cell, but there are many reasons for rejecting this solution to the present problem. Thus the equilibrium condition constitutes a practical limit to the extent of change in this case.

This is not to say that there is no way by which the engineer can achieve his objective. A different operating temperature will shift the equilibrium point. Or he might devise a means for separating the desired products out of the equilibrium mixture, leaving fresh reactants which would then react until equilibrium was re-established. In any event, it should be apparent that his solution to the problem must take the effect of equilibrium into account.

Equilibrium and stability. Three balls at rest on an irregular surface are shown schematically in Fig. 2.4. Each of the balls may be considered to be at equilibrium since forces are balanced and, in the absence of external disturbances, there is no tendency toward change. If work is expended to move each ball away from its equilibrium position, however, it can be seen that each of the three states of equilibrium has a unique characteristic: Ball A will return to its original equilibrium position when the displacing force is removed. In contrast, the slightest displacement in either direction will cause ball B to move to a new equilibrium position, while ball C will seek either its original position or a new one, depending on the extent of the displacement.

Ball A is said to be in a state of *stable equilibrium*, because its state is unaffected by temporary disturbances. It follows that the state of ball B is one of *unstable equilibrium*, and the state of ball C is commonly called *metastable equilibrium*. These three types of equilibrium are encountered in a wide

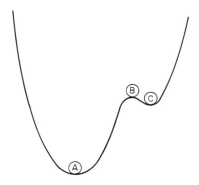

Fig. 2.4   Schematic representation of stable equilibrium (A), unstable equilibrium (B), and metastable equilibrium (C).

variety of thermodynamic systems. The condition of stable equilibrium ultimately limits the extent of change, but an intervening metastable state often requires special attention.

Criterion for stable equilibrium. The second law furnishes a suitable quantitative test for the existence of stable equilibrium. As noted in Sec. 2.5, "the entropy of an isolated system always increases or, in the limit, remains constant." Thus, when the entropy of an isolated system reaches a maximum, further change is impossible. This condition of maximum entropy in an isolated system corresponds to a state of stable equilibrium, for the state can be altered only if the restriction of isolation is removed and energy is brought in from the surroundings. In other words, the state of a system is one of stable equilibrium if any conceivable change of state at constant energy would decrease the entropy of the system. The mathematical equivalent of this statement is

$$\Delta S_E < 0 \qquad (2.21)$$

where the subscript E denotes the restriction of constant energy. A condition of stable equilibrium exists when this equation applies to all conceivable changes away from a given state.

Like the general mass and energy balance equations, Eq. (2.21) can be converted to other forms to fit special cases. One such form will be considered in Chap. 8. Otherwise, the prediction of equilibrium conditions is another topic outside the scope of this text. The importance of equilibrium as an aspect of change has presumably been satisfactorily demonstrated, and the student should be fully aware of the role of equilibrium in the overall problem of effecting a desired change.

HOW FAST THE CHANGE TAKES PLACE

The "which way" and "how far" questions both involve a consideration of the driving force or potential for change, the first question being concerned with the direction of the potential and the second with its disappearance. This leaves the *magnitude* of the potential to be considered. As might be expected, the magnitude of the potential is directly related to the "how fast" aspect of change or, more formally, the *rate* of change.

2.7 The Rate Concept

Definition of rate. Basically, the term *rate* refers to the extent of a change divided by the time interval over which the change is effected. If it takes 10 minutes to produce 20 pounds of product A in a chemical reactor, we can say that the *average* rate of production is 20 divided by 10, or two pounds per minute. The use of the word "average" is significant, for the given data provide no indication of the rate at any given instant during the process.

While a knowledge of average rate provides no clue to instantaneous rates, a knowledge of the latter will always permit the calculation of the average rate by virtue of the very definition of the word "average." Thus it is the instantaneous rate rather than the average rate which is a fundamental concept. Accordingly, let us tentatively define rate as "an infinitesimal change in any property or quantity divided by the corresponding infinitesimal time interval over which the change is effected." The corresponding mathematical definition is

$$\text{Rate} = \frac{d\Gamma}{d\theta}$$

in which Γ denotes any property or quantity whatsoever and θ is time.

Doubling the size of the reactor in the above example will clearly double the rate of production if all other conditions remain unchanged. The extent of the system has a similar effect on rates in general, and it is common practice to include an appropriate extensive factor in the rate definition so as to extend its applicability. The modified rate definition is

$$\text{Rate} = \frac{d\Gamma}{\Lambda d\theta} \tag{2.22}$$

in which Λ is a factor, such as length, volume, or surface area, that characterizes the extent of the system.

By definition, a steady-state flow process is one in which conditions at any point do not change with time, although they may change from point to point within the system. Eq. (2.22) may be applied to such a process if θ is interpreted as the *residence time* required for the flowing material to move from one point to another. A somewhat more effective approach is to let $\gamma = d\Gamma/d\theta$ be the rate at which the quantity Γ flows past a given point in the system. This rate will then change, not with time, but with position in the system. The latter may be expressed in terms of the extensive factor used in Eq. (2.22), and the steady-state rate equation becomes

$$\text{Rate} = \frac{d\gamma}{d\Lambda} \tag{2.23}$$

Eqs. (2.22) and (2.23) are mutually consistent,* and only the process characteristics need be considered in deciding which one to use. The rate definition can then be completed by specifying the particular physical variables represented by Γ and Λ together with the units to be used. It is customary to make the rate a positive quantity. Thus it will be necessary to incorporate a minus sign into the definition if the derivative is negative.

Rate correlation. The practical application of the rate concept requires that the engineer be able to predict the rate of change for a given process on the basis of information obtained elsewhere, usually under conditions somewhat removed from those pertinent to the proposed application. This makes it necessary to identify the quantitative relationship between a rate and the various environmental factors which affect it. The mathematical relationship between rate and environment is called the *rate correlation*.

The relationship between rate and driving force or potential is readily envisioned. The rate of flow between our two lakes, for example, is greatest when the levels are most widely different and will, in accordance with the equilibrium concept, diminish to zero as the levels become equal. We can also predict that the water will flow faster through a smooth concrete runway than it will through a rough earthen ditch of the same size. These observations, that is, that rate varies with both potential and resistance, are generally applicable to all rate processes.

For many processes the quantitative relationship is linear, and

$$\text{Rate} \propto \frac{\text{potential}}{\text{resistance}}$$

or

$$\text{Rate} = K\left(\frac{\text{potential}}{\text{resistance}}\right)$$

where K is the proportionality factor. A more complex function is required for some processes, but this fact does not detract from the general applicability of the development that follows.

For the most part, the experimental determination of the resistance and the proportionality factor K as separate quantities is not practicable. It

---

* Actually, both equations are special forms of a single generalized rate definition, $\text{Rate} = \frac{\partial^2\Gamma}{\partial\Lambda\partial\Theta}$. This definition reduces to Eq. (2.22) for a batch process and to Eq. (2.23) for a steady-state flow process.

will therefore be convenient to combine these variables into a single *rate coefficient*, thereby putting the rate correlation into the form

$$\text{Rate} = (\text{rate coefficient}) \times (\text{potential}) \tag{2.24}$$

Rate measurement. Because physical measurements can be made only over finite time intervals, instantaneous rates cannot be measured directly. Instead, the principles of differential calculus must be used to convert the raw data, taken over finite time intervals, to instantaneous rates. The recommended procedure for this conversion is presented in Appendix B.

A knowledge of instantaneous rate and the corresponding potential then permits the calculation of the rate coefficient in Eq. (2.24). In general, the coefficient will be independent of the potential but will depend on a number of other pertinent environmental factors, all of which must be investigated. The correlation of rate data may therefore require an extensive investigation before the relationship between the rate coefficient and environment can be expressed in quantitative form.

Process application. For a batch process, the rate definition given by Eq. (2.22) can be combined with the rate correlation, Eq. (2.24), to obtain the differential equation

$$d\theta = \frac{d\Gamma}{(\Lambda)(\text{rate coefficient})(\text{potential})} \tag{2.25}$$

In any particular application, Γ and Λ are replaced by specific physical variables, while a knowledge of environmental conditions presumably permits calculation of the rate coefficient. Eq. (2.25) may accordingly be integrated, provided the rate coefficient and potential are either constant or can be expressed as functions of Γ. The latter case will almost invariably bring the mass balance or the energy balance into use.

The integrated rate equation may then be solved for either (a) the time needed to carry out a specified change with a given potential; (b) the potential which will be required to effect a specified change in a given time; or (c) the extent of the change which can be effected with a given potential and in a specified time.

A similar procedure is applicable to steady-state flow processes. Eq. (2.23) replaces Eq. (2.22), and the differential rate equation becomes

$$d\Lambda = \frac{d\gamma}{(\text{rate coefficient})(\text{potential})} \tag{2.26}$$

Upon integration, the equation may be solved for (a) the extent of the system needed to carry out a specified change with a given potential; (b) the potential which will be required to effect a specified change in a system of a given size; or (c) the extent of the change which can be effected with a given potential in a system of a given size.

Mass- and energy-rate balances. In the course of developing the generalized mass balance, Eq. (2.2), it was emphasized that the balance must be applied over a specific time interval. If the time interval is infinitesimally small, the mass balance may be written

$$\delta M_i - \delta M_o = dM_s + \delta M_c \qquad (2.27)$$

where dM_s refers to the change in the mass of the system. It is sometimes advantageous to convert this equation to a rate form by dividing through by the time interval, $d\theta$. The result may be written

$$m_i - m_o = \frac{dM_s}{d\theta} + m_c \qquad (2.28)$$

in which m_i and m_o denote the instantaneous rates at which mass is entering and leaving the system, and m_c is the instantaneous rate at which mass is being converted to energy.

The general energy balance, Eq. (2.6), may be similarly converted to a rate form if desired. Either the mass-rate or energy-rate equation may then be reduced to a simplified form in accordance with the principles discussed earlier.

Summary. The rate concept is an extremely important one in chemical engineering, and the foregoing treatment hardly scratches the surface. Even so, the student should have acquired an introductory familiarity with the subject. A few specific applications will be considered in Chap. 9.

HOW THE CHANGE IS EFFECTED

Now that we are familiar with what might be termed the theoretical aspects of change, as discussed in the preceding sections, we can turn to their practical application in getting the job done—which is, after all, the ultimate objective of the chemical engineer. "Change A, B, and C into one ton per day of compound D," he was told in Chap. 1, and all of the theoretical considerations treated up to this point will go for naught unless he can come up with a sequence of specific and practical processes which will do just that. And so the question is, "How?"

2.8 Unit Changes

As was noted in Chap. 1, the first step in answering the "how" question is to break the desired overall change down into a series of component unit changes, each of which can be carried out as a separate step or in a separate piece of process equipment. Without a knowledge of the pertinent characteristics of the various unit changes, however, the engineer would be unable to determine whether a proposed change was practicable or, for that matter, even possible. Let us therefore consider the "how" question as it applies to specific types of unit change first, after which we can re-examine the problem of combining a series of such changes to effect a desired overall result.

It has been the practice in chemical engineering to designate all purely physical unit changes as *unit operations*, while chemical changes are *unit processes*. The distinction is somewhat arbitrary, since certain basic principles apply to all changes, both physical and chemical. For our purposes, it will be more convenient to classify the unit changes by objective: to effect a physical combination, a chemical reaction, or a physical separation; or to get material into a suitable state for one of these changes.

Physical combination. Since mixing is inherently a spontaneous process, physical combination can usually be effected by merely bringing the desired components together. Only two problems of any consequence are likely to be encountered: First, it is usually necessary that the mixture be homogeneous or nearly so, and adequate *contact time* or agitation must be provided. Additional steps—emulsification, for example—may be required to insure a uniform dispersion of immiscible components.

Second, the mixing process may result in the liberation of considerable heat, as when strong acids are diluted. In such cases it may be necessary to provide for heat removal either by circulating a suitable coolant through or around the mixing vessel, or by mixing in stages, with intermediate cooling following each stage.

Chemical reaction. The major considerations involved in effecting a chemical reaction are the reaction rate and the equilibrium point, both of which depend on pressure, temperature, and the composition and condition of the reacting mixture. The given reactants may also enter into a number of undesirable side reactions under the proper conditions. The effect of pressure, etc., on all the various reactions which might be encountered must therefore be known before the design of a reactor can be undertaken.

Many of the chemical reactions of industrial importance would be completely impracticable were it not for the availability of suitable catalysts which accelerate the desired reactions preferentially, thereby reducing reaction time while also minimizing the effect of side reactions. Thus information regarding the effect of catalysis may also be prerequisite to the reactor design, particularly since it may be necessary to provide for adequate contact between the catalyst and the reacting mixture.

Once the operating conditions have been set on the basis of the foregoing considerations, the size of the reactor will be determined by the desired throughput and by the reaction rate. As was the case with mixing, the design may be complicated to the extent that a uniform dispersion of the

reactants, products, and catalyst must be maintained, or that heat of reaction must be supplied or removed.

Physical separation. In terms of the end result, physical separation is
synonymous with *component* separation. Viewed as a technique, on the other
hand, it will usually mean *phase* separation, a phase being defined as "a
mechanically separate, homogeneous part of a heterogeneous system." Thus
a given system might consist of one or more solid phases, one or more liquid
phases (oil and water, for example, are mechanically separate), and a gas or
vapor phase. The overall problem of separating components, then, is two-
fold: First, each of the components to be separated must be induced to exist
preferentially in a different phase; and second, the phases themselves must
be separated from each other, thereby completing the component separation.

Phase separation is by far the easier of the two steps. A difference in the
densities of the phases will often provide a means for separation, for it is on
this basis that such separations as gas from liquid, liquid from solid, gas
from solid, and even solid from solid (consider panning for gold) are easily
effected, the lighter phase tending to rise above the heavier.

Another class of separating techniques exploits difference in size. Included
in this group are screening or sifting for the separation of solids, filtration
for solid-liquid separation, and the use of dust filters, entrainment separators,
or porous membranes for separating solids and liquids from gases. The
"molecular sieve" is an interesting recent addition to this category, with a
separation being effected on the basis of differences in molecular size.

Whereas all the techniques listed above serve only to separate phases,
others provide for the necessary component distribution within the phases.
Among them are distillation, evaporation, condensation, crystallization, and
drying, in which the separation of components is a direct result of the
creation of different phases. It is not surprising that the operations in this
category are of major importance to the chemical engineer.

When phase creation by one of the above techniques is not practicable,
it may be advantageous to introduce deliberately a second phase from an
external source. Thus a liquid might be brought in to absorb one component
out of a mixture of gases or to combine selectively with one of the components
in a liquid mixture; or a component in either a gaseous or liquid mixture
might be *ad*sorbed onto the surface of a solid adsorbent. Such operations
must obviously be followed by others which will recover the desired component from the new medium.

The operations which effect the transfer of a component from one phase
to another are commonly called *mass transfer operations*. The sizing of mass
transfer equipment involves a typical application of the mass balance and
the rate concept, but detailed design is somewhat more complicated. Adequate contact between phases is essential and may be provided in a variety

of ways. Further, many of the mass transfer operations involve simultaneous heat transfer. A few typical solutions to the general problem will be outlined in Chap. 11, but for the most part this important subject will not be considered in this text.

Preparatory changes. Preparation for physical combination, chemical reaction, or physical separation consists largely of getting the material to the desired temperature, pressure, and phase for the anticipated operation. Bulk transport, i.e., getting the material from one point in the plant to another, can also be included in this category. Thus the preparatory operations include heating and cooling, compression and expansion, vaporization and condensation, and fluid flow and materials handling.

Important though they are, these operations need not be considered at length here, for we are already familiar with their underlying principles. Heat transfer, for example, is fundamentally analogous to mass transfer, and the design of heat transfer equipment requires the application of the concepts of energy balance and rate. Again, since the detailed design of equipment is not easy it will not be considered in this text. The use of the energy balance and rate concepts in sizing heat transfer and fluid flow equipment will be considered in Chap. 9, however.

2.9 Unit Change Combinations

The two examples presented in Chap. 1 typify the way in which various unit changes can be assembled in sequence to effect a complex change. The student should find it helpful at this point to review Figs. 1.3 and 1.4 in the light of what has been discussed in the present section. In practice, the engineer has only the overall process as a starting point, and the problem of envisioning the various unit changes that are required is many times more difficult than the relatively straightforward analysis of an already prepared flow diagram.

To illustrate, let us conclude this section with a consideration of the relatively simple problem of recovering pure, solid copper sulfate from a five per cent aqueous solution. Our first impulse would probably be to say, "Boil it," and it is true that such a process would achieve the desired result. When we try to envision the equipment in which it could be carried out economically, on a continuous basis, and at a rate of several tons a day, however, it becomes apparent that this quick answer leaves much to be desired.

A practical process to accomplish the recovery would indeed start out with evaporation, but definitely not to the point of dryness. Further, the evaporation might be carried out in several stages at successively lower pressures (and, accordingly, lower temperatures), in order that the vapor (steam) driven off in one stage might be used as a source of heat in the next. Precipitated salt can be removed from the bottom of each stage as necessary but should be accompanied by enough residual liquid (*mother liquor*) to permit its being pumped through a heat exchanger where it might give up heat to the five-per-cent feed solution. Clear mother liquor, meanwhile, would be transferred to the next stage of evaporation for further concentrating.

The clear mother liquor leaving the last evaporator will be a saturated solution, and it should be possible to precipitate additional $CuSO_4$ by cooling the solution in a crystallizer. Filtration of the crystallizer effluent to separate liquid and solid would seem to be the next step, but filtration is somewhat uneconomical if the liquid-to-solid ratio in the feed stream is high. Accordingly, the crystallizer effluent might first be concentrated in a thickener, a device which effects continuous sedimentation or settling to produce a clear overflow stream and a concentrated, sludge-like underflow. The overflow could be recycled to the last evaporator, while the underflow would join the cooled evaporator-product stream en route to the filter.

Finally, the filtrate leaving the filter could also be recycled to the last evaporator, while the wet, solid salt could be conveyed to a drier for the removal of the remaining moisture. Thus evaporation, crystallization, heat exchange, sedimentation, filtration, and drying are all involved in the practical solution to this "simple" little problem. The solution is typical of the way in which the chemical engineer assembles several unit changes into an integrated combination to effect a single desired result.

HOW TO MEASURE AND CONTROL THE CHANGE

The chemical engineer is charged with the operation of processes as well as with their design. If the operation is to be efficient, he must be able to determine how well the plant is performing once it is running or *on stream*. Further, he must be able to take corrective action whenever it becomes apparent that the process is not operating under optimum conditions. Instrumentation for the measurement and control of key process variables is therefore a definite chemical engineering responsibility.

2.10 Measurement

Since it is not practicable to measure temperatures, pressures, flow rates, or compositions at all points in a process, the question of what to measure is a logical starting point for the solution of a process instrumentation problem. The answer comes from a careful examination of all cause-and-effect relationships involved in the process, and full use will be made of mass and energy balances and the rate equations in this initial analysis. As a result of this study, a number of variables will be earmarked for direct measurement, with the others to be determined indirectly by making simple calculations.

The particular type of instrument to be used for each measurement can then be specified. In some instances a simple indicating-type instrument which shows only the immediate value of the measured variable will be sufficient. In others it will be necessary to specify a more complex recording-type instrument that will produce a permanent record for subsequent study and analysis. The required degree of precision of measurement must also be considered, and may dictate the use of a particular sensing element. Even a simple variable such as temperature can be sensed in at least six different ways. The engineer must accordingly know the comparative advantages and limitations of all the various techniques if he is to specify the one best suited for any particular application.

Although the detailed solution of measurement problems will generally fall to engineers with special training in instrumentation, this does not relieve the chemical engineer of his overall responsibilities for efficient operation of processes. It is therefore important that he be aware of the role of measurement as an engineering aspect of change, but there is little to be gained by examining this rather specialized area in detail. Subsequent laboratory work will provide a satisfactory background.

2.11 Process Control

There can be no assurance that the operating conditions prescribed by the process designer will in fact prevail during actual operation unless adequate provision is made for regulation and control. Not only must the desired conditions be established initially; they must also be maintained in the face of unavoidable difficulties. It is this latter aspect which can be particularly troublesome, for many of the upsets to be encountered will be unforeseen as well as unavoidable.

The solution to the control problem starts with the same cause-and-effect analysis that was used for measurement. This study will make it possible to predict the consequences of departures from the prescribed operating conditions and will also suggest the counter-measures to be taken when upsets occur. Appropriate key variables can then be selected for independent control with the assurance that they, in turn, will effectively control the remaining variables.

While the technical details of control instrumentation are hardly within the scope of an introductory text, certain aspects which are common to all control systems are worth attention. It will be convenient to use a single, specific example to illustrate these aspects, but the student may be assured that the demonstrated principles are equally applicable to all other types of control problems.

Consider the water tank shown in Fig. 2.5(a). Let us suppose that we wish to maintain some pre-determined level in the tank, even though the rate at which water is withdrawn from the bottom of the tank changes

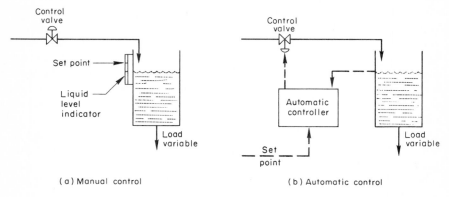

(a) Manual control   (b) Automatic control

Fig. 2.5   Schematic flow diagram for a liquid-level control system.

from time to time. While the latter rate will almost certainly be controlled elsewhere, it is not subject to independent control at the tank. Such uncontrolled variables are called *load variables*. The *measured variable* in this case is the level in the tank, and a mark might be made on the glass sight gage to indicate the desired level. The desired value of the measured variable is called the *set point* or *reference input*.

If the control is to be manual, an operator will check the gage-glass reading from time to time. When the reading does not agree with the set point, he will open or close the control valve in the supply line. This valve is the *final control element* in this case. He must then recheck the gage reading to determine the effect of his action and may have to readjust the valve setting, and so on. This cycle of operations describes a typical *control loop* in which a change at one point leads to a change at another and the latter, in turn, changes conditions at the first point all over again.

If the load variable fluctuates widely and rapidly, it can be seen that the full-time attention of the operator might be necessary to insure satisfactory control. The continuous monitoring and rapid response afforded by automatic control systems is obviously a significant advantage under such conditions. A typical system is shown in Fig. 2.5(b). A suitable indication of the level in the tank is transmitted to the control instrument, where it is compared with the set point. The difference or *error* between the two values then actuates a mechanism which will alter the setting of the valve in the supply line. Thus the operator need only adjust the set point to the desired value, and the control system will then carry out all the other steps.

Since an automatic instrument is incapable of making judgments, a specific relationship between error and corrective action must be built into the instrument. The three most common control modes are *proportional* control, for which the change in control valve setting would be directly proportional to the error; *derivative* control, where the valve change is proportional to the rate at which the error is changing; and *integral* control, for which the valve change is proportional to the area under the error-time curve. Since these control modes may also be used in combination, a wide variety of response characteristics is possible.

Although many different variables must be controlled, the final corrective action in almost every case will be the opening or closing of a valve. This situation is a logical consequence of the cause-and-effect relationships mentioned earlier. For example, how would one control the temperature in a large, gas-fired furnace? One obvious method would be to control the rate at which fuel gas is supplied to the burners. The final control element would therefore be a valve in the gas line.

Just as a chemical process involves the flow of mass and energy, so can a control system be considered to involve the flow of information or *signals*. The construction of a schematic signal-flow diagram is frequently advantageous. A typical diagram of this type is shown in Fig. 2.6. The arrows in the

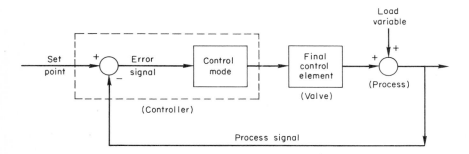

Fig. 2.6 Schematic signal-flow diagram for a typical closed-loop control system.

figure properly represent the flow of signals rather than mass or energy, and a comparison with Fig. 2.5(b) should be informative. In the actual control system, the signals can be transmitted electrically, pneumatically, hydraulically, or through mechanical linkages.

Process control has not always been considered one of the fundamental aspects of chemical engineering, but it is definitely an area of growing significance in view of the current trend toward automation. In any event, it can hardly be argued that control is not a fundamental aspect of change, for without effective control change could be put to only limited practical use.

THE COST OF EFFECTING THE CHANGE

It may seem strange that economic considerations as they pertain to change should be given a status equivalent to that of the laws of thermodynamics, the rate concept, unit operations, and process control. Actually, the economic aspects of change might even be considered to have precedence over these other considerations. The most meticulous attention to the technical aspects of change in designing or operating a plant will be to no avail unless the design and operation are consistent with fundamental economic principles.

2.12 Economic Considerations in Design

The extent to which the process designer must consider economic implications was outlined in the first chapter, but that account was somewhat misleading in two important respects: First, the process designer will seldom wait until his design is completed before he considers the economics of the process. Second, the impact of economics affects all areas of chemical engineering activity and not process design alone.

With respect to the first of these points, the importance of having economics *always* in mind cannot be over-emphasized. The successful process designer will consider cost implications at every step along the way, and will in fact project them as far ahead as possible. As a case in point, there is the story of a consultant who was asked to design a complicated plant for the production of a chemical by a new method. His first step was to make a materials or mass balance for the plant, and the entire project was immediately cancelled when he pointed out that the cost of the necessary raw materials would exceed the market value of the product!

Optimum economic design. As an example of the role of economics in process design, consider the problem of selecting the diameter of the pipe to be used in a simple piping system. The cost of the pipe itself can be minimized by using the smallest possible diameter. For a given flow rate, however, the velocity at which the fluid flows through the line must increase as the diameter decreases, and this will increase the pressure drop in the line.

A smaller diameter will consequently require the use of a larger and more expensive pump, and power costs will also be greater. The problem, then, is to specify the diameter which corresponds to a minimum total cost.

The first step in solving such a problem is to reduce all costs to a common basis. The piping and pump will require an initial expenditure for their purchase, while the cost of power is a continuing expense. The usual technique is to express all costs on an annual basis. Thus the cost of the piping and pump would be expressed in terms of annual charges for depreciation, maintenance, return on investment, etc. The pipe diameter corresponding to the minimum annual cost can then be selected.

A plot similar to that shown in Fig. 2.7 can be used to depict the basis

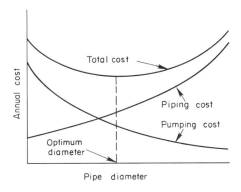

Fig. 2.7   Effect of pipe diameter on piping, pumping, and total costs.

for selection. Both piping cost and pumping cost (cost of pump plus cost of power) have been converted to an annual basis and plotted against pipe diameter. It can be seen that the two cost trends oppose one another as suggested above. But the total cost, obtained by the direct addition of the two component costs, goes through a minimum point, which clearly indicates the optimum diameter. Other typical applications of plots of this type will be considered in Chap. 11.

Other economic considerations. The impact of economics in other areas of chemical engineering is equally significant. Should a process unit now producing chemical A be modified to permit the production of chemical B? How frequently should a given process unit be shut down for routine maintenance? Should an obsolete but serviceable piece of equipment be replaced with newer and more efficient equipment? Which of two research projects should be suspended in the event of a cutback in research funds? Should a proposed plant be located close to a source of raw materials, close to a marketing area, or close to a good labor supply? Can plant expansion be justified?

These are but a few of the questions which can be answered only by a consideration of economics. In short, economic aspects pervade the entire field of chemical engineering, and the student is well advised to keep sight of this fact even though his next few courses will be almost entirely concerned with the technical aspects of change.

CONCLUSION

The importance of change to the chemical engineer was presumably made clear in the first chapter, and the present chapter has presented an introductory picture of the many considerations which are involved in putting change to practical use. Significantly, the student has now been exposed to *all* of the fundamental aspects of chemical engineering. Subsequent studies will be devoted to filling in details, thereby putting some substance on the framework already presented.

These subsequent studies will, for the most part, deal with each of the fundamental aspects of change in turn. It is hoped that the student will recognize this as an academic expedient, for none of the aspects herein listed can ever be completely excluded from consideration in actual practice. Accordingly, as new knowledge pertaining to each individual aspect is assimilated, its relation to all the other aspects should be carefully noted. Let the student never become so enamored of the trees that he overlooks the forest!

REVIEW, STUDY, AND DISCUSSION

2-1. Define system, surroundings, boundary, property, state, intensive property, extensive property, specific property, process, mass balance, basis, energy balance, energy, heat, work, enthalpy, Δ, work of expansion, shaft work, lost work, entropy, δ, reversible process, equilibrium, rate, rate correlation, potential, rate coefficient, unit operation, component, phase, mass transfer, load variable, set point, final control element, control loop, error, signal; the adjectives closed, open, isolated, adiabatic, homogeneous, and steady-state as applied to systems; the adjectives kinetic, potential, internal, and PV as applied to energy; the adjectives flow, batch, steady-state, unsteady-state, adiabatic, and irreversible as applied to processes.

2-2. State the first and second laws of thermodynamics both in words and mathematically.

2-3. How many different mass balances may be applied to the steady-state combustion of ethyl alcohol (C_2H_5OH) in air if the combustion is complete? If the combustion is not complete? How many energy balances may be applied?

2-4. Identify the intensive and extensive properties in the following list: mass, velocity, potential energy, distance, heat, color, electrical potential, equilibrium, elevation, friction, enthalpy, specific surface area.

2-5. By eliminating those terms which are zero or cancel out in each case, reduce the general energy balance equation to a simplified form applicable to the following:*

a) Any closed system; any steady-state open system.

b) Two metal blocks, isolated from the rest of the universe and initially at different temperatures, are brought together with the resulting flow of heat. System: the cold block; the hot block; both blocks.

c) Steam flows through a well-insulated turbine with negligible change in kinetic or potential energy, under steady-state conditions. System: the turbine.

d) A storage battery discharges across a resistance. System: the resistance.

e) Steam flows steadily through a horizontal, insulated nozzle. System: the nozzle; one pound of steam.

f) A heavy steel block slides slowly down an inclined plane until it comes to rest. System: the block.

g) Hot oil flowing through a jacketed pipe is cooled by water flowing through the jacket. Steady-state conditions prevail, the pipe is horizontal, and the outside of the jacket is well insulated. System: the pipe; the jacket; the entire heat exchanger.

h) An insulated surge tank is "riding" on a compressed air line. Line pressure starts to fall and air flows slowly out of the tank for several minutes. System: the tank; all the air which will remain in the tank when flow stops.

i) A pound of liquid is vaporized by heat and the vapor expands freely (no shaft work) to a lower pressure, where it is condensed by removing heat. The liquid is then compressed to return it to its original condition. System: the liquid; basis: the entire process. Will the heat of vaporization be greater than, equal to, or less than the heat of condensation?

2-6. A tennis ball is dropped onto a concrete sidewalk from a height of four feet. The ball is initially at rest at the same temperature as the sidewalk and the surrounding air. Discuss the energy and entropy changes

---

* Internal energy and enthalpy may be assumed to be straight-line functions of temperature. The basis for this assumption will be presented in Chap. 6.

pertaining to the ball as it bounces freely until it finally comes to rest on the walk.

2-7. A well-insulated tank contains gas under pressure, which leaks very slowly to the atmosphere through a slightly opened valve until, after a time, the valve is closed. Specify at least four practical systems which might be used to analyze this process. Indicate whether each system is open, closed, homogeneous, isolated, batch, steady-state, unsteady-state, or adiabatic, and whether the process the system undergoes is adiabatic, batch, reversible, continuous, steady-state, or unsteady-state. Reduce the energy balance equation to fit each case.

2-8. A closed system undergoes an adiabatic, reversible change from state 1 to state 2. If the same change in state is to be effected by a process which is neither adiabatic nor reversible, must heat be added or removed?

2-9. A fluid flows through an open, steady-state system and undergoes a non-adiabatic, reversible change at constant temperature without any work being done. Assuming that the potential and kinetic energy effects are negligible, show that $\Delta S = \Delta H / T$ for the fluid as it flows through the system.

2-10. Equilibrium and stability are not synonymous though they are often confused. Give an example of a stable but non-equilibrium situation.

2-11. Can a system which is in motion be considered to be at equilibrium? Explain.

2-12. A body initially at 100°F is to be heated by contact with a second body which will be maintained at a constant temperature of 200°F. Draw a rough (qualitative) temperature-time curve for the first body. How long will it take for the body to reach 200°F?

2-13. Draw a rough rate-potential curve for Prob. 2-12 and describe a suitable procedure for obtaining a quantitative graphical relationship between rate and potential, starting with experimental temperature-time data. Explain how the rate coefficient might then be determined.

2-14. Prepare a schematic flow diagram for the $CuSO_4$ recovery process described in Sec. 2.9.

2-15. A home heating system consists of a gas-fired furnace, a blower to circulate heated air, and a thermostat mounted on the wall somewhere in the home. Draw a schematic "process flow" diagram for the system. Draw the corresponding signal-flow diagram. Identify the various control system elements such as load variables, set points, measured variables, and final control elements.

2-16. List the specific factors which would have to be considered in answering each of the economic questions asked towards the end of Sec. 2.12.

2-17. Suggest another problem that might be amenable to solution through the preparation of a cost plot (such as that shown in Fig. 2.7). Prepare a sketch of the appropriate plot.

CHAPTER 3

The Engineering Method

The first two chapters have suggested that the engineer in general and the chemical engineer in particular can be identified with a specialized field of knowledge and the application of that knowledge to the solution of practical problems. There is another identifying characteristic of the engineer which is no less important; namely, the way he sets about solving his problems. It is this characteristic which has carried many a mediocre student past more knowledgeable classmates in the quest for success in engineering. Unless the would-be engineer assimilates the proper way of thinking (the *engineering method*) along with his knowledge of technical subject matter, his effectiveness as a solver of practical problems will be sharply reduced.

What, then, is the engineering method and why is it so important? And why isn't it included in the formal definition of engineering? To answer the latter question first, it is—but only by implication. The definition uses the words "judgment" and "economically," but makes no direct reference to what is perhaps the most important consideration in engineering practice: *time!*

The importance of economics as a fundamental aspect of engineering has already been emphasized. To bring time into consideration it should only be necessary to quote the old adage, "Time is money." The first company to get a new product on the market, for example, has a distinct economic advantage over its competitors. Other economic goals are similarly served

57

by minimizing the expenditure of time. As a consequence, the deadline for the solution to any given problem will, more often than not, be set by management's answer to the question, "How soon must we have an answer?" In other words, the complexity and difficulty of the problem will be given only secondary consideration in determining how much time should be allocated for its solution. Thus the engineer will almost invariably find himself working against time, and it is this influence of the time factor which gives rise to the engineering method.

3.1 How the Engineer Saves Time

By far the quickest way to solve a problem is simply to *guess* the answer. Such a procedure may appear to be difficult to justify, but it is a fact that in many respects the best engineer is the best guesser. We refer, of course, not to the wild guess but to the educated guess—the guess based on a thorough knowledge of pertinent engineering principles and, even more important, on sound engineering judgment.

Only by the rarest of coincidences will the engineer guess the exact answer to a problem. In fact, he makes no real attempt to do so, but merely guesses a range within which the answer should lie. Thus he might guess that the cost of constructing a new plant will be between ten and thirty million dollars, but could hardly justify a pure guess, educated though it might be, of $17,400,000. Significantly, even such a broad-range guess may constitute an acceptable solution to the problem. Should it be known that even a ten-million-dollar plant would be far from profitable, for example, there would be little point in spending five months on additional calculations to determine that the actual cost would in fact be $17,400,000.

In any event, there can be no argument over the fact that the engineering guess provides *an* answer, but not *the* answer, to the problem in the shortest possible time. The saving in time is obtained at the expense of the accuracy of the answer, and this relationship applies generally to all the engineer's time-saving methods: the greater the required accuracy, the greater the time needed to obtain the answer.

When the time available for solving a problem is not so short as to require an outright guess, the engineer can effect a considerable gain in the accuracy of his answer by making a slightly more detailed *estimate* rather than a pure guess. Here, he brings the full range of his knowledge and experience to bear and may even make a few rough but quantitative calculations. Thus the estimate represents a refined guess, and the extent to which it provides a better answer will depend directly on the degree of refinement introduced.

When the refinement reaches the point where extensive calculations become necessary, it is more generally referred to as an *approximation*. The engineer will still be making guesses even at this stage, but they will now be restricted to aspects of the problem which are of only secondary importance and will disappear completely as the approximate solution becomes more and more exact.

The time factor is not the only justification for the use of approximative methods. Often the physical and chemical data needed for the solution to a problem will be far from exact. Under such circumstances, it is illogical to expend time on rigorous calculations when the final answer can never be any more exact than are the data upon which it depends.

In summary, the engineer saves time in solving problems through the expedient use of guesses, estimates, and approximations to the extent that the available time, the available data, or the nature of the problem justify an inexact solution. This means that there is no single engineering answer to a particular problem. Given a "five-month" problem, for example, the engineer can and will, if asked, submit a five-minute answer, a five-hour answer, a five-day answer, or a five-week answer as well as a five-month answer. Although they will differ, these answers can all be considered to be correct, for each is merely a more accurate refinement of its shorter-time equivalent.

3.2 The Method of Successive Refinement

Approximative methods are equally appropriate even on those rare occasions when ample time and exact data for a complete and rigorous solution are known to be available. Suppose a process designer works on a process for several months and then concludes that it is economically impracticable. His time has not been wasted in a sense, for he has prevented the much greater waste which would have resulted had the plant been built and only then found to be impracticable. On the other hand, we must agree that his time *was* largely wasted if, through the judicious use of approximative methods, he could have reached the same conclusion at the end of his first week on the job rather than after several months.

Alternately, suppose an engineer is initially given two weeks to solve a two-week problem, but at the end of the first week he is told it will be necessary to have the answer the following day instead. If we assume that he has completed the first half of the problem at that point, it follows that he can present only the one-day solution to the second half, and much of his attention to detail during the first week will accordingly be wasted. He would certainly have been better off had he prepared a one-week answer to the entire problem in the first place.

Finally, suppose that an engineer is given two hours to determine the cost of a process involving four pieces of process equipment. He prepares a half-hour answer to each separate problem and finds that the respective costs are $10,000, $25,000, $3,000, and $150,000, for a total cost of $188,000. Assuming that the time available required the use of estimates and approximations in each case, would he not have been wiser to spend most of the two hours making a more careful approximation for the $150,000 item, even if it meant falling back on a rough estimate or even a guess for the others?

These three examples all make the same point: In each case the engineer could have used his time much more effectively had he made a quick initial guess or rough estimate and then made successive refinements to the initial answer as the remaining time permitted. The process designer might have saved himself months of unnecessary effort; the second engineer could have turned in a better answer to the total problem on short notice; and the initial guess or estimate made by the third engineer would have clearly indicated where his remaining time could be most profitably spent.

Other arguments favoring this approach to complex engineering problems can also be cited, but it should suffice to list them without examples. For the sake of completeness, the list below includes the three arguments presented above:

1) Attention is continually focused on the overall aspects of the problem, and all component parts of the solution may therefore be considered at all times in their relation to the problem as a whole.

2) Unnecessary calculations may be avoided when an approximate answer at any stage of the solution clearly shows that there is little point in continuing the solution.

3) An answer to the total problem will always be available should it be requested on short notice.

4) The early stages of the solution will indicate the optimum allocation of limited additional time.

5) Even the time spent in arriving at a rigorous ultimate answer may be considerably reduced. In the third illustration above, there would be little point in carrying out detailed calculations to determine the cost of the $3,000 item to within ten per cent if the available data were such that the cost of the $150,000 item could, at best, also be determined to within ten per cent.

6) Mistakes in the calculations are less likely to go undetected. If detailed calculations gave an answer of, say, 570, a decimal-point error would immediately be suspected had a previous approximation predicted an answer between 4,000 and 6,000.

Significantly, the method of successive refinement has only one disadvantage worthy of mention: If a solution is ultimately to be as exact as it is possible to make it, it *may* take slightly longer to arrive at the final answer by successive refinement. On the other hand, time may actually be saved in accordance with point (5) above. In any event, the other advantages of the method should more than compensate for any slight additional investment in time.

To many engineers, the engineering method means the use of guesses, estimates, and approximations to the extent that they are necessary. We contend here that approximative methods are advantageous whether necessary or not, and that the engineering method embraces the principle of successive refinement: a quick, highly approximative answer to the problem in the form of a guess or rough estimate, followed by successive refinement of the initial answer to any degree consistent with the required accuracy of the final answer, the availability and exactness of the pertinent data, and the availability of additional time.

Conservative design and the safety factor. If, because of the limitations of time or available data, the best possible answer to a given problem is still only an approximation, how can the engineer then proceed to design equipment with any assurance that it will serve its intended purpose in every respect? The answer to this question is two-fold:

First, the engineer takes care to see that his approximations are always on the conservative or safe side. Thus if approximative calculations indicate that a certain flow rate will be between 700 and 900 pounds per hour, he will size the pertinent equipment on the basis of the latter rate so as to be on the safe side in case of error.

Second, the engineer does not hesitate to use a *safety factor* when the occasion calls for one. Should he determine that a chemical reactor must have a volume of at least 200 cubic feet, he may apply a safety factor of 25 per cent and actually prescribe a volume of 250 cubic feet, again to be on the safe side. The cost associated with the increase in reactor volume can be looked upon as a form of insurance, for it will be small compared to that which would be incurred if a 200-cubic-foot reactor were to be installed and then found to be too small.

To those who do not understand the engineering method, a liberal safety factor (and factors of as much as 100 per cent are not uncommon) may appear to be a bold attempt to hide possible mistakes and general carelessness in the calculations. It can only be hoped that the student realizes that this is not the case, for the use of safety factors is a completely justifiable and necessary aspect of engineering.

General utility of the engineering method. Beginning engineering students are frequently distressed by the implications of the engineering method, for their prior studies have involved given information of unquestioned accuracy, little or no deviation from a straightforward problem-solving routine, and the ultimate determination of *the* correct answer to a problem. In the face of such a background, it is not surprising that the engineering method, with its frequent dependence on inexact data, optional guesswork and approximations, and multiplicity of correct answers, is often viewed with suspicion and even alarm.

The fact is that the basic features of the engineering method are widely used outside the field of engineering, and every student has already accepted and may even have used them in one way or another. For an example close at hand, consider the first two chapters of this text: Here we have the quick, highly approximative solution to the problem of teaching chemical engineering; this solution will be successively refined in the remainder of the text and in subsequent studies.

Psychologists recommend the use of the equivalent of the engineering approach in reading study assignments:* The first step in using a new text is to read the table of contents to get an overall picture of the book's scope. The student should then skip quickly through the assigned material, noting only major paragraph headings, figures, tables, etc. The next step is to skim over the text material itself, looking for the sense of the subject matter but ignoring details. And only after these three approximative solutions is it recommended that the student start at the beginning of the assignment and read through it carefully and thoroughly.

The student should find it interesting to speculate on the consequences of applying the engineering method to other non-engineering situations, and should even find it advantageous to adopt it from time to time. It might be profitably applied to the problem of making effective use of study time, for example.

3.3 A Routine for Problem-Solving

Whereas the engineering method represents what might be called a philosophy of problem-solving, an alternative interpretation of the term "method" leads to a consideration of the detailed steps involved in proceeding through almost any type of solution, be it a guess, estimate, approximation, or complete solution. These steps are generally well known, but are all too frequently disregarded in practice. The following paragraphs should serve to emphasize the importance of attacking problems in a logical and orderly manner.

Understanding the problem. The first step in solving any problem is to make sure that the problem itself is completely understood. Even though the *sense* of a problem may be grasped, a solution may be completely inappropriate if certain key words are overlooked. Conversely, one may pay strict attention to the individual words of the problem statement and yet fail to grasp their overall significance and sense.

---

* Morgan, C. T., and Deese, J., *How to Study*, McGraw-Hill Book Company, Inc., New York (1957).

In the case of a written problem statement, the engineering method may be helpful in avoiding these pitfalls. First, skim over the problem quickly to identify its general nature; second, read through the entire problem without stopping, to determine its overall sense; and finally, read it through again, this time slowly and carefully—sentence by sentence, phrase by phrase, word by word—until all details are firmly in mind. Question everything during this last step: "What does this mean?" "What is its significance?" "Does this imply things which are not specifically stated?"

The last question is particularly important, for many pertinent aspects of a problem may be stated only by implication and it may take some elementary deduction to identify them. As an example—and perhaps as a welcome respite from things technical—consider the following problem in logic:

The members of a small loan company are Mr. Black, Mr. White, Mr. Gray, Mrs. Brown, Miss Green, and Miss Blue. They hold the positions of manager, assistant manager, cashier, teller, stenographer, and clerk, though not necessarily respectively. The cashier is the stenographer's son-in-law. The assistant manager is the manager's grandson. Mr. Black is a bachelor. Mr. White is 22 years old. Miss Green is the teller's step-sister. Mr. Gray is the manager's nearest neighbor. Who holds each position with the company?

Let's see what elementary deduction does for us when it is applied to one of the statements above. Statement: "The cashier is the stenographer's son-in-law." Deduced implications: (1) The cashier is male; (2) the cashier is married; (3) the stenographer is married; (4) the stenographer is elderly; and (5) the cashier is a generation younger than the stenographer. Apply the same sort of analysis to each of the other statements, compare the results, and the problem is easily solved.

Statements in engineering problems will generally not be so subtle; nevertheless, important inferences can almost always be drawn. A few typical engineering statements are presented for analysis in the problem section at the end of the chapter, along with another logic problem thrown in for good measure. (Problems in logic and in engineering have much in common, for both require facts to be assembled in a logical manner as a prerequisite to a solution.)

Jotting down pertinent details in note form is urged as an aid to understanding the problem. Many students rely on underlining to emphasize salient points in written problems, but such points will be set more firmly in mind if they are rewritten in the student's own hand. A simple diagram will often provide a convenient rack on which to hang pertinent details. The use of a diagram is particularly recommended when mass or energy balances may be required, for it will show at a glance all flow streams of interest and will help to insure that no stream is overlooked when the numerical calculations are carried out.

Analyzing the problem. Once he is sure he understands all aspects of the problem, the engineer is well advised to sit back for a few minutes and think it over in terms of the basic principles likely to be involved in its solution. For the chemical engineer, this analysis might well consist of considering each of the various aspects of change in turn and deciding which ones will be pertinent. Will an energy balance be required? Is the rate concept involved? Must economic factors be considered? Indeed, the deliberate consideration of each aspect in turn should provide insurance against some fundamental aspect being completely overlooked.

The analysis step should also include a study of the problem from the viewpoint of the engineering method, with the considerations of major importance being sorted out for primary attention. This is probably a good point at which to make the first quick stab at an answer to the problem by means of a well-considered guess.

In most cases it is not advisable to start with the given information and plan the steps which will lead to the desired answer, even should such a procedure be possible. Instead, the engineer should start with the answer and work backwards toward the given information. The basis for this recommendation is the fact that *given* information will often be incomplete or partially extraneous and hence misleading, whereas there can be no doubt about *requested* information.

In general terms, the engineer's line of reasoning in the analysis step might go something like this: I am asked to determine Z; Z depends on W, X, and Y, and I know the quantitative relationship; X and Y are fundamental data (not necessarily given in the problem statement) and can be ascertained; W, however, depends on T, U, and V; and so forth, until finally F and G are found to be quantitatively related to A, B, and E, which are given in the statement of the problem. (C and D may also have been given in the problem statement, but they were not needed in the solution.)

Particular note should be made of the branches (X and Y, for example) off the main line connecting requested and given information. These branches may lead to side chains which must also be followed back to a suitable starting point. Thus the analysis step may involve blocking out the solution to secondary problems as well as envisioning the primary route through the original problem.

It is important that the analysis step be completed before any quantitative calculations are undertaken, lest time be wasted on calculations which will subsequently be found to lead up blind alleys. The analysis step is also generally prerequisite to any successive refinement beyond the initial guess. In dealing with comprehensive problems, the engineering method may be applicable to the analysis itself: The overall problem can first be broken down into a number of sub-problems, with the breakdown being used as a basis for an estimate of the answer. The consideration of detailed steps and further refining of the estimate would then follow.

It should be apparent that the detailed plan of the solution is of great value in successively refining earlier, approximate answers. The quantitative relationships set forth in the plan should provide an indication of the relative importance of the various factors involved in the solution, and the engineer can therefore decide which of these factors should be given immediate attention and which can be temporarily neglected.

The analysis step often leads to the realization that certain *process* information, ostensibly pertinent, is neither given directly nor implied in the problem statement. In such cases it is necessary to make one or more *assumptions* which are consistent with whatever information *is* available. Subject to the latter restriction, the usual practice is to make assumptions which simplify the problem. For example, as noted in Sec. 2.4, changes in kinetic and potential energy in process equipment are normally assumed to be negligible in the absence of information to the contrary. In any event, a clear statement of each assumption should be an integral part of the problem solution.

Collecting the necessary data. Only in the simplest problems is all the physical and chemical *data* (as opposed to information pertaining to process conditions) necessary for a solution likely to be given in the problem statement. When it is not, the engineer must not only be conversant with supplementary sources of data and the type of information to be found in such sources; he will also find it necessary to determine for himself exactly what additional data are required. As we have already seen, the analysis step should lead directly to the latter determination—but only if the engineer is able to recognize the end points of the various branches off the main-line plan, that is, those unknowns which need merely be looked up in a suitable reference.

The primary sources of supplemental data are engineering handbooks and periodicals. It is essential that the engineer be familiar with both. Perry's *Chemical Engineers' Handbook* (McGraw-Hill Book Co., Inc., New York, 1950) in particular is an invaluable source of information of interest to the chemical engineer and should almost invariably be consulted first. Other handbooks will also be helpful from time to time and the student will do well to acquaint himself with their general content. Among the more useful are Hodgman's *Handbook of Chemistry and Physics* (Chemical Rubber Publishing Co., Cleveland, 1958), Lange's *Handbook of Chemistry* (Handbook Publishers, Inc., Sandusky, Ohio, 1956), and Washburn's *International Critical Tables* (McGraw-Hill Book Co., Inc., New York, 1926).

When the desired information is not to be found in a handbook, the problem becomes more difficult, for a search of periodicals can be an arduous undertaking. It will be greatly simplified if the engineer is completely at home in a technical library and well versed in the use of *Chemical Abstracts* (and other similar reference indexes). The detailed procedure for making a search of periodicals is beyond the scope of the present treatment, but the beginning chemical engineer will find it advantageous to look into the proper use of library reference material on his own if he is not already experienced in searching for specific information.

An even more effective hedge against a time-consuming search is to have prior familiarity with those periodicals which are most likely to contain data and general information of interest. Among the chemical engineering journals which are pertinent in this respect are *Chemical Engineering Progress* and *The A.I.Ch.E. Journal*, both published by the American Institute of Chemical Engineers; *Industrial and Engineering Chemistry*, *Chemical and Engineering News*, and the *Journal of Chemical and Engineering Data*, published by the American Chemical Society; and *Chemical Engineering* (McGraw-Hill). If the beginning chemical engineer is at all serious about his profession, it is not too early to start reading one or more of these periodicals, even if only superficially.

As for the type of information likely to be found in any of these supplementary sources, data regarding physical and chemical properties are perhaps most widely available. General data pertaining to equilibria and rates of change may also be found, but are much less extensive. On the other hand, information about specific processes, process equipment, and process instrumentation and control is widely published. Cost data are also generally available. These observations should give the student a rough idea of the help that may be obtained from outside references, but there is no substitute for experience when it comes to predicting what may or may not be found.

What happens when the engineer has satisfied himself that needed information is nowhere to be found? If the student has really assimilated the material presented earlier in this chapter, he already knows the answer: in such a case the engineer falls back on a guess, an estimate, or an approximation. Specific data pertaining to a similar situation can be of considerable help under such circumstances and serve to assure the engineer that he can't be greatly in error. What is the density of tomato juice, for example? If this information cannot be found and experimental measurement is not possible, the engineer will probably use the density of water in his calculations, and allow for error by introducing a suitable safety factor when he arrives at a final answer.

If the missing data are so critical that even a reasonable approximation is not adequate, then the engineer has no recourse but to arrange for a laboratory investigation, time permitting. And if time does not permit? There will always be occasions when a satisfactory solution to a problem will be impossible under conditions imposed.

Completing the solution. Only rarely will an engineer make calculations of interest only to himself. If they are important, someone else may be called upon to check them; or, if subsequent revision becomes advisable, the job may fall to another engineer. In any event, the likelihood that others will find it necessary to go over the calculations in detail must be anticipated. Sketchy, "back-of-an-envelope" calculations are therefore completely out of place, for it should always be clear what was done, why it was done, and how it was done.

This means that the mathematical solution to a problem will contain words as well as figures, since explanation will frequently be called for. As noted in Chap. 2, for example, it will be necessary to identify the system around which a balance is made, or the particular component being balanced. Further, the sources of all supplemental data should be clearly specified, while any assumptions, guesses, or estimates should be carefully identified as such and explained. Symbols should be defined unless their meaning is obvious. Finally, since the numbers used in engineering problems always have physical significance, the extensive use of appropriate units and labels is definitely called for.

Due attention to the foregoing rules leaves only the numbers themselves to be considered. Needless to say, this is an extremely important consideration, for a simple mathematical error can be just as disastrous in its final effect as would be, say, a gross error in the analysis of the problem. The quantitative aspects of engineering calculations will be thoroughly treated in Chap. 4.

Considering the results. The engineer will naturally take every precaution to insure against error in each of the steps in problem solving, but can hardly lay claim to infallibility. Accordingly, as a final check on the validity of the solution, he should always ask himself, "Does the answer make sense? Is it completely consistent with the physical situation, with the results of other calculations, with prior experience, and with the dictates of engineering judgment?" If it is not, the answer should be viewed with suspicion, pending a careful recheck of the solution.

The opportunity to test an answer in this manner is a unique feature of engineering calculations. In pure mathematics there would be no cause to doubt an answer of -1000 in a given problem, assuming that the pertinent mathematical calculations had been done with care. But if the engineer was calculating the pressure in a vessel and came up with an answer of -1000 *millimeters of mercury*, he could be certain that something was wrong somewhere and would do some careful back-checking.

The use of the method of successive refinement provides a built-in test of the soundness of an answer, since prior answers provide a basis of comparison. Even so, the wise engineer will never accept *any* answer at face value unless he is completely convinced that it is reasonable. In this respect it is misleading to list consideration of the results as a separate step in the problem-solving routine, for it should actually be an integral part of the entire routine. The experienced engineer automatically checks his results after each separate calculation lest a mistake be carried over into his subsequent work. The sooner the beginner forms the same habit, the easier his engineering studies will be for him.

Communicating the results. The details of report writing do not fall within the scope of this text, but this is not to suggest that the engineer can dismiss his reporting obligations as being of minor importance. The significance of a problem solution to others can easily be obscured by ineffectual reporting. Perhaps more important to the engineer as an individual is the fact that the report is likely to be the only permanent record of his accomplishments, and a well-written report which presents a well-conceived and well-executed solution to a challenging problem can be a significant factor in promotions. As the saying goes, "It pays to advertise."

Reports, like problem statements, may be oral as well as written, and the engineer will frequently be called upon to discuss his work formally as well as informally with his colleagues, his immediate superiors, and, on occasion, with higher management. Thus speaking ability and writing ability are equally important. The aspiring engineering student will do well to cultivate both as part of his professional development. Interestingly enough, a recent survey of young engineers in industry disclosed that these were two specific areas in which they felt themselves to be most deficient.

The foregoing strongly suggests that an engineer cannot expect to get ahead on the strength of his technical competence alone, and this is indeed the case. Additional support for the argument that an engineer should have a firm humanistic-social background was presented in the first chapter. Thus the importance of non-technical studies is hardly subject to debate. Truly, they are as essential to the engineer's overall professional development as is the wealth of technical subject matter with which he must become familiar.

3.4 Conclusion

Starting with the premise that the engineer is fundamentally a problem solver, we have now considered how he goes about obtaining his solutions, both from the standpoint of the overall engineering method and from the standpoint of the detailed steps he follows in working from problem statement to desired answer. Hopefully, the student will have found himself wholly receptive to these ideas, for "he that complies against his will is of his own opinion still" and will hardly make any great effort to adopt new techniques for his own use.

Unfortunately, it is one thing to be convinced and yet another to put one's convictions into practice. The road paved with good intentions is well known. Only as the student actually uses the engineering method will he come to understand its full implications and gain confidence in its wide-spread practicability. To the extent that he succeeds in making it a natural part of his philosophy, he will add immeasurably to his engineering capability.

As for the problem-solving routine, the very obviousness of its recommendations makes them all the more susceptible to careless disregard, yet an oversight of any kind in using the routine can be disastrous. We therefore urge meticulous care in its use, even to the point of returning repeatedly to the text material to insure that nothing has been forgotten. In time it too will become a natural part of the student's approach to problem solving and, like the more general engineering method, will add much to his overall ability as an engineer.

REVIEW, STUDY, AND DISCUSSION

3-1. The construction of a petroleum refinery that will process 50,000 barrels of crude oil per day is proposed. What is a five-second answer to the problem of determining the cost of construction? Describe in general terms how an engineer would go about obtaining five-minute, five-hour, five-day, five-week, and five-month answers to the same problem.

3-2. As stated before, the greater the required accuracy of a problem answer, the greater the time needed to obtain it. Sketch the curve which might be expected if per cent accuracy were to be plotted against working time for a comprehensive problem. Discuss the advantages of the engineering method in terms of this plot.

3-3. Distinguish between the "one-hour solution" and the "one-quarter of the four-hour solution" to a four-hour problem. Compare the advantages and disadvantages of each.

3-4. Give an example of a non-engineering situation to which the engineering method might be applied. Discuss the advantages and disadvantages of the approach in this situation.

3-5. List and discuss briefly each of the routine steps in problem solving. Which step do you feel is most important? Why?

3-6. List as many implications as you can deduce from each of the following statements:

a) A salt solution is to be cooled from 200°F to 100°F, at which temperature precipitation should occur.

b) Compound A will be pumped to storage after being separated from B by filtration.

c) The final product will be water-washed to remove impurities.

d) The liquid mixture will be fed to the reactor from a well-agitated storage vessel.

e) Steam at atmospheric pressure will enter the exchanger at 220°F and will be cooled by heat exchange with a stream of crude oil.

f) Chemical X is leaking from a hole in the roof of the storage tank, and the odor is easily detectable at the base of the tank.

3-7. Given the fact that a gallon of paint should cover 400 square feet of surface, you are asked to determine how many circular wooden disks, each a foot in diameter, can be painted with a single gallon of paint. Describe how you would go about analyzing this simple problem and planning a solution. Will any assumptions be necessary? Is the engineering method applicable to such a simple problem?

3-8. A sophomore, a junior, and a senior are sitting in on a freshman class taught by Prof. Jones, Prof. Brown, and Prof. Smith. Coincidentally, the students' names are also Jones, Brown, and Smith, though not necessarily in that order. The following facts are known:

a) Prof. Jones lives in Jonesville, five miles from the college.

b) The sophomore lives half way between Jonesville and the college.

c) Prof. Smith earns exactly $8,000 a year.

d) Brown once beat the junior at tennis.

e) The sophomore's father earns exactly two-thirds as much as his next-door neighbor, who is one of the three professors.

f) The professor who lives right across the street from the college has the same name as the sophomore.

What is the senior's name?

CHAPTER 4

Engineering Calculations

The importance of quantitative calculations in engineering has been emphasized only by implication up to this point, in deference to the objective of presenting an overall picture of chemical engineering before examining its quantitative details. With the qualitative treatment now complete, a thorough consideration of numerical calculations is a necessary intermediate step before we move on to specific chemical engineering problems. Just as the apprentice carpenter learns how to use his saw, chisel, and plane before attempting to build a house, so must the would-be-engineer know how to use the tools of *his* trade before he can be fully effective as a solver of practical problems.

The term "tools" is intended to include techniques, as well as real devices (such as the slide rule). It is presumed that the student has long since mastered the basic techniques of arithmetic and algebra, but he is certainly less familiar with their practical adaptation to engineering calculations, particularly when modifications are dictated by the engineering method discussed previously. The present chapter accordingly considers the tricks of the trade used by the engineer in setting up and carrying out quantitative calculations.

71

UNITS, LABELS, AND DIMENSIONS

4.1 Basic Concepts

It has already been noted that the numbers used in engineering problems always have physical significance; therefore, the extensive use of appropriate *units* is essential. The pure number 600 means little to the engineer because it leaves unanswered the very pertinent question, "Six hundred what?" But as soon as units are added, the picture changes, for 600 *square feet* or 600°F or 600 *pounds per hour* all have distinct physical significance.

The proper designation of units will not always tell the whole story, for we may still be left wondering, "Six hundred pounds of what?" If a number is to be truly informative, it may be necessary to provide not only appropriate units but an explanatory *label* as well. Even a label such as 600 pounds *of water* per hour may not be sufficient, for it may be necessary to specify 600 pounds of water per hour *leaving the second heat exchanger* in order to eliminate any possible confusion.

A wide variety of units can be used to describe any given physical quantity. For example, *length* might be expressed in feet, meters, miles, Angstrom units, or light-years. In many situations it is convenient to adopt a generalized notation rather than specify particular units; a *dimension* is therefore defined as "a general term denoting any or all units pertaining to a given physical quantity." Thus the *dimension* of length embraces all conceivable *units* of length. This dimension is commonly symbolized by L, which may be read simply "length units".

Length, mass, time, and *temperature* are fundamental physical concepts, and their respective dimensions may be represented by L, M, θ, and T. The dimensions pertaining to other physical quantities may be readily obtained by properly combining these four fundamental dimensions. Thus, area, being the product of two lengths, must have the dimension L^2. Similarly, velocity has the dimension L/θ (sometimes written $L\theta^{-1}$) for it represents a length (distance) divided by time. Other derived dimensions, such as ML/θ^2 for force or ML^2/θ^2 for energy, are not quite so obvious, but their validity will be demonstrated in due course.

Even though the dimensions of force and energy may be derived from the four fundamental dimensions, these physical quantities are encountered so frequently in chemical engineering problems that it is often convenient to assign them fundamental dimensions of their own, F and E respectively. Thus pressure would have the dimension F/L^2, but, since F has been substituted for the more fundamental dimension ML/θ^2, pressure might also be characterized by $M/L\theta^2$.

Dimensional notation is always symbolic, whereas the designation of units requires the use of words, or at least their abbreviations. Unit notation is therefore less concise, and care must be taken to insure against misinterpretation. It is strongly recommended that the student form the habit of using parenthetical notation, in which adjacent units in a combination are separated by parentheses. There can be no misunderstanding the units of thermal conductivity, for example, if they are written $BTU/(hr)(ft^2)(°F/ft)$. The use of hyphens is also common, particularly for frequently encountered combinations such as ft-lb or hp-hr. But the possibility of misinterpretation in complex notation should be immediatedly obvious: $BTU/hr-ft^2-°F/ft$. The notation $BTU/hr/ft^2/°F/ft$ is to be particularly avoided.

A second possible source of confusion is the choice of abbreviations, for "abbreviated abbreviations" are used to a considerable extent, particularly within specialized fields. The chemical engineer will frequently encounter combinations such as psia, cfm, BPD, or fps, and should be able to interpret them. But he should use them himself only when sure that they will be equally familiar to those who may be called upon to interpret them. An engineer in the natural gas industry would have no trouble deciphering the units MMSCFSD, but the expression can easily baffle even a chemical engineer in another field. Some of the more common abbreviations of this type are tabulated in the back of the book.

4.2 Consistency of Units

Both labels and units may be important in setting up calculations as well as in giving full meaning to an answer. In the absence of units, there is no apparent restriction to the problem of adding 11 and 12 to get the obvious answer 23. But suppose the problem were to find the combined length of two pieces of pipe, one 11 feet long and the other 12 inches. The numbers are unchanged, addition is clearly indicated, and 11 plus 12 is still 23; the only thing now obvious about the answer it that it is wrong.

This example illustrates a point of great significance: Complete *consistency of units* is prerequisite to the numerical completion of indicated mathematical operations. Stated more specifically, this means that *all numbers joined by plus, minus, or equality signs must have the same units.* In the above illustration, we need merely convert the length of the first pipe to 132 inches, whereupon the addition becomes correct in terms of both numbers and units, for 132 inches plus 12 inches does in fact equal 144 inches.

A second principle pertaining to the consistency of units is perhaps even more significant: *When physical quantities undergo the operations of multiplication or division, the corresponding units must be subjected to the same operation, and the resulting combination of units will characterize the numerical answer.* Thus 12 men times 8 hours equals 96 "men times hours" or man-hours; 24 feet divided by 6 seconds is 4 "feet divided by seconds" or ft/sec; 16 inches times 2 inches equals 32 "inches times inches" or in.^{2}. The principle is directly applicable even when the initial units are already combinations: 4 ft/sec times 2 ft^2 equals 8 ft^3/sec.

An important corollary to this second principle is that a unit appearing in both the numerator and denominator of a combination of units may be cancelled in the same way that numbers are cancelled in the multiplication of fractions. For example, 4 ft/sec times 60 lb/ft^3 is 240 (ft)(lb)/(ft^3)(sec) in accordance with the second principle. Upon application of the corollary, however, the answer becomes simply 240 lb/(ft^2)(sec). Note that we have already made use of both the principle and its corollary in the pipe example above, for we determined the length of the first pipe to be 132 inches by multiplying 11 ft by 12 in./ft to get 132 (ft)(in.)/ft or 132 in.

It is interesting to note that the application of the corollary can lead to numbers which have no units, called *dimensionless* numbers. If an inclined plane rises 4 feet in 20 feet of length, we say it has a a pitch or slope of 0.2. Ostensibly, the latter is a dimensionless number; but since it was obtained by dividing 4 ft by 20 ft, we might also conclude that it is characterized by the units ft/ft, or, more particularly, feet of rise per foot of length.

Many other numbers generally considered dimensionless can be assigned appropriate units as an aid in insuring unit consistency. The most important of these are percentages and molecular weights. Suppose a salt solution contains 10 per cent salt. From the unit standpoint, this means that there are 10 *pounds of salt per hundred pounds of solution*—or, alternately, 0.1 pounds of salt per pound of solution—thereby identifying the pertinent units. Similarly, molecular weights can be considered to have units of pounds per pound-mole or grams per gram-mole. We will examine mole units and their application in due course.

Note that the last two examples involved labels as well as units; this will be the case in most practical problems. Labels can be as important as units in setting up calculations, for labels survive multiplication and division in the same way that units do. Thus 300 pounds of water divided by 15 pounds of salt does not lead to a dimensionless answer in the strictest sense, but to 20 *pounds of water per pound of salt*. This concept assumes even greater importance when mixed units are involved: 834 pounds of alcohol divided by 8.34 pounds of water per gallon does not equal 100 gallons of anything, even though lb divided by lb/gal equals gallons.

Labels also survive addition and subtraction, but the requirement of consistency may be obscured by a change in nomenclature. If 10 pounds *of hydrogen* are added to 10 pounds *of oxygen* to obtain 20 pounds *of gas* (hardly an improper operation) it might appear that labels have been mixed. It is only necessary to recognize that the *gas* in this case is simply *hydrogen plus oxygen*, whereupon it becomes apparent that both units and labels are consistent.

The two principles of consistency, together with the corollary to the second principle, may seem to be ridiculously simple, for there is nothing particularly complicated about them. Yet they constitute one of the most powerful tools available to the engineer in setting up calculations in a form which will lead to the correct numerical answer. The wise engineer will never write down a combination of numbers without checking, either mentally or as a separate calculation on the side, the consistency of units and labels in accordance with the principles given above. The student who cultivates the same habit will save himself many a false step in solving comprehensive problems.

4.3 Unit Conversion

When the units associated with the numerical quantities to be substituted into a given relationship are not initially consistent, it is necessary to convert one or more of the quantities to a consistent set of units. Unit conversion is not always as simple as it was in the pipe example already cited, but the meticulous application of the principles set forth in the preceding section will always show the way.

Suppose 500 gallons of water is to be converted to cubic feet. The conversion factor is known to be 7.48 gal/ft^3, but is the conversion effected by multiplication or division? A quick check of the units gives the answer: gallons divided by gal/ft^3 yields the desired cubic feet, whereas gallons multiplied by gal/ft^3 leads to gal^2/ft^3. Ridiculous as this answer is, many a young engineer who should know better has performed the numerical multiplication without thinking and duly labeled his answer "cubic feet".

The same type of analysis is applicable to the cancellation of labels. To illustrate, let us reconsider our 10 per cent salt solution: From the standpoint of units alone, there is no bar to dividing 100 pounds of solution by 10 pounds of salt per pound of solution. But from the label standpoint, such a procedure is highly inadvisable, unless, of course, the engineer really wants an answer expressed in "square pounds of solution per pound of salt."

Careful analysis of units is even more essential when complex combinations of units are to be converted. This situation arises all too frequently, since laboratory data are almost invariably reported in metric units, whereas engineering calculations are usually carried out in English units. Specific conversion factors for most combinations of interest are to found in handbooks; but a handbook will not always be available, and the engineer may have to fall back on component factors which are already familiar to him.

Let us demonstrate the technique in a final example of the efficacy of unit analysis:

The overall factor for converting gm/(cm²)(sec) to lb/(ft²)(hr) is to be calculated from known conversion factors of 2.54 cm/in., 12 in./ft, 60 sec/min, 60 min/hr, and 453.6 gm/lb. First we write down the initial units in the "built-up" style:

$$\frac{\text{gm}}{(\text{cm}^2)(\text{sec})}$$

Then we tackle each individual unit in turn, introducing the pertinent factor or factors, while checking unit cancellation to see whether multiplication or division is called for. Thus, to convert grams to pounds, we can make direct use of the gm/lb factor, but do we multiply or divide? A check of unit consistency indicates division. This is most conveniently indicated by reciprocal multiplication:

$$\frac{\text{gm}}{(\text{cm}^2)(\text{sec})}\left(\frac{\text{lb}}{\text{gm}}\right)$$

Note that the gram units can now be cancelled out.

Using only the given information, we cannot convert directly from centimeters to feet, but we can go from centimeters to inches and then to feet. The conversion of seconds into hours is similarly effected, with unit cancellation being checked at each step and duly indicated in the resulting expression:

$$\frac{\text{gm}}{(\text{cm}^2)(\text{sec})}\left(\frac{\text{lb}}{\text{gm}}\right)\left(\frac{\text{cm}}{\text{in.}}\right)^2\left(\frac{\text{in.}}{\text{ft}}\right)^2\left(\frac{\text{sec}}{\text{min}}\right)\left(\frac{\text{min}}{\text{hr}}\right)$$

Collecting the units which remain uncancelled, we see that we have indeed succeeded in obtaining lb/(ft²)(hr). It now becomes a simple matter to substitute the corresponding numbers into the expression to obtain the desired overall factor for conversion:

$$\left(\frac{1}{453.6}\right)(2.54)^2(12)^2(60)(60) = 7375$$

Hence any number having the units gm/(cm²)(sec) can be converted to lb/(ft²)(hr) by multiplying by 7375 (slide-rule accuracy). The factor itself, in accordance with the principles of unit combination, must have the units lb/(ft²)(hr) divided by gm/(cm²)(sec).

An experienced engineer can usually write down the numerical expression directly while performing all unit cancellations mentally, and the student should practice toward that end. But the most important thing is to be sure that the conversion is carried out correctly, and, if setting up the units separately will help, by all means do it. The ability to do the job mentally will come soon enough with practice.

4.4 Some Special Units

Mass based on molecular weight. Many chemical engineering calculations are most conveniently carried out in mole units. The student has presumably already encountered the concept of the *gram-molecular-weight*, usually shortened to *gram-mole* (with the final "e" frequently dropped), in chemistry. To review the concept briefly, a gram-mol represents "that quantity of any material which has a weight in grams equal to the molecular weight of the material." Since different materials have different molecular weights, the gram-mol is a variable quantity of matter—but a quantity which is still uniquely defined for any given material.

In engineering calculations it is usually more convenient to work with pound-mols rather than gram-mols, but the same basic definition applies: A pound-mol (commonly abbreviated lb-mol or simply mol), represents that quantity of any material which has a weight in pounds equal to the molecular weight of the material. Thus 2 mols of carbon (MW = 12) corresponds to 24 pounds of carbon, while 14 pounds of nitrogen (MW = 28) is equivalent to 0.5 mols.

We can see from the foregoing that the conversion of pounds to mols or mols to pounds is simple enough: mols times molecular weight gives pounds, and pounds divided by molecular weight gives mols. In either case, the application of the principles of unit consistency leads to the conclusion that molecular weight as used in such calculations must have the units lb/lb-mol. Recognition of this fact will frequently be helpful in setting up problems involving the cancellation of units.

Despite its extensive use, the pound-mol will often be discarded in favor of the gram-mol, the kilogram-mol, or the ton-mol in accordance with the dictates of convenience. Similarly, there may be situations in which it will be preferable to use pound-atoms instead of pound-mols. If the student really understands the mol concept, he will have no difficulty in extending it to cover any of these analogous units.

Absolute temperature. Many of the property relationships encountered in chemical engineering require the use of *absolute* temperatures, rather than temperatures expressed in the more common units of degrees Fahrenheit or Centigrade. The student should have encountered the concept of absolute temperature in chemistry, and only a brief review will be presented here:

The two absolute temperature scales in common use are the Rankine and Kelvin scales. One Kelvin degree (K°) covers the same temperature *interval* as one Centigrade degree (C°), but a temperature *level* of 0°K corresponds to -273.2°C. Thus

$$(T \text{ in } °K) = (t \text{ in } °C) + 273.2 \tag{4.1}$$

but

$$\Delta T \text{ in } K° = \Delta t \text{ in } C° \tag{4.2}$$

The distinction between temperature level and temperature interval or change should be kept firmly in mind at all times, for its neglect can obviously result in serious errors. We shall consistently place the degree symbol *before* the scale abbreviation to denote *level*, and *reverse* the order to denote *interval*, so as to emphasize the distinction. Thus 100°C is the boiling point (level) of water, whereas ice water must be heated 100 C° (interval) to bring it to its boiling point.

Absolute zero on the Rankine scale corresponds to −459.7°F, but one degree covers the same temperature interval on either scale. Thus

$$(T \text{ in } °R) = (t \text{ in } °F) + 459.7 \tag{4.3}$$

and

$$\Delta T \text{ in } R° = \Delta t \text{ in } F° \tag{4.4}$$

The interval covered by one C° or K° is 1.8 times as large as that covered by one F° or R°. The conversion factor for converting from one *interval* scale to the other is accordingly 1.8 R°/K°, or 1.8 F°/C°. The same relationship applies to temperature *levels* in degrees Rankine or Kelvin, since the zero points on both scales are coincident. The pertinent factor is thus 1.8°R/°K. To relate Centigrade and Fahrenheit levels, on the other hand, it is necessary to allow for the fact that 0°C is equivalent to 32°F, and

$$(t \text{ in } °F) - 32 = 1.8(t \text{ in } °C) \tag{4.5}$$

Absolute temperatures expressed in degrees Kelvin or Rankine *must* be used in many thermodynamic calculations. The chemical engineer is well advised to use absolute units in *all* calculations unless the use of other units is specifically prescribed—or when only intervals and not levels are to be treated.

Absolute pressure. The use of absolute pressures is similarly called for in chemical engineering calculations, but many pressure-measuring devices in common use indicate *gage pressure*, or the pressure above or below atmospheric pressure. Gage pressures must therefore be corrected to absolute values before calculations are undertaken, and the correction is accomplished by simply adding the atmospheric pressure to the gage reading.

For example, a gage pressure of 10 psig (pounds per square inch gage) corresponds to an absolute pressure of 24.7 psia, assuming atmospheric pressure to be 14.7 psi. Similarly, a vacuum of 100 mm Hg means a gage pressure of −100 mm Hg, and is equivalent to an absolute pressure of 660 mm Hg, again assuming atmospheric pressure to 14.7 psi, which corresponds to 760 mm Hg. Conversion equivalents for pressure units in common use are tabulated in the back of the book.

MASS, FORCE, AND WEIGHT

4.5 Dimension of Force

It was suggested earlier that force is not a fundamental concept from the dimensional standpoint, since it can be expressed in terms of mass, length, and time. It was also suggested that it is generally convenient to assign a special dimension to force instead of depending entirely on a more complex derived dimension. It should be immediately apparent that there must be important restrictions pertaining to such an assignment if we are to maintain complete consistency among the dimensions—and units—of force, mass, length, and time. This section will consider the relationship among these variables and will, at the same time, provide an excellent illustration of the way in which the principles of unit consistency can be put to practical use.

In its most familiar form, Newton's second law of motion states that force is equal to mass times acceleration, or, $F = Ma$. (This is admittedly not the most rigorous statement of the law, but it will suffice for almost all applications of interest to chemical engineers, and the exceptions are safely left out of this text.) Now let us apply what we have learned about units and dimensions to Newton's law: The mass term in the equality will have the fundamental dimension of mass itself, $\mathbf{M}$. Acceleration, on the other hand, is a derived concept dimensionally speaking. Since it represents velocity $(\mathbf{L}/\boldsymbol{\theta})$ divided by time, it must have the dimension $\mathbf{L}/\boldsymbol{\theta}^2$. The product of M times a, then, must have the dimension $\mathbf{ML}/\boldsymbol{\theta}^2$ in accordance with the second principle of unit consistency.

At this point the first principle becomes pertinent, since F and the Ma product are joined by an equality sign. Thus F, force, must also have the dimension $\mathbf{ML}/\boldsymbol{\theta}^2$ if unit consistency is to be maintained. This is precisely the dimension presented earlier. The force dimension, $\mathbf{F}$, can now be introduced as a convenience symbol to replace the group $\mathbf{ML}/\boldsymbol{\theta}^2$ in the same way that H (enthalpy) was introduced to replace $U + PV$. Thus, by definition, $\mathbf{F} = \mathbf{ML}/\boldsymbol{\theta}^2$.

4.6 Units of Force

In metric units, with mass in grams, length in centimeters, and time in seconds, the corresponding units of force are $(\text{gm})(\text{cm})/\text{sec}^2$, and this combination is called a *dyne*. The equivalent unit in the English system is the *poundal*, corresponding to one $(\text{lb})(\text{ft})/\text{sec}^2$. The practice of giving a special name to frequently encountered combinations of units is not uncommon. As a matter of fact, all units except those pertaining directly to mass, length, time, and temperature represent special combinations of the units of these basic concepts, although in many cases a numerical factor is also involved.

The erg, for example, is one dyne-centimeter, or one $(gm)(cm^2)/sec^2$, while a joule represents 10^7 ergs.

In most chemical engineering work, the unit of force is the pound. Since mass is also measured in pounds, it is necessary to differentiate between the two meanings of the term whenever confusion might result. Accordingly, the pound-force is commonly symbolized by lb_f and the pound mass by lb_m. It now remains only to establish a specific relationship between these two units in accordance with the general relationship between force and mass.

4.7 Force-Mass Relationship

When the acceleration being considered is that due to the earth's gravitational field, Newton's law may be written $F = Mg$, where $g = 32.17$ ft/sec² at sea level. A pound-force may then be defined as the force that results when one pound-mass is subjected to an acceleration of 32.17 ft/sec². Suppose we substitute these values into Newton's law:

$$1 \text{ lb}_f = (1 \text{ lb}_m)(32.17 \text{ ft/sec}^2)$$

Two discrepancies are immediately apparent: First, the relationship is numerically incorrect; and second, the units are inconsistent, for the units on both sides of the equality sign are nowhere near the same.

If we insist on measuring force in pounds, then, it is apparent that we will have to include a conversion factor in this expression. This factor, commonly denoted by g_c, is introduced into the left-hand side:

$$(g_c)(1 \text{ lb}_f) = (1 \text{ lb}_m)(32.17 \text{ ft/sec}^2)$$

Solving this relationship for g_c (and following the rules for preserving units), we find that

$$g_c = 32.17 \text{ (lb}_m)(\text{ft})/(\text{lb}_f)(\text{sec}^2)$$

This dimensional constant, sometimes called the *gravitational constant*, is extremely important in chemical engineering calculations. It is a true constant, and should not be confused with the gravitational *acceleration*, g, which can take on various values. Both the numerical value and the units of g_c should be committed to memory. Perhaps the easiest scheme is to memorize Newton's law in the form $g_cF = Ma$, for the units of g_c are readily deduced from this expression.

In many applications g and g_c will appear in ratio to each other. If g is equal to 32.17 ft/sec², as, for practical purposes, it is anywhere on the earth's surface, their numerical values will cancel out. Their units, on the other hand, do not cancel, for they are not the same. A check of the unit combination shows g/g_c to have the units lb_f/lb_m, and the ratio accordingly constitutes a conversion factor for getting from pounds-mass to pounds-force and back again. As noted above, the factor will have a numerical value of unity only when g is equal to 32.17 ft/sec²; but other values for the acceleration are readily substituted when the occasion demands.

When does one use the gravitational constant? Whenever it is needed to make the units come out right. Beginning chemical engineers are often suspicious of this "fudge factor" aspect of the constant, but it is a perfectly legitimate consequence of our decision to use the pound-force as the primary unit of force. Were we not quite so stubborn, we could dispense with g_c entirely by simply accepting the poundal as the unit of force, as physicists do. Or, we might retain the pound-force and instead join the proponents of the *slug* as the primary unit of mass; a slug is one $(lb_f)(sec^2)/ft$, in accordance with Newton's law and the dictates of dimensional consistency.

Two simple—but important—examples should suffice to illustrate the use of g_c. First, let us calculate the potential energy possessed by a mass of 20 pounds when it is 50 feet above sea level. At first glance, 20 pounds times 50 feet would appear to equal 1000 ft-lbs of energy. But a foot-pound of energy corresponds to a *force* of one pound moving through a distance of one foot, and the correct expression is therefore ft-lb$_f$ and not ft-lb$_m$. We must therefore convert lb$_m$ to lb$_f$, which we do by introducing the factor g/g_c. Thus the symbolic expression for potential energy is not simply Mz (z being the elevation), but Mgz/g_c. Were we to express mass in slugs, on the other hand, the correct expression would be simply Mgz.

As a second example, consider the calculation of kinetic energy. It may be recalled from physics that kinetic energy equals one-half mass times velocity squared or, in English units, $(lb_m)(ft/sec)^2$. How does one go about converting this to ft-lb$_f$? Again we might be tempted to bring in g/g_c, but we would be left with unwanted units of ft/sec². This suggests using only g_c. A check of the unit combination shows that it belongs in the denominator, and the resulting units are found to be simply ft-lb$_f$ when cancellation is completed. Hence kinetic energy can be symbolized by $Mu^2/2g_c$. (What will the corresponding expression be if the mass is in slugs?)

Mass and weight. The distinction between mass and weight is somewhat subtle, but it is nevertheless one of which the engineer should be aware. Strictly speaking, *weight* refers to the gravitational force exerted on a body, and it is accordingly expressed in pounds-force rather than in pounds-mass. Since, as has been noted, the lb$_m$-to-lb$_f$ conversion factor (g/g_c) is equal to unity for almost all situations of interest to chemical engineers, there is a tendency to use the terms weight and mass interchangeably.

It should be recognized, however, that, whereas mass is a true property of matter, weight depends on environment as well. Thus one pound-mass will *weigh* exactly one pound (force) wherever $g = 32.17$ ft/sec²; but the same mass would weigh only $\frac{1}{6}$ of a pound or so on the moon, for example, where the gravitational acceleration is approximately $\frac{1}{6}$ as great. In outer space, the same mass would be weightless. Extensive chemical engineering activity on the moon or in space may appear to be remote, but it will still be well to keep the distinction between mass and weight in mind.

4.8 Energy Units

The concept of energy as the product of a force times the distance through which it moves correctly indicates that the dimension of energy must be **FL** or, substituting $\mathbf{F} = \mathbf{ML}/\boldsymbol{\theta}^2$, $\mathbf{ML}^2/\boldsymbol{\theta}^2$. (Note that numerical conversion factors are omitted in dimensional notation. It is tacitly assumed that consistent units will be used.) As was done in the case of the force dimension **F**, the convenience symbol **E** may be introduced to represent the dimension of energy. It is equal to $\mathbf{ML}^2/\boldsymbol{\theta}^2$ by definition.

The ft-lb$_f$ is a satisfactory unit for energy in the form of work, internal energy, and, as has already been demonstrated, kinetic and potential energy. It also applies to enthalpy ($H = U + PV$) if P is expressed in lb/ft^2 and V is in ft^3, since the PV product will then be in ft-lb$_f$. Energy in the form of heat or thermal energy, on the other hand, is normally expressed in calories or British Thermal Units (BTU). A calorie represents the quantity of heat required to raise the temperature of one gram of water one Centigrade degree, while a BTU is the quantity of heat required to raise the temperature of one *pound* of water one *Fahrenheit* degree. As here stated, neither of these definitions is exact, but they will suffice for almost all engineering applications. The conversion factor relating the two units is 252 cal/BTU.

The relationship between heat and work was first demonstrated in a classical experiment by J. P. Joule, a British physicist, in the mid-nineteenth century. Joule succeeded in raising the temperature of water by mechanical stirring only, and was able to relate quantitatively the temperature rise to the amount of work done on the water by the stirrer. Subsequent investigations by others ultimately indicated that one BTU of heat is approximately equal to 778 ft-lb$_f$ of work. The conversion factor relating the units of ft-lb$_f$ and BTU is accordingly 778 ft-lb$_f$/BTU.

Although both heat and work appear in the general energy balance equation developed in Chap. 2, the principle of unit consistency requires that a single common unit of energy be used. Either the ft-lb$_f$ or the BTU might be used, but the use of the latter will be more convenient in most chemical engineering work. Literature data pertaining to internal energy and enthalpy are normally reported in BTU units, but it will be necessary to convert work, kinetic energy, and potential energy to BTU before numerical calculations are undertaken.

It was stated in Chap. 2 that kinetic and potential energy effects are frequently negligible in problems of interest to chemical engineers. It should now be clear why this is so. In the case of potential energy (Mgz/g_c), assuming g/g_c to be unity, a one-pound mass would have to have an elevation of 778 feet to possess 778 ft-lb$_f$ or one BTU of energy. Similarly, the substitution of numerical values into the expression for kinetic energy, $Mu^2/2g_c$, will show that a one-pound mass must have a velocity of 224 ft/sec if its kinetic energy is to be one BTU. In contrast, the condensation of one pound-mass of steam at atmospheric pressure is accompanied by an energy change of 970 BTU. Thus kinetic and potential energy effects may safely be neglected under normal circumstances.

This completes the discussion of units, dimensions, labels, consistency, and conversion, but they will be encountered again and again in setting up and solving practical engineering problems. As was noted earlier, these concepts constitute one of the most powerful tools at the engineer's command. Many an avenue of attack on a problem will open up when they are applied conscientiously; and many an otherwise valid solution will be rendered worthless when they are ignored. The sooner the student assimilates these principles, the sooner he will benefit from their use.

NUMERICAL CALCULATIONS

In the course of determining the factor for converting $gm/(cm^2)(sec)$ to $lb/(ft^2)(hr)$ in Sec. 4.3, it was shown that the answer could be obtained by carrying out the mathematical operations indicated by the expression

$$\left(\frac{1}{453.6}\right)(2.54)^2(12)^2(60)(60)$$

In most engineering calculations the application of the principles of unit consistency and conversion will yield a similar string of numbers to be multiplied, divided, squared, etc., and the final step will be to carry out the indicated operations to obtain an answer. The more important methods and techniques applicable to this final step will now be considered.

4.9 Alternative Methods of Computation

In the completely general case, computation can be carried out in a number of different ways. An obvious way is to make long-hand calculations, and a desk calculating machine might be used to simplify the task. A third possibility would be the use of a table of logarithms, while the slide rule represents still another calculating aid. Finally, if the student has been duly imbued with the spirit of the engineering method, he will also accept the idea of approximating, estimating, or even guessing the answer within varying limits of accuracy. The choice among these methods will be dictated by such considerations as the availability of calculating aids, the complexity of the calculations, the degree of accuracy required, and the time available for the computation.

Long-hand calculations, even if carried out on a desk calculator, are time-consuming, and the extensive nature of the usual computation makes them susceptible to the introduction of errors. On the other hand, they will yield the most accurate answer, for there is no limit to the number of significant figures that can be retained. Applied to the example computation, long-hand calculation yields an answer of 7373.2571428 . . . It can be anticipated that 11 or more significant figures will be of little use, even if their retention could be justified.

The use of logarithms permits the solution of problems involving fractional roots and powers, neither of which can be handled either long-hand or on a desk calculator. Otherwise, the use of logarithms differs from long-hand calculation only in that it converts the operations of multiplication and division into addition and subtraction. The conversion takes time but errors are less likely. Four to six-place accuracy is possible, depending on the extent of the tables. Six-place tables give an answer of 7373.25 for the foregoing problem.

By far the most rapid calculating aid is the slide rule, with which this same problem can be run off in 30 seconds or less. We have already reported a slide-rule answer of 7375, although it might easily have been read 7370 or 7380. As we shall see shortly, any of these answers will be sufficiently accurate for most engineering calculations. Like logarithms, the slide rule permits the determination of fractional roots and powers. Because of the importance of slide-rule work in engineering, a separate section is devoted to techniques pertinent to its use.

As for the approximation or estimate, it may surprise the student to learn that an answer can usually be predicted to within 3 or 4 per cent without any calculating device whatsoever, and in as little time as it takes to use a slide rule. The ability to make quick mental calculations can be an important asset to the engineer and, fortunately, is something anyone can acquire with practice. It, too, will be given detailed attention shortly.

This discussion would not be complete without some mention of the impact of digital and analog computers on modern engineering calculations. These machines make it possible to solve highly complex problems which would not be amenable to solution otherwise, and they can be expected to assume an even more important role as time goes on. Their capabilities and limitations will not be considered here, except to note that they supplement rather than replace the other methods of calculation. Indeed, complete familiarity with the techniques presented in this chapter is perhaps the best possible preparation for subsequent work with computers.

The foregoing consideration of various computing methods bears a striking resemblance to the earlier development of the engineering method: Here again we have a multiplicity of answers, a time factor to be considered, and the distinct possibility that a rigorous calculation cannot be justified since one of the quicker methods may be completely adequate. Unless the student has had some prior instruction in the concept of significant figures, he may not fully appreciate the last point. A brief consideration of this subject will be advisable before we turn to other aspects of numerical calculation.

4.10 Significant Figures

Engineering calculations will almost invariably involve decisions regarding the extent to which figures can or should be rounded off. These decisions are partially based on the required accuracy of the answer, but should also reflect the precision of given information and supplementary data. Accordingly, after each mathematical operation we should ask ourselves how many of the digits in the answer are trustworthy or significant, and discard the rest.

The rules for determining significant figures are fairly simple. First, given information or data are generally assumed to have an uncertainty of ± 1 in the last significant figure reported. Thus a temperature of 74.8°F presumably means a temperature within the range between 74.7 and 74.9°F, unless other limits of precision are specifically indicated, e.g., a temperature of 75 ± 5°F. The plus-or-minus one rule is applicable regardless of the position of the decimal point, although some doubt may arise when one or more zeros precede the decimal point. The uncertainties associated with the numbers 856 and 8.56 would be ± 1 and ± 0.01, respectively; additional information is required to determine whether 8560 has an uncertainty of ± 10 or only ± 1, for the zero may or may not be significant. However, note that the number 0.800 definitely implies an uncertainty of only ± 0.001, since the zeros are superfluous otherwise.

In addition and subtraction, the uncertainties associated with the numbers involved in the operation are additive. If 5.47 is added to 38.6, the answer of 44.07 should be rounded off to 44.1, for the uncertainty would be ± 0.11. This follows from the presumed uncertainties of 0.01 and 0.1 in the original numbers. The addition of uncertainties is particularly important when two numbers of similar magnitude are to be subtracted, for it will frequently be found that little significance can be attached to the answer: 16.592 minus 16.57 is 0.022; but, since the original uncertainties total 0.011, it can be seen that this answer is only certain within ± 50 per cent.

In multiplication and division, *percentage* uncertainties are approximately additive. 1.20 times 24 is 28.8, but the original uncertainties are one part in 120 and one part in 24. Accordingly, the uncertainty in the product is approximately $(1/120 + 1/24)(28.8) = 1.4$. Were 1.20 to be divided by 24 the uncertainty in the quotient of 0.05 would be $(1/120 + 1/24)(.05) = 0.0025$, approximately.

The rules governing the rounding-off operation can be stated briefly to complete the treatment of significant figures: When the digit following the last digit to be retained is less than 5, the retained digit is not changed; if the first digit to be dropped is more than 5, the last retained digit is increased by 1; and if the digit to be dropped is 5, the last retained digit is left unchanged (if even) or increased by 1 (if odd).

Returning to the sample conversion calculation, we see that the slide-rule answer is wholly adequate from the standpoint of significant figures; this will be the case in most chemical engineering calculations. As a matter of fact, the use of the slide rule automatically eliminates non-significant figures, thereby relieving the engineer of this responsibility to a considerable extent. Occasionally, however, slide-rule accuracy will not suffice, and the engineer must resort to more precise methods of calculation. The foregoing discussion of significant figures should provide a basis for recognizing those situations in which greater accuracy is desirable and justifiable.

4.11 Locating the Decimal Point

A mislocated decimal point in the answer to any computation will make that answer wrong by at least 90 per cent. Indeed, only one other aspect of an answer, its algebraic sign, is more important than the location of the decimal point. The determination of sign is usually a simple matter, but careful deliberation may be required to establish the proper location of the decimal point. This is particularly true of slide-rule calculations in which several numbers of widely different magnitudes are combined by successive multiplication and division, for decimal point location is not automatically fixed in slide-rule work.

There are methods for keeping track of the decimal point while operating a slide rule, but we recommend against their use for three reasons: First, they require that attention be divided between decimal point and the numbers themselves during slide-rule operation, making errors more likely. Second, the use of a separate calculation to establish the decimal point provides an independent check of the slide-rule answer. Third, the utility of the slide rule is severely restricted when the decimal point must be considered during its use, since only C and D scale calculations are practicable.

The recommended method for locating the decimal point involves the direct application of the engineering method: We make a quick estimate or gross approximation of the answer by freely rounding off the given figures to obtain numbers that are easily combined mentally or in long-hand. Thus in the unit conversion example, 453.6 might be rounded off to 500, $(2.54)^2$ to 6, $(12)^2$ to 150, and $(60)^2$ to 4000, and the resulting simplified expression would be

$$\frac{(6)(150)(4000)}{500}$$

The calculation may now be completed mentally: 4000 divided by 500 is 8, times 150 is 1200, times 6 is 7200. The fact that we come so close to the actual slide-rule answer is coincidental, for we might just as easily have come up with 5000 or 10,000. In either case the slide rule yields the numbers 7375, and we can be sure that the correct answer, complete with decimal point, is 7375 and not 737.5 or 73,750.

In general, as illustrated above, little care need be exercised in rounding off the given numbers. When many numbers are involved, though, it may be necessary to make the round-off errors cancel each other to some extent to avoid a misleading result. We did this quite by chance in the example, since we rounded upwards in both numerator and denominator, but intentional compensation is hardly necessary in a simple case such as this.

While the rounding-off step is relatively easy, the subsequent calculation of the decimal point may not be, for it will not always be feasible to carry the decimal point straight through the approximation as we did above. Two alternative procedures may be recommended, depending on the complexity of the problem. These will be illustrated by considering a hypothetical problem in its rounded-off form:

$$\frac{(.05)(70)(4000)(5)}{(.8)(900)}$$

The determination of the decimal point can be greatly facilitated by expressing each number as a single digit times 10 to the appropriate power; hence

$$\frac{(5)(10^{-2})(7)(10^1)(4)(10^3)(5)}{(8)(10^{-1})(9)(10^2)}$$

If we then collect the digits and the combined powers of 10 separately, we have

$$\frac{(5)(7)(4)(5)}{(8)(9)} \times 10^1$$

and the decimal point determination becomes easy: 5 times 7 is 35, divided by 72 is roughly $\frac{1}{2}$, times 20 is 10; and, finally, times 10^1 is 100.

The second method, a mental version of the first, is applicable to less complex problems. Given the product $(3000)(120)$, for example, we need only multiply 3 by 12 to get 36 and then tack on the four zeros to get 360,000. Cancellation can also be effective. In the complex example above, we can change 0.05 to 5 if we also change 4000 to 40. Then the zeros in 70 and 40 may be cancelled with those in 900 to yield

$$\frac{(5)(7)(4)(5)}{(.8)(9)}$$

which is readily handled mentally.

Generally speaking, it will be quicker and easier to effect cancellation to the fullest possible extent before resorting to the use of powers of 10. There is also an obvious advantage to having many numbers assembled into a single combination, for this permits some freedom of choice in the order of cancellation and in the order in which the final mental calculations are carried out. Compare, for example, the sequence used in the second paragraph above with that which is perhaps more obviously applicable to the same problem in its cancelled form: This time, we might say 0.8 times 9 is approximately 7, which cancels 7 in the numerator and leaves only $(5)(4)(5)$ to be considered.

The principles involved in decimal point determination are not difficult, but practice will be required before the student will have full confidence in the result. Such practice is well-advised in view of the great importance of the correct decimal point. We are reminded of a cartoon showing two engineers on a river bank overlooking a collapsed bridge. One is looking at his slide rule and saying to the other, "Doggone it, I misplaced the decimal point."

The moral is clear: Even a complete mastery of technical subject matter is of little use unless the engineer can consistently come up with the right numerical answer to his problem, and the decimal point is an essential part of that answer. Don't let a simple decimal point be the nail for want of which the shoe, horse, and rider are all lost.

4.12 Slide-Rule Techniques

The student who does not already own a *good*, *log-log* slide rule is well advised to invest in one immediately. It may be some time before the use of the log-log scales will be important, but mistakes are far less likely when one is using a slide rule with which he is completely familiar. The sooner one starts using the rule which will be his sidearm for many years to come, the better.

A brief summary of basic slide-rule techniques is found in Appendix A. It should be helpful not only to the student learning the use of the slide rule for the first time, but also to those who may have been using it regularly but who have never advanced beyond simple C and D-scale multiplication and division. Unless the student is already completely familiar with the use of the CI, CF, DF, and CIF scales in the latter operations and with the use of the LL scales in problems involving roots and powers, we strongly urge the study of Appendix A at the earliest opportunity, followed by the conscientious use of the techniques presented therein until they become habit.

Although the slide rule is a tremendously effective aid to calculation, there is no substitute for common sense and good judgment in its use. As we have already noted, it will be sufficiently accurate for the majority of engineering calculations; but there will be occasions when an extra significant figure or two will be desirable. The alert engineer will be quick to recognize such occasions, but should also be aware that he may still be able to avoid longhand, machine, or logarithmic computation. A few typical tricks for improving on normal slide-rule accuracy follow, and it is hoped that the student will be duly encouraged to dream up his own for other situations.

An additional significant figure or two can almost always be obtained by factoring the numbers to be handled. Consider the product $(.987)(45,000)$. By direct slide-rule multiplication we obtain an answer of 44,400. But if we rewrite the problem in the form

$$(1 - .013)(45,000) = 45,000 - (.013)(45,000)$$

and carry out a slide-rule multiplication on the new product, we can obtain an answer of 44,415 upon subtraction and have gained two significant figures. This technique will frequently be advisable when working with percentages; but, since slide-rule manipulation takes no cognizance of the decimal point, it is equally applicable in other situations.

The division of two almost equal numbers affords another opportunity to improve accuracy, and this situation will frequently be encountered in temperature calculations in thermodynamics. Straightforward division of 525 by 520 gives an answer of 1.01. But if we recognize that $525/520$ is equal to $1 + 5/520$, we can obtain an answer of 1.00962. A similar procedure could be applied to the quotient $515/520$, with a subtraction replacing the addition.

The addition or subtraction of reciprocals is another operation that recurs in chemical engineering calculations. Consider the difference $1/313.6 - 1/342.4$: The slide-rule reciprocals are 0.00319 and 0.00292, giving a difference of 0.00027. Cross-multiplication prior to division saves one slide-rule step and also yields an extra significant figure in the answer:

$$\frac{1}{313.6} - \frac{1}{342.4} = \frac{342.4 - 313.6}{(313.6)(342.4)} = \frac{28.8}{(313.6)(342.4)} = 0.000268$$

For a more complex application of the factoring technique, consider the product $(7.281)(.2415)$. Let each number be factored into the closest two-digit round number plus or minus a correction and the resulting binomial product expanded. Slide-rule multiplication followed by simple addition or subtraction will then give several more significant figures than will direct multiplication. Thus, with the usual disregard for decimal point,

$$(72.81)(24.15) = (73 - .19)(24 + .15)$$
$$= (73)(24) + (73)(.15) - (.19)(24) - (.19)(.15)$$
$$= 1752 + 10.95 - 4.56 - .0285 = 1758.36$$

with slide-rule multiplication used throughout. The answer obtained by direct multiplication would be read 1758 or perhaps even 1757. In contrast, the slide-rule product of 73 times 24 should definitely be read 1752 and not 1753, since inspection tells us that the last digit in the product must be a 2.

The student may contend that the foregoing problem could be solved more quickly long-hand. This may be; but our purpose was to demonstrate typical methods for extending slide-rule accuracy, and it must be admitted that the factoring method is effective. If these few examples convince the student that factoring can be a useful supplement to straightforward slide-rule calculation, they have served their purpose.

4.13 Pertinence of the Engineering Method

As we have seen, slide-rule calculation is a two-step process involving decimal-point determination as well as actual slide-rule manipulation. That these steps should be carried out in the order listed and not the other way around need not be emphasized if the engineering method has been fully assimilated. Note that the decimal-point determination alone provides an answer to the problem, whether followed up by the slide rule or not, whereas the slide rule alone does not even indicate the order of magnitude of the answer.

If the engineer is fully alert, he will even recognize situations in which slide-rule follow-up to the determination of decimal point is entirely unnecessary. Consider the combined multiplication and addition, $(.146)(37.2) + (67)(384)$. By gross approximation, the two products are seen to be about 5 and 25,000, respectively. Is there any point whatsoever in refining the first product on a slide rule, in view of its relative magnitude compared to the second? The second product gives a slide-rule answer of 25,700; the first product will therefore be completely lost when the sum is rounded off in accordance with the rules for handling significant figures.

The foregoing strongly suggests roughing out the entire solution to a problem before undertaking slide-rule work, lest time be wasted on calculations which need only be approximated. Suppose it had taken an entire page of calculations to obtain the number 37.2 used in the problem above. How much time and effort might have been saved had the engineer skimmed rapidly over the page and merely satisfied himself that the answer would be somewhere between 10 and 100.

The idea of working out an approximate but complete solution to a problem before picking up a slide rule is frequently hard for the beginning engineer to accept, for it opposes his natural inclination to be thorough and methodical. Yet the pertinence of the engineering method to quantitative calculations can hardly be denied, for the above illustration is in no way atypical. Although it will take considerable will-power to resist the temptation to finish each separate calculation in turn rather than to wait until the entire picture is clear, we submit that such effort will ultimately pay off in greatly increased efficiency in problem solving.

4.14 Mental Arithmetic

It was suggested earlier that the ability to make quick mental calculations can be an important asset to the engineer. The rapid determination of the decimal point is one aspect of this ability, but there are also numerous occasions when a more accurate approximation is desirable and slide-rule calculation is not practicable for one reason or another. For this reason a few basic principles of mental arithmetic are presented below. The treatment is admittedly somewhat superficial, but it will serve to identify some of the typical techniques involved.

For all but the simplest problems, mental arithmetic is made easier if given decimal points can be shifted arbitrarily to points of maximum convenience. This suggests that the proper location of the decimal point in the answer should be determined in a separate rough approximation. Such a procedure will be assumed in the examples which follow, and decimal points will be shifted freely or ignored completely just as they are during slide-rule manipulation. Also, all steps in the calculations will be written out in detail for purposes of clarity. With practice, one can develop the ability to make such calculations mentally or, at worst, to use only a few numbers on scratch paper.

Basically, it can be asserted that the common arithmetic operations increase in difficulty in the order addition, subtraction, multiplication, and division. This contention sets the stage for the general principles which underly most techniques for mental calculation: Reduce any given computation to a lower order of difficulty or, more generally, carry out the indicated operation using rounded-off numbers and then apply a correction based on a less-difficult operation.

As a first example of the application of the principle consider the sum
$481 + 93$. Presumably this can be done mentally without difficulty. But
the difference $481 - 93$ requires greater concentration and may even
necessitate pencil and paper work for many students. If we mentally rewrite
the problem in the form $481 - (100 - 7)$, equal to $481 - 100 + 7$, the
mental subtraction is easy and so is the corrective addition. Thus we have
converted a subtraction to a less difficult addition, so to speak.

Moving on to multiplication, let us consider the product $(83)(18)$. Here
again we can "factor" to simplify the problem, mentally rewriting 18 as
$20 - 2$. Then $(83)(18) = (83)(20) - (83)(2)$. Mental multiplication reduces
this to $1660 - 166$, and the corrective subtraction is easily accomplished. In
this illustration, then, we have reduced a multiplication to a subtraction for
practical purposes.

The use of reciprocals frequently makes it possible to reduce a division
to a simpler multiplication. With a little concentration, 310 can be mentally
divided by 250; but how much simpler the problem becomes if we recognize
that 0.25 (note the arbitrary decimal point shift) is the reciprocal of 4 and
that the problem can therefore be rewritten $(310)(4)$, an easily handled form.
Reciprocals may also be used to convert a difficult multiplication into a
simpler, round-number division. Consider the conversion of an area of 16.9
square feet to square inches, requiring the determination of the product
$(16.9)(144)$. Neither to these numbers has an exact round-number reciprocal, but 0.144 is very nearly the reciprocal of 7. Dividing 169 by 7 yields
241, which compares very favorably with the slide-rule answer to the
original problem, 243.

Many of the numbers which are recurrent in chemical engineering calculations can, with a suitable shift of decimal point, be conveniently replaced
by round-number reciprocals or simple fractions. Thus 144 and 14.7 be-
come $\frac{1}{7}$, 62.4 is $\frac{5}{8}$, 778 is $\frac{7}{9}$, 379 is $\frac{3}{8}$, 8.34 is $\frac{1}{12}$, 7.48 is $\frac{3}{4}$, 29 is $\frac{2}{7}$, 32.17 is $\frac{1}{3}$,
22.4 is $\frac{2}{9}$, and 453.6 is $\frac{4}{9}$. The student should recognize some of these numbers,
while the others will become familiar later on.

The use of a factoring, reciprocal, or round-fraction technique will not
always be feasible, and recourse to other methods will frequently be necessary. One alternative method involves compensatory round-off, and is
particularly appropriate when two numbers of approximately equal magnitude are to be handled. In such a case, little error will result if one number
is changed slightly to a convenient round number and the other is changed
an equal amount to compensate. The changes will be in the opposite direction in multiplication and in the same direction in division.

To illustrate, let us square 2.54 as we had to do in an earlier example.
This can be done by replacing $(254)(254)$ with $(250)(258)$—subtracting 4
from the first term and adding 4 to the second. Then $\frac{1}{4}$ of 258 (the reciprocal

technique) is 645. The actual slide rule answer is also 645. Similarly, (56) (5.35) is approximately (595)(500), and half of 595 is 2975. This differs by only 1 per cent or so from the slide-rule answer of 294. As for division, 38/.37 is approximately 41/40 or 1025, compared with a slide-rule answer of 1027.

The round-off technique may even be applied to dissimilar numbers if the magnitude of the round-off is made proportional to the magnitude of the number rounded off. For example, (83)(37) might be approximated by (77)(40), the round-off of 3 on 37 being compensated for by a round-off of 6 on 83, since 83 is approximately twice 37. The resulting answer of 308 compares very favorably with the slide-rule answer of 307. Similarly, 61/18 is approximately equal to 67/20 or 335. The slide-rule answer is 339.

Another method that may be useful on occasion comes from the series expansion

$$\frac{1}{a \pm x} = \frac{1}{a} \mp \frac{x}{a^2} + \frac{x^2}{a^3} \mp \cdots$$

When a is large compared to x, only the first two terms need be considered, and even then a gross approximation of the second term will generally suffice. The technique is most useful when $a = 1$, in which case $1/(1 \pm x)$ becomes simply $1 \mp x$. Thus $1/.95$ should equal 1.05 to a very good approximation, and does. This type of approximation is accurate within 1 per cent or so if x is not more than 0.1.

For an example of the more general case, consider the reciprocal $\frac{1}{37}$. Rewriting the denominator as $40 - 3$ and applying the series expansion, we obtain $\frac{1}{40} + 3/1600$ or $0.225 + .002$ (approximated) $= 0.027$, which is in direct agreement with the slide-rule answer. Note that 37 might also have been approximated by $\frac{3}{8}$ to obtain an answer of 267, or compensatory round-off might have been used to get $1075/40 = 269$ or perhaps $109/40 = 272$. The relative accuracy of alternative techniques is unpredictable, and a choice among them can usually be based on convenience.

When calculations involving roots or powers are to be carried out without the aid of log tables or a slide rule, it will be helpful to remember that the base-10 log of 2 is approximately 0.301 (actually 0.30103). Starting with this value, one can construct a reasonably accurate log table by setting up successive multiples of 2 while adding the logs. If characteristics are disregarded, the following table will be obtained:

No.:	2	4	8	1.6	3.2	6.4	1.28	2.56	5.12
Log:	.301	.602	.903	.204	.505	.806	.107	.408	.709

Rearranging in ascending order,

No.:	1.28	1.6	2	2.56	3.2	4	5.12	6.4	8
Log:	.107	.204	.301	.408	.505	.602	.709	.806	.903

The mantissa of the logarithm of any desired number can now be approximated to within ± 0.003 or so by linear interpolation. And if it is remembered that $\ln_e = 2.303(\log_{10})$, one has ready access to natural logs as well.

As was the case with the techniques for improving on slide-rule accuracy, it might be argued that in some instances a complete long-hand calculation could be completed as rapidly as a less rigorous approximation. If the student finds this to be true, it is only because he does not have the same working familiarity with approximative methods as he does with long-hand calculations. We strongly urge the practice of the techniques presented herein at every opportunity, until they become firmly rooted and available for use as needed. Such practice will bring both facility and confidence, and will add significantly to the student's overall engineering ability.

4.15 Trial-and-Error Solutions

So far, we have considered approximative methods as an alternative to more rigorous calculations. In many of the problems of interest to chemical engineers, an initial approximation or even a pure guess is absolutely essential to the successful solution of the problem. Such solutions, in which an initial estimated or guessed answer is tested to see how well it fits a given relationship, are called *trial-and-error* solutions.

Consider the relatively simple relationship $xe^x = 133.5$. An analytical solution to this transcendental relationship is not possible, but it can be solved by trying successive values of x until the value which satisfies the equation is found. Thus if $x = 1$, $e^x = 2.72$ and the product is also 2.72, much too small. For $x = 2$, $e^x = 7.4$ and the product is 14.8. Jumping to $x = 4$, $e^x = 54.5$ and the product is 218. This indicates that the next trial should be between 2 and 4, and we will repeat the trial-and-error until the correct answer is obtained. Typically, the complete solution might require six trials or more, depending for the most part on how skillful or lucky one is in assuming new values for x on the basis of previous trials.

In most applications of this kind, the number of trials can be reduced significantly by the following procedure: First, examine the given relationship to see if one part is more sensitive to changes in the value of the unknown than the rest. In the above example, we have already seen that a two-fold change in x, from 2 to 4, results in a seven-fold change in e^x, from 7.4 to 54.5. The exponential part of the relationship is therefore more sensitive to changes in x than is x itself. Second, rearrange the relationship to put the more sensitive part to the left of the equality sign and everything else to the right; or, $e^x = 133.5/x$. Finally, assume a value for the unknown, substitute it into the right side only, and solve the resulting expression for the remaining unknown. Trying $x = 3$, $e^x = 133.5/3 = 44.5$, from which x is found to be

3.8. The problem is solved when the assumed and calculated values agree.

The advantage of this technique is that the magnitude and direction of the discrepancy or error between the assumed and calculated values will usually suggest a logical value to be used in the next trial. In the example, the rearranged equation makes it clear that x must lie between 3 and 3.8, because trying a value larger than 3 will result in a calculated value less than 3.8. Furthermore, since the right side of the equation is less sensitive to changes in x, a large change in the trial value should yield a much smaller change in the calculated value. In other words, the correct value of x should be much closer to 3.8 than to 3, and we might elect to try $x = 3.7$: $e^x = 133.5/3.7 = 36.1$, from which $x = 3.59$. x is now known to lie between 3.7 and 3.59 and to be much closer to the latter. Trying $x = 3.62$, $e^x = 133.5/36.2 = 36.9$ and $x = 3.61$. A more accurate slide-rule answer is not possible.

A second example should serve to emphasize the utility of the recommended technique. In a typical application of the van der Waals equation (to be encountered later), it might be necessary to solve the equation

$$\left(4 + \frac{1540}{V^2}\right)(V - 1.12) = 394$$

Were this to be expanded, it would result in a cubic equation in V that can be solved analytically only with considerable difficulty. A trial-and-error solution is almost always quicker. Experience in the use of the equation tells us that the second bracketed term is more sensitive to changes in V than the first; hence the recommended rearrangement is

$$V = 1.12 + \frac{394}{4 + 1540/V^2}$$

As a first trial, let V be infinite to eliminate the V^2 term entirely. By inspection, it can be seen that V is approximately 100. Substituting this value for V^2, $V = 1.12 + 394/4.154 = 1.12 + 94.9 = 96.0$. This time, a qualitative analysis indicates that trying a lower value of V in the V^2 term will yield a still lower calculated value—but one which should close to 96.0 in any event. Thus we might elect to try $V = 95$ or perhaps 95.5 for the second trial. As it happens, $V = 95.5$ is the solution to the problem.

The frequent use of graphical or tabular data in chemical engineering leads to another type of problem which may be solvable only by trial-and-error. Typically, such problems involve two unknowns and only one analytical equation, with the table or graph being used in lieu of a second equation. The procedure outlined above is directly applicable to such problems. A practical example will be presented in Chap. 5.

It should be noted that trial-and-error solutions are amenable to graphical treatment. In the $xe^x = 133.5$ example, we might have plotted xe^x vs. x

and picked off the value of x corresponding to $xe^x = 133.5$. In most cases, the proper use of the recommended technique will yield an answer almost in the time it takes to hunt up a suitable sheet of graph paper. A rough plot may help as a guide to better values to be used in successive trials but, generally speaking, a complete graphical solution will not be as rapid as the corresponding trial-and-error attack.

The trial-and-error method is another aspect of chemical engineering which frequently bothers the beginning student, for he may feel that it is akin to pulling himself up by his own bootstraps. Actually, it is not only a perfectly legitimate procedure, but it may even be the quickest route to the solution of a problem that is also solvable by relatively straightforward analytical techniques. Try the trial-and-error method on the quadratic equation $0.1x^2 + 4x - 8 = 0$, rearranged to $x = 2 - .025x^2$. Temporarily neglecting the last term, we see that x is approximately 2. Substituting this value into the right side, $x = 2 - .10 = 1.9$. Trying $x = 1.91$, $x = 2 - .091 = 1.909$. A solution based on the quadratic formula would almost certainly take much longer.

(Note that this method does not indicate the other root, which is -41.9. Physical restrictions almost always rule out answers which are wholly acceptable from the purely mathematical standpoint, and we might even know in advance that x lies between 0 and 2 in the above example. In such a case there would be no point in seeking out the other root.)

4.16 Graphical Methods

The graphical representation of data and even the graphical solution of complex problems plays an important part in chemical engineering. For the most part, specific graphical methods will be considered as the need for their use arises, but there are a few basic principles which should be known by way of general preparation. Among such are the characteristics of semi-logarithmic and logarithmic plots and the techniques for graphical integration and differentiation. The student who feels a need for instruction in these principles will find a brief treatment in Appendix B.

4.17 Conclusion

The extensive detail that has characterized the discussion in this chapter is in no way disproportionate to the importance of the subject matter to the success of an engineer—or an engineering student, to cite a more immediate challenge. Indeed, it is more than likely that the student will find unexpected uses for many of the recommended techniques in other courses. Their importance in chemical engineering, meanwhile, will be repeatedly demonstrated, starting with the next chapter. In due course the student will have learned for himself that the complete mastery of these techniques is absolutely essential.

The successful engineer must be able to *come up with the answers* to the problems assigned to him. As long as engineering problems are quantitative in nature, the ability to set up and carry out the calculations is no less important than an understanding of theoretical principles. The wise student will not let either aspect be an Achilles heel.

REVIEW, STUDY, AND DISCUSSION

4-1. Specify suitable dimensions, units, and labels for each of the underlined numbers in the following:

a) A 10 per cent (wt) HCl solution enters a reactor and 50 per cent of the HCl reacts. 50 per cent of 10 per cent is 5 per cent.

b) A mixture of chlorine and air analyzing 95 per cent chlorine by volume is fed to a reactor in which some of the chlorine reacts. The effluent stream contains 10 per cent chlorine by volume. 95 minus 10 is 85.

c) Normal butane enters a reactor and is converted to iso-butane with a conversion of 45 per cent.

d) *A* and *B* are fed to a mixing tank in a mass ratio of 3 to 1.

e) The specific gravity of aluminum is 2.7.

f) A filter cake contains 55 per cent solids by volume, and the interstitial space between the solid particles is 35 per cent (volume) full of water. 35 per cent of 45 per cent is 15.75 per cent.

g) A plot is made of the pressure in a tank (*y* axis) vs. time. The slope of the line at one point on the plot is −0.60.

4-2. Using only the factors given below, set up the sequence of unit cancellations which will permit the calculation of overall factors for each of the conversions listed and specify the units of the overall factors. (Actual calculations need not be carried out.)

Given factors: g and g_c, 12 in./ft, 2.54 cm/in., 10 mm/cm, 453.6 gm/lb, 60 sec/min, 60 min/hr, 1.8 F°/C°, 252 cal/BTU, 778 ft-lb$_f$/BTU, 7.48 gal/ft^3, 62.4 lb$_m$/ft^3 (for water). Conversions:

a) Velocity: ft/min to cm/sec.

b) Density: gm/cm^3 to lb/ft^3.

c) Volume: cm^3 to gal.

d) Energy: ft-lb$_f$ to cal.

e) Heat flux: BTU/(hr)(ft^2) to cal/(sec)(cm^2).

f) Heat capacity: cal/(gm)(C°) to BTU/(lb$_m$)(F°).

g) Thermal conductivity: BTU/(hr)(ft²)(F°/ft) to cal/(sec)(cm²)(C°/cm).

h) Viscosity: gm/(cm)(sec) to (lb$_f$)(sec)/ft².

i) Pressure: lb$_f$/in.² to mm of Hg. (Density of mercury is 13.6 gm/cm³.)

4-3. Prove that the conversion factor relating gm-mols to lb-mols is 453.6 gm-mols/lb-mol.

4-4. Convert 14°F to °C and to °R. Convert each answer to °K. Which route between °F and °K is more convenient? Which route gives the more accurate answer? Convert 14F° to C°, R°, and K°.

4-5. It is reported that the contents of a batch reaction vessel undergo a pressure rise of 20 psi during the course of the reaction. Does this mean psia or psig? Explain.

4-6. When one end of a spring is firmly anchored, a man must exert a pull of 50 pounds to stretch it one inch. Compare the relationship between pull and stretch on the earth with that on the moon, with the spring in both a vertical and a horizontal position. Repeat the comparison for the case of a steel block hanging from one end of the spring (or from a rope running over a pulley when the spring is horizontal).

4-7. Specify dimensions in terms of **M, L, θ,** and **T** for heat capacity and thermal conductivity. (See Prob. 4-2 for typical units.)

4-8. Since force, mass, length, and time are related through Newton's second law, it should be possible to set up a dimensional system based on any three of the four concepts. Determine the dimensions of velocity, viscosity, power (energy/time), and thermal conductivity in both the **F-M-L-T** and **F-M-θ-T** systems. (See Prob. 4-2 for typical units.)

4-9. From a consideration of Newton's second law, determine the numerical conversion factors needed to relate slugs to lb$_m$ and poundals to lb$_f$.

4-10. Complete each of the following calculations and express the answer in the proper number of significant figures: $0.44 + 60.0 + 0.1 + 0.02$; $45,000 - 285$; $0.66/1.1$; $(2.0)(0.01234)$; $0.666/2.22$; $(125 \pm 5)(0.300)$.

4-11. Using rough approximations, establish the location of the decimal point in each of the unit conversions of Prob. 4-2.

4-12. Approximate the numerical answer to each part of Prob. 4-2 to the best of your ability without resorting to long-hand calculations or the use of a slide rule.

4-13. Determine the slide-rule answer to each part of Prob. 4-2.

4-14. The flow of a fluid through a pipe is characterized by a *dimensionless* Reynolds number equal to $Du\rho/\mu$, in which D is the pipe diameter, u the fluid velocity, ρ the fluid density, and μ the fluid viscosity. Calculate the Reynolds number for a fluid flowing through a 2-inch pipe at 300 ft/min and having a density of 1.2 gm/cm³ and a viscosity of 0.209×10^{-4} (lb$_f$)(sec)/ft².

4-15. Overwhelmed by the space age, we propose that the velocity of space vehicles be measured in etaoins per shrdlu, where an etaoin is equivalent to one $(lb_f)(min^2)/lb_m$ and a *square* shrdlu is one $(lb_m)(in.)/lb_f$. What is the speed in miles per hour of a space vehicle moving at a rate of 0.015 et/sh?

4-16. An accelerometer is to be designed to measure the acceleration of a space vehicle. It will consist of a partially-evacuated cylinder, 0.5 inches in diameter, positioned with its axis along the line of flight. When the vehicle is traveling at constant velocity, a small piston inside the cylinder will rest against its forward end. The piston will be made of steel and will have a density of 487 lb_m/ft^3.

When the vehicle accelerates, the inertial force will move the piston to the rear, compressing the gas in the cylinder, and the degree of acceleration will be indicated by the increase in pressure. It has been decided that the pressure should not exceed 760 mm of Hg lest there be leakage of gas past the piston.

Assuming frictional effects to be negligible, specify the maximum thickness of the piston if accelerations up to 10 g's are to be measured.

4-17. What value of x satisfies the relationship $x(\log x) = 150$?

4-18. A typical chemical equilibrium calculation might yield a relationship of the form

$$3 = \frac{(1-x)(4-x)}{x(5-x)^2}$$

where it is known that x lies between 0 and 1. What value of x satisfies this relationship?

The following problems are based on the material to be found in Appendix B:

4-19. When a reaction rate coefficient expressed in reciprocal seconds is plotted against reciprocal temperature $(1/°K)$ on semi-log paper (coefficient on the log scale), a straight line results. If the rate coefficient increases by a factor of 3 when the temperature is raised from 400°K to 410°K, what is the numerical slope of the line? What are the units of the slope?

4-20. A log-log plot of heat-transfer coefficient (y axis) vs. velocity of a flowing fluid has a slope of 0.8. What units might this number have? When $u = 5$ ft/sec, the plot indicates that $h = 500$ BTU/(hr)(ft²)(F°). What is the value of h when $u = 12.7$ ft/sec? Calculate the slope which would result were u to be expressed in ft/min instead of in ft/sec.

4-21. Evaluate $\int_1^{10} (1/w)dw$ by graphical integration. Compare the result with that obtained by the usual analytical method.

4-22. Using the data given in the first two columns of Table B-1, Appendix B, prepare a plot of $\Delta\theta/\Delta x$ vs. x and construct an equivalent equal-area curve denoting instantaneous reciprocal rate as a function of x. Compare the results with those given in the last column of Table B-1. Is this method an acceptable alternative to the method used in Appendix B? Explain.

PART II

Properties and Property Relationships

Primary attention may be focused on one or two of the fundamental aspects of change in the course of solving any particular problem; but no one aspect can be set apart as being most important under all circumstances. Still, it is not until it has been clearly established *what* changes that any of the other aspects become completely meaningful. It is therefore logical that we give first priority to the *what* question and its answer, "The properties and states of systems." A working knowledge of physical and chemical properties and the pertinent relationships among them will then provide a background for the subsequent consideration of the other aspects of change.

It is not the purpose of the next three chapters to provide a complete treatment of physical and chemical properties. Rather, we propose to continue to apply the engineering method to the chemical engineering curriculum, refining the concepts presented in Chap. 2 to some extent but still leaving many details for future investigation. For example, it will suffice for our purposes to know that temperature is a measure of the "hotness" or "coldness" of a system, and we need not concern ourselves with the kinetics of molecular motion.

Since free use will be made of some of the terms which were defined formally in Chap. 2, it may be advisable to review the definitions of a system, property, state, process, phase, and related terms before proceeding. Alternately, the formal definition of any term can be reviewed as the need arises. In no event should the importance of fully understanding these terms and their usage be overlooked. Meticulous interpretation of them is essential if the material which follows is to be assimilated.

CHAPTER 5

P-$\underline{V}$-T Behavior of Pure Substances

In defining the terms *state* and *property* in Chap. 2, it was noted that the state of a system is identified through the properties of the system, and that all properties are identical for identical states. It was also pointed out that a change in one property may be accompanied by an unavoidable change in another. The fact that the specification of one property may make it impossible to specify another independently gives rise to two very important questions: (1) What properties can be specified independently in the course of defining or identifying a state? (2) Once a particular state has been defined by specifying certain properties, how does one ascertain other properties associated with that state?

Answers to these questions are developed in this chapter and the two to follow. The initial development is restricted to a consideration of the properties of pressure, specific volume (or its reciprocal, density), and temperature, these being the properties most frequently used to identify or define a state, since they are all amenable to direct measurement and control. Since these properties are all intensive, it is not necessary to consider the extent of a system in the initial analysis. Energy, entropy, and composition, the other properties of major interest to chemical engineers, are treated in Chaps. 6 and 7.

103

5.1 Properties and State Identification

Experimental observations. Since the interrelationship among properties is experimentally determinable, let us begin our analysis by envisioning
a simple laboratory experiment: A known quantity of a pure gas is confined
within a cylinder fitted with a movable piston and a pressure gage, and the
entire apparatus is immersed in a constant-temperature oil bath as shown in
Fig. 5.1. With the gas temperature maintained constant by the surrounding

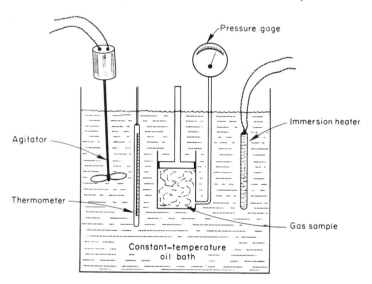

Fig. 5.1 Schematic diagram of laboratory apparatus for obtaining P-$\underline{V}$-T data.

bath, the gas can be compressed to any desired degree by placing different
weights atop the piston to change the pressure. Doing this demonstrates,
not unexpectedly, that the piston comes to rest at a height which is directly
related to the applied pressure and to the temperature of the bath. With
the quantity of gas and the cross-sectional area of the cylinder known, the
height is readily converted to an equivalent specific volume.

Were we to calculate specific volumes for various successively higher
pressures while the apparatus is held at a relatively high, constant temperature T_1, we would obtain data which would yield an *isotherm* or constant-
temperature curve similar to that labeled *a-b* in Fig. 5.2. The hyperbolic
shape of this curve is typical of the P-$\underline{V}$ behavior of a gas during isothermal
expansion or compression, and repeating the entire experiment at any
higher constant temperature T_2 would yield a similar curve as indicated by
the line *c-d* in Fig. 5.2.

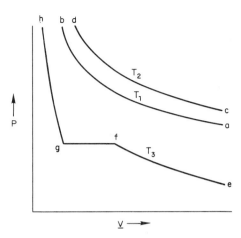

Fig. 5.2 Typical experimental *P-V* isotherms for a pure material.

A consideration of the region between and around the isotherms T_1 and T_2 in Fig. 5.2 clearly indicates that the specification of values for any two of the three properties P, V, and T defines the location of a point on the plot, whereupon the value of the third property is uniquely fixed. States in this region are said to have two *degrees of freedom*, meaning that any two properties will suffice to define the state and, consequently, that no more than two properties may be specified arbitrarily or independently.

At a much lower temperature T_3, the same experimental technique might yield an isotherm similar to curve *e-f-g-h* in Fig. 5.2, the general hyperbolic shape being altered by the presence of a straight, horizontal line segment. The underlying phenomenon is readily surmised, for a marked change in volume at constant pressure and temperature is possible only if the system is undergoing a phase change—in this case either evaporation or condensation, depending on the direction in which the system moves along the curve.

Starting at point *e*, the isotherm portrays a typical compression process until the point *f* is reached. The terms *gas* and *vapor* are frequently used interchangeably in this region, but the latter more strictly refers to states not too far removed from point *f* or its equivalent. At this point, commonly referred to as the *dew point*, the first drop of liquid will appear as the vapor starts to condense. When a vapor is at its dew point, it is said to be *saturated;* the term *superheated* is applied to vapor states to the right of the dew point.

Similarly, the liquid existing at point *g* is said to be a *saturated liquid*, and curve *g-h* typifies the isothermal expansion (or compression) of a *subcooled* liquid. It will be noted that the line is almost vertical, in keeping with the fact that liquids are only slightly compressible. Point g itself is called the *bubble point*, since the first bubble of vapor will appear at this point when the pressure on a subcooled liquid is reduced at constant temperature.

An analysis similar to that made at higher temperature will show that there are two degrees of freedom in both the superheated vapor and subcooled liquid regions. A somewhat different situation exists between the dew and bubble points, where saturated liquid and saturated vapor coexist. In this region, it can be seen that the temperature T_3 corresponds to a unique pressure, and that, once the temperature is specified, pressure is not an independent variable. Conversely, specifying a pressure within the two-phase region automatically fixes the temperature as well. The obvious implication is that there is only one degree of freedom within this region.

In contrast to this restriction, it would appear that the specific volume of a two-phase system can vary all the way from that of a saturated liquid to that of a saturated vapor, even when both pressure and temperature are known. The explanation lies in the fact that the specific volume of a vapor-liquid mixture depends on the relative *quantities* of liquid and vapor, and specific volume is no longer a true intensive property. If a two-phase system is viewed as a combination of two single-phase systems, it should be apparent from Fig. 5.2 that the specific volumes of both the pure saturated vapor and pure saturated liquid *are* fixed, once pressure or temperature is specified.

Effect of composition. The foregoing observations hold for any pure substance, meaning a single element or chemical compound. This is not to say that identical results will be obtained with all pure substances. As we shall see shortly, only *ideal* or *perfect* gases have identical $P\text{-}\underline{V}\text{-}T$ relationships. All other substances must be specifically identified if a particular state is to be defined. This aspect of the definition of state is not normally counted as a degree of freedom, even though it involves an independent specification.

When two pure substances are combined to form a binary mixture, the composition of the system becomes a pertinent factor. The sum of the mol fractions being unity, composition can be stated in terms of the mol fraction of either component. The selected mol fraction can be considered to be a state variable, along with temperature, specific volume, and pressure. The new variable creates an additional degree of freedom which may be superimposed on those associated with a pure substance. Thus a superheated vapor or subcooled liquid, previously shown to have two degrees of freedom as a pure substance, will have three degrees of freedom if a second component is present.

The Gibbs phase rule. Were we to examine other cases involving varying numbers of components and phases, we would find that the number of components N_c, the number of phases N_p, and the number of degrees of freedom N_f are always related in the same way, the quantitative relationship being

$$N_f = N_c - N_p + 2 \qquad (5.1)$$

This relationship was first advanced in 1875 by J. Willard Gibbs, an American mathematician and physicist, and is known as the *Gibbs phase rule.*

The phase rule gives answer to one of the questions raised at the beginning of this chapter: In order to define a state, it is necessary to specify at least as many intensive properties as there are degrees of freedom indicated by the phase rule. Once this has been done, the state is fixed—and so are all other intensive properties, since all properties are identical for identical states.

PROPERTY RELATIONSHIPS

Application of the phase rule to a pure substance ($N_c = 1$) indicates that there can never be more than two degrees of freedom, since N_p must be equal to or greater than one. At most, then, only two properties can be specified arbitrarily, and all other properties must be determinable from the known values of these two. The existence of quantitative relationships for this purpose is clearly implied. Our immediate concern will be for relationships pertaining to pressure, specific volume, and temperature. These properties will in turn be related to specific energy and entropy in Chap. 6.

5.2 The P-V Diagram

If the experimental procedure used to obtain the three isotherms shown in Fig. 5.2 were to be repeated for other temperatures, a family of curves similar to those shown in Fig. 5.3 would result. The locus of all dew and bubble points is clearly indicated by the dashed lines which form the dome in the figure, with two phases existing at all points within the dome and only a single phase elsewhere. The liquid region lies to the left of the dome and the vapor region to the right.

The *P-V* diagram clearly constitutes a quantitative relationship which can be used to determine the value of one property when the other two are known. Cross-plotting to obtain *P-T* or *T-V* diagrams is also feasible, with *V* and *P*, respectively, being represented parametrically on such diagrams. All three types of diagram have distinct disadvantages: First, interpolation with respect to the parameter is not particularly easy. Second, such plots tell nothing about other thermodynamic properties of considerable importance, such as energy and entropy. And, perhaps most important, it is

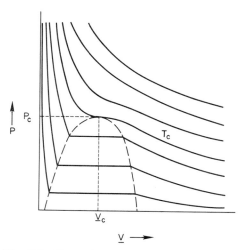

Fig. 5.3   Typical P-$\underline{V}$ diagram for a pure material.

necessary to prepare a separate plot for every substance of interest to chemical engineers.

Tabular representation of P-$\underline{V}$-T data circumvents the first two of these disadvantages. Interpolation is easier, and properties other than pressure, specific volume, and temperature can easily be included in the table. Notable examples are the familiar "Steam Tables"*, which present pressure, specific volume, temperature, enthalpy, entropy, and internal energy data for saturated liquid water, saturated water vapor, and superheated vapor. An abridgment of these tables is presented in Appendix C.

Numerous attempts have been made to generalize P-$\underline{V}$-T data so that a single plot or table might be used for all substances. The P-$\underline{V}$ diagram provides considerable insight into the basis for most generalized correlations. One aspect in particular of the P-$\underline{V}$ diagram deserves specific consideration before other methods of representing P-$\underline{V}$-T data are investigated.

Critical phenomena. It is apparent from Fig. 5.3 that, as the saturation pressure (and temperature) increases, the dew and bubble points approach each other until, at the top of the dome, they become coincident at a single point. This point, at which the properties of the saturated liquid and saturated vapor become identical, is called the *critical point*. It establishes a corresponding *critical temperature* T_c, a *critical pressure* P_c, and a *critical volume* $\underline{V}_c$. These are shown on Fig. 5.3.

The absence of a two-phase region above the critical point makes it possible to vaporize a liquid without ever passing it through a two-phase state:

---

* J. H. Keenan, and F. G. Keyes, *Thermodynamic Properties of Steam* (New York: John Wiley & Sons, Inc., 1937).

A pure liquid lying to the left of the dome can be heated at constant volume to a temperature above T_c, further heated at constant pressure to a volume well beyond $\underline{V}_c$, and then cooled at constant volume into the vapor region to the right of the dome. The condensation of a vapor can be similarly effected by following the reverse path.

This raises the interesting question of whether the material is in a liquid or vapor state at any point above P_c. The question has no real answer, for the properties of liquid and vapor become identical at the critical point. Above this point it is not possible to distinguish between the two phases, since the phases themselves do not exist as such. It is common practice to sidestep the issue by referring to all states above the critical point as *fluid* rather than as liquid or gaseous.

The phenomena associated with the critical point have considerable theoretical significance, in addition to their obvious physical significance. We will take cognizance of one theoretical aspect very shortly, but for the most part a thorough treatment of critical phenomena is beyond the scope of this text.

5.3 Equations of State

An alternative method of representing P-$\underline{V}$-T data would be to write an analytical expression or *equation of state* which fits data similar to that shown in Fig. 5.3. It can be anticipated that such an equation must be quite complex if it is to predict all the isotherms shown in the figure with satisfactory accuracy. As an example, consider the Beattie-Bridgeman equation, widely used for rigorous P-$\underline{V}$-T calculations:

$$P = \frac{RT(1 - C_o/\underline{V}T^3)}{\underline{V}^2} [\underline{V} + B_o(1 - b/\underline{V})] - \frac{A_o}{\underline{V}^2}(1 - a/\underline{V})$$

in which a, b, A_o, B_o, and C_o are constants for any given substance and must be determined empirically. It can be seen that the use of such an equation is very laborious, particularly when it is to be solved for specific volume.

The complexity of the Beattie-Bridgeman equation is in marked contrast to the simplicity of another equation of state, the familiar *ideal gas law:*

$$P\underline{V} = RT \qquad (5.2)$$

This is one of the earliest equations of state. It embodies the laws of Charles, Boyle, and Avogadro in relating the pressure, volume, temperature, and number of molecules in gaseous systems. Unlike the Beattie-Bridgeman equation with its six constants, five of which must be determined separately for each different material, the ideal gas law involves only the single constant R, which has the same value for all gases when $\underline{V}$ is expressed in units of volume per *mole* of material.

Although the ideal gas law is reasonably accurate at very low pressures (atmospheric or less, for practical purposes), it may be in error by as much as 75 per cent under other conditions, and is best regarded as providing a quick, approximate solution subject to further refinement as the occasion demands and time permits. It will be used repeatedly in chemical engineering calculations, in many cases with complete justification. It is hoped, however, that the student will always recognize its approximate nature and will never regard it as the universal answer to all P-$\underline{V}$-T calculations.

A somewhat more accurate—but more complex—equation of state is the van der Waals equation already encountered in Sec. 4.15:

$$(P + a/\underline{V}^2)(\underline{V} - b) = RT \tag{5.3}$$

Unlike the Beattie-Bridgeman equation, which is almost wholly empirical, the van der Waals equation has some theoretical significance. The $a/\underline{V}^2$ term purports to correct the ideal gas law for inter-molecular attraction, while the b term corrects for the volume actually occupied by the molecules themselves. The constants a and b must be determined separately for each different material.

The generalized compressibility factor. The accuracy required in most engineering calculations does not require the use of a very complex equation of state such as the Beattie-Bridgeman equation, yet the direct use of the ideal gas law will frequently be unsatisfactory. In such situations the use of a modification of the ideal gas law will result in an appreciable gain in accuracy without significantly altering the simplicity of the basic law. The modification consists of a correction factor inserted into the ideal gas law to bring it into agreement with experimental data. The resulting equation of state is

$$P\underline{V} = ZRT \tag{5.4}$$

in which the corrective term Z is called the *compressibility factor*.

At first glance it would appear that very little has been accomplished by this modification. Z is not only a function of pressure and temperature but also depends on the particular material being considered, and it would almost seem that Eq. (5.4) must be solved in order to determine the proper value of Z to be substituted into it. Fortunately, a most significant relationship known as the *law of corresponding states* comes to our aid:

According to this law, *all substances deviate from ideality to the same extent when they exist in comparable states with respect to the critical point.* This statement can be made more meaningful if we define a dimensionless *reduced pressure* for any substance, equal to the actual absolute pressure divided by the critical pressure for the substance: $P_r = P/P_c$. Similarly, *reduced temperature* equals the actual temperature divided by the critical temperature (*both in °R or °K*), or, $T_r = T/T_c$. The law of corresponding states then requires that the deviation from ideality—that is, the value of the compressibility factor Z—be the same for all substances existing at the same conditions of reduced pressure and reduced temperature.

The law of corresponding states permits the preparation of a single plot of Z vs. P_r, with parameters of T_r, which may be used to determine·the compressibility factor for any gas whatsoever, provided only that the critical properties of the gas are known. Such a plot is presented in Appendix C-6, and critical properties for a number of typical materials are given in Appendix C-5.

A substantial gain in accuracy may be effected by the use of the compressibility factor instead of the uncorrected ideal gas law, but it should not be inferred that the method is completely rigorous. The law of corresponding states is only approximately correct, and the values of Z given by Appendix C-6 accordingly represent *average* values for a wide variety of materials, with considerable deviation possible in specific applications. Even so, the use of Eq. (5.4) and Appendix C-6 will suffice for most engineering purposes and is recommended whenever specific experimental data are not available.

5.4 Gas-Phase P-V̲-T Calculations

The gas law constant. It has already been noted that the gas law constant, R, has the same value for all gases, and it only remains to provide for unit consistency in selecting the proper value of R to be used in any particular calculation. Eq. (5.2) indicates that R must have the units $PV̲/T$. With P commonly expressed in psia, V̲ in ft³/lb-mol, and T in °R, a value which is worth committing to memory is

$$R = 10.73 \text{ (psia)(ft}^3)/(\text{lb-mol})(°R)$$

Other values which will frequently be useful are presented in the back of the book.

EXAMPLE 5.1. Calculate the specific volume of ethane (C_2H_6) at 1500 psia and 120°F using (a) the ideal gas law; (b) the van der Waals equation of state; and (c) the generalized compressibility factor. (Perry's Handbook gives an experimental value of 0.04822 ft³/lb.)

Solution. The given temperature must first be converted to degrees Rankine, and 120°F ≈ 580°R.

(a) The ideal gas law may then be solved for V̲:

$$V̲ = RT/P = (10.73)(580)/1500 = 4.15 \text{ ft}^3/\text{lb-mol}$$

Dividing by the molecular weight of 30 yields 0.1383 ft³/lb, rather poor agreement with the experimental value.

(b) The van der Waals constants for ethane, obtained from the literature, are $a = 1391$ (atm)(ft^6)/(lb-mol)^2 and $b = 1.028$ ft^3/lb-mol. Substituting known values into Eq. (5.3), with due attention to unit consistency, yields

$$\left(\frac{1500}{14.7} + \frac{1391}{\underline{V}^2}\right)(\underline{V} - 1.028) = \left(\frac{10.73}{14.7}\right)(580)$$

A trial-and-error solution of this equation gives $\underline{V} = 1.89$ ft^3/lb-mol, equivalent to 0.063 ft^3/lb.

(c) Using values of P_c and T_c from Appendix C-5,

$$P_r = P/P_c = 1500/(48.2)(14.7) = 2.12$$
$$T_r = T/T_c = 580/(306)(1.8) = 1.05$$

Note the use of appropriate conversion factors to make P_r and T_r dimensionless. For $P_r = 2.12$ and $T_r = 1.05$, Z is found to be approximately 0.362 from Appendix C-6.

Instead of recalculating $\underline{V}$ via Eq. (5.4), we should recognize that the new value of $\underline{V}$ is simply the ideal gas value multiplied by 0.362. Hence

$$\underline{V} = (0.1383)(.362) = 0.0501 \text{ ft}^3/\text{lb}$$

for an error of less than 5 per cent from the experimental value.

EXAMPLE 5.2. Eighty pounds of carbon dioxide are to be stored in a 10.5 cubic-foot tank. What maximum temperature can be tolerated if the pressure in the tank is not to exceed 1000 psia?

Solution. $\underline{V} = 10.5/80 = 0.1313$ ft^3/lb. Multiplying by the molecular weight of 44 gives 5.77 ft^3/lb-mol. From Appendix C-5, $P_c = 72.9$ atm and $P_r = 1000/(72.9)(14.7) = 0.935$. $T_c = 304°$K, but T_r cannot be calculated since T is unknown. This makes it impossible to determine Z directly, and a trial-and-error solution will be necessary. It will be facilitated if we rewrite the compressibility factor equation in the form

$$Z \doteq P\underline{V}/RT = P\underline{V}/R(T_c T_r)$$
$$= (1000)(5.77)/(10.73)(304)(1.8) T_r$$
$$= 0.983/T_r \tag{5.5}$$

Eq. (5.5) must now be solved simultaneously with Appendix C-6. The solution can be expedited by plotting the equation directly on the figure, using T_r as the independent variable to facilitate plotting. For T_r equal to 1.15, 1.20, and 1.25, Eq. (5.5) gives corresponding values for Z of 0.854, 0.819, and 0.786. These three points may be plotted on Appendix C-6, and a line drawn through them intersects the vertical line $P_r = 0.935$ at $Z = 0.81$. The difficulty in finding T_r by interpolation can be circumvented by calculating it instead: $T_r = 0.983/.81 = 1.21$, from which $T = T_c T_r = (304)(1.8)(1.21) = 663°$R $\approx 203°$F. The use of the ideal gas law would have predicted a temperature of only 78°F, whereas the experimental value is approximately 200°F.

A similar trial-and-error procedure would be applicable were the compressibility factor method to be used to determine the pressure corresponding to a known temperature and specific volume. Substituting known values and $P = P_c P_r$ into the compressibility factor equation will yield a reduced equation of the form $Z = K P_r$, in which K is a known constant, to be solved simultaneously with Appendix C-6.

Standard conditions. Whereas 10 lb$_m$ of a given gas denotes a specific quantity and cannot be misinterpreted, 10 cubic feet of the same gas could mean almost any quantity, since gas volumes depend on pressure and temperature as well as on the amount of gas present. Still, it is often advantageous to specify gas quantities in volumetric units. This can be done as long as the pressure and temperature are also specified. Alternately, we might agree in advance that all volumetric quantities will imply a particular combination of pressure and temperature, called *standard conditions*, unless other conditions are specifically indicated.

The use of standard conditions is common practice. There is a reference to a standard state of 760 mm Hg and 0°C in chemistry, under which conditions one gram-mol of any *ideal* gas occupies 22.4 liters. In English units these conditions are equivalent to a pressure of one atmosphere and a temperature of 32°F, and a *pound*-mol of any ideal gas will occupy 359 cubic feet under these conditions. The abbreviations SCF (standard cubic feet) or ft³ STP (cubic feet at standard temperature and pressure) are frequently used to call attention to the fact that standard conditions are pertinent.

Unfortunately, there is considerable disagreement over what constitutes standard conditions. Temperature variations are particularly common, with 32°F, 60°F, and 70°F all being considered standard by various engineering groups. Standard conditions of one atmosphere and 60°F are quite common in chemical engineering, for example, and a pound-mol of any ideal gas occupies 379 cubic feet under these conditions.

Under the circumstances, the student is well-advised to be sure he knows what is meant by standard conditions when interpreting volumetric data. Conversely, standard conditions should be clearly identified in all original work—e.g., 4500 SCF (32°F, 1 atm). We will adopt the latter conditions as standard in this text, and recommend memorization of the figure 359 cubic feet per pound-mol under these conditions.

Ideal gas volumes at other than standard conditions are readily calculated by correcting the standard volume for pressure and temperature. The quantitative relationship is

$$\frac{V}{\underline{V}^{\circ}} = \left(\frac{P^{\circ}}{P}\right)\left(\frac{T}{T^{\circ}}\right) \tag{5.6}$$

in which the superscript degree denotes standard conditions, and the terms without superscript pertain to any other conditions. Memorization of this equation is hardly necessary, for it is well known that volume varies directly with temperature and inversely with pressure.

EXAMPLE 5.3. Repeat Ex. 5.1(a) using Eq. (5.6) in lieu of the ideal gas law.

Solution. At standard conditions, the specific volume of ethane is 359 ft³/ lb-mol. At 1500 psia and 120°F, then,

$$\underline{V} = (359) \left(\frac{14.7}{1500}\right)\left(\frac{580}{492}\right) = 4.15 \text{ ft}^3/\text{lb-mol}$$

Since this method is based on the ideal gas law, we should expect to get the same answer as was obtained previously.

5.5 The Two-Phase Region

The phase rule permits only one degree of freedom when a pure substance exists as a two-phase mixture. This leaves two properties to be determined. The determination is straightforward if a P-$\underline{V}$ diagram is available, but an equation of state can only be solved for a single unknown. In the absence of a complete P-$\underline{V}$ diagram or its equivalent, then, an additional relationship is needed to supplement the equation of state and permit the determination of both unknown properties. A brief, qualitative consideration of the phenomena associated with vapor-liquid equilibrium is advisable before the necessary relationship is identified.

Vapor pressure. Consider a liquid which completely fills the space in a cylinder closed off at one end by a movable piston. If the piston is withdrawn slightly in an attempt to create a vacuum above the liquid surface, it will be found that some of the liquid will evaporate to fill the new volume with vapor at a pressure which depends only on the temperature of the liquid. Further, any additional increase in volume at constant temperature will only result in the evaporation of more liquid at the same pressure, since, in accordance with the phase rule, the temperature alone fixes the state for a two-phase mixture of a pure substance.

This pressure, exerted by the vapor in equilibrium with a saturated liquid at any given temperature, is called the *vapor pressure*. It is identically equal to the saturation pressure corresponding to the given temperature, and is therefore pertinent in calculations involving pure saturated vapor or pure saturated liquid as well as to two-phase mixtures. In subsequent references, vapor pressure will be denoted by the symbol p^*.

Some typical vapor pressure data are included in Appendix C-1, and more extensive data may be found in any of the handbooks mentioned in Chap. 3 or in various chemical periodicals. The various generalized correlations which have been proposed for the relationship between vapor pressure and temperature lie outside the scope of the present treatment. However, there is one observation which will facilitate interpolation between the values given in tabulations of experimental data:

Over reasonable ranges of temperature, the relationship between vapor pressure and temperature is closely approximated by an equation of the form

$$\log p^* = A + B/T \qquad (5.7)$$

in which A and B are constants for a particular substance. The substitution of values for two known (p^*, T) points into this equation yields two expressions which can be solved simultaneously for the two constants A and B. With the constants known, Eq. (5.7) may then be used to determine the vapor pressure at any temperature not too far removed from those used in evaluating the constants. Alternately, the equation can be solved for T when vapor pressure is known.

Until numerical values for the constants A and B have been determined, any *absolute* units may be used for p^* and T in Eq. (5.7). Similarly, a natural logarithm may be substituted for the base-10 logarithm given in the equation. The choice of units and logarithm base will be reflected in the calculated values for A and B. It follows that when specific numerical values for these constants have been calculated or are given, the use of the units and logarithm base to which they correspond is mandatory.

EXAMPLE 5.4. The vapor pressure of methyl chloride is 1.0 atm at $-24.0°C$ and 60 atm at 137.5°C. Estimate the temperature at which methyl chloride has a vapor pressure of 20 atm.

Solution. The given temperatures must be converted to absolute units: $-24.0°C \approx 249.2°K$ and $137.5°C \approx 410.7°K$. Substituting these values and the corresponding pressures into Eq. (5.7) and subtracting one of the resulting expressions from the other to eliminate A yields

$$\log 60 - \log 1 = B/410.7 - B/249.2$$

or

$$\log \frac{60}{1} = 1.778 = \frac{(249.2 - 410.7)B}{(410.7)(249.2)}$$

from which $B = -1127°K$. (Although it makes no difference in this example, converting the difference of two logarithms to the logarithm of a quotient is generally recommended to minimize slide-rule error. The cross-multiplication on the right-hand side of the above equation serves the same purpose, as was noted in Sec. 4.12.)

The value for B may now be substituted back into Eq. (5.7), along with either of the given datum points to get A:

$$\log 1 = 0 = A - 1127/249.2 = A - 4.52$$

and $A = 4.52$. The vapor pressure of methyl chloride over the given temperature range is therefore approximated by the relationship

$$\log p^* = 4.52 - 1127/T$$

for p^* in atmospheres and T in degrees Kelvin. Substituting $p^* = 20$ atm
yields $T = 350°K$. This answer, even though based on an interpolation
between two widely separated points, is in excellent agreement with the
temperature of $350.5°K$ given in Perry's Handbook. Linear interpolation,
on the other hand, would have predicted a temperature of $301.3°K$.

Quality. In the absence of experimental data, the specific volume of a
saturated vapor can be calculated from an appropriate equation of state
once the saturation pressure and temperature are known. Depending on the
information available, it may be possible to determine the specific volume
of the saturated liquid in a similar manner. Otherwise, it may be necessary
to assume the liquid volume to be negligible compared to the vapor volume
and, as an approximation, to disregard the former. With the specific volumes
of saturated liquid and vapor thus known or approximated, the specific
volume of a two-phase mixture can be calculated if the relative quantities
of liquid and vapor are known. The percentage of vapor in a two-phase
mixture is commonly called the *quality* of the mixture.

The quantitative relationship between the specific volume of a two-phase
mixture, $\underline{V}_M$, and the specific volumes of the saturated liquid ($\underline{V}_L$) and
saturated vapor ($\underline{V}_V$) of which it is composed is

$$\underline{V}_M = q\underline{V}_V + (1 - q)\underline{V}_L \tag{5.8}$$

where q is the fraction of the mixture which is vapor (and $100q$ is the quality
of the mixture). This equation states simply that the volume of the mixture
is equal to the volume of saturated vapor plus the volume of saturated
liquid. The relationship may be solved for the vapor fraction, q, to obtain
the equation

$$q = \frac{\underline{V}_M - \underline{V}_L}{\underline{V}_V - \underline{V}_L} \tag{5.9}$$

Eq. (5.9) has an interesting graphical corollary. A typical isotherm passing
through the two-phase region of a P-$\underline{V}$ diagram is shown in Fig. 5.4, with
the points L, V, and M denoting saturated liquid, saturated vapor, and
mixture, respectively. Quality can be shown to increase *linearly* from zero
at point L to 100 at point V. The fact that the increase is linear is significant,
for it provides the basis for the *inverse lever arm* principle which will frequently
be applicable in chemical engineering calculations:

For a system at any point M on a saturation line, the linear relationship
requires that the fraction of saturated vapor in the mixture be equal to the
ratio of the line lengths $\overline{LM}/\overline{LV}$, while the fraction of saturated liquid is
given $\overline{MV}/\overline{LV}$. Note that, although pure saturated vapor lies at the right

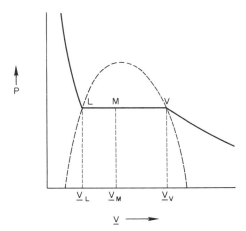

Fig. 5.4   P-$\underline{V}$ diagram showing typical location of a two-phase mixture, *M*.

end of the line, the vapor fraction in the mixture is indicated by the *left*-hand line segment; hence the inverse aspect of the lever-arm principle.

Since the lengths of the line segments appear only in a dimensionless ratio, they can be measured by any suitable method or scale. It is usually most convenient to make direct use of the scale provided on the abscissa of the plot. Thus, as can be seen from Fig. 5.4,

$$q = \overline{LM}/\overline{LV} = \frac{V_M - V_L}{\underline{V}_V - \underline{V}_L} \tag{5.9a}$$

A comparison of Eqs. (5.9) and (5.9a) shows the condition of linearity to be consistent with the concept of additive volumes.

EXAMPLE 5.5. Calculate the volume occupied by 0.5 pounds of methanol having a quality of 76 per cent at 426°F.

Solution. The presence of two phases means that the system must be at a pressure equal to the vapor pressure at 426°F, $\approx$ 886°R $\approx$ 492°K $\approx$ 219°C. Using the data in Appendix C-1, this temperature is bracketed by the two (p^*, T) points (50 atm, 214.0°C) and (60 atm, 224.0°C). A vapor pressure calculation similar to that made in Ex. 5.4 yields $A = 5.64$, $B = -1920°K$, and, at 492°K, $p^* = 55$ atmospheres.

The procedure demonstrated in Ex. 5.1(c) may now be used to calculate the specific volume of the saturated vapor at 492°K and 55 atmospheres. The calculation yields $P_r = 0.70$, $T_r = 0.96$, $Z \cong 0.64$, and $\underline{V}_V = 7.53$ ft^3/lb-mol. The lower portion of Appendix C-6 makes it possible to estimate the specific volume of the saturated liquid. For $P_r = 0.70$ and $T_r = 0.96$,

$Z \cong 0.14$ and $\underline{V}_L = 1.65$ ft³/lb-mol. Substituting q, $\underline{V}_V$, and $\underline{V}_L$ into Eq. (5.8),

$$\underline{V}_M = (.76)(7.53) + (.24)(1.65)$$

$$= 5.72 + .40 = 6.12 \text{ ft}^3/\text{lb-mol}$$

Note that the assumption of negligible liquid volume would lead to an error of less than 7 per cent, and that even this error would decrease with increasing quality. Since the quality encountered in most practical applications is upwards of 90 per cent, it can be seen that a rough estimate of liquid specific volume will generally suffice.

For a molecular weight of 32, 6.12 ft³/lb-mol is equivalent to 0.191 ft³/lb, and 0.5 lbs of methanol will occupy 0.0955 cubic feet under the conditions given.

When only the specific volume and quality of a two-phase mixture are known initially, an estimate of the liquid specific volume will make it possible to solve Eq. (5.8) for the specific volume of the saturated vapor. The equation of state and the vapor pressure equation must then be solved simultaneously for pressure and temperature. A trial-and-error solution will be necessary.

5.6 Extensive Properties

It is important to remember that the phase rule pertains to intensive properties only. The extent of the system constitutes an additional variable which must be handled separately. By definition,

$$\underline{\Gamma} = \Gamma/M \tag{5.10}$$

where Γ denotes any extensive property. This equation provides a bridge between the extent of a system and the intensive properties subject to the phase rule. Its use in relating V to $\underline{V}$ has already been demonstrated in Exs. 5.2 and 5.5. Examples involving other extensive properties will be presented in Chap. 6.

The presence of a mass term in Eq. (5.10) correctly suggests that the general mass balance may also be pertinent in problems involving extensive properties. This fundamental relationship was developed in Sec. 2.3 as Eq. (2.2) and is repeated here for convenience of reference:

$$M_i - M_o = M_2 - M_1 + M_c \tag{2.2}$$

It should be remembered that the use of this equation requires the specification of both a basis and a system.

5.7 The Solid State

The solid state has been ignored in the foregoing discussion of P-$\underline{V}$-T relationships, but this does not imply that it is of little importance to the chemical engineer. On the contrary, the physical properties of solids are of growing importance in view of the constantly increasing demand for solid materials of extreme purity—a demand which must be filled by the chemical engineer and his close associate, the metallurgical engineer.

Still, by far the greater majority of chemical engineering calculations pertain to the properties of liquids and gases. We therefore consider the foregoing development to be sufficient for an introductory text. A minor exception is the brief mention of properties pertaining to energy and chemical activity in subsequent chapters.

5.8 Summary

In the order in which they were developed in this chapter, the quantitative relationships pertinent to the P-$\underline{V}$-T behavior of pure substances are

1) The phase rule,
$$N_f = N_c - N_p + 2 \tag{5.1}$$

2) an equation of state such as
$$P\underline{V} = ZRT \tag{5.4}$$

3) a vapor pressure relationship such as
$$\log p^* = A + B/T \tag{5.7}$$

4) the concept of additive volumes for two-phase mixtures,
$$\underline{V}_M = q\underline{V}_V + (1 - q)\underline{V}_L \tag{5.8}$$

5) the extensive-intensive property relationship,
$$\underline{\Gamma} = \Gamma/M \tag{5.10}$$

6) the general mass balance,
$$M_i - M_o = M_2 - M_1 + M_c \tag{2.2}$$

This summary provides a convenient check list, but it is no substitute for a clear understanding of the significance of all six equations. Supplementary concepts such as critical phenomena, reduced properties, and the compressibility factor plot are equally important. The principles presented in this chapter are the cornerstones which support an impressive thermodynamic structure. It is therefore essential that the student master them, for such mastery will be invaluable in the subsequent study of thermodynamics.

In the meantime, the material already presented can be put to direct use as the example problems quite clearly indicate. The problems which follow will provide additional evidence of the practical utility of this material and will, at the same time, give the student a brief glimpse of some of the thermodynamic concepts which lie ahead. If the problems prove difficult, the odds are that a significant implication of the problem statement has been missed. A closing example should serve to illustrate this important point:

EXAMPLE 5.6. A horizontal cylinder is separated into two chambers by a freely-floating (frictionless) piston. One chamber contains 5 lbs of methyl alcohol, the other an equal quantity of ethylene, and the two chambers may be heated or cooled independently. At one point in a series of tests, when the piston is exactly centered in the cylinder, the methanol chamber is at 426°F and the ethylene chamber is at 124°F. How much liquid methanol, if any, is present under these conditions?

Solution. Two restrictions which are essential to the solution of this problem can easily be overlooked if the problem statement is not scrutinized to detect indirect implications. First, the fact that the piston is frictionless means that the pressures in the two chambers must be the same at all times. Second, the centered piston makes the volumes of the two chambers equal and, since the masses are also equal, the specific volumes must be the same. The pressure and specific volume equalities suggest that an examination of conditions in one chamber may be helpful in determining conditions in the other.

It is also essential to recognize the fact that the presence of any liquid methanol means that the pressure must be equal to the vapor pressure of methanol at 426°F. This conclusion, it should be noted, temporarily disregards the possibility that *all* the methanol exists as a sub-cooled liquid, and this possibility must be checked out. The most logical procedure would appear to be to assume that the methanol exists as a two-phase mixture with quality and to let the calculations disprove this assumption if it is erroneous.

The vapor pressure of methanol at 426°F was found to be 55 atmospheres in Ex. 5.5, wherein $\underline{V}_V$ and $\underline{V}_L$ were also found to be 7.53 and 1.65 ft³/lb-mol, respectively. If the specific volume in the methanol chamber lies between these two values, the existence of a two-phase mixture is confirmed. A greater specific volume would indicate the presence of superheated vapor only, while a lower value would indicate the presence of subcooled liquid only. In either of these eventualities, the given data are not sufficient to permit the calculation of all properties of interest.

The specific volume in the methanol chamber cannot be calculated directly, but that in the ethylene chamber is fixed by the known temperature and tentative pressure of 55 atmospheres. The equation-of-state calculation yields $\underline{V} = 5.54$ ft³/lb-mol, with $P_r = 1.10$, $T_r = 1.15$, and $Z \cong 0.715$. Since $\underline{V}$ in the methanol chamber is also 5.54 ft³/lb-mol, a two-phase mixture is present. Quality can now be calculated from Eq. (5.8), but the use of Eq. (5.9) is more direct:

$$q = \frac{5.54 - 1.65}{7.53 - 1.65} = \frac{3.89}{5.88} = 0.661$$

Thus 33.9 per cent of the methanol is in the liquid state, and $(.339)(5) = 1.70$ pounds of liquid are present under the given conditions.

REVIEW, STUDY, AND DISCUSSION

5-1. Define isotherm, degree of freedom, vapor, dew point, saturated vapor, superheated vapor, saturated liquid, subcooled liquid, bubble point, critical point, equation of state, ideal gas, compressibility factor, reduced pressure, reduced temperature, standard conditions, vapor pressure, and quality.

5-2. State the Gibbs phase rule, the law of corresponding states, and the inverse-lever-arm principle.

5-3. Two gas samples have been loaded into cylinders in preparation for P-$\underline{V}$-T tests as depicted in Fig. 5.1. One cylinder contains pure A and the other a mixture of A and B, but the lab technician failed to label them and no longer knows which is which. Describe a simple test for determining which container holds which sample in the absence of any data pertaining to physical properties.

5-4. It is quite difficult to make accurate experimental measurements of critical volume. From a consideration of Appendix C-6, explain why this should be so.

5-5. The concept of *residual volume*, defined as the ideal gas volume minus the actual volume, is useful in thermodynamics. Calculate the residual volume of ethylene (C_2H_4) at 90°F and 70 atm.

5-6. Ethane (C_2H_6) is stored in a closed vessel at 100 atm and 400°F. What will be the pressure in the vessel if the temperature falls to 120°F?

5-7. Given $R = 10.73$ (psia)(ft³)/(lb-mol)(°R), calculate the numerical value of the gas law constant if the units are to be (a) BTU/(lb-mol)(°R); (b) cal/(gm-mol)(°K).

5-8. Gaseous methane (CH_4) under pressure is to be cooled to $-265°F$ by adiabatic expansion in a turbo-expander. What discharge pressure should be specified if the methane is to leave the expander as a saturated vapor?

5-9. Vapor pressure data can be used to estimate the enthalpy change which accompanies vaporization through the use of the Clausius-Clapeyron equation:

$$\frac{d(\ln p^*)}{dT} = \frac{\Delta \underline{H}}{RT^2}$$

Using the vapor pressure data given in Appendix C-1, determine $\Delta \underline{H}$ of vaporization for ammonia at 0°F. (Perry's Handbook lists an experimental value of 568.9 BTU/lb.)

5-10. A vertical cylinder having a cross-sectional area of 0.05 ft² is closed off at the top by a movable piston. It contains 0.10 lbs of propane (C_3H_8) at an initial pressure of 400 psia and a temperature of 200°F. The propane is to be compressed isothermally until it is 50 per cent liquid. What final pressure will be required? How far will the piston travel during the process?

5-11. How many pounds of sulfur dioxide can be stored in a 100-cubic-foot tank at a pressure of 200 psia and a temperature of 150°F?

5-12. Carry out the calculations described in Ex. 5.6 to confirm the given intermediate and final answers. Include the calculations necessary to confirm the answers carried over from Ex. 5.5.

5-13. Calculate the dew point temperature and pressure in the vessel described in Prob. 5-6.

5-14. Thermodynamic calculations frequently require the evaluation of $\int \underline{V} dP$ along a path of constant temperature. Evaluate the integral for the compression of nitrogen from 10 atm to 100 atm at a constant temperature of $-188°F$, (a) assuming the ideal gas law to be applicable; (b) using the compressibility factor equation of state. Express the answer in BTU/lb-mol.

5-15. A small tank of propylene (C_3H_6) is immersed in a constant-temperature bath and a pressure gage attached to the tank reads 205 psi. A lab technician attempts to raise the pressure to 240 psia by adding more propylene from a second tank. A decreasing pressure in the second tank tells him that propylene is flowing into the test tank, but the gage continues to read 205 psi. He finally concludes that the gage is stuck, disconnects the second tank, and turns to other tasks.

Some time later he notices that propylene is leaking from the disconnected supply line and that the gage reading has dropped to 163 psi. Puzzled, he stops the leak and turns up the bath temperature to see what will happen. To his surprise, the gage responds properly. (Subsequent tests indicate that the gage was working properly at all times.) He then decides to raise the bath temperature still further in an attempt to reach the desired pressure of 240 psia.

    a) Why did the gage reading remain unchanged initially?

    b) Sketch the path of the entire process on a P-$\underline{V}$ diagram.

    c) For what temperature should the bath temperature control be set to reach the desired pressure?

CHAPTER 6

Energy and Entropy for Pure Substances

Although pressure, temperature and specific volume are often considered to be the primary state variables, properties associated with energy and entropy are no less important to the chemical engineer. The latter topics were treated in an introductory fashion in Chap. 2 and are now to be given detailed attention. A review of Secs. 2.4 and 2.5 is suggested in preparation for the material which follows. An understanding of the concepts presented in Chap. 5 is also essential, since these concepts provide a basis for relationships involving energy and entropy.

6.1 Fundamental Thermodynamic Equations

Three fundamental relationships are of critical importance in thermodynamics, for they are the starting point for the derivation of many other relationships having diverse applications. Two of the fundamental equations are the general energy and entropy balances developed in Chap. 2. Since the earlier development is considered to be adequate, the two balances are presented here without discussion:

$$-\Delta_{oi}[(\underline{H} + \underline{KE} + \underline{PE})M] + Q - W =$$
$$\Delta_{21}[(\underline{U} + \underline{KE} + \underline{PE})M] - E_c \qquad (2.6)$$

$$-dS_{oi} + \frac{\delta Q}{T} + \frac{\delta lw}{T} = dS_{21} \qquad (2.16)$$

(Note that the pertinence of the mass balance is implied by the presence of extensive properties in both equations.)

The third fundamental relationship is essentially a mathematical statement of the fact that the change in internal energy, which embraces all forms of energy except kinetic and potential, is equal to the algebraic sum of the changes in all these other forms of energy. In most chemical engineering applications only thermal, mechanical, and chemical energy are pertinent. Further, mechanical effects are generally limited to those associated with the expansion or compression of a gas. For these conditions,

Δ (internal energy) $= \Delta$ (thermal energy) $+$
$$\Delta \text{ (mechanical energy)} + \Delta \text{ (chemical energy)}$$

It can be shown that the mathematical equivalent of the foregoing equality is, in differential form,

$$dU = TdS - PdV + (\overline{G}_A dM_A + \overline{G}_B dM_B + \ldots) \qquad (6.1)$$

in which $\overline{G}_A$ and $\overline{G}_B$ are the chemical potentials of components A and B, and the only change in mechanical energy is that due to expansion or compression of the system. For the pure, non-reacting substances of interest at present, $dM_A = dM_B = 0$, and Eq. (6.1) reduces to

$$dU = TdS - PdV \qquad (6.2)$$

The following derivation pertains to this reduced form only, and its extension to include chemically-reacting systems will be considered in Chap. 8. However, we recommend that the general relationship given by Eq. (6.1) be remembered, rather than the reduced form given by Eq. (6.2), since the reduced form is readily derived by setting dM_A and dM_B equal to zero.

The fact that properties depend on state only and are independent of path or process has a significant corollary: If any relationship which involves properties only can be shown to be valid for any particular process, it must be equally valid for all possible processes. Eq. (6.2) falls into this category and is most easily derived by considering the special case of a reversible process:

For a closed system not subject to kinetic or potential energy changes, Eq. (2.6) reduces to $\Delta U = Q - W$ or, in differential form, $dU = \delta Q - \delta W$. If such a system undergoes a reversible process, the latter equation can be modified to $dU = TdS - \delta W$ since, for a reversible process, Eq. (2.16) reduces to $\delta Q = TdS$. The derivation of Eq. (6.2) may now be completed by showing that, for a reversible process, $\delta W = PdV$.

It was stated in Sec. 2.4 that work of expansion occurs when a system expands (or is compressed) against a resisting force or pressure. Since $P_R = F_R/A$ and $dV = Ads$, it can be seen that $\delta W = P_R dV$ is directly equivalent to $\delta W = F_R ds$, the subscripts serving to remind us that it is the *resisting* force or pressure which is significant. The fact that no work is done when a gas expands into a vacuum is thereby accounted for, but also makes it clear that the system pressure and the resisting pressure need not be the same.

It is at this point that the restriction of reversibility becomes pertinent. If an expansion or compression process is to be reversible, the system pressure and the resisting pressure must differ only infinitesimally and, in the limit, $P = P_R$. Thus $\delta W = PdV$ *for a reversible process* and Eq. (6.2) follows. As has already been pointed out, the equation must be equally valid for any process, reversible or not, since it involves only properties which are independent of path or process.

By definition, $\underline{\Gamma} = \Gamma/M$; hence $d\underline{\Gamma} = d\Gamma/M$ for a system of constant mass, i.e., a closed system. Also, $x_A = M_A/M$ and $dx_A = dM_A/M$. These relationships permit the conversion of either Eq. (6.1) or (6.2) to a per-unit-mass basis by simply dividing through by the mass of the system:

$$dU = TdS - Pd\underline{V} + (\overline{G}_A dx_A + \overline{G}_B dx_B + \dots) \qquad (6.3)$$

$$d\underline{U} = TdS - Pd\underline{V} \qquad (6.4)$$

6.2 The Convenience Functions

Enthalpy, H, was introduced in Sec. 2.4 as a convenience function to replace the recurring combination $U + PV$. Two additional convenience functions are in common use. The first, called the *Helmholtz work function*, replaces the combination $U - TS$ and will be denoted by the symbol A. The second, to be denoted by the symbol G, is called the *Gibbs free energy function* and replaces the combination $U + PV - TS$, equal to $H - TS$ and also to $A + PV$. It will be shown in Chap. 8 that the Gibbs free energy function G is directly related to the chemical potential $\overline{G}$ used in Eq. (6.1).

The equations which define H, A, and G may all be written in several alternative forms. Only those pertaining to enthalpy will be listed since the analogous forms for the other two functions will be immediately obvious:

1) By definition,

$$H = U + PV \qquad (6.5)$$

2) The definition can be differentiated to obtain

$$dH = dU + d(PV) = dU + PdV + VdP \qquad (6.6)$$

3) The differential form can be integrated between limits to obtain a finite difference form:

$$\Delta H = \Delta U + \Delta(PV) \qquad (6.7)$$

4) dU can be eliminated from the differential form by substituting from Eq. (6.1),

$$dH = TdS - PdV + (\overline{G}_A dM_A + \overline{G}_B dM_B + \ldots) + PdV + VdP$$
$$= TdS + VdP + (\overline{G}_A dM_A + \overline{G}_B dM_B + \ldots) \qquad (6.8)$$

5) For constant M_A and M_B, Eq. (6.8) reduces to

$$dH = TdS + VdP \qquad (6.9)$$

6) Since each term of each of the above equations contains an extensive property, any of the equations can be converted to a per-unit-mass basis by dividing through by the mass of the system.

The fifth alternative form given above is particularly useful, and it will be advantageous to summarize the four equations of this type:

$$dU = TdS - PdV \qquad (6.2)$$

$$dH = TdS + VdP \qquad (6.9)$$

$$dA = -SdT - PdV \qquad (6.10)$$

$$dG = -SdT + VdP \qquad (6.11)$$

All these relationships are subject to the same restriction; namely, they apply to closed systems subject to expansion or contraction and heat effects only. When chemical reaction is also to be provided for, it will be necessary to use the more general form represented by Eq. (6.8).

6.3 Mathematical Derivations

Many useful relationships can be derived from Eqs. (6.1) through (6.11). There is no need to identify all possible derivations or even the more important ones at this point. Instead, those techniques which are generally pertinent to the derivations will be illustrated. The student may then make use of the same techniques to derive any desired relationship as the occasion demands.

Two techniques, division by a finite quantity and the imposition of restrictions, have already been demonstrated. Eq. (6.2) was divided through by M to obtain Eq. (6.4), and division by T, S, P, V, or any other quantity would have been equally proper. Eq. (6.2) itself, on the other hand, was obtained by imposing the restriction of constant M_A and M_B on Eq. (6.1). The fact that a given relationship is under restriction is generally indicated by subscript. Thus the notation $dH_P = TdS_P$ indicates that this relationship, derived from Eq. (6.9), is valid only for a constant-pressure process.

Strictly speaking, each of the equations presented so far should include a number of subscripts to denote restrictions such as constant surface area (no surface energy effects), constant total mass, or, in some cases, constant M_A and M_B. Were all pertinent subscripts to be used meticulously, the notation in most thermodynamic equations would be almost hopelessly cumbersome. The customary practice is to state primary restrictions separately and to use subscripts to denote any additional restrictions imposed during the course of a particular development.

Division by a differential is a third technique which is often useful. This technique was demonstrated in Sec. 2.7 when the differential form of the mass balance was divided through by $d\theta$ to obtain a mass-rate balance. As a more immediate example, it can be seen that Eq. (6.9) may be divided by dP to obtain $dH/dP = TdS/dP + V$.

Restrictions may be imposed either before or after division by either a finite quantity or a differential. The addition of the restriction of constant entropy to the above example would yield

$$\left(\frac{dH}{dP}\right)_S = V \tag{6.12}$$

Partial derivative notation is properly called for in this expression, but is not essential as long as the subscript is retained to identify the variable to be held constant. As a matter of fact, the notation actually used has definite advantages since it emphasizes the fact that the derivative is composed of two separate differentials which may be separated by multiplying through by dP_S if desired. We shall adopt the practice of using ordinary derivative notation together with pertinent subscripts in lieu of partial derivatives.

Two partial derivatives can be combined by multiplication or division *if they are subject to the same restriction*, and the restriction will be retained in the answer. To illustrate, Eq. (6.12) will be multiplied through by $\left(\dfrac{dP}{dT}\right)_S$:

$$V\left(\frac{dP}{dT}\right)_S = \left(\frac{dH}{dP}\right)_S \left(\frac{dP}{dT}\right)_S = \left(\frac{dH}{dT}\right)_S$$

Note that the same result might have been obtained by dividing Eq. (6.9) through by dT while holding S constant.

6.4 Point Functions

It has been repeatedly emphasized that properties are independent of path or process. In mathematics, variables which do not depend on path are called *point functions* or .*perfect differentials*. Point functions have three characteristics which have direct application in thermodynamics. These characteristics will first be identified in general terms, and the thermodynamic consequences will be examined in the next section.

Given any point function $u = u(x,y)$, one can immediately write

$$du = \left(\frac{du}{dx}\right)_y dx + \left(\frac{du}{dy}\right)_x dy \tag{6.13}$$

In essence this equation states that, since u is independent of path, the change in u in going from one point to another can be determined by evaluating the change with x along a path of constant y and adding to it the change with y along a path of constant x.

The second pertinent characteristic of point functions is the fact that the second partial derivatives are equal, or,

$$\frac{d}{dy}\left(\frac{du}{dx}\right)_y = \frac{d}{dx}\left(\frac{du}{dy}\right)_x \tag{6.14}$$

which is equivalent to saying that the order of differentiation is immaterial. An alternative statement of this equality results if Eq. (6.13) is written in the form

$$du = M\,dx + N\,dy \tag{6.15}$$

where $M = \left(\dfrac{du}{dx}\right)_y$ and $N = \left(\dfrac{du}{dy}\right)_x$. Substitution into Eq. (6.14) yields

$$\frac{dM}{dy} = \frac{dN}{dx} \tag{6.16}$$

The third characteristic of point functions is derivable from Eq. (6.13). If the equation is divided through by dy while u is held constant, the result is

$$0 = \left(\frac{du}{dx}\right)_y \left(\frac{dx}{dy}\right)_u + \left(\frac{du}{dy}\right)_x$$

or

$$\left(\frac{du}{dx}\right)_y \left(\frac{dx}{dy}\right)_u \left(\frac{dy}{du}\right)_x = -1 \tag{6.17}$$

The form of Eq. (6.17) can be readily recalled if it is remembered that the variables appearing in the numerator, denominator, and subscript of each term form a rotating sequence: $u, x, y; x, y, u; y, u, x$. The sequence may be started with any of the three variables and applied in any consistent order.

6.5 Thermodynamic Properties as Point Functions

Path independence. The phase rule permits two degrees of freedom when a pure substance exists as a single phase. Any two properties may be specified to define the state, whereupon all other properties should be determinable as functions of the two specified properties. Suppose a state is fixed by specifying pressure and temperature. There must then be a relationship $H = H(P, T)$ which will permit the determination of the enthalpy. Since H is a point function, it follows from Eq. (6.13) that

$$dH = \left(\frac{dH}{dT}\right)_P dT + \left(\frac{dH}{dP}\right)_T dP \tag{6.18}$$

Had the state-defining properties been entropy and pressure, the resulting differential equation would be

$$dH = \left(\frac{dH}{dS}\right)_P dS + \left(\frac{dH}{dP}\right)_S dP \qquad (6.19)$$

This same equation might have been derived in an entirely different manner: If Eq. (6.9) is divided through by dS while P is held constant, the result is $T = \left(\frac{dH}{dS}\right)_P$. Eq. (6.19) follows directly when this expression and Eq. (6.12) are substituted back into Eq. (6.9).

Eq. (6.18) or its equivalent is the first step in relating changes in internal energy, enthalpy, and entropy to the changes in pressure, temperature, and specific volume discussed in the preceding chapter. The next step will be to express the two partial derivatives in terms of known or determinable properties, and the change in U, H, or S can then be calculated. The evaluation of the partial derivatives will be treated in Secs. 6.6 and 6.7.

The Maxwell relations. Eqs. (6.2), (6.9), (6.10), and (6.11) all have the same form as Eq. (6.15) and must therefore have corollaries equivalent to Eq. (6.16):

$$\left(\frac{dT}{dV}\right)_S = -\left(\frac{dP}{dS}\right)_V \qquad (6.20)$$

$$\left(\frac{dT}{dP}\right)_S = \left(\frac{dV}{dS}\right)_P \qquad (6.21)$$

$$\left(\frac{dS}{dV}\right)_T = \left(\frac{dP}{dT}\right)_V \qquad (6.22)$$

$$-\left(\frac{dS}{dP}\right)_T = \left(\frac{dV}{dT}\right)_P \qquad (6.23)$$

These equations are often referred to as the *Maxwell relations*. The last two are particularly useful, for they will make it possible to replace derivatives involving entropy with equivalent derivatives which involve only pressure, temperature, and volume.

Change of restricted variable. Three of the Maxwell relations would appear to be a direct consequence of the arbitrary decision to define the three convenience functions H, A, and G. This is not the case, since all four Maxwell relations can be derived directly from the fundamental relationship, Eq. (6.2), without going through the convenience functions. If Eq. (6.17) is written in terms of T, V, and S, it will be found that

$$\left(\frac{dT}{dV}\right)_S = -\left(\frac{dS}{dV}\right)_T \left(\frac{dT}{dS}\right)_V$$

Eq. (6.22) will result when this expression is inserted into Eq. (6.20) and the two constant-volume derivatives are combined. Similar derivations would yield Eqs. (6.21) and (6.23).

The foregoing derivation illustrates the practical application of Eq. (6.17) as a means of removing a variable from the subscript position, where it cannot be cancelled out, and placing it in the derivatives where it can be eliminated by cancellation.

6.6 Energy as a Function of Temperature

Eqs. (6.18) and (6.19) suggest that the change in any thermodynamic property can be expressed as a function of the changes in any two other properties selected as independent variables. It will usually be most convenient to use pressure and temperature as independent variables, although the substitution of specific volume for pressure is occasionally advantageous. Only energy and temperature are treated in the present section, but a consideration of pressure, volume, and entropy will follow.

The fundamental relationship. For water, at least, a suitable relationship between energy and temperature is built into the definition of the BTU as a unit of energy: Each Fahrenheit degree of temperature change corresponds to an energy change of one BTU per pound of water. Thus if 500 pounds of water are heated from 70°F to 95°F, an energy increase of 12,500 BTU is indicated.

If the foregoing calculation is written in the form of an equation, a flagrant case of unit inconsistency is at once apparent:

$$(500 \text{ lb})(25\text{F}°) \overset{?}{=} 12,500 \text{ BTU}$$

Suppose we tentatively eliminate the inconsistency by introducing a conversion factor as we did to resolve the $F = Mg$ dilemma. The factor must have a numerical value of unity, and, if introduced into the left-hand side of the equality, must also have the units of BTU/(lb)(F°). In symbolic notation, then,

$$MC\Delta T = \Delta E \tag{6.24}$$

with M denoting mass, ΔE the energy change, and C the conversion factor of 1 BTU/(lb)(F°).

The factor C is commonly called the *heat capacity*, and would appear to be adequately defined by Eq. (6.24). However, it should be remembered that energy depends on pressure or specific volume as well as on temperature. It will therefore be advisable to adopt a more fundamental definition,

$$C = T\left(\frac{dS}{dT}\right) \tag{6.25}$$

and to show that this definition is consistent with Eq. (6.24) and other familiar applications of the heat capacity concept.

Pressure and volume effects can be eliminated by restricting the use of C to constant pressure or constant volume processes. At constant volume, Eq. (6.2) can be divided through by dT and combined with Eq. (6.25) to obtain

$$C_V = T\left(\frac{dS}{dT}\right)_V = \left(\frac{dU}{dT}\right)_V \tag{6.26}$$

At constant pressure, a similar combination of Eqs. (6.9) and (6.25) yields

$$C_P = T\left(\frac{dS}{dT}\right)_P = \left(\frac{dH}{dT}\right)_P \tag{6.27}$$

Eqs. (6.26) and (6.27) can be considered to define C_V and C_P, but it is apparent that they are both consequences of the more fundamental definition given by Eq. (6.25).

If C_V is independent of temperature, Eq. (6.26) can be integrated to obtain $C_V\Delta T = \Delta U$ or, upon multiplication by M, $MC_V\Delta T = \Delta U$. Similarly, Eq. (6.27) becomes $MC_P\Delta T = \Delta H$. Either of these expressions may be used to replace Eq. (6.24), depending on whether the water was heated at constant volume or at constant pressure, and the fundamental definition of C can be seen to be wholly consistent with the tentative development presented initially.

Heat capacity as a property. Despite the popular use of the term *heat* capacity, the use of C_V and C_P is in no way restricted to problems involving the transfer of heat. In Joule's classical experiment, for example, the temperature of water was raised by stirring only, rather than by transferring heat, but the heat capacity could still be used to relate the temperature rise to the corresponding energy change. The term *specific heat* is also common, and refers to the ratio of the heat capacity of any given material to that of water. Since the heat capacity of water is unity, however, heat capacity and specific heat are numerically equal, and the two terms are interchangeable for practical purposes.

The fact that heat capacity reflects only a temperature-energy relationship and does not depend on the method or process employed to effect a change in temperature or energy makes it a true property. Like all properties, it varies from one substance to another and from one state to another. The variation with pressure or specific volume can be calculated from P-V-T data, but the variation with temperature and from substance to substance is usually determined by direct experiment:

Were a 0.1-lb sample of steel at an initial temperature of 270.2°F to be plunged into 12 pounds of water at an initial temperature of 70.0°F, heat would flow from the steel to the water with a consequent rise in water temperature. For these particular masses and initial temperatures, the water temperature, upon reaching thermal equilibrium, would be found to be 70.2°F. (This assumes no heat loss to the surroundings, which include the container holding the water. In practice a correction would be made for the heat absorbed by the container.)

Under constant pressure conditions, the energy increase of the water during this experiment would be, in accordance with the integrated form of Eq. (6.27),

$$\Delta H = MC_P \Delta T = (12)(1)(0.2) = 2.4 \text{ BTU}$$

If the first law of thermodynamics is to be satisfied, this same quantity of energy must come from the steel. Thus the steel undergoes an energy change of -2.4 BTU during a process which is also characterized by a temperature change of $-200\text{F}°$. The constant-pressure heat capacity of steel can accordingly be calculated from the integrated form of Eq. (6.27),

$$C_P = \Delta H / M \Delta T = -2.4/(.1)(-200) = 0.12 \text{ BTU}/(\text{lb})(\text{F}°)$$

(Note the use of the proper sign convention with respect to the numbers substituted for both ΔH and ΔT.)

C_P was tacitly assumed to be independent of temperature in the foregoing example, but this is not true of most materials. Temperature dependency is usually taken into account by substituting a function of temperature for C_V or C_P before Eq. (6.26) or (6.27) is integrated. Should C_P be a linear function of T, for example, Eq. (6.27) could be written $dH = (a + bT)dT$ and then integrated. Other common analytical expressions for the relationship between C and T are $C = a + bT + cT^2$ and $C = a + bT + c/T^2$. In each case a, b, and c are constants requiring experimental evaluation. Experimental heat capacity data are widely reported in the literature, and an abridged tabulation will be found in Appendix C-2.

EXAMPLE 6.1. Calculate the enthalpy change which will result when 500 pounds of gaseous HCl are cooled from 250°F to 100°F. $C_P = 6.70 + 0.0084\,T$ cal/(gm-mol)(C°), with T in °K.

Solution. It should be recalled from Prob. 4-12 that heat capacities in cal/(gm-mol)(C°) and in BTU/(lb-mol)(F°) are numerically equal. This equality does not alter the fact that C_P is given as a function of T in degrees Kelvin. Unit consistency will be preserved by converting 250°F and 100°F to 394.5°K and 311°K, respectively. Substituting for C_P in Eq. (6.27) and integrating,

$$\Delta H = \int_{394.5}^{311} (6.70 + 0.00084\text{T})dT$$

$$= (6.70)(311 - 394.5) + (.00042)[(311)^2 - (394.5)^2]$$

$$= -559 - 25 = -584 \text{ cal/gm-mol}$$

$$\therefore \ \Delta H = (-584)(1.8)\left(\frac{500}{36.5}\right) = -14{,}400 \text{ BTU}$$

the factor of 1.8 converting cal/gm-mol to BTU/lb-mol.

An alternative procedure would be to determine C_P as a function of temperature in degrees Rankine or Fahrenheit. For T' in °R, $T = T'/1.8$ and $C_P = 6.70 + 0.00084\,T'/1.8 = 6.70 + 0.000467\,T'$. To convert to °F, set $T' = t + 459.7$ to obtain $C_P = 6.70 + (.000467)(t + 459.7) = 6.70 + .000467t + .214 = 6.91 + 0.000467t$. It is suggested that the student satisfy himself that this expression, when used with the given Fahrenheit temperature limits, will yield the same answer as is given above.

Mean heat capacity. When heat capacity varies with temperature, it will frequently be convenient to determine a *mean heat capacity* which, when multiplied by a temperature change, will yield the corresponding energy change without any integration being necessary. Thus

$$\Delta \underline{H}_P = C_{P(m)}(T_2 - T_1) \tag{6.28}$$

where the subscript (m) denotes the mean value of C_P. If this expression is compared with the integrated form of Eq. (6.27),

$$\Delta \underline{H}_P = \int_{T_1}^{T_2} C_P d T$$

the relationship between $C_{P(m)}$ and C_P itself is seen to be

$$C_{P(m)} = \frac{\int_{T_1}^{T_2} C_P d T}{T_2 - T_1} \tag{6.29}$$

EXAMPLE 6.2. Calculate the mean heat capacity of gaseous HCl between 311°K and 394.5°K.

Solution. The integral in Eq. (6.29) was evaluated in the course of solving Ex. 6.1, and is equal to 584 cal/gm-mol. Hence

$$C_{P(m)} = \frac{584}{394.5 - 311} = 7.00 \text{ cal}/(\text{gm-mol})(\text{C°})$$

$$= 7.00 \text{ BTU}/(\text{lb-mol})(\text{F°})$$

When C_P is a *linear* function of temperature, the mean C_P over any temperature range is equal to C_P itself at the mean temperature. (The student can readily prove this to his own satisfaction by setting up a one-step graphical integration as outlined in Appendix B.) In Ex. 6.2, the mean temperature is 352.8°K, and the mean C_P is therefore

$$6.70 + (.00084)(352.8) = 7.00 \text{ cal}/(\text{gm-mol})(\text{C°})$$

Note that the use of this relationship could have replaced the more laborious integration carried out in Ex. 6.1. The engineer should always be on the lookout for such shortcuts, but should remember that this one is only valid when C_P is a linear function of temperature.

Ex. 6.2 correctly implies that integration will generally be necessary to determine $C_{P(m)}$. Once a value has been determined, however, it may be used repeatedly without further integration. The fact that $C_{P(m)}$ varies with the temperature range over which it is applied can be provided for by using the same lower limit—25°C is a popular choice—for all calculations and tabulating values of $C_{P(m)}$ for various upper limits. A typical tabulation of mean heat capacities, based on 25°C as a lower limit, for HCl might include the following points:

T, °C:	25	100	200
$C_{P(m)}$:	6.95	6.98	7.02

These data say that the mean heat capacity *between* 25°C and 100°C is 6.98, *between* 25°C and 200°C is 7.02, and at 25°C (*between* 25°C and 25°C, so to speak) is 6.95. The use of data such as these can best be illustrated by an example:

EXAMPLE 6.3. Recalculate ΔH for the HCl of Ex. 6.1 using the mean heat capacities given above.

Solution. The temperature limits given in Ex. 6.1 were 100°F (37.8°C) and 250°F (121°C). The corresponding values of $C_{P(m)}$, interpolated from the above table, are 6.96 and 6.99, respectively. It is noteworthy that these two values do *not* average out to 7.00, which we already know to be the mean heat capacity between the two given temperatures. It cannot be over-emphasized that the tabulated data are usable directly only when the lower limit of the temperature range is 25°C.

The fact that H, being a property, is independent of path makes it possible to introduce a limit of 25°C arbitrarily: Instead of going directly from 121°C to 37.8°C, let us first cool from 121°C to 25°C and then reheat to 37.8°C. The validity of such a technique should be apparent from the mathematics:

$$\Delta H = H_2 - H_1 = H_{37.8°} - H_{121°}$$
$$= H_{37.8°} - H_{121°} + (H_{25°} - H_{25°})$$
$$= (H_{37.8°} - H_{25°}) + (H_{25°} - H_{121°})$$

The two interpolated values for $C_{P(m)}$ may now be used to evaluate each of the above groupings separately:

$$\Delta H = (6.96)(37.8 - 25) + (6.99)(25 - 121)$$
$$= 89 + (-671) = -582 \text{ cal/gm-mol}$$

which agrees with the previous answer within the limits of slide-rule accuracy.

Relationship between C_P and C_V. A comparison of Eqs. (6.26) and (6.27) clearly indicates that C_P and C_V are inherently different and cannot be used interchangeably. Still, they are quite obviously related since they evolve from a common definition. It will be shown in Sec. 6.8 that they are related quantitatively by the equation

$$C_P - C_V = T\left(\frac{dP}{dT}\right)_V \left(\frac{d\underline{V}}{dT}\right)_P \qquad (6.30)$$

The partial derivatives in this expression can be determined for the material and conditions of interest by differentiation of the pertinent P-V-T data. If the ideal gas law is applicable, for example, Eq. (6.30) reduces to

$$C_P - C_V = R \qquad (6.31)$$

Heat capacity data are almost exclusively reported in terms of C_P rather than C_V. The use of Eq. (6.30) will accordingly be necessary if C_V is to be used in Eq. (6.26) to calculate the change in internal energy with temperature. The alternative technique is to use the available C_P data in Eq. (6.27) to evaluate the change in enthalpy with temperature. The change in internal energy can then be obtained from the relationship $\Delta U = \Delta H - \Delta(PV)$.

6.7 Effect of Pressure and Volume on Energy

If Eq. (6.4) is divided through by $d\underline{V}$ with a restriction of constant temperature, the result is

$$\left(\frac{d\underline{U}}{d\underline{V}}\right)_T = T\left(\frac{d\underline{S}}{d\underline{V}}\right)_T - P$$

The Maxwell relation given by Eq. (6.22) makes it possible to substitute $\left(\frac{dP}{dT}\right)_V$ for $\left(\frac{d\underline{S}}{d\underline{V}}\right)_T$ to obtain

$$\left(\frac{d\underline{U}}{d\underline{V}}\right)_V = T\left(\frac{dP}{dT}\right)_V - P \qquad (6.32)$$

Since the right-hand side of this equation can be evaluated from P-$\underline{V}$-T data or an equation of state, a practical method of determining the change in internal energy with volume at constant temperature has been derived. A parallel derivation, using Eqs. (6.9) and (6.23), leads to a relationship for the change in enthalpy with pressure at constant temperature:

$$\left(\frac{d\underline{H}}{dP}\right)_T = \underline{V} - T\left(\frac{d\underline{V}}{dT}\right)_P \qquad (6.33)$$

The relative ease with which $\left(\frac{dP}{dT}\right)_V$ or $\left(\frac{d\underline{V}}{dT}\right)_P$ can be evaluated will generally dictate the choice between Eqs. (6.32) and (6.33). Even when the initial and final volumes are given and ΔU is to be determined, for example, it may be advisable to use Eq. (6.33) rather than Eq. (6.32). P-$\underline{V}$-T data or an equation of state can always be used to calculate pressures corresponding to the given volumes, and the definition of enthalpy makes it possible to convert $\Delta \underline{H}$ to $\Delta \underline{U}$ and vice versa.

EXAMPLE 6.4. A gas at 500°F and 60 atm pressure is to be expanded isothermally to atmospheric pressure. Calculate the change in enthalpy if the equation of state is

$$P = \frac{RT}{\underline{V} - b} - \frac{a}{T\underline{V}^2}$$

in which $a = 7.7 \times 10^5$ (atm)(ft⁶)(°R)/(lb-mol)², $b = 0.69$ ft³/lb-mol, and consistent units are used for P, $\underline{V}$, T, and R.

Solution. A pressure-explicit equation of state such as that given here is easily solved for $\left(\dfrac{dP}{dT}\right)_P$, whereas the evaluation of $\left(\dfrac{d\underline{V}}{dT}\right)_P$ is quite laborious. The use of Eq. (6.32) is accordingly indicated, even though the initial and final volumes must be calculated by trial and error and $\Delta \underline{H}$ rather than $\Delta \underline{U}$ is to be determined. The trial-and-error calculations yield initial and final specific volumes of 11.27 and 701 ft³/lb-mol, respectively. Then

$$T\left(\frac{dP}{dT}\right)_V = T\left(\frac{R}{\underline{V} - b} + \frac{a}{T^2\underline{V}^2}\right) = \frac{RT}{\underline{V} - b} + \frac{a}{T\underline{V}^2}$$

$$T\left(\frac{dP}{dT}\right)_V - P = \left(\frac{RT}{\underline{V} - b} + \frac{a}{T\underline{V}^2}\right) - \left(\frac{RT}{\underline{V} - b} - \frac{a}{T\underline{V}^2}\right) = \frac{2a}{T\underline{V}^2}$$

$$d\underline{U}_T = \left[T\left(\frac{dP}{dT}\right)_V - P\right]d\underline{V}_T = \frac{2a}{T\underline{V}^2}d\underline{V}_T$$

$$\Delta \underline{U}_T = \int_{\underline{V}_1}^{\underline{V}_2} \frac{2a}{T\underline{V}^2}\,d\underline{V}_T = -\frac{2a}{T\underline{V}_2} + \frac{2a}{T\underline{V}_1} = \frac{2a(\underline{V}_2 - \underline{V}_1)}{T\underline{V}_2\underline{V}_1}$$

$$= \frac{(2)(7.7 \times 10^5)(690)}{(960)(701)(11.27)} = 140 \text{ (atm)(ft}^3)/\text{lb-mol}$$

$$\Delta \underline{H} = \Delta \underline{U} + \Delta(P\underline{V}) = \Delta \underline{U} + P_2\underline{V}_2 - P_1\underline{V}_1$$
$$= 140 + (1)(701) - (60)(11.27)$$
$$= 140 + 701 - 676.2 = 164.8 \text{ (atm)(ft}^3)/\text{lb-mol}$$

$$\frac{(164.8)(14.7)(144)}{778} = 448 \text{ BTU/lb-mol}$$

The student who wishes to satisfy himself that this method of solution is easier than the direct use of Eq. (6.33) is invited to try the latter.

The right-hand sides of both Eq. (6.32) and Eq. (6.33) vanish for an ideal gas. Thus the internal energy of an ideal gas does not change with volume, nor does enthalpy change with pressure. Further, for an ideal gas at constant temperature, $\Delta(P\underline{V}) = \Delta(RT) = 0$, making $\Delta \underline{U}$ and $\Delta \underline{H}$ identically equal. Thus both properties are independent of pressure *and* volume, or, they vary with temperature only.

In the absence of an equation of state or exact data, the engineering solution to a problem such as Ex. 6.4 involves the use of a generalized plot which, like the compressibility factor plot, is based on the law of corresponding states. Either $\dfrac{\underline{H}^\circ - \underline{H}}{T_c}$ or $\dfrac{\underline{H}^\circ - \underline{H}}{T}$ may be plotted against reduced pressure with parameters of reduced temperature. $\underline{H}^\circ$ is the enthalpy in the ideal-gas state, where enthalpy is independent of pressure, and $\underline{H}$ is the enthalpy at the pressure used to enter the chart. Two separate chart readings are necessary to determine $\Delta \underline{H}$ between two non-ideal states: Values for $\underline{H}^\circ - \underline{H}_1$ and $\underline{H}^\circ - \underline{H}_2$, obtained from the chart at P_{r_1} and P_{r_2}, can be combined algebraically to get $\underline{H}_2 - \underline{H}_1$.

Eqs. (6.32) and (6.33) apply to liquids and solids as well as to gases, but the change of internal energy and enthalpy with pressure or volume is usually negligible. If saturated liquid water at 100°F is compressed isothermally from its saturation pressure of 0.95 psia to 400 psia, for example, its enthalpy will change by less than 2 per cent and its specific volume by approximately 0.1 per cent. Unless very high pressures are involved or extreme accuracy is required, the energy content and specific volume of liquids and solids can safely be assumed to be functions of temperature only.

6.8 Entropy Relationships

The variation of entropy with temperature at constant volume or pressure is given by the two equations which followed the definition of heat capacity, C, in Sec. 6.6. Upon rearrangement, they give

$$\left(\frac{d\underline{S}}{dT}\right)_V = \frac{C_V}{T} \tag{6.34}$$

and

$$\left(\frac{d\underline{S}}{dT}\right)_P = \frac{C_P}{T} \tag{6.35}$$

The use of absolute temperatures is particularly essential in entropy calculations. It can be seen from the above equations that the English-system units for entropy must be BTU/°R.

The relationships between entropy and pressure or volume at constant temperature are

$$d\underline{S}_T = \left(\frac{d\underline{S}}{d\underline{V}}\right)_T d\underline{V} = \left(\frac{dP}{dT}\right)_V d\underline{V} \tag{6.36}$$

and

$$d\underline{S}_T = \left(\frac{d\underline{S}}{dP}\right)_T dP = -\left(\frac{d\underline{V}}{dT}\right)_P dP \tag{6.37}$$

Both left-hand equalities are identities; the right-hand equalities come from the Maxwell relations given by Eqs. (6.22) and (6.23). The right-hand partial derivatives can be evaluated by differentiating pertinent P-$\underline{V}$-T data.

For an ideal gas, it will be found that

$$d\underline{S}_T = (R/\underline{V})d\underline{V} = -(R/P)dP \tag{6.38}$$

which integrates to

$$\Delta S_T = R(\ln \underline{V}_2/\underline{V}_1) = -R(\ln P_2/P_1) \tag{6.39}$$

Note that entropy, unlike internal energy or enthalpy, *does* vary with pressure or volume at constant temperature, even when the ideal gas law is applicable.

When ideal-gas behavior cannot be assumed, it is customary to modify Eq. (6.39) by replacing the pressure, P, with a new variable called the *fugacity*, f, thereby correcting for non-ideality:

$$\Delta \underline{S}_T = -R(\ln f_2/f_1) \tag{6.40}$$

Fugacity may be defined formally by the two relationships

$$RT \, d(\ln f) = (\underline{V}dP)_T \tag{6.41}$$

and

$$f \to P \text{ as } P \to 0$$

The latter restriction is necessary to account for ideal behavior at low pressures.

The law of corresponding states provides a basis for evaluating fugacity: The ratio f/P can be shown to be a function of reduced pressure and reduced temperature, just as is the compressibility factor. Thus a single plot of f/P vs. P_r with parameters of T_r will suffice for the determination of the fugacity of any gas under any conditions of interest. The plot need not be presented here, but it will be used repeatedly in the subsequent study of thermodynamics, since the concept of fugacity has many applications in addition to those involving the change of entropy with pressure at constant temperature.

6.9 Paths of Convenience

Many of the processes of interest to chemical engineers follow paths along which pressure, volume, and temperature all change, whereas the use of any of the relationships so far developed requires that one of these three properties be constant. This dilemma can be resolved by utilizing the fact that property changes are independent of path and depend only on the initial and final states of the system. It follows that property changes may be evaluated along *any* path between given end states, even though the given process follows a particular path. The specified path can therefore be replaced with a *path of convenience* insofar as the calculation of property changes is concerned.

The availability of relationships applicable to constant-temperature, constant-pressure, and constant-volume processes suggests that the selected path of convenience should consist of a combination of these special paths. A typical analysis is shown in Fig. 6.1, where a given complex path has been replaced by an equivalent two-step path along which first pressure and then temperature is held constant. The relationships already presented

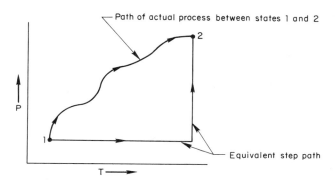

Fig. 6.1 Schematic plot showing substitution of a combination of constant-pressure and constant-temperature steps for any given process path.

permit the calculation of the energy and entropy changes for each of the component steps. Using enthalpy as an example, the mathematical derivation is

$$\Delta \underline{H} = \underline{H}_2 - \underline{H}_1 = \underline{H}_2 - \underline{H}_1 + (\underline{H}_{P_1, T_2} - \underline{H}_{P_1, T_2})$$
$$= (\underline{H}_{P_2} - \underline{H}_{P_1})_{T_2} + (\underline{H}_{T_2} - \underline{H}_{T_1})_{P_1}$$

Substituting from Eqs. (6.33) and (6.27),

$$\Delta \underline{H} = \int_{P_1}^{P_2} \left[\underline{V} - T \left(\frac{d\underline{V}}{dT} \right)_P \right]_{T_2} dP + \int_{T_1}^{T_2} C_{P_1} dT \qquad (6.42)$$

The student should have no difficulty writing corresponding equations for internal energy and entropy. (Note that the definition of C_V suggests the use of a constant-volume step rather than a constant-pressure step for internal energy.)

In many practical problems the change in enthalpy or entropy is known from the start, making it necessary to solve Eq. (6.42) or its equivalent for P_1, P_2, T_1, or T_2, rather than for $\Delta \underline{H}$ or $\Delta \underline{S}$. The following example illustrates this important point as well as the general path-of-convenience technique.

EXAMPLE 6.5. Calculate the change in internal energy for the gas of Ex. 6.4 if the expansion is to be isenthalpic instead of isothermal. At atmospheric pressure, $C_P = 7.20 + 0.0036\,T$ cal/(gm-mol)(K°) with T in °K.

Solution. Let the gas first be expanded from 60 atm to 1 atm at a constant temperature of 500°F (533.5°K) and then heated or cooled at a constant pressure of 1 atm to the unknown final temperature, this path of convenience being suggested by the given C_P correlation. The fact that $\Delta \underline{H} = 0$ for the entire process can then be used to calculate the final temperature via Eq. (6.42), whereupon $\Delta \underline{U}$ is readily determinable.

From Ex. 6.4, $\Delta \underline{H}$ for the constant-temperature step is 448 BTU/lb-mol $\approx$ 249 cal/gm-mol. Substituting this value, the given C_P correlation, and $\Delta \underline{H} = 0$ into Eq. (6.42),

$$0 = 249 + \int_{533.5}^{T_2} (7.20 + .0036T)dT$$
$$-249 = 7.20(T_2 - 533.5) + .0018[T_2{}^2 - (533.5)^2]$$

from which $T_2 = 506.1°K$. At this temperature and $P = 1$ atm, trial-and-error solution of the equation of state given in Ex. 6.4 yields $\underline{V} = 666$ ft³/lb-mol and

$$\Delta \underline{U} = \Delta \underline{H} - \Delta(P\underline{V}) = 0 - [(1)(666) - (60)(11.27)]$$
$$= 0 - 666 + 676.2 = 10.2 \text{ (atm)(ft}^3)/\text{lb-mol} \approx 27.8 \text{ BTU/lb-mol}$$

Theoretically, a constant-temperature step followed by a constant-volume step could also be used to evaluate $\Delta \underline{U}$ once the final temperature is fixed. However, it would be necessary to calculate C_V from Eq. (6.30), in which $\left(\frac{d\underline{V}}{dT}\right)_P$ appears. The difficulty of evaluating this derivative for a pressure-explicit equation of state can be sidestepped by making use of the $\Delta \underline{U}$-$\Delta \underline{H}$ relationship as illustrated in the foregoing solution.

Variation of C_P and C_V. The differential form of Eq. (6.42) is

$$d\underline{H} = \left[\underline{V} - T\left(\frac{d\underline{V}}{dT}\right)_P\right]_T dP + C_P dT \tag{6.43}$$

Although this equation bears little resemblance to Eq. (6.9), $\underline{H}$ is still a point function and the cross-partials in Eq. (6.43) must be equal. Thus

$$\left(\frac{dC_P}{dP}\right)_T = \frac{d}{dT}\left[\underline{V} - T\left(\frac{d\underline{V}}{dT}\right)_P\right]_P$$
$$= \left(\frac{d\underline{V}}{dT}\right)_P - T\left(\frac{d^2\underline{V}}{dT^2}\right)_P - \left(\frac{d\underline{V}}{dT}\right)_P$$
$$= -T\left(\frac{d^2\underline{V}}{dT^2}\right)_P \tag{6.44}$$

An analogous derivation yields

$$\left(\frac{dC_V}{d\underline{V}}\right)_T = T\left(\frac{d^2P}{dT^2}\right)_V \tag{6.45}$$

Eqs. (6.44) and (6.45) show that C_P and C_V vary with pressure and volume unless the partial derivatives vanish, as they do for an ideal gas. Heat capacity data generally pertain to ideal gas conditions, and are therefore directly applicable only at low pressures. Since the form of a particular equation of state may make the evaluation of the partials in Eqs. (6.44) and (6.45) impracticable, an alternative technique is frequently advantageous when a gas is known to be non-ideal:

Suppose it is desired to determine the change in enthalpy in going from state 1 to state 2 along the path shown in Fig. 6.2, and that C_P is known for

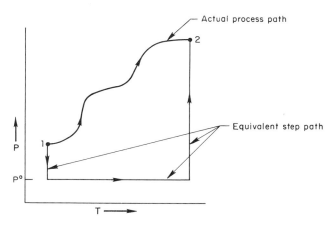

Fig. 6.2   Schematic plot showing three-step equivalent path.

the ideal-gas state. Should the assumption of ideal behavior at P_1 be permissible, the two-step path of convenience shown earlier in Fig. 6.1 will suffice. Non-ideal behavior at P_1 can be provided for either by correcting the ideal-gas C_P in accordance with Eq. (6.44) or by utilizing the three-step path of convenience shown in Fig. 6.2, P° being a pressure low enough to validate the assumption of ideal behavior. The three-step path might also be used to determine the mean C_P at any pressure of interest, as demonstrated in Ex. 6.6.

EXAMPLE 6.6. Using the data given in Ex. 6.5, calculate the mean C_P between 506.1°K and 533.5°K at 60 atmospheres.

Solution. By definition, $C_{P(m)} = \Delta \underline{H}_P / \Delta T$. Since ΔT is specified, we need only calculate $\Delta \underline{H}$ in going from 506.1°K to 533.5°K at $P = 60$ atm. With C_P known at atmospheric pressure, the pertinent path of convenience will involve (1) isothermal expansion from 60 atm to 1 atm at constant $T = 506.1°K$; (2) heating from 506.1°K to 533.5°K at constant $P = 1$ atm; and

(3) compressing from 1 atm to 60 atm at constant $T = 533.5°K$. Summing the $\Delta\underline{H}$'s for these three steps will yield the desired $\Delta\underline{H}$.

$\Delta\underline{H}$ for step (1) can be calculated by the method illustrated in Ex. 6.4. The calculations yield $\underline{V} = 10.54\ ft^3/lb\text{-mol}$ at 60 atm and 506.1°K and $\Delta\underline{H} = 289\ cal/gm\text{-mol}$. Since the total $\Delta\underline{H}$ for the other two steps is already known to be zero from Ex. 6.5, $\Delta\underline{H}$ for the complete process is also 289 cal/gm-mol and

$$C_{P(m)} = \frac{289}{533.5 - 506.1} = 10.55\ cal/(gm\text{-mol})(K°)$$

(At atmospheric pressure, over the same temperature range, $C_{P(m)} = 9.10$ cal/(gm-mol)(K°).)

Relationship between C_P and C_V. The equivalent of Eq. (6.43) for entropy is

$$d\underline{S} = C_P\frac{dT}{T} - \left(\frac{d\underline{V}}{dT}\right)_P dP \tag{6.46}$$

this relationship following from Eqs. (6.35) and (6.37). Multiplying through by T/dT and imposing the restriction of constant volume yields

$$T\left(\frac{d\underline{S}}{dT}\right)_V = C_V = C_P - T\left(\frac{d\underline{V}}{dT}\right)_P\left(\frac{dP}{dT}\right)_V$$

which, upon rearrangement, gives the relationship between C_P and C_V which was presented without proof in Sec. 6.6:

$$C_P - C_V = T\left(\frac{dP}{dT}\right)_V\left(\frac{d\underline{V}}{dT}\right)_P \tag{6.30}$$

6.10 Effect of Phase Changes

Thermodynamic analysis. Just as energy and entropy can be related to $P\text{-}\underline{V}\text{-}T$ data for single-phase processes, so is it possible to derive equally useful expressions applicable to processes involving a change of phase. The development which follows will be restricted to vaporization and condensation processes, but the principles are equally applicable to other types of phase changes such as freezing, melting, sublimation, and recrystallization.

Consider a saturated liquid being vaporized at any given constant temperature to form a saturated vapor. For a pure substance, the given saturation temperature also fixes the saturation pressure in accordance with the phase rule, and the process must therefore take place at a point (T, p^*) on the vapor pressure curve. The free energy equation presented in Sec. 6.2,

$$dG = -SdT + VdP \tag{6.11}$$

shows dG to be zero for any constant-temperature, constant-pressure process, and it follows that, for either vaporization or condensation,

$$G_V = G_L \tag{6.47}$$

where the subscripts V and L refer to saturated vapor and saturated liquid.

Now let the process be displaced along the vapor pressure curve from (T, p^*) to $(T + dT, p^* + dp^*)$. The displacement will change the free energy of both liquid and vapor in accordance with Eq. (6.11), or,

$$d\underline{G}_V = -\underline{S}_V dT + \underline{V}_V dp^*$$

$$d\underline{G}_L = -\underline{S}_L dT + \underline{V}_L dp^*$$

But, since Eq. (6.47) applies to both the new point and the original point, $d\underline{G}_V$ must equal $d\underline{G}_L$. Accordingly,

$$-\underline{S}_V dT + \underline{V}_V dp^* = \underline{S}_L dT + \underline{V}_L dp^*$$

and rearrangement yields

$$\frac{dp^*}{dT} = \frac{\underline{S}_V - \underline{S}_L}{\underline{V}_V - \underline{V}_L} \tag{6.48}$$

This equation, called the *Clapeyron equation*, is obviously significant, for it relates the entropy change accompanying vaporization or condensation to quantities determinable from P-$\underline{V}$-T data.

The Clapeyron equation is readily transformed to permit the determination of the corresponding enthalpy change. By definition, $\Delta\underline{G} = \Delta\underline{H} - \Delta(T\underline{S})$. With both $\underline{G}$ and T constant for the conditions of interest, this reduces to $\Delta\underline{S} = \Delta\underline{H}/T$, and substitution into Eq. (6.48) yields

$$\frac{dp^*}{dT} = \frac{\underline{H}_V - \underline{H}_L}{T(\underline{V}_V - \underline{V}_L)} \tag{6.49}$$

Thus only vapor pressure data and a knowledge of the volume change accompanying a change of phase are needed for the calculation of the corresponding entropy and enthalpy changes. The change in internal energy, of course, can be calculated from the definition of enthalpy.

The utility of Eq. (6.49) can be extended considerably by making two simplifying assumptions. First, if the specific volume of the saturated liquid is small in comparison to that of the saturated vapor, $\underline{V}_V - \underline{V}_L \cong \underline{V}_V$. The concept of the compressibility factor then makes it possible to substitute $\underline{V}_V = ZRT/p^*$, and

$$\frac{dp^*}{dT} = \frac{p^*(\underline{H}_V - \underline{H}_L)}{ZRT^2}$$

or

$$\frac{d(\ln p^*)}{dT} = \frac{\underline{H}_V - \underline{H}_L}{ZRT^2} \tag{6.50}$$

Finally, if the vapor phase can be considered to behave as an ideal gas, Z is unity and drops out. These simplifications are attributed to Clausius, and the ideal-gas form of Eq. (6.50) is commonly called the *Clausius-Clapeyron equation.*

If $\Delta \underline{H}/Z$ is constant, Eq. (6.50) integrates to

$$\ln p^* = A - \frac{\Delta \underline{H}}{ZRT} \qquad (6.51)$$

where A is the constant of integration. This equation is identical in form to the vapor pressure correlation given by Eq. (5.7) and provides the theoretical basis for the latter. The student may recall an earlier contact with this interrelationship in Prob. 5-9.

The enthalpy change accompanying constant-temperature vaporization is commonly called the *latent heat of vaporization.* Latent heats of freezing, fusion (melting), sublimation, etc., are analogous concepts. The contrasting term *sensible heat* refers to the enthalpy possessed by a system by virtue of its temperature level. It is noteworthy that both latent and sensible heat pertain to enthalpy rather than to heat as defined for thermodynamic purposes.

Properties of two-phase mixtures. Not all processes will involve complete vaporization or condensation, and it is often necessary to determine the properties of vapor-liquid mixtures having *quality*. Since pressure and temperature are independent of quality and the calculation of specific volume has already been treated in Sec. 5.5, only energy and entropy remain to be considered.

Although Eq. (5.8),

$$\underline{V}_M = q\underline{V}_V + (1 - q)\underline{V}_L \qquad (5.8)$$

was presented as a means of calculating the specific volume $\underline{V}_M$ of a liquid-vapor mixture having a quality $100q$, identical relationships are applicable to internal energy, enthalpy, and entropy. In general,

$$\underline{\Gamma}_M = q\underline{\Gamma}_V + (1 - q)\underline{\Gamma}_L \qquad (6.52)$$

where $\underline{\Gamma}$ denotes any of these properties.

Fixing either pressure or temperature automatically determines all specific properties of the saturated vapor and saturated liquid, that is, the values denoted by $\underline{\Gamma}_V$ and $\underline{\Gamma}_L$ in Eq. (6.52). A knowledge of any one property of the mixture, corresponding to $\underline{\Gamma}_M$, will therefore make it possible to solve the equation for q. All other "$\underline{\Gamma}_M$" properties can then be calculated, for q and the appropriate values for $\underline{\Gamma}_V$ and $\underline{\Gamma}_L$ are now known. The following example should make the procedure clear:

EXAMPLE 6.7. Calculate the enthalpy, entropy, and internal energy of a one-pound mixture of liquid water and water vapor which occupies a volume of 0.2182 cubic feet at a temperature of 600°F.

Solution. The following data may be obtained from the Steam Tables, for the given temperature of 600°F:

	Volume ft³/lb	Enthalpy BTU/lb	Entropy BTU/(lb)(°R)
Liquid:	0.0236	616.8	0.8130
Vapor:	0.2668	1165.2	1.3305

(Saturation pressure = 1543.2 psia)

Since $\underline{V}_M = 0.2182$ is given, Eq. (6.52) can first be written for volume and solved for q:

$$0.2182 = 0.2668q + 0.0236(1 - q)$$

from which $q = 0.80$. This value, together with the enthalpy data from the Steam Tables, can now be substituted into Eq. (6.52), written for enthalpy,

$$\underline{H}_M = (.80)(1165.2) + (.20)(616.8)$$

from which $H_M = 1055.5$ BTU/lb. Similarly, $\underline{S}_M$ may be found to be 1.2270 BTU/(lb)(°R). It is suggested that the student confirm this result as well as $U_M = 993.1$ BTU/lb.

In the absence of energy and entropy data such as that given in the Steam Tables, the Clapeyron equation or one of its simplified forms can be used to determine $\underline{\Gamma}_V - \underline{\Gamma}_L$, but neither $\underline{\Gamma}_V$ or $\underline{\Gamma}_L$ can be determined separately. In such situations a rearrangement of Eq. (6.52),

$$q = \frac{\underline{\Gamma}_M - \underline{\Gamma}_L}{\underline{\Gamma}_V - \underline{\Gamma}_L} \quad \text{or} \quad 1 - q = \frac{\underline{\Gamma}_V - \underline{\Gamma}_M}{\underline{\Gamma}_V - \underline{\Gamma}_L} \tag{6.53}$$

will still permit the determination of quality and the *change* in any property in going from saturated liquid or saturated vapor to a mixture of quality. The use of Eq. (6.53) will be illustrated in Ex. 6.8.

The determination of quality is somewhat more difficult when neither pressure nor temperature is given as a state-defining property, since the properties of the saturated vapor and liquid cannot then be determined directly. Some of the graphical plots of thermodynamic data to be discussed in the next section may be helpful in such cases. Alternately, the pressure and temperature may be determined by trial-and-error. Problems of this type will not be treated here, but the student should find it worthwhile to envision a suitable procedure. The technique used to solve Prob. 5-13 should point the way.

6.11 Thermodynamic Data

Reference states. The importance of using absolute units in calculations pertaining to pressure and temperature was emphasized in Chap. 4. In contrast, energy and entropy calculations will generally involve *relative* values. Insofar as energy is concerned, this is due to the fact that absolute values are non-existent, since a suitable absolute zero for energy has never been established. The third law of thermodynamics establishes an absolute zero for entropy, but the use of absolute entropies is neither necessary nor particularly convenient in most problems.

The student has already encountered many purely relative scales of measurement such as gage pressure, Centigrade temperature, and elevation. In each of these examples a value of zero has been assigned to some arbitrary condition or *reference state*—atmospheric pressure, the freezing point of water, and elevation at mean sea level, respectively—and relative values for other states may then be specified in a consistent manner. That the assignment is entirely arbitrary is apparent from the fact that another relative temperature scale, every bit as valid as the Centigrade scale, is based on the assignment of a zero value to the freezing point of a saturated salt solution. We refer, of course, to the Fahrenheit scale.

The amount by which any property *changes* depends only on the size or extent of the unit of measurement, and is completely independent of reference state. Indeed, the entire concept of reference states depends on this fact. The statement that a system in some given state x has a relative enthalpy H_x' referred to reference state o really means that

$$H_x' = H_x - H_o \qquad (6.54)$$

where H_x and H_o are the true enthalpies for the two states x and o. Eq. (6.54) should be kept firmly in mind, for it represents a concept which will be invaluable whenever it becomes necessary to change from one reference state to another. A typical calculation of this type will be presented at the end of this section.

Heat (Q) and work (W), not being properties, are also independent of reference state just as property changes are. These facts make it unnecessary to identify a specific reference state in many problems. In others either the initial or final conditions for the particular process of interest can be arbitrarily selected as the reference state. Note, for example, that no mention of reference states was made in developing the many relationships presented earlier in this chapter.

It should be emphasized that internal energy and enthalpy are not independent, being related by the equation which defines enthalpy. Hence only one of these properties may be assigned an arbitrary reference state, whereupon relative values for both are uniquely determined. Entropy is an independent concept and different reference states for energy and entropy are permissible. Even so, confusion will generally be avoided by using a single reference state in any particular problem.

The reference state concept is not particularly difficult to understand, and it should be readily assimilated once the student starts working problems calling for its use. Specific examples will be encountered in due course.

Presentation of data. The possibility of including data pertaining to internal energy, enthalpy, and entropy in tabulations of P-$\underline{V}$-T data has already been mentioned, the Steam Tables being a primary example. Such tables normally include values of $\underline{V}_L$, $\underline{V}_V$, $\underline{H}_L$, $\underline{H}_V$, $\underline{S}_L$, and $\underline{S}_V$ as functions of either saturation pressure or temperature in the two-phase region*; and $\underline{V}$, $\underline{H}$, and $\underline{S}$ as functions of temperature and pressure for superheated vapor. Tables for many of the materials of interest to chemical engineers are available, and the student will find himself using such tables repeatedly in thermodynamic calculations.

Although energy and entropy parameters are not normally shown on simple P-$\underline{V}$-T diagrams, other forms of graphical representation do include these properties, with pressure-enthalpy, temperature-entropy, and enthalpy-entropy diagrams being most frequently encountered. The latter is commonly referred to as a *Mollier diagram*, and generally shows parameters of temperature, pressure, and, in the two-phase region, quality. Similarly, temperature-entropy diagrams usually show parameters of pressure, enthalpy, and, frequently, specific volume. All of these diagrams will become familiar to the student in due course.

Values of internal energy, enthalpy, or entropy reported in the literature will always be relative values with respect to a particular reference state. Care in their use is accordingly indicated, particularly if a problem requires the use of data from more than one source. In the latter situation it may be necessary to resolve the use of two different reference states, as indicated in the following example.

EXAMPLE 6.8. A table of properties for saturated ammonia in Perry's Handbook lists $\underline{H} = 0$ for saturated liquid ammonia at $-40°F$. Elsewhere in Perry, a table of properties for aqueous ammonia solutions gives $\underline{H} = 0$ for pure, saturated liquid ammonia at $32°F$. Calculate the amount by which values read from the first table should be corrected to make them agree with those in the second.

Solution. For a given state x, let $\underline{H}_x{}'$ denote the value read from the first table and $\underline{H}_x{}''$ denote the corresponding value read from the second table. Using Eq. (6.54), $\underline{H}_x{}' = \underline{H}_x - \underline{H}_{-40°}$ and $\underline{H}_x{}'' = \underline{H}_x - \underline{H}_{32°}$. Subtracting one expression from the other to eliminate $\underline{H}_x$ and rearranging the result gives $\underline{H}_x{}'' = \underline{H}_x{}' + (\underline{H}_{-40°} - \underline{H}_{32°})$, and the parenthetical term is the desired correction factor. It may be evaluated from either table. Using the first table, $\underline{H}'_{32°} = 77.9 \text{ BTU/lb} = \underline{H}_{32°} - \underline{H}_{-40°}$. Therefore $\underline{H}_x{}'' = \underline{H}_x{}' -$

---

* The subscripts f and g are used in lieu of L and V, respectively, in the Steam Tables and similar tabulations.

77.9, and any value in the second table may be obtained by subtracting 77.9 from the corresponding value in the first table. Stated another way, this means that the subtraction of 77.9 from all values given in the first table will change the reference state of that table to $\underline{H} = 0$ for saturated liquid ammonia at 32°F.

The foregoing problem is not so difficult that the correct answer could not, with a little thought, be obtained by inspection. This will not always be the case, and the student is well advised to remember the technique illustrated.

6.12 Summary

Although detailed attention has been given the relationships needed to calculate the changes in energy and entropy which accompany changes in temperature, pressure, specific volume, or phase, these relationships are subservient to the much broader concept of the path of convenience. Both the basic concept and the quantitative relationships which support it can best be summarized by demonstrating their application to a comprehensive problem. The example should provide a clearer insight into the overall aspects of thermodynamic calculations and thereby give fuller meaning to the material covered in the present chapter. It also affords a glimpse of the subject matter yet to come in the chemical engineering curriculum.

One final observation is appropriate: In view of the inviting simplicity of the ideal gas law and its attendant energy relationships, it would indeed be convenient if all gases always behaved ideally. Never let the wish be father to the thought. Instead, it will be well to maintain a healthy suspicion regarding ideality and to make a deliberate decision to use the ideal gas law only when the pressure is near or below one atmosphere, or when a rough approximation is either necessary or sufficient at higher pressures.

EXAMPLE 6.9. Steam flows continuously through an adiabatic, reversible turbine, entering at 300 psia and 700°F and discharging at 90°F. Calculate the horsepower delivered by the turbine for a steam rate of 5,000 lb/hr, (a) assuming only P-$\underline{V}$-T and C_p data to be available; and (b) using Steam Table data.

Solution. This is clearly an energy balance problem, and the logical first step is to specify a basis, define a system, and reduce the general energy balance. The given steam rate suggests a basis of one hour. Either the steam itself or the turbine might be taken as the system: the steam is a closed, unsteady-state system; the turbine is an open, steady-state system. When a choice is possible, the latter is almost invariably more advantageous because, since *the system* does not expand, work of expansion need not be considered.

With the turbine as the system and, in the absence of information to the contrary, with the assumption that kinetic and potential energy effects are negligible, the general energy balance reduces to $M\Delta\underline{H} = -W$. Since M is 5,000 for the selected basis of one hour, it only remains to calculate $\Delta\underline{H}$ in order to determine W. This we expect to do by selecting a suitable path of convenience connecting the two end states.

But what *is* the final state? Presumably it takes two properties to define it, and only a final temperature is given in the problem statement. Here is an excellent example of given information which is not stated directly but must be inferred: An adiabatic, reversible process is also isentropic in accordance with Eq. (2.15), and hence $\underline{S}$ in the final state must be the same as it is initially. Thus the two properties defining the final state are, in effect, temperature and entropy.

The next step, then, is to determine the final pressure corresponding to the known temperature and entropy. A three-step path of convenience similar to that shown in Fig. 6.2 is indicated. First let the steam be expanded to ideal-gas conditions at a constant temperature of 700°F. The change in entropy for this step will be calculated from either Eq. (6.36) or (6.37), depending on which of the partial derivatives is more easily evaluated from the given P-$\underline{V}$-T data or equation of state. Second, let the steam cool from 700°F to 90°F at constant pressure or constant volume, and $\Delta\underline{S}$ for this step be calculated from Eq. (6.34) or (6.35). Finally, at a constant temperature of 90°F, either Eq. (6.36) or (6.37) may again be used to determine a final pressure such that the algebraic sum of the entropy changes for all three steps will be zero.

Were the necessary calculations to be carried out, a final pressure of 12 psia or so would be obtained. We might now be tempted to proceed with the $\Delta\underline{H}$ calculation, but we should remember that the wise engineer always inspects his results for consistency as he obtains them. At face value, a final pressure of 12 psia is not unreasonable, but what if a phase change occurred during the process? The foregoing procedure tacitly assumed only changes in temperature and pressure to be pertinent, but will the turbine make the same assumption? A check of the vapor pressure data should answer the question and turns out to be a most pertinent precaution: the saturation temperature corresponding to a pressure of 12 psia is almost 200°F!

In other words, condensation will definitely be encountered and will be accompanied by a substantial change in entropy which was not taken into account in the original calculations. The initial answer of 12 psia must therefore be rejected, but it now becomes highly probable that the final state will be a mixture of liquid and vapor at 90°F and hence at the corresponding saturation pressure, which is 0.698 psia. The next step, then, is to calculate $\Delta \underline{S}$ for the condensation. This may be done by differentiating the vapor pressure equation to determine the slope of the vapor pressure curve at $T = 90°F$, and then using Eq. (6.48) to obtain $\Delta \underline{S}$ of condensation. $\Delta \underline{V}$ for use in the equation is presumably known from the given P-$\underline{V}$-T data.

When the value of $\Delta \underline{S}$ so determined is added algebraically to the entropy changes previously calculated for the constant-temperature and constant-pressure steps, it will be found that only partial condensation is required to make $\Delta \underline{S} = 0$ for the overall process. A quality calculation is accordingly indicated, and Eq. (6.53b) can be utilized. The numerator will be the needed entropy change due to partial condensation, while the denominator will be the change for total condensation as calculated from Eq. (6.48).

The calculation of the enthalpy change can now be carried out using the same path of convenience as was used for entropy. Note that the form of the given P-$\underline{V}$-T data may dictate the use of Eq. (6.32) rather than Eq. (6.33). $\Delta \underline{H}$ for the partial condensation might be obtained by applying Eqs. (6.49) and (6.53b). Since $\Delta \underline{S}$ for this step is already known, however, a quicker method is to make use of the relation $\Delta \underline{S} = \Delta \underline{H}/T$ which is applicable to phase changes at constant temperature.

It might be anticipated that a much simpler solution is possible when pertinent thermodynamic data are available, and this is very much the case. In using the Steam Tables, one might first look up 700°F in the temperature table and find the corresponding saturation pressure to be 3094.1 psia. Or, entering the pressure table at 300 psia, the corresponding saturation temperature is found to be 417.33°F. In either case it is clear that the initial steam is superheated rather than saturated. The initial conditions will therefore be found in the superheat table and, for 300 psia and 700°F, the table gives $\underline{S} = 1.6742$ BTU/(lb)(°R) and $\underline{H} = 1367.4$ BTU/lb.

For $T = 90°F$, the temperature table gives $\underline{S}_f = 0.1115$ and $\underline{S}_g = 2.0073$. Since $\underline{S}_1 = \underline{S}_2 = 1.6742$ lies between these two values, the final state must be a two-phase mixture having quality. Eq. (6.52) or (6.53) can accordingly be written for entropy and solved to obtain $q = 0.824$. (Had the initial and final value of $\underline{S}$ been greater than 2.0073, it would be concluded that the steam was still superheated at 90°F. Similarly, a value less than 0.1115 would indicate a subcooled liquid at this temperature.)

With q known, Eq. (6.52) or (6.53) may be written for enthalpy and solved for $\underline{H}_M = \underline{H}_2$, using $\underline{H}_L = 58.0$ and $\underline{H}_V = 1100.1$ from the temperature table at $T = 90°F$. The calculation yields $\underline{H}_2 = 916.6$ BTU/lb, and $\Delta \underline{H}$ for the process is therefore $916.6 - 1367.4 = -450.8$ BTU/lb. Then $W = -M\Delta \underline{H} = -(5,000)(-450.8) = 2,254,000$ BTU/hr ≈ 885 hp.

REVIEW, STUDY, AND DISCUSSION

6-1. Define enthalpy, Helmholtz work function, Gibbs free energy function, point function or perfect differential, Maxwell relation, C_P, C_V, heat capacity, specific heat, mean heat capacity, path of convenience, fugacity, latent heat, sensible heat, quality, reference state.

6-2. Write the three fundamental thermodynamic equations. Define all symbols used.

6-3. Derive equations for the Gibbs free energy function equivalent to Eqs. (6.5) through (6.9).

6-4. State and illustrate by example the three pertinent properties of perfect differentials.

6-5. Derive Eq. (6.23) without making use of the free energy convenience function.

6-6. The heat capacity of sulfur dioxide is given by the relationship $C_P = 7.116 + 0.009512\,T - 3.511 \times 10^{-6}\,T^2$, cal/(gm-mol)(K°), where T is in °K. Derive an equivalent expression for C_P in units of BTU/(lb-mol)(F°) and in terms of t in °F.

6-7. Sulfur dioxide is to be cooled from 1000°F to 200°F at a constant pressure of 1 atm.

a) Calculate the change in enthalpy in BTU/lb.

b) What is the enthalpy of sulfur dioxide at 1000°F referred to a reference state of 200°F?

c) What is the internal energy of sulfur dioxide at 200°F referred to a reference state of 1000°F? Specify an alternative to the method used in solving this problem.

d) Calculate the mean molal heat capacity of sulfur dioxide between 77°F and 1000°F.

e) What is the enthalpy of sulfur dioxide at 200°F referred to a reference state of 77°F?

f) The mean molal C_P of sulfur dioxide between 77°F and 600°F is 10.62 BTU/(lb-mol)(F°). Calculate the enthalpy change which will result when SO_2 is heated from 200°F to 600°F.

6-8. Given $C_P = a + bT$, prove that $C_{P(m)}$ between T_1 and T_2 is equal to $a + b\left(\dfrac{T_1 + T_2}{2}\right)$.

6-9. Molal heat capacities at constant pressure for carbon dioxide have been determined at a number of different temperatures as follows:

T, °C:	0	100	200	300	500
C_P:	8.61	9.69	10.51	11.22	12.24

T, °C:	750	1000	1250	1500	1750
C_P:	13.07	13.58	13.93	14.15	14.26

Calculate the mean molal heat capacity of CO_2 between 25°C and 1750°C.

6-10. Gasoline at 150°F enters a heat exchanger at a rate of 12,000 pounds per hour and gives up heat to 40 gpm of cooling water. $C_P = 0.5$ BTU/(lb)(F°) for the gasoline. If the water enters the exchanger at 55°F, what is the lowest possible temperature to which the gasoline can be cooled, (a) if the two streams flow through the exchanger in opposite directions? (b) if the two streams flow through the exchanger in the same direction?

6-11. Prove that Eq. (6.31) reduces to Eq. (6.32) for an ideal gas.

6-12. Derive Eq. (6.33). Show that the right-hand side vanishes for an ideal gas.

6-13. Differentiate the van der Waals equation (Sec. 5.3) and evaluate the right-hand side of Eq. (6.32) to show that $(d\underline{U}/d\underline{V})_T = a/\underline{V}^2$ for a van der Waals gas.

6-14. Nitrogen expands from 100 atm to 10 atm at a constant temperature of $-188°F$. Compare the change in entropy given by Eq. (6.40) with that obtained when ideal-gas behavior is assumed. [Note: the answer to Prob. 5-14 may be used to determine the fugacity ratio needed in Eq. (6.40).]

6-15. Derive an integrated expression for the change in $\underline{U}$ and $\underline{H}$ at constant temperature for a gas which obeys the Linde equation of state,

$$ \underline{V} = \frac{AT}{P} - \frac{C + EP}{T^3} + D + FP $$

in which A, B, C, D, E, and F are empirical constants.

6-16. Air at 70°F and a pressure of 10 psig flows continuously through a preheater at a rate of 10,000 ft³/hr (measured at inlet conditions). To what temperature will the air be heated if the preheater delivers 40,000 BTU/hr? C_P for air is $6.45 + 0.001649T - 0.1945 \times 10^{-6}T^2$, with T in °K and C_P in BTU/(lb-mol)(F°).

6-17. 500 pounds per hour of gaseous HCl are to flow through a heat exchanger and be cooled from 250°F to 100°F. $C_P = 6.70 + 0.00084T$ cal/(gm-mol)(K°) for T in °K. At what rate should cooling water flow through the exchanger if it is to enter at 55°F and leave at 80°F?

6-18. A constant-volume bomb contains methane (CH_4) at 80°F and 1 atm. How much heat (BTU/mol of methane) must be added to raise the temperature of the methane to 125°F? It may be assumed that methane behaves ideally at 1 atm and that the van der Waals equation applies at higher pressures, with $a = 581.2$ (atm)(ft⁶)/(lb-mol)² and $b = 0.6855$ ft³/lb-mol. (Suggestion: make use of the relationship given in Prob. 6-13.)

6-19. A gas at an initial pressure of 30 atmospheres is to be expanded isenthalpically from $\underline{V}_1 = 10$ ft³/lb-mol to atmospheric pressure. The pertinent equation of state is

$$ P = \frac{RT}{\underline{V}} - \frac{a}{\underline{V}^2} $$

where $a = 1600$ (atm)(ft^6)/(lb-mol)^2. Calculate the final specific volume if the mean C_P at atmospheric pressure for the temperature range of interest is 7.0 BTU/(lb-mol)(F°).

6-20. Repeat Prob. 6-19 for a final pressure of 10 atm.

6-21. Derive a vapor-pressure relationship for acetone at 50°C. Use the relationship together with Eq. (6.51) to approximate the latent heat of vaporization of acetone at 50°C.

6-22. Assuming $\Delta \underline{H}/Z$ to be constant, integrate Eq. (6.50) between the limits used for the vapor-pressure relationship derived in Prob. 6-21. Solve the resulting expression for $\Delta \underline{H}$ and compare the answer with that to Prob. 6-21.

6-23. Carry out the calculations described in part (a) of Ex. 6.9 assuming the van der Waals equation to be applicable and the pertinent constants to be $a = 1400$ (atm) (ft^6)/(lb-mol)^2 and $b = 0.82$ ft^3 per lb-mol.

6-24. A saturated liquid at a pressure only slightly below the critical pressure is to be cooled at constant volume until the pressure is 1 atm. Sketch the path for this process on a P-$\underline{V}$ diagram. On the same plot, show the path of convenience which would be used to calculate $\Delta \underline{H}$ for the process.

6-25. Use the Steam Tables to determine $\Delta \underline{H}$ and $\Delta \underline{U}$ for the process of Prob. 6-24 if the initial pressure is 2400 psia. How much heat must be removed per pound of steam?

6-26. Steam flows continuously through an adiabatic throttling valve, entering at 200 psia and discharging at 14.7 psia and 250°F. Calculate the specific volume of the steam at the inlet to the valve.

CHAPTER 7

Properties of Multi-Component Mixtures

The pure-substance concepts presented in the last two chapters are, to a considerable extent, directly applicable to systems comprising more than one component. The state of a mixture, like the state of a pure substance, can be described in terms of pressure, temperature, specific volume, enthalpy, entropy, etc. Why, then, should it be necessary to devote a separate chapter to the properties of multi-component mixtures? The answer to this question is two-fold.

First, the extensive properties of a mixture cannot be determined by simply adding the corresponding properties of the pure components in many cases. Mass, of course, is always additive in accordance with the principle of conservation. But volume, for example, may not be additive; witness the fact that mixing one quart of water with one quart of alcohol will yield only 1.93 quarts of mixture. Further, since mixing is inherently an irreversible process, it should be obvious that the entropy of a mixture will *always* be greater than the sum of the entropies of the pure components in the absence of heat effects. These and similar observations clearly indicate the need for special relationships for the calculation of extensive properties for mixtures.

Second, the mixing of two or more pure substances to form a mixture introduces one completely new variable which has not been considered

154

previously, namely, composition or concentration. Since specification of the composition of a mixture is prerequisite to any quantitative consideration of other properties, it is appropriate that we give this aspect first attention. Once we have a working familiarity with the composition variable, we can return to consider the other properties of multi-component mixtures.

7.1 Units for Composition

Mass or weight per cent. Probably the most straightforward method of expressing composition or analysis is to specify the percentage of each of the components by weight. Strictly speaking, mass is perhaps a more appropriate word than is weight, but the two are completely interchangeable even when the lb_f-to-lb_m conversion factor is not unity, since the same factor will be applied to each component in any case. We shall arbitrarily use the terms per cent by weight and weight per cent, but it should be remembered that the corresponding mass terms are equally correct.

The significance of an analysis expressed in weight per cent was indicated in the earlier discussion of units, labels, and dimensions. To say that a mixture contains 25 per cent A by weight is to say that there are 25 pounds of A per 100 pounds of mixture; hence the number 25 may be considered to have the units *lbs of A per 100 lbs of mixture*. An alternative would be to say that the mixture contains 0.25 weight fraction of A, or, 0.25 *lbs of A per lb of mixture*.

It should hardly be necessary to point out that the foregoing observations are not restricted to the pound as a unit of weight. In more general terms, it might be said that 25 weight per cent A means 25 *parts* (by weight) of A per 100 parts (by weight) of mixture, or 0.25 parts (by weight) of A per part of mixture.

Volume per cent. Even though volumes may not be additive for many mixing processes, there are situations of practical interest in which they are. In such cases it may be convenient to express compositions in volume per cent or volume fraction rather than by weight. Everything which has already been said about weight per cent and weight fraction is equally applicable to a volumetric basis.

Compositions of solid and liquid mixtures are conventionally expressed in weight per cent. Gas compositions, on the other hand, are commonly expressed in volume per cent. In the absence of information to the contrary, these conventions may be assumed to apply. Thus 25 per cent A may be taken to mean weight per cent if the mixture is liquid or solid but means volume per cent if the mixture is gaseous. Both conventions will be used throughout the rest of this text, and the student is advised to take due note of them.

Mol per cent. It was suggested in Chap. 4 that the weight of a pure material might be expressed in pound-molecular-weights or mols, even though the quantity of mass represented by a mol is a variable which depends on the molecular weight of the substance. This concept is readily extended to mixtures, and it will frequently be convenient to express composition in mol per cent or mol fraction. Thus 15 mol per cent A means 15 mols of A per 100 mols of mixture or 0.15 mols of A per mol of mixture. The same interpretation applies to gram-mols, ton-mols, or other similar units.

If the components of a mixture are elements or compounds to which a specific molecular weight is applicable, it is a simple matter to convert mols to pounds by multiplying by the molecular weight, provided this is done component by component. Note, however, that the concept of mol per cent involves mols of mixture as well as mols of the pure components. It should therefore be possible to define a molecular weight for a mixture as well as for its separate components. This aspect of molal analyses will be treated in Sec. 7.2.

Partial pressure. For theoretical purposes, the partial pressure of a component in a gaseous mixture may be defined as the pressure which would be exerted by that component if it alone filled the total volume at the same temperature. For an ideal gas, this means that

$$p_A V = N_A R T \qquad (7.1)$$

where p_A is the partial pressure of component A, N_A is the number of mols of A in the mixture, and V is the *total* volume of the mixture.

The ideal gas law also applies to the mixture itself,

$$PV = NRT \qquad (7.2)$$

where P is the total pressure and N is the mols of total mixture. Eqs. (7.1) and (7.2) may be combined to yield

$$p_A = \left(\frac{N_A}{N}\right) P = y_A P \qquad (7.3)$$

where y_A is the mol fraction of A in the mixture. For an ideal gas, then, partial pressure equals mol fraction times total pressure. This relation leads directly to Dalton's law of partial pressures, which states that the total pressure of an ideal-gas mixture is equal to the sum of the partial pressures of the components.

For practical purposes, it will be more convenient to let partial pressure *be defined* by Eq. (7.3), whether the gas behaves ideally or not, and we shall adopt this definition. Thus partial pressure, as here defined, is *always* equal to mol fraction times total pressure, and the sum of the partial pressures is always equal to the total pressure. On the other hand, only for an ideal gas will the partial pressure of a component equal the pressure which would be exerted by that component if it alone filled the total volume at the same temperature.

Rearrangement of Eq. (7.3) shows the mol fraction of a component to be equal to the partial pressure divided by the total pressure. This quotient might be considered to constitute a *pressure fraction* by analogy. In other words, the concentration of a component in a gaseous mixture can be specified by stating the total pressure and the partial pressure of the component.

Expression in ratio form. For a two-component mixture of A and B, the statement that the mixture contains 8.2 lbs of A per lb of B is certainly just as informative as a percentage composition would be, and the use of ratios such as this will occasionally be advantageous. The ratio method is not restricted to two-component systems, although it does not indicate a complete analysis if additional components are present. The moisture content of a gas mixture is often expressed in mols of moisture per mol of *moisture-free* gas, even though the "dry" gas may consist of several components. The advantages of this method of expressing composition or partial composition will be demonstrated in due course.

Other expressions for composition. A variety of expressions which indicate the composition of mixtures have been developed for use in special applications and should be familiar to the chemical engineer. Some of the more common of these are presented here; others will be treated in greater detail in Sec. 7.4.

Percentage by weight has already been shown to be equivalent to parts (by weight) of the component per hundred parts of mixture. For very small concentrations it will be somewhat more convenient to deal with parts (by weight) per *million* parts of mixture. Parts per million is commonly abbreviated *ppm*. Thus a water sample might contain 150 ppm of dissolved $CaSO_4$, meaning 150 pounds (grams) of $CaSO_4$ per million pounds (grams) of solution. The use of *ppb*, or parts per billion, is also becoming common.

Composition may also be expressed in mixed units, that is, a combination of weight and volume or mol and volume units. The hardness of water is often reported in grains per gallon—grains of hardness (primarily dissolved calcium salts) per gallon of water, a grain being 1/7000 of a pound. Similarly, concentrations in gm-mols of solute per liter of solvent or per liter of solution are commonly used by chemists. The interpretation of such expressions should occasion no difficulty since they carry specific labels and units.

7.2 Calculations Pertaining to Composition

Whereas the experienced engineer need give little conscious thought to calculations pertaining to composition, such calculations are all too frequently a source of considerable difficulty for beginning engineers. Should the student find this to be the case, he might find it advisable to review the first part of Chap. 4, because the difficulty can usually be traced to a questionable understanding of the principles of unit consistency.

Quantity-percentage conversions. The relationship which defines weight fraction,

$$x_A = \frac{M_A}{M_M} \tag{7.4}$$

can clearly be solved for either the weight fraction, the quantity of component A, or the quantity of total mixture (M_M) when values for two of the three variables are known. Similar relationships are readily written for volumetric or molal quantities. The calculations are so straightforward that they hardly deserve further comment, but there is one observation which should be made:

When the quantity of total mixture is to be determined, it should be expressed immediately in the form M_A/x_A without going through the intermediate step in substituting values into Eq. (7.4) as it stands. The validity of the recommended procedure is readily demonstrated by mentally solving Eq. (7.4) for M_M, but it may also be deduced from the principles of unit cancellation: (lbs of A) divided by (lbs of A per lb of mixture) must yield lbs of mixture upon cancellation. Thus if 75 lbs of A are present in a mixture which analyzes 30 weight per cent A, the total quantity of mixture must be 75/.30 or 250 lbs.

The beginning engineer often distrusts this direct procedure and insists on solving the relationship $75 = 0.30M_M$ instead. As he writes the equation, he is likely to be saying to himself, "75 is (equals) 0.30 of (times) M_M." The recommended alternative is to say "75 is (*divided by*) 0.30 of (*equals*) M_M." This mnemonic scheme may be helpful until a working familiarity with the calculation is attained. Although both methods clearly give the same answer, the latter is more direct and eliminates an extra, unnecessary step.

Change-of-base calculations. In view of the two conventions regarding the use of weight per cent for liquids and solids and volume per cent for gases, it can be anticipated that it will often be necessary to convert from one base to another. Conversion from or to mol units will also be necessary from time to time. The calculations are not difficult, and it is only necessary that the molecular weight and density or specific volume of each component be known.

The basic principle for such calculations is the fact that each component can and must be converted separately. Given so many pounds of A, for example, we can readily determine the equivalent number of mols or cubic feet. The quantities of all other components are similarly converted, one by one, and the total quantity in mol or volumetric units can then be obtained by addition. The final conversion to mol or volume fraction or per cent is a simple matter.

Conversions from mols to volume, volume to mols, or mols or volume to weight are handled in the same way. In all cases the calculations can be simplified by using an arbitrary quantity of mixture as a basis. The most advantageous basis will generally be a round-number quantity in lbs, cubic feet, or mols, depending on whether the given initial analysis is by weight, volume, or mols. The procedure can best be illustrated by example:

EXAMPLE 7.1. A hydrocarbon mixture contains 10 per cent pentane, 70 per cent hexane, and 20 per cent heptane by volume. The specific gravities of the three components are 0.63, 0.659, and 0.679 respectively, and the component volumes may be assumed to be additive. Calculate the corresponding composition in weight per cent.

Solution. A volumetric basis is indicated since the given analysis is by volume. A basis of 100 cubic feet would be suitable, but would make it necessary to convert the given specific gravities to English-unit densities. The latter conversion can be avoided by selecting a basis of 100 cc instead of 100 cubic feet, since specific gravity is identically equal to density in gm/cc.

Basis: 100 cc of mixture, = 10 cc pentane, 70 cc hexane, 20 cc heptane. The desired conversion is effected by converting each of these quantities to an equivalent number of grams:

$$(10)(.630) = 6.3 \text{ gms pentane}$$
$$(70)(.659) = 46.1 \text{ gms hexane}$$
$$(20)(.679) = \underline{13.58} \text{ gms heptane}$$
$$66.0 \text{ gms mixture}$$

from which

$$6.3/66 = 0.0955, \quad \text{or} \quad 9.55 \text{ per cent pentane}$$
$$46.1/66 = 0.699, \quad \text{or} \quad 69.9 \text{ per cent hexane}$$
$$13.58/66 = 0.206, \quad \text{or} \quad \underline{20.60} \text{ per cent heptane}$$
$$100.0$$

The fact that the percentages total slightly more than 100.00 is due to slide-rule inaccuracy, and suggests that the 69.9, being most doubtful in the last significant figure, should perhaps be replaced by 69.85 as determined by difference from 100.00.

Note that the density of the mixture is obtained as a by-product of the above calculation. The 100 cc used as a basis were found to weigh 66 gms, and the density of the mixture is therefore 0.66 gm/cc.

EXAMPLE 7.2. A mixture of nitrogen and carbon dioxide contains 5 lbs of N_2 per lb of CO_2. Express the analysis of the mixture in mol per cent.

Solution. A weight basis is indicated, but a basis of 6 lbs of mixture (5 lbs of N_2 plus 1 lb of CO_2) is preferable to a basis of 100 lbs of mixture, since the calculations will be simplified. For the recommended basis

$$5/28 = 0.1787 \text{ mols } N_2$$
$$1/44 = \underline{0.0227} \text{ mols } CO_2$$
$$0.2014 \text{ mols of mixture}$$

from which

$$.1787/.2014 = 0.887, \quad \text{or} \quad 88.7 \text{ per cent } N_2$$
$$.0227/.2014 = 0.113 \quad \text{or} \quad \underline{11.3} \text{ per cent } CO_2$$
$$100.0$$

Here again the calculations yield a by-product, for it can be seen that 6 lbs is equivalent to 0.2014 mols. The quotient 6/.2014, equal to 29.8, clearly has the units of lbs/mol. These are precisely the units assigned to molecular weight itself. Accordingly, we can consider 29.8 to be the molecular weight of the mixture, by definition. It will frequently be desirable to calculate the molecular weight of a mixture, and this may always be done by the foregoing procedure.

Mol-volume-pressure relationship. Consider an ideal-gas mixture containing 31 mols of N_2, 12 mols of CO_2, and 7 mols of O_2. The corresponding volumetric analysis, at standard conditions, can be obtained by applying the conversion factor 359 ft³/mol. Thus

$$(31)(359) = \text{ft}^3 N_2$$
$$(12)(359) = \text{ft}^3 CO_2$$
$$\underline{(7)(359)} = \text{ft}^3 O_2$$
$$(50)(359) = \text{ft}^3 \text{ total mixture}$$

It can be seen that the 359 factor will cancel out completely when each component volume is divided by the total volume to obtain volume fraction. This leads to the significant conclusion that mol per cent and volume per cent are identical for ideal-gas mixtures.

Since partial pressure has already been defined so as to make mol fraction always equal to pressure fraction, the entire relationship among mol fraction, pressure fraction, and volume fraction can be summed up by stating that *mol fraction equals pressure fraction equals, for ideal gases, volume fraction.* It will be well to keep this relationship in mind, for it has many applications.

Ratio-percentage conversion. A knowledge of the percentage analysis of a mixture obviously makes it possible to calculate the ratio of the quantity of any one component or combination of components to that of another or combination of others. The reverse calculation is a bit more troublesome, particularly when only a partial analysis is available. Since this situation is most frequently encountered in problems involving the moisture content of a gas, we shall demonstrate the calculation for this specific case and trust the student to recognize its general applicability.

Consider a gas mixture which contains Y mols of moisture per mol of dry gas. The use of the term "dry gas" may appear to be improper in this situation since the mixture clearly contains moisture, but this term is conventionally used to denote the sum total of all components other than water vapor. Thus Y is simply the ratio of the mols of water vapor to the total mols of all other components. It follows that $(1 + Y)$ mols of *wet* gas will contain Y mols of moisture plus 1 mol of other components, and the mol fraction of moisture in the wet mixture is given by

$$y = \frac{Y}{1 + Y} \tag{7.5}$$

(x rather than y is commonly used to denote mol fraction in liquids and solids. The corresponding mol ratio would be denoted by X.)

EXAMPLE 7.3. Dry air may be considered to analyze 21 per cent oxygen and 79 per cent nitrogen*. Calculate the analysis of a sample of air which contains 0.08 mols of water vapor per mol of dry air.

Solution. The given analysis is in volume per cent, equal to mol per cent. Each mol of dry air is accompanied by 0.08 mols of water vapor for a total of 1.08 mols, and $0.08/1.08 = 0.074$ mol fraction water vapor. Also, $0.21/1.08 = 0.1945$ mol fraction oxygen. The mol fraction of nitrogen, by difference from unity, is 0.7315.

Analyses are often reported on a *dry basis*—mols per mol of moisture-free mixture—even though moisture is present. The utility of dry-basis analyses lies in the fact that moisture content may vary, depending on a variety of factors, and it will often be advantageous to use figures which are independent of such variation. On a dry basis, air is always 21 per cent oxygen and 79 per cent nitrogen, whereas the composition on a *wet basis* will obviously change with the amount of moisture present.

Eq. (7.5) may be solved for Y to obtain

$$Y = \frac{y}{1 - y} \tag{7.6}$$

and this equation can also be derived by reasoning analogous to that used in arriving at Eq. (7.5): A gas which contains y mols of moisture per (1) mol of total (wet) gas must contain $(1 - y)$ mols of dry gas. The expression for mols of moisture per mol of dry gas given in Eq. (7.6) follows immediately.

Hopefully, the student will resist the temptation to memorize either Eq. (7.5) or (7.6). These equations are readily reasoned out from a consideration

---

* Actually, air analyzes 20.99 per cent oxygen, 78.03 per cent nitrogen, and 0.98 per cent argon, carbon dioxide, and other minor constituents. Since the latter components are largely inert, it is the common practice to include them with the nitrogen for all calculations in which their presence is not of specific interest.

of the pertinent units, and a fallible memory is a poor substitute for straight-forward logic. Equivalent relationships may be utilized in working with mass, volume, or pressure fractions and ratios.

EXAMPLE 7.4. The partial pressure of the water vapor in a sample of air is 2 psia. The total pressure is 14.7 psia. Calculate the moisture content in mols per mol of dry air.

Solution. Using pressures in Eq. (7.6),

$$\frac{2}{14.7 - 2} = 0.1575$$

This is the ratio of the partial pressure of the water vapor to that of the dry air and is equal to the mols of water per mol of dry air, since pressure ratio and mol ratio are the same.

One other type of ratio calculation will be pertinent from time to time: Suppose a combustion process is to be supplied with enough air to furnish 165 mols of oxygen, and it is necessary to determine how much nitrogen will accompany the oxygen. One technique is to calculate the total quantity of air first: $165/.21 = 786$ mols of air. The nitrogen can then be obtained by difference and is seen to be 621 mols.

A more direct procedure is possible if it is recognized that the quotient $79/21$ (or $.79/.21$) represents the mol ratio of nitrogen to oxygen. Thus multiplying 165 by $79/21$ will give mols of nitrogen directly, without the necessity of first calculating mols of total air. The student will do well to take careful note of this technique, for he will have frequent use for it.

EXAMPLE 7.5. A combustion process yields a flue gas which analyzes 85.95 per cent nitrogen, 8.78 per cent CO_2, and 5.27 per cent oxygen, all on a dry basis, and also contains 0.1756 mols of water vapor per mol of dry gas. (a) What is the analysis of the gas on a wet basis? (b) What is the analysis of the gas on a nitrogen-free basis? (c) How many mols of water vapor will be present in a quantity of gas which contains 395 mols of CO_2?

Solution. A partial solution to this example will be presented without comment. The student can test his comprehension of the material presented in this section by confirming the given results and completing the solution.

Basis: 100 mols of dry gas, $= 85.95$ mols N_2, 8.78 mols CO_2, 5.27 mols O_2, and 17.56 mols H_2O for a total of 117.56 mols of wet gas.

On a wet basis,

$$\left(\frac{85.95}{117.56}\right)(100) = 73.1 \text{ per cent } N_2, \text{ etc.}$$

On a nitrogen-free basis,

$$\left(\frac{8.78}{117.56 - 85.95}\right)(100) = 27.8 \text{ per cent } CO_2, \text{ etc.}$$

For part (c),

$$(395) \left(\frac{17.56}{8.78}\right) = 790 \text{ mols } H_2O \text{ per } 395 \text{ mols } CO_2$$

7.3 Composition of Two-Phase Mixtures

If a two-component liquid mixture is heated from a subcooled state at constant pressure, it will start to vaporize when the bubble point is reached just as a pure substance will. The vaporization of the mixture will then differ from that of a pure substance in that the more volatile component will vaporize preferentially, thereby increasing the concentration of the less-volatile component in the residual liquid. In turn, the reduced volatility of the residual liquid makes it necessary to raise the temperature in order to continue the vaporization.

Since these same phenomena will occur again at the higher temperature, it is apparent that the temperature must continue to rise throughout the vaporization process, and that the residual liquid will always have a composition different from that of the vapor in equilibrium with it. It can be seen that the vaporization of a mixture differs considerably from that of a pure substance, the latter being characterized by a constant temperature and identical liquid and vapor compositions.

The T-x diagram. Let us imagine that we have vaporized several mixtures of A and B of varying initial compositions and have carefully determined, at a constant pressure, the temperatures at which vaporization started and at which it was complete—i.e., the bubble and dew points—for each composition. The dew points and bubble points might then be plotted against composition of the mixture as shown by the small circles in Fig. 7.1, on which the boiling points of pure A and pure B are properly shown as single points.

When a smooth curve is drawn through all the bubble points and a second through all the dew points, it should be clear that two phases exist only within the area bounded by the two curves. Above the dew-point line all mixtures will be superheated vapors, while below the bubble-point line they will be subcooled liquids. Further—and this is a most significant observation—the dew-point line represents the locus of all saturated vapor compositions, and the bubble-point line similarly represents the locus of all saturated liquid compositions.

A temperature-composition or T-x diagram such as Fig. 7.1 can be used to determine the composition of two-phase mixtures as follows: A two-phase mixture at equilibrium consists of a saturated liquid and a saturated vapor at the same temperature. If a horizontal line corresponding to the temperature is drawn on the diagram, then, the equilibrium liquid and vapor

compositions must be given by the points of intersection with the bubble-
and dew-point lines, respectively. Such a line has been drawn on Fig. 7.1

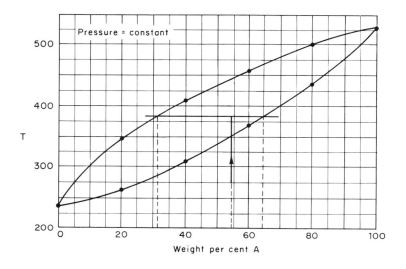

Fig. 7.1 Typical temperature-composition diagram for a two-component system.

for a temperature of 385°, and it can be seen that saturated vapor analyzes
31.5 per cent A and saturated liquid 65 per cent A at this temperature.

The equilibrium compositions, being fixed by temperature (and pressure)
alone, are completely independent of the total composition of the mixture,
provided only that the total composition is such that the mixture lies within
the two-phase region at the temperature of interest. Outside this region any
mixture is either all liquid or all vapor, and the composition is simply that
of the mixture itself.

The foregoing does not imply that the total composition of a two-phase
mixture is not of interest. Once the equilibrium liquid and vapor compositions have been determined for a given temperature, the total composition
establishes the relative *quantities* of liquid and vapor. The inverse-lever-arm
principle is directly applicable to the latter calculation just as it is in the
case of pure substances.

If a subcooled liquid containing 54 per cent A is heated to 385°, for
example, the inverse-lever-arm rule indicates the mixture will be approximately $\frac{2}{3}$ liquid and $\frac{1}{3}$ vapor at that temperature. For a more accurate
determination, we can use the abscissa scale to measure line lengths just as

was done in pure-substance calculations. The weight fraction of vapor in the mixture is therefore

$$\frac{65 - 54}{65 - 31.5} = 0.329$$

For 100 lbs of the original mixture, there will be 32.9 lbs of vapor analyzing 31.5 per cent A and 67.1 lbs of liquid analyzing 65 per cent A at 385°. The vapor accordingly contains $(32.9)(.315) = 10.35$ lbs of A while the liquid contains $(67.1)(.65) = 43.65$ lbs of A. It can be seen that the 54 lbs of A originally present are all accounted for.

The student should be able to confirm his understanding of the vapor-liquid relationships indicated on a T-x diagram by checking the answers to the following problems based on Fig. 7.1:

EXAMPLE 7.6. To what temperature must a liquid mixture analyzing 50 per cent A be heated before it will start to vaporize? (340°)

EXAMPLE 7.7. What will be the composition of the first vapor to appear in Ex. 7.6? (18 per cent A)

EXAMPLE 7.8. At what temperature will the vaporization of Ex. 7.6 be complete? (435°)

EXAMPLE 7.9. What will be the composition of the last drop of liquid to disappear when the mixture of Ex. 7.6 reaches its dew point? (79 per cent A)

EXAMPLE 7.10. What are the compositions of the equilibrium liquid and vapor phases at 400°? (Liquid is 70 per cent A, vapor is 37 per cent A)

EXAMPLE 7.11. What fraction of the original mixture of Ex. 7.6 is vapor at 400°? (0.61)

EXAMPLE 7.12. How many lbs of B are present in the liquid phase for the conditions of Ex. 7.11? (11.70 lbs per 100 lbs of original mixture)

EXAMPLE 7.13. To what temperature must the mixture of Ex. 7.6 be heated to vaporize half of it? (390°, determined by drawing horizontal lines by trial-and-error to find the one which is bisected by the vertical line at 50 per cent A)

Presentation of phase-equilibria data. The T-x diagram portrays the general nature of the relationships pertinent to vapor-liquid equilibria, but it is not the only—or even the most common—method of presenting data. Indeed, the data themselves are not normally obtained by determining bubble and dew points as has been implied, but rather by actually analyzing the equilibrium phases at various temperatures. Thus the T-x diagram has been used primarily as a convenient medium for introducing the general subject of phase equilibria. In passing, it might be noted that not all T-x diagrams will have the same "cigar-shaped" two-phase region shown in Fig. 7.1, for many variations are possible. Some of these variations will be encountered in subsequent course work.

A popular alternative to the T-x diagram as a means of presenting equilibrium data for *binary* (two-component) systems is the x-y plot, on which the mol fraction (x) of the more volatile component in the liquid phase is plotted against the equilibrium mol fraction in the vapor phase (y). Like the T-x plot, the x-y plot pertains to a specific constant pressure, but temperature is a built-in parameter, since each point on the x-y line corresponds to a different temperature. We will have the occasion to use x-y plots in due course.

Another alternative is to plot or tabulate values of the *equilibrium constant*, K, as a function of pressure and temperature, K for any component being equal to y/x for that component. This method of data presentation is particularly advantageous when systems comprising more than two components are to be treated, since the K-value for any component may be considered to be independent of the overall composition of the mixture to a good approximation.

Equilibrium data for binary systems may also be expressed in terms of *relative volatility* (α), defined as the ratio of K for the more volatile component to that for the less volatile component. Thus, if B is the more volatile component in a mixture of A and B,

$$\alpha = \frac{K_B}{K_A} = \frac{y_B/x_B}{y_A/x_A} = \frac{y_B x_A}{x_B y_A} = \frac{y_B(1 - x_B)}{x_B(1 - y_B)} \tag{7.7}$$

The last equality makes it clear that a knowledge of the relative volatility, α, will permit the determination of y_B as a function of x_B.

Theoretical relationships. Quantitative expressions relating equilibrium phase compositions are readily derivable from thermodynamic considerations, but rigor depends on the experimental evaluation of some of the terms. As a consequence, the engineer is more likely to use the experimental data directly when they are available. Still, analytical relationships will be useful as a means of predicting equilibrium compositions in the absence of specific experimental data, particularly if certain simplifying assumptions are permissible. The theoretical basis for such relationships will be outlined, but a rigorous derivation is best deferred to a more intensive study of thermodynamics.

It was shown in Sec. 6.2 that, for a pure substance,

$$d\underline{G} = -\underline{S}dT + \underline{V}dP \tag{6.11}$$

and the restriction of constant temperature may be imposed to obtain

$$d\underline{G}_T = \underline{V}dP_T = RT\,d(\ln f) \tag{7.8}$$

The latter equality follows from the definition of fugacity given in Sec. 6.8. If a unit mass of a substance moves from the liquid to the vapor phase at constant temperature, Eq. (7.8) can be integrated between limits to obtain

$$\underline{G}_V - \underline{G}_L = RT \ln \left(\frac{f_V}{f_L}\right) \tag{7.9}$$

At equilibrium, however, $\underline{G}_V = \underline{G}_L$ in accordance with the development in Sec. 6.10, and Eq. (7.9) can therefore be satisfied at equilibrium conditions only if

$$f_V = f_L \tag{7.10}$$

In other words, the fugacities of the liquid and vapor phases must be equal when a pure substance exists as a two-phase, equilibrium mixture.

The proof is too involved to be presented here, but it can similarly be shown that Eq. (7.10) applies separately to each component when a multi-component system exists as a two-phase, equilibrium mixture. With the symbol $\bar{f}$ denoting the fugacity of a component in a mixture, then, the equality

$$\bar{f}_V = \bar{f}_L \tag{7.11}$$

holds for each component at equilibrium, and there are as many fugacity equalities as there are components in the system.

Let us now define an ideal solution as one for which the component volumes are additive.* This concept should not be confused with that of an ideal gas, for even non-ideal gases tend to form ideal solutions. Many liquids also form ideal solutions, although others (alcohol and water, for example) do not. A significant characteristic of ideal solutions is the fact that the fugacity of any component in the solution is equal to the mol fraction times the fugacity of the component were it to exist as a pure substance at the same temperature and total pressure. Thus

$$\bar{f} = yf \tag{7.15}$$

for each component in an ideal solution, either liquid or vapor. Eq. (7.15) is known as the *Lewis-Randall rule* and is presented here without proof.

---

* A mathematical statement of this condition is

$$\overline{V}_j = \underline{V}_j \tag{7.12}$$

in which j denotes any component in the mixture and $\overline{V}_j$ is the change in the total volume of the mixture per unit quantity of j added while temperature, pressure, and the masses of all other components are held constant. Thus

$$\overline{V}_j = \left(\frac{\partial V}{\partial M_j}\right)_{T,P,M_A,M_B,\cdots} \tag{7.13}$$

If M is in mols, the partial derivative is called the *partial molal volume* of component j. Partial molal quantities for other extensive properties may be similarly defined, i.e.,

$$\overline{\Gamma}_j = \left(\frac{\partial \Gamma}{\partial M_j}\right)_{T,P,M_A,M_B,\cdots} \tag{7.14}$$

where Γ is any extensive property. Note that $\overline{\Gamma}$ is identically equal to $\underline{\Gamma}$ for any component in a pure, unmixed state.

The fact that many liquid solutions are not ideal is usually provided for by introducing an *activity coefficient*, γ, into Eq. (7.15) as a correction factor. The Lewis-Randall rule then makes it possible to write Eq. (7.11) in the form

$$(y f_V)_j = (\gamma x f_L)_j \tag{7.16}$$

with the subscript j indicating that this equation applies to each component in the system. γ will be unity for ideal liquid solutions, but its evaluation depends on experimental data otherwise.

For a two-phase mixture existing at a pressure P and a temperature T, $(f_V)_j$ will be the fugacity of pure j at P and T. It can be evaluated by calculating P_r and T_r and obtaining f/P from a generalized plot as outlined in Sec. 6.8. Then $(f_V)_j = (f/P)P$. For an ideal gas, $f/P = 1$ and $(f_V)_j$ is identically equal to P.

The evaluation of $(f_L)_j$ requires the use of a path of convenience. First, the vapor pressure of component j at temperature T is determined. Next, $(f_V)^*_j$ is evaluated at p^*_j and T, using the procedure described in the preceding paragraph. But, since vapor and liquid are in equilibrium at p^* and T, Eq. (7.10) applies and the fugacity of pure liquid j at p^*_j and T is therefore the same as $(f_V)^*_j$. It remains only to correct for the change in pressure in going from p^*_j to P, the pressure of the original mixture. The right-hand equality in Eq. (7.8) may be integrated and used for this purpose, and the value of $(f_L)_j$ to be substituted into Eq. (7.16) is thus obtained. Since $(f_V)_j$ was evaluated previously and γ_j is assumed to be known, the substituted form of Eq. (7.16) accordingly gives y_j as a function of x_j and equilibrium phase compositions can be calculated.

Simplifying assumptions. The following assumptions are not unreasonable in many cases of practical interest: (1) Ideal-gas behavior prevails at p^*_j and T. This means that $(f/P)^* = 1$ and hence $(f_V)^*_j = (f_L)^*_j = p^*_j$, the vapor pressure of j at temperature T. (2) The change of liquid fugacity with pressure is negligible, making $(f_L)_j = (f_L)^*_j = p^*_j$. (3) The liquid phase is an ideal solution for which $\gamma_j = 1$. (4) Ideal-gas behavior prevails at P and T; hence $(f_V)_j = P$.

When these assumptions are permissible, Eq. (7.16) can be simplified to

$$y_j P = p_j = x_j p^*_j \tag{7.17}$$

and y_j and x_j are seen to be directly related once the system pressure and temperature are specified, since p^*_j is evaluated at the system temperature. This equation is known as *Raoult's law*.

A slightly more general form of Eq. (7.17), not subject to the restriction that the liquid solution behave ideally, is

$$y_j P = p_j = \gamma_j x_j p^*_j \tag{7.18}$$

In very dilute solutions, as x_j approaches zero, the product $\gamma_j p^*_j$ is found to be a constant at any given system temperature. For such conditions Eq. (7.18) is commonly written in the form

$$y_j P = p_j = x_j H'_j \tag{7.19}$$

and is known as *Henry's law*. H'_j, the Henry's law constant, is a function of temperature only.

It can be shown that when Henry's law is valid for the dilute component in a binary mixture, Raoult's law is valid for the concentrated component. This relationship makes it possible to calculate H': Given y (or x) for the concentrated component, we can solve Raoult's law for x (or y). x and y for the dilute component may then be determined from the relationships $\Sigma x = 1$ and $\Sigma y = 1$. Finally, with x and y for the dilute component known, Henry's law can be solved for H'.

A special case of Eq. (7.17) arises when all but one of the components in the gas phase are essentially insoluble in the equilibrium liquid. Such components are called *non-condensibles*. Written for a single condensible component c, with x_c equal to one for practical purposes, Eq. (7.17) reduces to

$$y_c P = p_c = p^*_c \tag{7.20}$$

That is, at equilibrium the partial pressure of the condensible component is equal to its vapor pressure. Any mixture of water vapor in air constitutes an important example of systems falling into this category. Some consequences of Eq. (7.20) will be considered in the next three sections.

7.4 Composition Related to Saturation

Dew point. In Chap. 5, a saturated vapor was defined as one which is at its dew point and hence on the verge of condensing. An analogous definition is applicable to a non-condensible gas mixture containing a condensible vapor: the mixture is said to be at its *dew point* and *saturated* with respect to the condensible component if the component is on the verge of condensation. The condensible component must satisfy Eq. (7.20) under such conditions, since the presence of the first infinitesimal quantity of equilibrium liquid is implied.

The foregoing makes it possible to fix the concentration of a condensible component in a gas-vapor mixture by specifying the dew point temperature and pressure: Consider an unsaturated mixture stated as having a dew point at a temperature T^* and a total pressure P^* (not to be confused with vapor pressure, p^*). Were the mixture to be cooled or compressed to bring it directly to the dew point, there could be no condensation prior to reaching that point, in accordance with the definition of dew point. Consequently the mol fraction of vapor in the mixture, y_c, would be the same at the dew point as it was originally. At the dew point, however, Eq. (7.20) becomes applicable and can be solved for y_c, since $P = P^*$ is known and p^*_c is presumed to be a known function of T^*.

When only the dew point temperature of a given mixture is specified, the corresponding dew point pressure may be assumed to be that of the mixture itself. That is, the given dew point temperature is the temperature at which the mixture would become saturated were it to be cooled *at constant pressure*. Similarly, when only the dew point pressure is specified, it is implied that the mixture would become saturated at that pressure were it to be compressed *isothermally* from the given pressure and temperature. The following example should help to clarify the various relationships among dew point, partial pressure, vapor pressure, and total pressure.

EXAMPLE 7.14. A mixture of benzene vapor and nitrogen at 108°F and 2 atm pressure has a dew point of 79°F. (a) Calculate the mol fraction of benzene in the mixture. (b) To what pressure must the mixture be compressed to reduce the mol fraction of benzene by 80 per cent if the compression is to be isothermal at 108°F?

Solution. At 79°F (26.1°C) the vapor pressure of benzene is 100 mm Hg or 0.132 atm. In accordance with Eq. (7.20) this must also be the partial pressure of the benzene in the mixture at its dew point of 79°F and 2 atm. The corresponding mol fraction, equal to p/P, is $0.132/2 = 0.066$ mols of benzene per mol of mixture. Since there is no change in composition between 108° and 79°, the mol fraction in the mixture at 108°F is also 0.066.

For the compression process, the composition will again remain unchanged until the dew point is reached, at which point the partial pressure, equal to $0.066P$, must equal the vapor pressure. At 108°F (42.2°C), the vapor pressure is 200 mm Hg or 0.263 atm; hence

$$0.066P = 0.263 \quad \text{and} \quad P = 3.99 \text{ atm}$$

This is the dew point pressure corresponding to a temperature of 108°F, and there will be no condensation up to this point.

If the compression is continued, benzene will condense while the remaining gas mixture will always be saturated. Eq. (7.20) therefore applies, and the partial pressure of the benzene in the vapor phase must always be equal to the vapor pressure of 0.263 atm. In the given problem, the final mol fraction in the vapor phase is to be $(.20)(.066) = 0.0132$. At the end of the process, then,

$$P = \frac{p}{y} = \frac{.263}{.0132} = 20 \text{ atm}$$

The student who accepts this answer without question has already forgotten either an important part of Chap. 5 or one of the restrictions underlying Eq. (7.20): Ideal-gas behavior can safely be assumed only at pressures near atmospheric, and it is conceivable that Eq. (7.20), based on the assumption of ideality, is not valid at 20 atmospheres. It will be well to investigate the extent to which benzene behaves ideally at the latter pressure:

From Appendix C-5, $P_c = 48.6$ atm and $T_c = 562°K$; hence $P_r = 20/48.6 = 0.412$ and $T_r = 568/(1.8)(562) = 0.56$. From Appendix C-6, $Z < 0.75$ and ideality is not indicated. In the absence of a generalized f/P plot, we will still accept the answer of 20 atmospheres, but we now recognize it for what it is, namely, an expedient approximation.

The alert student may wonder about the effect of non-ideal behavior for the nitrogen. It has no effect whatsoever because it was not necessary to apply Eq. (7.20) to the nitrogen.

EXAMPLE 7.15. How many mols of liquid benzene will be recovered for each mol of mixture subjected to the compression process of Ex. 7.14(b)?

Solution. Since the original and final concentrations are 0.0660 and 0.0132 mols of benzene per mol of mixture, respectively, the solution would appear to be

$$0.0660 - 0.0132 = 0.0528 \text{ mols recovered/mol mixture}$$

Unfortunately appearances are deceiving, for here is another case in which labels are as significant as units: The condensation of benzene changes the total quantity of mixture, and mols of benzene per mol of *final* mixture cannot be subtracted from mols of benzene per mol of *original* mixture.

The foregoing should immediately suggest the use of analyses on a dry basis (in this case, dry means benzene-free). Initially, the mixture contains $0.0660/0.934 = 0.0707$ mols of benzene per mol of nitrogen; finally, it contains only $0.0132/0.9868 = 0.0134$ mols per mol. The two mol ratios *can* be subtracted, since the quantity of nitrogen remains constant throughout the process. Thus the liquid recovered will be 0.0573 mols of benzene per mol of nitrogen, and, since there are 0.934 mols of nitrogen per mol of original mixture,

$$(.0573)(.934) = 0.0535 \text{ mols recovered/mol mixture}$$

Relative saturation. The partial pressure of the condensible component in an unsaturated mixture must be less than its vapor pressure at the same temperature. The actual mol fraction of the condensible component is equal to p/P, while the mol fraction would be p^*/P if the mixture were saturated *at the same total pressure*. If the actual mol fraction is divided by the mol fraction at saturation, the total pressure cancels out to leave only p/p^*. This ratio is called the *relative saturation* of the mixture, or,

$$\text{Relative saturation} = \frac{p}{p^*} = \frac{y}{y^*} \tag{7.21}$$

in which y^* denotes the mol fraction at saturation just as p^* denotes the vapor pressure, or partial pressure at saturation. Relative saturation is often expressed in per cent rather than as a ratio or fraction.

Note that temperature, pressure, and relative saturation effectively fix the concentration of the condensible component in a mixture: Temperature fixes the vapor pressure p^*; relative saturation then fixes the partial pressure via Eq. (7.21); and, finally, the mol fraction of the condensible component is equal to the partial pressure divided by the total pressure. Conversely, relative saturation can be calculated from a knowledge of temperature, pressure, and mol fraction.

Per cent saturation. In dry-basis analyses the concentration of the condensible component is expressed in mols per mol of dry gas rather than as a mol fraction. As was noted in Sec. 7.2 and again in Ex. 7.15, this practice exploits the fact that the quantity and composition of the dry gas are independent of changes in condensible content. The advantage of mol-ratio analyses is incorporated into the definition of *per cent saturation*,

$$\text{Per cent saturation} = \frac{Y}{Y^*} (100) \tag{7.22}$$

in which Y is the actual mol ratio of condensible component to dry gas and Y^* is the ratio which would exist were the gas to be saturated at the same temperature and total pressure.

The fact that $Y = y/(1 - y)$ and mol ratio equals pressure ratio makes it possible to write Eq. (7.22) in an equivalent form,

$$\text{Per cent saturation} = \frac{\dfrac{y}{1-y}}{\dfrac{y^*}{1-y^*}} (100) = \frac{\dfrac{p}{P-p}}{\dfrac{p^*}{P-p^*}} (100) \tag{7.23}$$

A comparison of Eqs. (7.21) and (7.23) clearly shows per cent saturation and per cent *relative* saturation to be inherently different, and care must obviously be exercised if the two concepts are not to be confused.

EXAMPLE 7.16. A mixture of water vapor and air is 55 per cent saturated at 90°F and 20 psia. Calculate the mol fraction and partial pressure of the water vapor in the mixture and the per cent relative saturation. (For water at 90°F, $p^* = 0.698$ psia.)

Solution. All of the principles required for the solution of this problem have already been treated. The solution will be presented without comment and its confirmation left as an exercise.

$$Y^* = \frac{.698}{20 - .698} = 0.0362$$

$$Y = (.0362)(.55) = 0.0199$$

(a) $$y = \frac{.0199}{1 + .0199} = 0.0195 \text{ mol fraction water}$$

(b) $$p = (.0195)(20) = 0.39 \text{ psia}$$

(c) $$\frac{.39}{.698}(100) = 55.9 \text{ per cent relative saturation}$$

The reverse calculation is suggested as an additional exercise; that is, given a *relative* saturation of 55 per cent, what is the per cent saturation at 90°F and 20 psia? (The answer is 54.1 per cent, with $Y = 0.0196$ mols of water per mol of dry air.)

It should not be inferred from the foregoing that per cent saturation and per cent relative saturation are always approximately equal. At 200°F, for example, at which temperature $p^* = 11.525$ psia, it will be found that 55 per cent relative saturation is equivalent to only 34.2 per cent saturation.

Humidity. Although the concepts of per cent saturation and per cent relative saturation apply to any mixture of a condensible vapor and a non-condensible gas, it is the common practice to substitute the word *humidity* for saturation when the components are water vapor and air. Similarly, the symbol H is substituted for Y and is called the *molal humidity*, being the mols of water vapor per mol of dry air. Humidity may also be expressed in weight units, but conversion to molal units will usually be necessary or advisable as a prelude to quantitative calculations.

Actually, the distinction between humidity and its more general counterpart, saturation, serves little useful purpose. There is a growing tendency to use the terms interchangeably in practice, and only the purist would criticize an engineer who spoke of a benzene-nitrogen mixture, for example, as having a humidity of 0.05 pounds of benzene per pound of dry gas.

7.5 Wet- and Dry-Bulb Thermometry

A final method for specifying the composition of gas mixtures containing a condensible vapor involves the use of *wet-* and *dry-bulb temperatures*. The development of the pertinent relationships provides an excellent opportunity to demonstrate the practical application of the rate concept presented in Chap. 2 and will be presented in detail for this reason.

Evaporation is a rate process involving the transfer of mass from a liquid phase to a contiguous gas or vapor phase. The pertinent rate is the quantity, commonly expressed in mols, of liquid evaporated per unit time, $dN/d\theta$. Further, the factor which characterizes the extent of the system in inter-phase mass transfer processes is the interfacial area of contact between the two phases. In accordance with the general rate concepts presented in Sec. 2.7, then, the rate definition for such processes is

$$\text{Rate} = \frac{dN}{Ad\theta} \tag{7.24}$$

and the corresponding rate correlation is

$$\text{Rate} = k(\Gamma_L - \Gamma_V) \tag{7.25}$$

where k is the rate coefficient or *mass-transfer coefficient,* and $(\Gamma_L - \Gamma_V)$ is the appropriate driving force, yet to be specifically identified.

One of the identifying characteristics of any driving force is the fact that it disappears at equilibrium. Eqs. (7.10) and (7.11) show that fugacity satisfies this requirement, and experimental rate studies confirm the implication that the driving force for mass transfer is a fugacity difference. Substituting $\bar{f}$ for Γ in Eq. (7.25) and combining the result with Eq. (7.24) yields the differential rate equation

$$\frac{dN}{Ad\theta} = k(\bar{f}_L - \bar{f}_V) \tag{7.26}$$

Finally, if conditions are such that the simplifying assumptions leading to Raoult's law are justified, the fugacities in Eq. (7.26) can be replaced with the vapor pressure and partial pressure, respectively, to obtain

$$\frac{dN}{Ad\theta} = k(p^* - p) \tag{7.27}$$

Unless the two phases are at the same temperature, the evaporation process will also involve the flow of heat. If Q is the heat absorbed by the liquid, the pertinent heat-transfer rate equation is

$$\frac{\delta Q}{Ad\theta} = h(T_V - T_L) \tag{7.28}$$

where h is the heat-transfer coefficient and T_V and T_L are the temperatures of the vapor and liquid phases, respectively. The development of this equation parallels that of Eq. (7.27).

Now let us consider a gas at temperature T_V flowing across the surface of a small quantity of liquid at temperature T_L, initially equal to T_V. If the gas is saturated with respect to the liquid, there will be no evaporation, since $p = p^*$ at saturation and the driving force in Eq. (7.27) is zero. If, on the other hand, the gas is *not* saturated, p will be less than p^* and evaporation will result. Furthermore, the rate of evaporation as given by Eq. (7.27) will vary with p; and the lower the concentration of the condensible component in the gas phase, the greater will be the rate of evaporation.

At this point another factor must be considered, namely, the latent heat of vaporization. With T_V initially equal to T_L, heat cannot flow from gas to liquid since there is no driving force for heat transfer. Any evaporation must therefore result in the conversion of sensible heat to latent heat within the liquid phase, and the temperature of the liquid will accordingly drop as the liquid loses sensible heat.

As soon as T_L falls below T_V, however, heat can and will flow from gas to liquid, and the rate of heat transfer will increase as T_L continues to drop. At the same time, the rate of evaporation will be decreasing because the change in T_L also reduces the vapor pressure p^*. Ultimately, the liquid temperature will reach a steady-state value, to be designated T_{wb}, such that the rate of heat transfer from the gas phase is just sufficient to supply the necessary heat of vaporization. The mathematical equivalent of this statement, with ΔH_v denoting the latent heat of vaporization in BTU/mol, is

$$\frac{\delta Q}{d\theta} = (\Delta H_v)\frac{dN}{d\theta} \qquad (7.29)$$

Eqs. (7.27), (7.28), and (7.29) may be combined to obtain

$$hA(T_V - T_{wb}) = (\Delta H_v)kA(p^* - p) \qquad (7.30)$$

and a final rearrangement yields

$$\frac{k}{h}(\Delta H_v)(p^* - p) = T_V - T_{wb} \qquad (7.31)$$

Assuming the existence of a generalized correlation which will permit the evaluation of the ratio k/h, Eq. (7.31) provides a means of determining the partial pressure of the condensible component in a gas-vapor mixture from a knowledge of T_V and T_{wb}. The latter temperature automatically fixes both p^* and ΔH_v, and the equation can therefore be solved for p if T_V and T_{wb} are known. Note that T_V and T_{wb} will approach each other as p increases, and will be identical at saturation when $p = p^*$.

The steady-state liquid temperature T_{wb} may be measured experimentally by soaking a cloth wick in the liquid, wrapping the wick around the bulb of a thermometer, and exposing this *wet bulb* to the gas stream. When steady-state conditions have been established, the thermometer will read the desired temperature. In the absence of a moving gas stream the same effect can be achieved by moving the wet-bulb thermometer rapidly about in the stagnant gas. In either case the resulting temperature is appropriately called the *wet-bulb temperature*, and the use of the symbol T_{wb} can be seen to have a logical basis.

The gas temperature T_V can be obtained with an ordinary thermometer. By analogy this is often referred to as a dry-bulb thermometer, and T_V is called the *dry-bulb temperature*. A *sling psychrometer* is often used to measure both wet- and dry-bulb temperatures simultaneously. This instrument consists of a light-weight metal frame, on which the thermometers are mounted, with a swiveled handle attached to its upper end. The operator can grasp the handle and swing the instrument about in a circle so as to insure a constant supply of fresh gas at the wet bulb.

7.6 The Psychrometric Chart

Graphical representation of the relationships described in the preceding sections has obvious advantages when repetitive humidity calculations must be undertaken. The most popular form of graphical representation is the *psychrometric chart*, a plot of humidity vs. dry-bulb temperature with per cent saturation, wet-bulb temperature, and adiabatic cooling lines (to be discussed shortly) shown parametrically. A chart for the air-water system at atmospheric pressure will be found in Appendix C-7, and similar plots for a number of other systems may be found in the literature.

A typical psychrometric chart is shown schematically in Fig. 7.2. Simple

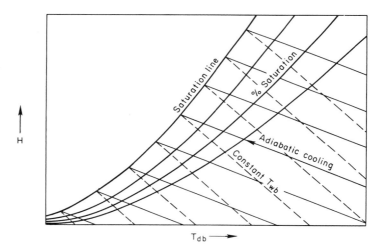

Fig. 7.2 Schematic psychrometric chart showing relationships among variables.

heating and cooling in the unsaturated region correspond to movement along a horizontal line on the chart, since the humidity does not change until condensation occurs. The intersection of any horizontal line with the saturation line locates a dew point, and the dew point temperature is the dry-bulb temperature at the point of intersection. It should also be noted that wet- and dry-bulb temperatures are equal at saturation. The wet-bulb temperature associated with any given line of constant T_{wb} is thus equal to the dry-bulb temperature at which the line intersects the saturation line.

Except for the combination of humidity and dew point, both of which fix only an ordinate, a knowledge of any two of the variables shown on the psychrometric chart will fix a single point on the chart, and all other properties can then be determined. The utility of the basic chart may be extended by plotting additional relationships if desired. Typical additions, not shown in Fig. 7.2, are plots of the specific volume of the dry gas, specific volume of the saturated gas, and latent heat of vaporization as functions of dry-bulb temperature. The heat capacity of the moist gas, expressed in BTU per pound of *dry* gas per Fahrenheit degree, may also be plotted as a function of humidity. This heat capacity is commonly called the *humid heat*.

If an unsaturated gas is brought into contact with a liquid, it can be simultaneously humidified and cooled in accordance with the relationships discussed in Sec. 7.5. When the temperature of the liquid is such that all the latent heat of vaporization comes from the gas, the humidification-cooling process is called *adiabatic cooling* or *adiabatic saturation*. The temperature of the gas will fall as its humidity rises, and an application of the pertinent mass and energy balances provides a quantitative relationship between temperature and humidity. Typical paths are shown in Fig. 7.2.

Coincidentally, the wet-bulb temperature lines and the adiabatic cooling lines are identical for the air-water system; hence separate adiabatic cooling lines are not shown on the chart in Appendix C-7. Similar charts for other vapors would show separate families of lines for wet-bulb temperature and adiabatic cooling as per Fig. 7.2.

The chart in Appendix C-7 may also be used for mixtures of water vapor and non-condensible gases other than air with but one modification: If the gas contains a significant quantity of a tri-atomic component such as carbon dioxide, the wet-bulb temperature lines are slightly steeper. All other relationships shown by the chart remain unchanged. It should be emphasized that the chart can be used only for gases at atmospheric pressure. At other pressures it will be necessary to fall back on the analytical relationships presented earlier in this chapter.

TABLE 7.1

T_{db}, °F	T_{wb}, °F	H	% Sat'n	Dew Pt, °F
100	75	0.021	30	65
95	84	0.036	60	80
131	125	0.148	80	124
75	63	0.015	50	55
187	130	0.151	10	125
165	105	0.057	10	94
174	135	0.190	24	132
143	117	0.108	40	114
86	81	0.035	80	79

EXAMPLE 7.17. Starting with the underlined figures in each line of Table 7.1, use the psychrometric chart in Appendix C-7 to confirm the other values given on the same line in the table.

EXAMPLE 7.18. Use the psychrometric chart in Appendix C-7 to determine the vapor pressure of water at 108°F.

Solution. At saturation, $p^* = p = yP$. At 108°F and 100 per cent saturation, the chart shows $H = H^* = 0.09$ mols of water vapor per mol of dry air. The corresponding mol fraction is accordingly $0.090/1.090 = 0.083$, from which

$$p^* = yP = (.083)(14.7) = 1.22 \text{ psia}$$

(The Steam Tables indicate a vapor pressure of 1.20 psia at 108°F.)

EXAMPLE 7.19. A mixture of water vapor and air is 20 per cent saturated at 159°F. Determine the final temperature, humidity, dew point, etc., if the saturation is increased to 70 per cent by (a) cooling at constant pressure; (b) adiabatic saturation at constant pressure; (c) isothermal compression.

Solution. (a) Follow a line of constant $H = H_1 = 0.092$ to 70 per cent saturation. At this point, $T_{db} = 120°F$, $T_{wb} = 110.5°F$, and the dew point is 109°F.

(b) Follow a line of constant wet-bulb temperature (identical to adiabatic cooling line for air-water system) from given initial conditions to the final saturation. For $T_{wb} = 115°F$, the final conditions are $T_{db} = 125°F$, dew point 114°F, and $H = 0.107$ mols/mol.

(c) Since the pressure will change, the atmospheric-pressure chart can be used only to find the initial (and final) humidity of 0.092 mols per mol and, if desired, to determine the vapor pressure at 159°F as illustrated in Ex. 7.18. Thereafter the pertinent calculations, to be confirmed by the student, are as follows:

$$H^* = \frac{0.092}{.70} = 0.131$$

$$y^* = \frac{0.131}{1.131} = 0.116$$

$$p^* = 4.63 \text{ psia at } 159°F$$

$$P = \frac{p^*}{y^*} = \frac{4.63}{.116} = 40.0 \text{ psia}$$

$$p = yP = \frac{0.092}{1.092} (40.0) = 3.37 \text{ psia}$$

The dew point is the temperature at which $p^* = p = 3.37$ psia, and is found to be 146°F. The determination of the wet-bulb temperature would require the use of Eq. (7.31).

```
32  —   0 8071
40  —   0 7948
50      0 7786
        0 7090
100     0 6997
        0 6509
150
        0 6056
200
```

$$28.94 \;\tfrac{\#}{mole}$$
$$\overline{\qquad\qquad\qquad}$$
$$0 6137 \;\tfrac{\#}{ft^3}$$

$$\underline{187}$$

$$\rho_T = \rho_V + \rho_A$$

EXTENSIVE PROPERTIES OF MIXTURES

7.7 Volume

If two or more components form an *ideal solution*, the sum of the component volumes will equal the volume of the mixture, since such behavior is the basis for the definition of an ideal solution. Ideal gases always form ideal solutions and, as has been noted previously, even non-ideal gases tend to form ideal solutions. The volume of a gaseous mixture might therefore be closely approximated by simply adding up the volumes of the pure components as determined through the use of separate compressibility factors.

EXAMPLE 7.20. Estimate the specific volume of air at 50 atm and $-150°F$.

Solution. From Appendix C-5, $P_c = 33.5$ atm and $T_c = 126°K$ for nitrogen, and $P_c = 50.1$ atm and $T_c = 155°K$ for oxygen. For nitrogen, then,

$$P_r = \frac{50}{33.5} = 1.49; \qquad T_r = \frac{310}{(1.8)(126)} = 1.37$$

From Appendix C-6, $Z \cong 0.81$ and

$$\underline{V} = \frac{ZRT}{P} = \frac{(.81)(.73)(310)}{50} = 3.67 \text{ ft}^3/\text{lb-mol}$$

Similarly, for oxygen

$$P_r = \frac{50}{50.1} = 1.00; \qquad T_r = \frac{310}{(1.8)(155)} = 1.11; \qquad Z \cong 0.71$$

$$\underline{V} = \frac{ZRT}{P} = \frac{(.71)(.73)(310)}{50} = 3.21 \text{ ft}^3/\text{lb-mol}$$

Assuming additive volumes, the specific volume of air at the given conditions is therefore

$$(.79)(3.67) + (.21)(3.21) = 2.90 + 0.67$$
$$= 3.57 \text{ ft}^3/\text{lb-mol}$$

An alternative procedure for determining the volume of gaseous mixtures involves the use of *pseudo-critical* properties, defined by the relationships

$$P_{sc} = (yP_c)_A + (yP_c)_B + \ldots \tag{7.32}$$
$$T_{sc} = (yT_c)_A + (yT_c)_B + \ldots \tag{7.33}$$

where y is the mol fraction of the component, P_c and T_c are its critical properties, and the subscripts $A, B, \ldots$, denote the various components. In other words, the pseudo-critical properties of a mixture are simply the molal average critical properties.

The pseudo-critical properties can be used to obtain a single reduced pressure and reduced temperature for the mixture in the same way that these properties are determined for pure substances. A single value of Z may then be obtained from the compressibility factor plot and substituted into the equation of state to obtain the desired volume.

EXAMPLE 7.21. Repeat the Ex. 7.20 using the concept of pseudo-critical properties.

Solution. Following the procedure outlined above,

$$P_{sc} = (.79)(33.5) + (.21)(50.1) = 37.0 \text{ atm}$$

$$T_{sc} = (.79)(126) + (.21)(155) = 132°\text{K}$$

$$P_r = \frac{50}{37} = 1.35; \qquad T_r = \frac{310}{(1.8)(132)} = 1.30; \qquad Z \cong 0.79$$

$$\underline{V} = \frac{ZRT}{P} = \frac{(.79)(.73)(310)}{50} = 3.58 \text{ ft}^3/\text{lb-mol}$$

It can be seen that the two methods give answers which are in good agreement. Thermodynamically speaking, the use of pseudo-critical properties is preferable to the assumption of additive volumes. Unfortunately, there is no corresponding generalized procedure for liquids. Experimental data will therefore be required for all cases in which the liquid mixture is not ideal, with the assumption of ideality being a last resort when experimental data are not available.

7.8 Energy

If the overall energy balance presented in Sec. 2.4 is written for the steady-state mixing of two components to form a mixture or solution, it reduces to

$$H_i - H_o + Q - W = 0 \tag{7.34}$$

or
$$(M_A \underline{H}_A + M_B \underline{H}_B) - M_S \underline{H}_S + Q - W = 0 \tag{7.35}$$

in which A and B refer to the components being mixed and S denotes the final mixture. Obviously $M_S = M_A + M_B$; and in most mixing applications W will be negligible in comparison with the other terms even if the mixing process is accompanied by agitation. The reduced energy balance applicable to most mixing problems is therefore

$$(M_A + M_B)\underline{H}_S - (M_A \underline{H}_A + M_B \underline{H}_B) = Q \tag{7.36}*$$

This relationship has two significant consequences. First, the enthalpy of the final mixture depends on the reference states used for both A and B, since $\underline{H}_A$ and $\underline{H}_B$ will be relative values. Thus the specification of the enthalpy

---

* For batch mixing, the equivalent of Eq. (7.36) involves internal energies rather than enthalpies. In most practical applications $\Delta(PV)$ is small and can safely be neglected, in which case $\Delta H = \Delta U$. Thus Eq. (7.36) is commonly applied to both batch and steady-state mixing processes.

of a mixture will always require the identification of as many reference states as there are components in the mixture.

Second, $\underline{H}_S$ for any given mixture depends on Q, the *heat of solution*, as well as on the reference states used for the pure components of the mixture. This dependence correctly implies that experimental data must be available if Eq. (7.36) is to be put to practical use. The usual practice is to determine experimental values of Q as a function of solution composition for a single set of experimental conditions. Heat capacity data plus the concept of paths of convenience developed in Chap. 6 then permit the calculation of Q or $\underline{H}_S$ for any other conditions of interest.

Isothermal heat of solution. One popular method of presenting the necessary experimental data is that used in Fig. 7.3, in which heat of solution

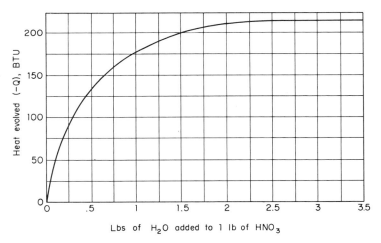

Lbs of H_2O added to 1 lb of HNO_3

Fig. 7.3   Isothermal heat of solution for aqueous nitric acid at 18°C. Plotted from data in *International Critical Tables* (New York: McGraw-Hill Book Company, Inc., 1926), **V**.

is plotted as a function of the quantity of water added to one pound of nitric acid. The caption under the figure calls attention to a most important restriction: The data are directly applicable only to processes in which water at 18°C is mixed with HNO_3 at 18°C to obtain a solution which is also at 18°C. Appropriate techniques for solving non-isothermal mixing problems will be presented in due course.

To demonstrate the utility of Fig. 7.3, let us first write Eq. (7.36) for the particular case of mixing water with one pound of HNO_3. Using the subscripts w and a to denote water and acid, respectively,

$$(1 + M_w)\underline{H}_S - (1)\underline{H}_a - M_w\underline{H}_w = Q \qquad (7.37)$$

Since we expect to obtain Q from Fig. 7.3, $\underline{H}_a$ and $\underline{H}_w$ must be the enthalpies of pure HNO_3 and pure water at 18°C, and $\underline{H}_S$ will be the enthalpy of the final solution at 18°C. Note, however, that Q is independent of the choice of reference states; hence any desired reference states may be selected. By far the most convenient choice is to specify reference states of pure water at 18°C and pure HNO_3 at 18°C so that $\underline{H}_a = \underline{H}_w = 0$. Eq. (7.37) then reduces to

$$(1 + M_w)\underline{H}_S = Q \qquad (7.38)$$

With Q given as a function of M_w by Fig. 7.3, $\underline{H}_S$ may be calculated for any desired concentration.

EXAMPLE 7.22. Calculate the specific enthalpy of a 40 per cent nitric acid solution at 18°C referred to pure HNO_3 at 18°C and pure water at (a) 18°C; (b) 0°C.

Solution. The given weight per cent must first be converted to a weight ratio to permit the use of Fig. 7.3:

$$\frac{.60}{.40} = 1.5 \text{ lbs } H_2O \text{ per (1) lb } HNO_3$$

Then, from Fig. 7.3, 200 BTU are evolved when 1.5 lbs of water and 1 lb of HNO_3 are mixed isothermally at 18°C. Using Eq. (7.38) for part (a) with $Q = -200$ and $M_w = 1.5$, it can be seen that $\underline{H}_S = -200/2.5 = -80$ BTU/lb, the desired answer.

For part (b), the reference state techniques described in Sec. 6.11 may be used to evaluate $\underline{H}_w$ for pure water at 18°C referred to pure water at 0°C,

$$\underline{H}_w = \underline{H}_{18°C} - \underline{H}_{0°C} = \int_0^{18} C_p dT$$
$$= (1)(18 - 0) = 18 \text{ cal/gm, } \times 1.8 = 32.4 \text{ BTU/lb}$$

Substituting in Eq. (7.37) this time, with $\underline{H}_a = 0$ as before,

$$(1 + 1.5)\underline{H}_S - (1.5)(32.4) = -200$$

from which $\underline{H}_S = -60.6$ BTU/lb.

The foregoing example should make it clear that data such as that presented in Fig. 7.3 make it possible to determine the enthalpy, at 18°C, of a solution of any concentration of interest referred to any desired reference states. Enthalpies so determined may then be used in Eq. (7.36) to obtain the heat of solution for *any* mixing process carried out isothermally at 18°C as the following example illustrates.

EXAMPLE 7.23. How much heat will be evolved when 100 lbs of a 75 per cent nitric acid solution at 18°C are mixed isothermally with 125 lbs of a 12 per cent solution?

Solution. In this case the subscripts A and B in Eq. (7.36) refer to 75 per cent acid and 12 per cent acid, since these are the "components" being mixed. The pertinent enthalpies are calculated by the procedure illustrated in Ex. 7.22: For 0.333 lbs of water per lb of HNO_3 in the 75 per cent solution, $Q \cong -110$ BTU from Fig. 7.3 and Eq. (7.38) yields $\underline{H}_{75\%} = -110/1.333 = -82.5$ BTU/lb. A similar calculation, to be confirmed by the student, yields $\underline{H}_{12\%} \cong -25.8$ BTU/lb.

Next, since Eq. (7.36) is to be solved for Q, $\underline{H}_S$, the enthalpy of the final solution, must also be evaluated. A simple mass-balance calculation is necessary to determine the concentration of the final solution:

Total mass balance: $100 + 125 = 225$ lbs final solution

HNO_3 balance: $(.75)(100) + (.12)(125) = 90$ lbs HNO_3 in final solution

$$\frac{90}{225}(100) = 40\% \ HNO_3 \text{ in final solution}$$

The enthalpy of a 40 per cent solution at 18°C was found to be -80 BTU/lb in Ex. 7.22. Note that all enthalpies have been referred to the same reference states of pure HNO_3 and pure water at 18°C. The use of the same reference states throughout a given problem is essential.

Substituting the pertinent masses and enthalpies into Eq. (7.36),

$$(100 + 125)(-80) - (100)(-82.5) - (125)(-25.8) = Q$$
$$-Q = 18,000 - 8,250 - 3,220 = 6,530 \text{ BTU evolved}$$

Effect of temperature. It is significant that Eq. (7.36) is restricted to isothermal mixing at 18°C only when a value of Q obtained from Fig. 7.3 is to be substituted into it. Otherwise, the equation is generally applicable to mixing at any temperature or combination of temperatures provided the pertinent enthalpies are properly evaluated.

EXAMPLE 7.24 Repeat Ex. 7.23 for the case of 75 per cent acid at 40°C being mixed with 12 per cent acid at 18°C to obtain a final solution at 18°C. $C_p = 0.6$ BTU/(lb)(F°) for 75 per cent nitric acid.

Solution. The solution is the same as that to Ex. 7.23 except that $\underline{H}_{75\%}$ must be evaluated at 40°C instead of 18°C. In the completely general case, the evaluation of $\underline{H}$ at 18°C is prerequisite to its evaluation at any other temperature, since heat-of-solution data must be obtained from Fig. 7.3. Here, $\underline{H}$ at 18°C is already known to be -82.5 BTU/lb and, using the given C_p data,

$$\underline{H}_{40°C} = \underline{H}_{18°C} + \int_{18}^{40} C_p dT$$
$$= -82.5 + (1.8)(0.6)(40 - 18) = -58.7 \text{ BTU/lb}$$

Substitution of this value, together with the values obtained previously for the other enthalpies, into Eq. (7.36) yields $-Q = 8,910$ BTU evolved.

An alternative approach to non-isothermal mixing problems utilizes the path-of-convenience concept: The components to be mixed may be heated or cooled to 18°C, mixed isothermally, and the resulting mixture then heated or cooled to the desired final temperature. Summing up the ΔH's calculated for each separate step will yield the overall enthalpy change which is equal to Q for the given non-isothermal process.

Applying this technique to Ex. 7.24, the heat evolved when 100 lbs of 75 per cent acid are cooled from 40°C to 18°C will be

$$-Q = -\Delta H = -M \int_{40}^{18} C_p dT$$
$$= -(100)(1.8)(0.6)(18 - 40) = 2380 \text{ BTU}$$

The additional heat which will be evolved when mixing takes place isothermally at 18°C has already been determined to be 6,530 BTU in Ex. 7.23. The total heat evolved will therefore be $6,530 + 2380 = 8,910$ BTU, the same answer as was obtained by the original method.

The H-x diagram. The fact that Fig. 7.3 or its equivalent for other systems makes it necessary to calculate enthalpies for each concentration of interest suggests making the calculations once and for all and preparing an auxiliary plot of specific enthalpy vs. concentration. The resulting enthalpy-composition, or H-x, diagram is the second popular method of presenting heat-of-solution data. The availability of heat capacity data makes it possible to include isotherms for temperatures other than 18°C on the same diagram, and a typical H-x diagram is shown in Fig. 7.4.

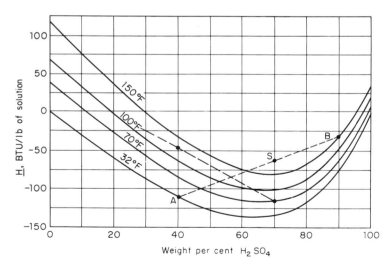

Fig. 7.4 Enthalpy-concentration diagram for aqueous sulfuric acid. ($\underline{H}$ referred to pure liquid H_2SO_4 and pure liquid water at 32°F.)

Specific enthalpies for use in Eq. (7.36) may be read directly from such a diagram whether the mixing is isothermal or not, and the equation may then be solved for Q. Alternately, if Q is specified, the equation may be solved for $\underline{H}_A$, $\underline{H}_B$, or $\underline{H}_S$ and the corresponding temperature obtained from Fig. 7.4.

Unlike Fig. 7.3, which does not depend on reference states, Fig. 7.4 is based on the particular reference states noted in the caption. As was pointed out in Chap. 6, these same reference states should be used consistently whenever use is made of enthalpy values obtained from the figure. This observation applies to H-x diagrams in general.

EXAMPLE 7.25. 70 per cent sufuric acid is to be produced by mixing 40 per cent acid at 32°F with 90 per cent acid at 150°F. If the final solution is to be at 100°F, how many BTU must be removed per pound of 70 per cent acid produced?

Solution. From Fig. 7.4, $\underline{H}_{40\%} = -110$ BTU/lb at 32°F, $\underline{H}_{90\%} = -32$ BTU/lb at 150°F, and $\underline{H}_{70\%} = -102$ BTU/lb at 100°F. For a basis of one pound of 70 per cent acid, the necessary quantities of 40 and 90 per cent acid may be calculated by applying the pertinent mass balances:

Total mass balance: $M_{40\%} + M_{90\%} = 1$

H$_2$SO$_4$ balance: $(.40)(M_{40\%}) + (.90)(M_{90\%}) = .70$

Simultaneous solution of these two equations yields $M_{40\%} = 0.40$ and $M_{90\%} = 0.60$. Substituting in Eq. (7.33),

$$(1)(-102) - (.4)(-110) - (.6)(-32) = Q$$

from which $Q = -38.8$ BTU/lb of 70 per cent acid produced.

Graphical methods. It was noted in Chap. 4 that graphical solutions would be possible in many types of chemical engineering problems, and mixing problems are particularly amenable to graphical techniques when an H-x diagram is available. Consider the straight line A-S-B in Fig. 7.4, and let the coordinates of these three points be denoted by $(x_A, \underline{H}_A)$, $(x_S, \underline{H}_S)$, and $(x_B, \underline{H}_B)$, respectively. From the concept of similar triangles,

$$\frac{\overline{BS}}{\overline{SA}} = \frac{x_B - x_S}{x_S - x_A} = \frac{\underline{H}_B - \underline{H}_S}{\underline{H}_S - \underline{H}_A} \tag{7.39}$$

Now let the solution represented by point A be mixed with that represented by point B, and let the quantities mixed and the final temperature be such that the resulting mixture is represented by the point S. The pertinent mass balance for the H$_2$SO$_4$ involved in the process is

$$M_A x_A + M_B x_B = (M_A + M_B)x_S = M_A x_S + M_B x_S$$

and rearrangement yields

$$M_A(x_S - x_A) = M_B(x_B - x_S)$$

or

$$\frac{M_A}{M_B} = \frac{x_B - x_S}{x_S - x_A} \tag{7.40}$$

A comparison of Eqs. (7.39) and (7.40) shows the inverse-lever-arm principle to be applicable to the line A-S-B, since $M_A/M_B = \overline{BS}/\overline{SA}$. Further, it can be seen that the scale of either the ordinate or the abscissa may be used to represent the pertinent line lengths.

The comparison also yields

$$\frac{M_A}{M_B} = \frac{\underline{H}_B - \underline{H}_S}{\underline{H}_S - \underline{H}_A}$$

and this equality may be rearranged to obtain

$$(M_A + M_B)\underline{H}_S - (M_A\underline{H}_A + M_B\underline{H}_B) = 0 \qquad (7.41)$$

Eq. (7.41), it can be seen, is the same as Eq. (7.36) written for the special case of adiabatic mixing. In other words, when point S lies on a straight line connecting points A and B, it represents the result of adiabatic mixing.

The foregoing relationships provide the basis for a simple graphical procedure for solving mixing problems. Any two of the three points A, S, and B will establish a straight line upon which the third point must lie if the mixing is adiabatic, and the exact location of the third point can be determined by application of the inverse-lever-arm principle. If the actual mixing process is *not* adiabatic, a path of convenience involving adiabatic mixing plus heating or cooling of either A, B, or S may be utilized. The following example illustrates this technique.

EXAMPLE 7.26. 400 lbs of 40 per cent sulfuric acid at 125°F are to be prepared by diluting 100 lbs of 70 per cent acid at 70°F with a weak acid. (a) What weak acid concentration should be used? (b) At what temperature should the weak acid be fed to the mixer if the mixing process is to be adiabatic? (c) Calculate the heat of mixing if the weak acid enters the mixer at 70°F.

Solution. Locate the 70 per cent acid on the 70°F isotherm and the 40 per cent acid on the 125°F isotherm (interpolated) and draw a straight line through the two points. (See Fig. 7.4.) For adiabatic mixing, the weak acid must lie on an extension of the line. A mass balance shows 300 lbs of weak acid to be required, and this quantity corresponds to the line segment between 0.70 and 0.40. The line segment corresponding to the 100 lbs of strong acid must be one-third as long and will therefore extend from 0.40 to 0.30. Hence the concentration of the weak acid should be 30 per cent. The corresponding enthalpy is -25 BTU/lb and the interpolated temperature approximately 115°F. This is the temperature at which the weak acid must be fed if the mixing process is to be adiabatic.

For the non-adiabatic case, let adiabatic mixing follow pre-heating of the weak acid from 70°F ($H = -56$ BTU/lb) to 115°F, this being a path of convenience. For the pre-heating,

$$Q = \Delta H = H_2 - H_1 = 300[-25 - (-56)] = 9300 \text{ BTU}$$

Since $Q = 0$ for the subsequent adiabatic mixing, the total heat of mixing for the equivalent non-adiabatic process is also $+9300$ BTU (absorbed).

Heat of solution data are available for most of the systems of interest to chemical engineers. If the student understands the principles which have been presented in this section, he should have no trouble interpreting such data and putting them to practical use.

7.9 Entropy

Since mixing is inherently an irreversible process, it must be characterized by an increase in entropy. The procedure for calculating the entropy change involves setting up a completely reversible path connecting the given end states and then evaluating the entropy change from an application of the fact that $\int T dS = Q$ for a reversible process. The details of this procedure are left to subsequent study of thermodynamics.

7.10 Conclusion

Complete familiarity with the various methods for specifying the composition of multi-component mixtures and for converting from one basis to another is an essential attribute of the chemical engineer. It is for this reason that the topic has been given detailed attention, and the problems which the student will encounter in the future will be much less difficult if these basic principles have been mastered.

The relationships pertaining to energy effects are somewhat more specialized but no less important. It is significant that they evolve directly from the general mass and energy balance equations, and any difficulty in assimilating them can probably be traced to an inadequate grasp of these two fundamental principles.

The graphical procedures presented towards the end of the chapter may appear to be even more specialized, and it must be admitted that the corresponding analytical calculations are not overly laborious. When more comprehensive problems are presented in Chap. 13, however, it will quickly become apparent that graphical methods provide an effective means of avoiding the drudgery of many repetitive calculations.

REVIEW, STUDY, AND DISCUSSION

7-1. Define per cent as used in gas analyses, per cent as used in liquid and solid analyses, partial pressure, pressure fraction, ppm, dry-basis analysis, molecular weight of a mixture, dew point, bubble point, saturated liquid, saturated vapor, binary system, equilibrium constant, relative volatility, ideal solution, partial molal volume, activity coefficient, non-condensible component, relative saturation, per cent saturation, humidity, wet-bulb temperature, dry-bulb temperature, adiabatic cooling, pseudo-critical properties, heat of solution, isothermal heat of solution, adiabatic mixing.

7-2. State the relationship among mol, pressure, and volume per cent; the composition of dry air; the relationships between analyses on a wet and dry basis; Raoult's law; Henry's law.

7-3. Two mols of carbon dioxide and 10 lbs of oxygen are added to 2000 SCF of nitrogen.

a) Calculate the analysis of the resulting mixture in mol per cent, weight per cent, and volume per cent. Ideal gas behavior may be assumed.

b) Calculate the mol and weight ratios for $N_2:O_2$, $CO_2:N_2$, and $(O_2 + CO_2):N_2$. What is the analysis of the mixture on a CO_2-free basis?

c) How many mols of "air" might be removed from the mixture?

d) Calculate the analysis of the mixture on an air-free basis.

e) Calculate the molecular weight of the mixture.

f) Calculate the density of the mixture at standard conditions and at 20 psia and 150°F.

g) Another mixture of the same composition contains 300 lbs of CO_2. How many mols of mixture are present? How many pounds? How many standard cubic feet?

h) A third mixture of the same composition contains 8 mols of oxygen. How many mols of CO_2 are present?

i) Nitrogen is to be removed from the original mixture until the weight fraction of oxygen is twice its original value. How many pounds of nitrogen must be removed? What will be the percentage composition of the final mixture?

7-4. a) A fuel is to be burned with air containing 2 per cent moisture. If 2 mols of oxygen are supplied per mol of fuel burned, how many mols of nitrogen will also be supplied? How many mols of water vapor?

b) If the stack gas leaving the furnace contains one mol of CO_2, 0.5 mols of O_2, 2.243 mols of H_2O, and 9.4 mols of N_2, what is the percentage analysis of the gas?

c) How many mols of H_2O are present per mol of dry gas?

d) What is the analysis of the gas on a dry basis?

e) What is the analysis of the gas in weight per cent?

f) What is the molecular weight of the gas?

7-5. Refer to Fig. 7.1. A superheated vapor mixture analyzing 25 per cent A and 75 per cent B by weight is to be cooled and condensed. Assume the molecular weight of A to be 50 and that of B to be 30.

a) What is the bubble point of the mixture? The dew point?

b) At what temperature in the two-phase region should the liquid and vapor be separated so as to obtain a liquid containing the maximum possible concentration of A? A liquid analyzing 36 per cent A?

c) What are the equilibrium phase compositions at 325°? What fraction of the original vapor is condensed at this temperature?

d) At what temperature will condensation be 75 per cent complete? What are the equilibrium phase compositions at this temperature? How many pounds of A, per 100 pounds of original mixture, will be present in the liquid phase?

e) When condensation is 50 per cent complete, the two phases are separated and the pure liquid phase is then heated until it is 50 per cent vaporized. What will be the composition of the residual liquid? How many pounds of this liquid can be obtained from each pound of the original 75-25 mixture?

f) Describe a method for obtaining a liquid analyzing 10 per cent A from a vapor analyzing 90 per cent A. Indicate pertinent temperatures and the approximate yield of liquid per pound of vapor processed.

7-6. Refer to Fig. 7.1. Calculate the equilibrium constant for component A and the relative volatility of the A-B system at 400°. Use the molecular weights given in Prob. 7-5.

7-7. Assuming Raoult's law to be applicable and that Fig. 7.1 applies at a pressure of 18 psia, calculate the vapor pressure of A at 500°.

7-8. Assuming Raoult's law to be applicable, calculate the equilibrium phase compositions for a mixture of ethane and propane at 5 atm pressure and $-32°C$. If a vapor mixture analyzing 60 per cent ethane is compressed isothermally at $-32°C$, at what pressure will the first drop of liquid form?

7-9. At 10°C and atmospheric pressure, the solubility of CO_2 in water is 0.2318 gms per 100 gms of water, and the vapor pressure of CO_2 is 653.6 psia. Calculate the composition of the CO_2-H_2O vapor in equilibrium with a saturated liquid solution at 10°C, (a) assuming Raoult's law to be applicable to the CO_2; (b) assuming Raoult's law to be applicable to the water. Is the liquid an ideal solution? What is the value of the Henry's law constant for CO_2 under the given conditions?

7-10. A mixture of acetone and air at 173.5°F and 17 psia has a dew point of 83°F. Calculate the percentage analysis of the mixture.

7-11. Calculate the relative saturation and the per cent saturation of the mixture of Prob. 7-10.

7-12. Air at 150°F and 25 psia is 50 per cent saturated with water vapor. Calculate the per cent relative humidity and the dew point of the mixture.

7-13. Use Eqs. (7.21) and (7.23) to prove that per cent saturation can never be greater than per cent relative saturation for any given mixture. Under what conditions are the two percentages equal?

7-14. Air at 120°F and atmospheric pressure is 90 per cent saturated with water vapor. We propose to reduce the humidity by cooling to condense out most of the water and then reheat the air to 120°F. The available refrigeration will permit cooling to 50°F. Use analytical relationships to determine

a) the temperature at which condensation will begin.

b) the temperature to which the air should be cooled to obtain a final humidity (at 120°F) of 40 per cent.

c) the minimum relative humidity obtainable with the proposed process.

d) the quantity of water (mols per mol of dry air) which would be removed for the conditions of part (c).

7-15. Repeat Prob. 7-14 using the psychrometric chart in the Appendix.

7-16. Air is to be humidified in a wetted-wall column in which the air flows up the center of the column while a film of water flows down the inside wall. The air is initially at 60°F and atmospheric pressure, and has a wet-bulb temperature of 50°F. The inlet water temperature will be 65°F. To what temperature should the air be preheated before it enters the column if the water temperature is to be held constant throughout the column?

7-17. Air at 90°F and atmospheric pressure has a dew point of 49°F. It is to be processed to obtain 90 per cent humidity and a dry-bulb temperature of 80°F. Specify a suitable sequence of process steps if the humidification step is to be carried out adiabatically. Indicate pertinent temperatures and humidities.

7-18. How many pounds of a gaseous mixture analyzing 40 per cent ethane and 60 per cent ethylene can be stored in a 1000-cubic-foot tank at 60 atm and 80°F?

7-19. Repeat Prob. 7-18 using an alternative method.

7-20. How much heat will be evolved when 480 lbs of 75 per cent HNO_3 are mixed with 1300 lbs of 10 per cent HNO_3, (a) if mixing is isothermal at 18°C? (b) if the 75 per cent acid is at 100°F, the 10 per cent acid at 150°F, and the final mixture is to be at 18°C? $C_p = 0.6$ BTU/(lb)(F°) for 75 per cent acid, and 0.905 for 10 per cent acid.

7-21. Repeat Prob. 7-20 for H_2SO_4 using Fig. 7.4 only to obtain the pertinent enthalpy data. To what temperature should the 10 per cent acid be pre-cooled so that it might be mixed adiabatically with 75 per cent acid at 70°F to yield a final mixture at 100°F?

7-22. Solve Prob. 7-21 graphically.

CHAPTER 8

Property Changes in Chemical Reactions

The most obvious consequence of a chemical reaction is a change in composition. In general this will not be the only consequence, for a chemical reaction may also result in a change of temperature, pressure, volume, phase, or form of energy. Any one of these changes may be of primary interest in a given application, but the others can never be completely ignored. The interrelationships among these properties are accordingly pertinent and will be treated in this chapter.

8.1 Change of Composition

The qualitative application of the mass balance to chemical reactions was treated briefly in Chap. 2. The concepts presented in the intervening chapters have paved the way for quantitative calculations.

Consider the typical combustion reaction

$$2\,C_2H_6 + xO_2 \rightarrow yCO_2 + zH_2O$$

The balancing of this reaction involves the direct, quantitative application of the mass-balance principle to chemical change. The fact that the carbon, hydrogen, and oxygen must all balance is a direct consequence of the law of conservation of mass; that is, the mass balance must be satisfied for each of these elements individually. Thus the presence of 4 mols of carbon on the left-hand side of the reaction calls for 4 mols on the right, and it immediately follows that $y = 4$. Similarly, a hydrogen balance yields $z = 6$, and, with the oxygen on the right-hand side now known to be 7 mols, it follows that $x = 7$. The balanced reaction is thus

$$2 \ C_2H_6 + 7 \ O_2 \rightarrow 4 \ CO_2 + 6 \ H_2O \qquad (8.1)$$

The reaction coefficients clearly denote *mol* quantities. It follows that an early step in the solution of any problem involving chemical reaction should be the conversion of given quantities into mol units. The continued use of such units throughout the solution is also indicated, with the conversion to mass or volume being made only when it becomes absolutely necessary. A significant advantage of this procedure is the fact that mol units are readily converted to either volume or mass, and their use therefore provides considerable flexibility.

There is one consequence of the use of mol units which should be kept in mind. Eq. (8.1) correctly shows 9 mols of reactants to be converted to 10 mols of products, and it must be concluded that total mols need not be conserved. Total mass *is* conserved, however, and mass units must accordingly be used whenever a total-mass balance is pertinent.

It is noteworthy that the above reaction is also balanced if written

$$4 \ C_2H_6 + 14 \ O_2 \rightarrow 8 \ CO_2 + 12 \ H_2O$$

or even

$$C_2H_6 + \tfrac{7}{2} \ O_2 \rightarrow 2 \ CO_2 + 3 \ H_2O \qquad (8.2)$$

In other words, a balanced chemical reaction tells us nothing whatsoever about the *absolute* quantities of reactants and products, but only fixes *relative* quantities. For example, the 7 in Eq. (8.1) is not simply mols of oxygen but rather mols of oxygen per 2 mols of ethane (or per 4 mols of carbon dioxide formed, etc.). This ratio obviously reduces to $\tfrac{7}{2}$ mols of oxygen per (1) mol of ethane. The latter ratio justifies the form of Eq. (8.2), even though the purist might insist that only integers can be used as coefficients in chemical reactions.

EXAMPLE 8.1. Calculate the quantity and composition of the product mixture resulting from the combustion of 165 lbs of ethane in accordance with Eq. (8.2).

Solution. The molecular weight of ethane is 30, and $165/30 = 5.5$ mols of ethane to be burned. Using coefficient ratios from Eq. (8.2),

$$(5.5)(2) = 11.0 \text{ mols } CO_2 \text{ produced}$$

$$(5.5)(3) = 16.5 \text{ mols } H_2O \text{ produced}$$

$$[\text{Also, } (5.5)(3.5) = 19.25 \text{ mols } O_2 \text{ consumed}]$$

The total quantity of product mixture is 27.5 mols, and this figure may be converted to pounds or cubic feet if desired. The composition of the mixture will be found to be 40 per cent CO_2 and 60 per cent H_2O, assuming all of the water produced remains in the vapor state.

Coefficient ratios are not the only ratios indicated by a balanced chemical reaction. In complex problems it may be advantageous to utilize *internal* ratios such as one mol of carbon per mol of CO_2, $\frac{1}{2}$ mol of oxygen per mol of H_2O, or 3 mols of hydrogen per mol of ethane. The validity of such ratios should be obvious, and the following example illustrates their utility.

EXAMPLE 8.2. Carbon is to be burned with a limited quantity of oxygen to produce a product mixture containing CO and CO_2 in a mol ratio of 7:1. How much oxygen will be required for each 20 mols of carbon burned?

Solution. The normal first step would be to write and balance the pertinent chemical reaction, but no less than four are possible in this case:

$$C + \tfrac{1}{2} O_2 \rightarrow CO; \qquad CO + \tfrac{1}{2} O_2 \rightarrow CO_2;$$
$$C + O_2 \rightarrow CO_2; \qquad CO_2 + C \rightarrow 2\,CO$$

The dilemma can be sidestepped by recognizing the significance of the internal ratios 1 mol of carbon per mol of CO and 1 mol of carbon per mol of CO_2: Each mol of CO and each mol of CO_2 contains one mol of carbon, regardless of how it is formed. If carbon is to be conserved, it follows that the combustion of 20 mols of carbon must yield 20 mols of $(CO + CO_2)$. Since these two components are to be produced in a ratio of 7:1, the product mixture must be $\frac{7}{8}$ CO and $\frac{1}{8}$ CO_2. Thus $(20)(\frac{1}{8}) = 2.5$ mols of CO_2 must be produced, leaving $20 - 2.5 = 17.5$ mols of CO. The internal ratios of 1 mol of O_2 per mol of CO_2 and $\frac{1}{2}$ mol of O_2 per mol of CO now become pertinent, and the total O_2 in the product mixture is $(1)(2.5) + (.5)(17.5) = 11.25$ mols. An oxygen balance shows that this is the quantity of oxygen required for the specified process.

The fact that the completion of the mass balance for chemical processes does not depend on an ability to write specific reaction equations is highly significant. The illustrated technique will be put to frequent use, and complete confidence in the use of internal ratios should be developed as quickly as possible.

Effect of excess reactants. When reactants are made available in the same ratio in which they will react they are said to be supplied in *stoichiometric* proportion, or in the stoichiometric amount. The stoichiometric quantity of any reactant is therefore the quantity which is *theoretically required* for the complete conversion of other reactants.

A reactant supplied in excess of the stoichiometric amount is called an *excess reactant.* Conversely, any reactant not supplied in excess is called a *limiting reactant,* since the reaction cannot proceed beyond the point where such a reactant is completely consumed. When a reactant is supplied in excess, the *percentage excess* is always calculated as a percentage of the theoretical or stoichiometric requirement, not of the amount actually supplied.

The balancing principles discussed previously are readily extended to cover the presence of excess reactants. The balanced reaction equation indicates the stoichiometric quantity, and this may be subtracted from the quantity of reactant actually supplied to determine the excess amount. The excess remains unchanged by the reaction and will be present in the product mixture when the reaction is complete. The pertinent calculations are illustrated in Ex. 8.3.

Effect of inert components. Reactants of 100 per cent purity are the exception rather than the rule when reactions are carried out on an industrial scale. Any non-reacting impurities or *inerts* introduced with the reactants will be present in the product mixture and can be accounted for by a straightforward mass balance.

EXAMPLE 8.3. Propane is to be burned with 25 per cent excess air to form carbon dioxide and water vapor. Calculate the composition of the stack gas leaving the furnace and the quantity of gas (SCF) which will be produced per ton of propane burned.

Solution. The pertinent chemical reaction is

$$C_3H_8 + 5 O_2 \rightarrow 3 CO_2 + 4 H_2O$$

but the product mixture will contain unreacted oxygen and all the nitrogen introduced with the air as well as the indicated products of combustion. A simple block flow diagram such as is shown in Fig. 8.1 is a convenient aid in problem analysis. Note that the air has been broken down to show

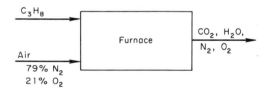

Fig. 8.1   Block flow diagram for Example 8.3.

its elemental constituents and that the qualitative balance has been completed by showing both nitrogen and unused oxygen as components of the stack gas.

The balanced reaction equation shows that each mol of propane burned will require 5 mols of O_2 and will yield 3 mols of CO_2 and 4 mols of H_2O. The air theoretically required will contain 5 mols of oxygen, and 25 per cent excess air will mean 25 per cent excess oxygen. Since per cent excess is a percentage of the theoretical quantity by definition, $(.25)(5) = 1.25$ mols of excess O_2, and the total O_2 supplied in the air is 6.25 mols. Then (6.25) $(79/21) = 23.5$ mols of N_2 must also enter with the air.

A check of the block flow diagram shows that all components in the stack gas have been determined: 3 mols CO_2, 4 mols H_2O, 23.5 mols N_2, and 1.25 mols excess O_2, for a total of 31.75 mols. The corresponding percentage analysis is 9.45% CO_2, 12.6% H_2O, 74.0% N_2, and 3.94% O_2.

Finally, $2000/44 = 45.4$ mols of propane ($MW = 44$) actually burned. Since each mol yields 31.75 mols of stack gas,

$$(45.4)(31.75)(359) = 518,000 \text{ SCF of stack gas}$$

per ton of propane burned. Note that the analysis of the gas is independent of the actual quantity of propane burned.

Effect of incomplete reaction. Equilibrium conditions place an absolute limit on the extent to which any reaction can proceed. Further, since reaction rates approach zero as equilibrium is approached, it is often economically advantageous to sacrifice degree of completion in order to obtain a higher overall reaction rate. As a consequence, reactions which do not go to completion are quite commonly encountered in chemical engineering. Any unconverted reactants must be accounted for in the product mixture, and the calculations parallel those illustrated in Ex. 8.3.

The *percentage conversion* of any reactant is the percentage of that reactant which undergoes reaction. The percentage conversion of a limiting reactant is also called the *degree of completion* of the reaction. In the case of simultaneous reactions, the percentage conversion generally refers to the total conversion of the component, regardless of the reaction or reactions involved or the products to which it is converted. The term *yield* or *percentage yield*, on the other hand, refers to the degree of conversion to a particular product of interest. The terms conversion and yield are often used loosely and should be interpreted with care.

It is possible to include excess reactants, unconverted reactants, and even inert components in an overall, pseudo-chemical reaction. For the reaction considered in Ex. 8.3, the result would be

$$C_3H_8 + 6.25\,O_2 + 23.5\,N_2 \rightarrow 3\,CO_2 + 4\,H_2O + 1.25\,O_2 + 23.5\,N_2$$

While such an equation is wholly consistent with the overall mass balance, there is little to be gained by its use. The coefficients can be obtained only through the calculations presented in Ex. 8.3; once these calculations have been made, an overall reaction equation reveals nothing that is not already known.

Simultaneous and successive reactions. When more than one reaction is involved in a given process, it is frequently advantageous to combine two or more reactions to obtain a single reaction equation which characterizes the entire process. Such combinations should never be effected without careful analysis to insure that specified yields are not being altered.

Suppose two *simultaneous* reactions are encountered when hot carbon is brought into contact with steam:

$$C + H_2O \rightarrow CO + H_2$$
$$C + 2\,H_2O \rightarrow CO_2 + 2\,H_2$$

If these two reactions should be added directly to obtain a single equivalent reaction

$$2\,C + 3\,H_2O \rightarrow CO + CO_2 + 3\,H_2$$

the result indicates that the product mixture will contain equal quantities of CO and CO_2; yet other information may indicate that a $CO:CO_2$ ratio of $9:1$ is to be expected. This is equivalent to stating that 90 per cent of the carbon will enter the first reaction and the remainder the second.

The inconsistency can be resolved by modifying the coefficients of the original reactions *before* they are combined. For the hypothesized $9:1$ ratio, a suitable modification would be

$$9\,C + 9\,H_2O \rightarrow 9\,CO + 9\,H_2$$
$$C + 2\,H_2O \rightarrow CO_2 + 2\,H_2$$

These two reactions *can* be combined to obtain

$$10\,C + 11\,H_2O \rightarrow 9\,CO + CO_2 + 11\,H_2$$

in which the specified $CO:CO_2$ ratio is clearly provided.

Similar care must be exercised when successive reactions are combined. Suppose ammonia is to be synthesized according to the reaction

$$N_2 + 3\,H_2 \rightarrow 2\,NH_3$$

and that all of the ammonia thus formed will subsequently be oxidized to nitric acid:

$$NH_3 + 2\,O_2 \rightarrow HNO_3 + H_2O$$

The two reactions may be combined even though they may occur at different points in the overall process. Doubling the second reaction to permit the cancellation of the NH_3 from both sides of the combination, we obtain

$$N_2 + 3\,H_2 + 4\,O_2 \rightarrow 2\,HNO_3 + 2\,H_2O$$

and this reaction correctly describes the overall process.

Suppose, however, that only 95 per cent of the NH_3 formed in the first reaction will be oxidized in the second. For each two mols of NH_3 formed in the first reaction, then, only 1.9 mols will be oxidized. The two reactions to be combined are therefore

$$N_2 + 3\,H_2 \rightarrow 2\,NH_3$$
$$1.9\,NH_3 + 3.8\,O_2 \rightarrow 1.9\,HNO_3 + 1.9\,H_2O$$

and the resulting combination is

$$N_2 + 3\,H_2 + 3.8\,O_2 \rightarrow .1\,NH_3 + 1.9\,HNO_3 + 1.9\,H_2O$$

In this case, little has been gained by deriving the proper combination since, for all practical purposes, it was necessary to solve the problem before the combination could be effected. It can only be concluded that there is no substitute for the logical analysis of any given problem followed by the step-by-step application of the pertinent mass-balance relationships until the solution is obtained.

8.2 Change of Energy

Consider a chemical reactor operating continuously under steady-state conditions with kinetic energy, potential energy, and work effects either absent or negligible. For the reactor as a system, the general energy balance reduces to

$$Q = H_o - H_i \tag{8.3}$$

in which the subscripts o and i clearly refer to the product and reactant streams, respectively. Q is commonly called the *heat of reaction* in this application.

The corresponding equation for an unsteady-state batch reaction is

$$Q - W = U_2 - U_1 \tag{8.4}$$

in which the W term accounts for any work of expansion. Should the reaction be carried out at constant volume as is frequently the case, W is zero and Eq. (8.4) reduces to

$$Q = U_2 - U_1 \tag{8.5}$$

For reaction at constant pressure, on the other hand,

$$W = \int PdV = P\Delta V = \Delta(PV) = P_2V_2 - P_1V_1$$

Substituting into Eq. (8.4) and rearranging,

$$Q = (U_2 + P_2V_2) - (U_1 + P_1V_1) = H_2 - H_1 \tag{8.6}$$

Since the subscripts 2 and 1 refer to products and reactants, respectively, Eqs. (8.6) and (8.3) are identical. Reaction energy calculations are normally carried out in terms of enthalpy, with pressure-volume products introduced when necessary to obtain Eq. (8.4) or (8.5) as a final step.

The energy effects associated with chemical reactions parallel those associated with mixing in two important respects. First, as is implied by the above equations, the reference states used for the reactants and products are not entirely independent. The reference state for one component, either a reactant or a product, is automatically fixed by the energy balance when reference states have been selected for all other components. Second, the availability of experimental data is prerequisite to the practical application of these equations.

Standard heat of formation. Most heat of reaction data are reported in terms of *standard heats of formation*. By definition, the heat of formation of a compound is the enthalpy change which would result were the compound to be formed from its constituent *elements*. Thus the heat of formation of sodium sulfate is the enthalpy change associated with the reaction

$$2 \, Na + S + 2 \, O_2 \rightarrow Na_2SO_4$$

even though such a reaction might never be carried out in the laboratory. Although it may appear to be unrealistic, this definition facilitates the consistent interpretation of the data and makes it unnecessary to write out the reaction itself when the data are reported.

Since heats of reaction vary with reaction temperature (and to a lesser extent with pressure), it is essential that the conditions to which a given heat of formation applies be clearly understood. Standard heats of formation refer to isothermal reaction at a stated temperature—usually 25°C—and to reactants and products in an agreed upon *standard state*. The usual standard state is the pure (unmixed) element or compound at atmospheric pressure.

EXAMPLE 8.4. The standard heat of formation of liquid sulfuric acid, as reported in the literature, is -193.69 kcal/mol. Interpret this data.

Solution. Were pure hydrogen, pure sulfur, and pure oxygen to react to form pure liquid sulfuric acid, the reaction to be carried out isothermally at 25°C and at a constant pressure of one atmosphere, the reaction would be accompanied by an enthalpy change of -193.69 kilo-calories for each gram-mol of acid formed; or

$$\underline{H}_{H_2SO_4} - (\underline{H}_{H_2} + \underline{H}_S + 2\underline{H}_{O_2}) = -193.69 \text{ kcal/mol} \qquad (8.7)$$

under the conditions specified. A somewhat more common way of expressing the same information is

$$H_2 + S + 2 \, O_2 \rightarrow H_2SO_4; \qquad \Delta H° = -193.69 \text{ kcal/mol} \qquad (8.8)$$

with the superscript degree indicating the pertinence of standard conditions.

Care must be exercised in interpreting the units kcal/mol in Eqs. (8.7) and (8.8) and similar expressions. First, the fact that the energy change is expressed in metric units correctly suggests that gm-mols rather than lb-mols are intended. Second, it can be seen that kcal per mol of acid is not the same as kcal per mol of oxygen. In energy balance expressions such as Eq. (8.7) it is suggested that the units be considered as those applicable to each of the $\underline{H}$'s in the equation; and in the alternative expressions typified by Eq. (8.8) the mol designation be considered to identify only the pertinent mass units associated with the indicated enthalpy change, since the *number* of mols of each material is indicated by the coefficients in the reaction equation.

Standard heats of formation for a number of compounds are tabulated in Appendix C-3a.

Standard heat of reaction. Eq. (8.7) can clearly be multiplied through by any desired positive or negative number, and the entire equation can be added to or subtracted from a similar equation written for another compound. The validity of these operations makes it possible to calculate the standard heat of any reaction if the heats of formation of the reactants and products are known. The technique can best be illustrated by example.

EXAMPLE 8.5. Calculate the standard heat of reaction at 25°C for the reaction

$$FeS_2 + 2\,O_2 \rightarrow Fe + 2\,SO_2$$

given heats of formation of -38.62 and -70.94 kcal/mol for FeS_2 and SO_2, respectively.

Solution. The desired enthalpy change is

$$\Delta H^\circ = \underline{H}_{Fe} + 2\underline{H}_{SO_2} - \underline{H}_{FeS_2} - 2\underline{H}_{O_2}$$

For the formation of FeS_2,

$$\underline{H}_{FeS_2} - \underline{H}_{Fe} - 2\underline{H}_S = -38.62 \text{ kcal/mol}$$

Since 2 mols of SO_2 appear in the given reaction, the corresponding equation for the formation of SO_2 will be multiplied through by 2 to obtain

$$2\underline{H}_{SO_2} - 2\underline{H}_S - 2\underline{H}_{O_2} = -141.88 \text{ kcal/mol}$$

If the equation for FeS_2 is subtracted from this equation, $\underline{H}_S$ will cancel out to yield

$$\underline{H}_{Fe} + 2\underline{H}_{SO_2} - \underline{H}_{FeS_2} - 2\underline{H}_{O_2} = -141.88 - (-38.62) = -103.26 \text{ kcal/mol}$$

which is the desired standard heat of reaction.

An equivalent procedure makes use of the form of Eq. (8.8). The formation equations for the products of the desired reaction are written in the usual manner, but those for the reactants are reversed, with the sign on ΔH° also being reversed. One or more of the equations may be multiplied through by a coefficient as necessary to give the desired reaction when the formation equations are added. Using this technique, the solution to Ex. 8.5 takes the form

$$
\begin{array}{lll}
2\,S + 2\,O_2 \rightarrow 2\,SO_2; & \Delta H^\circ = -141.88 \text{ kcal/mol} \\
FeS_2 \rightarrow Fe + 2\,S; & \Delta H^\circ = +\ 38.62 \text{ kcal/mol} \\
\hline
FeS_2 + 2\,O_2 \rightarrow Fe + 2\,SO_2; & \Delta H^\circ = -103.26 \text{ kcal/mol}
\end{array}
$$

Note that when the two reactions are added, 2 mols of sulfur appear on both sides and may be cancelled.

Standard heat of combustion. Experimental data are sometimes reported in terms of *standard heats of combustion*, that is, reaction with oxygen, rather than as heats of formation. The products of combustion must also be reported if the data are to be meaningful, and it is particularly important to note whether any water formed is in the liquid or vapor state. Otherwise, heat of combustion data are directly analogous to heats of formation. For example, the standard heat of combustion of liquid toluene at 25°C is -934.5 kcal/mol, the products of combustion being CO_2 and $H_2O(l)$. Hence

$$C_6H_5CH_3 + 9\ O_2 \rightarrow 7\ CO_2 + 4\ H_2O(l); \qquad \Delta H° = -934.5 \text{ kcal/mol}$$

or

$$7\underline{H}_{CO_2} + 4\underline{H}_{H_2O(l)} - \underline{H}_{C_6H_5CH_3} - 9\underline{H}_{O_2} = -934.5 \text{ kcal/mol}$$

Other heats of combustion are listed in Appendix C-3b.

It is sometimes necessary to use both heat of formation and heat of combustion data to determine the heat for a specified reaction. The procedures illustrated in Ex. 8.5 are still pertinent although somewhat more complicated. The introduction of the combustion reaction(s) into the calculation may necessitate the arbitrary introduction of formation reactions for CO_2 or H_2O to eliminate these compounds from the final equation.

EXAMPLE 8.6. Toluene is to be nitrated to produce trinitrotoluene (TNT) according to the reaction

$$C_6H_5CH_3 + 3\ HNO_3 \rightarrow C_7H_5(NO_2)_3 + 3\ H_2O(l)$$

Calculate the heat of reaction at 25°C.

Solution. A standard heat of formation of -41.35 kcal/mol for nitric acid may be obtained from the literature, but only heats of combustion are reported for toluene and TNT. Accordingly, the first step in the solution is to write the combustion reactions, using the respective heats of combustion of -934.5 and -821.0 kcal/mol. The reported products of combustion associated with these values are CO_2, N_2, and $H_2O(l)$; hence

$$C_6H_5CH_3 + 9\ O_2 \rightarrow 7\ CO_2 + 4\ H_2O(l); \qquad \Delta H° = -934.5 \text{ kcal/mol}$$

$$\tfrac{3}{2}\ N_2 + \tfrac{5}{2}\ H_2O(l) + 7\ CO_2 \rightarrow C_7H_5(NO_2)_3 + \tfrac{21}{4}\ O_2;$$
$$\Delta H° = +821.0 \text{ kcal/mol}$$

Note that the TNT reaction has been reversed so as to put the TNT on the right side, since it appears on that side in the desired reaction, and that the sign on $\Delta H°$ has been reversed accordingly. Similarly, the formation equation for HNO_3 will be reversed and multiplied through by 3:

$$3\ HNO_3 \rightarrow \tfrac{3}{2}\ H_2 + \tfrac{3}{2}\ N_2 + \tfrac{9}{2}\ O_2; \qquad \Delta H° = +124.05 \text{ kcal/mol}$$

If all three equations are now combined and like terms cancelled, the result will be found to be

$$C_6H_5CH_3 + 3\,HNO_3 \rightarrow C_7H_5(NO_2)_3 + \tfrac{3}{2}\,H_2O(l) + \tfrac{3}{2}\,H_2 + \tfrac{3}{4}\,O_2;$$
$$\Delta H° = +10.55 \text{ kcal/mol}$$

The heat of formation of $H_2O(l)$ may now be introduced arbitrarily to eliminate the unwanted O_2 and H_2 from the above reaction. Using the reported value of -68.32 kcal/mol and multiplying the formation equation through by $\tfrac{3}{2}$,

$$\tfrac{3}{2}\,H_2 + \tfrac{3}{4}\,O_2 \rightarrow \tfrac{3}{2}\,H_2O(l); \qquad \Delta H° = -102.48 \text{ kcal/mol}$$

When this equation is added to the previous equation and like terms are cancelled, the result is

$$C_6H_5CH_3 + 3\,HNO_3 \rightarrow C_7H_5(NO_2)_3 + 3\,H_2O(l);$$
$$\Delta H° = -91.9 \text{ kcal/mol}$$

and the desired heat of reaction has been obtained.

Note that the final combination automatically gives the correct number of mols of water on the right-hand side of the equation. This is no coincidence, for the combination of the appropriate reactions, *properly balanced*, will always yield the desired final reaction.

Effect of temperature and pressure. The fact that heats of formation and heats of reaction derived therefrom pertain to reactions occurring at 25°C is no bar to the solution of problems involving other temperatures, for it will be recalled that ΔH is independent of path. Thus reactants at any given temperature can be cooled or heated to 25°C and converted at that temperature, after which the products can be heated or cooled to any desired final temperature. The sum of the enthalpy changes for all three steps is the total change in enthalpy for the entire process.

In rigorous calculations the effect of pressure must also be considered. The procedure is the same as that used to account for the effect of temperature, that is, it involves the selection of a path of convenience connecting the two end states, with the reaction itself considered to occur at 25°C and atmospheric pressure. Pressure effects will be small unless fairly high pressures are involved, and they can be neglected in many applications.

EXAMPLE 8.7. Calculate the heat of reaction when carbon monoxide at 25°C is burned with oxygen at 200°C to form carbon dioxide at 600°C. The standard heats of formation of CO and CO_2, obtained from the literature, are -26.42 and -94.05 kcal/mol, respectively. Mean heat capacities over the temperature ranges of interest, also obtained from the literature, are 7.16 and 11.11 cal/(mol)(C°) for the oxygen and carbon dioxide, respectively.

Solution. The calculation for the heat of reaction at 25°C is

$$\underline{H}_{CO_2} - \underline{H}_{O_2} - \underline{H}_C = -94.05 \text{ kcal/mol}$$
$$(-) \quad \underline{H}_{CO} - \tfrac{1}{2}\underline{H}_{O_2} - \underline{H}_C = -26.42 \text{ kcal/mol}$$
$$\overline{\underline{H}_{CO_2} - \underline{H}_{CO} - \tfrac{1}{2}\underline{H}_{O_2}} = -67.63 \text{ kcal/mol}$$

The desired enthalpy change can then be broken up into three parts as follows:

$$\Delta H = \underline{H}_{CO_2,600°} - (\underline{H}_{CO,25°} + \tfrac{1}{2}\underline{H}_{O_2,200°})$$
$$= (\underline{H}_{CO_2,600°} - \underline{H}_{CO_2,25°}) + [\underline{H}_{CO_2,25°} - (\underline{H}_{CO,25°} + \tfrac{1}{2}\underline{H}_{O_2,25°})]$$
$$+ \tfrac{1}{2}(\underline{H}_{O_2,25°} - \underline{H}_{O_2,200°})$$

The given heat capacity data may be used to evaluate the two parenthetical terms, and the terms in the brackets represent the heat of reaction at 25°C, already calculated. Thus

$$\Delta H = \frac{(11.11)(600 - 25)}{1000} + (-67.63) + \frac{(7.16)(25 - 200)}{(2)(1000)}$$
$$= 6.39 - 67.63 + (-0.63) = -61.87 \text{ kcal/mol CO burned.}$$

8.3 *Change of Temperature, Pressure, or Volume*

The procedure illustrated in Ex. 8.7 can obviously be used to calculate the change in temperature which will result from a given reaction if $Q(= \Delta H)$ is specified. The temperature which results when a reaction is carried out adiabatically is often of particular interest and is called the *adiabatic* or *theoretical reaction temperature.* The equivalent terms adiabatic or theoretical *flame* temperature are often used in conjunction with combustion reactions.

EXAMPLE 8.8. Calculate the adiabatic flame temperature for combustion of carbon monoxide at 25°C with air at 25°C.

Solution. The pertinent reaction is

$$CO + \tfrac{1}{2}O_2 \rightarrow CO_2$$

and the half mol of O_2 will be accompanied by $(.5)(79/21) = 1.88$ mols of N_2. The pertinent energy balance is therefore

$$Q = \Delta H = 0 = 1.88\underline{H}_{N_2,T°} + \underline{H}_{CO_2,T°} - \underline{H}_{CO,25°} - (1.88\underline{H}_{N_2,25°} + 0.5\underline{H}_{O_2,25°})$$
$$= 1.88(\underline{H}_{N_2,T°} - \underline{H}_{N_2,25°}) + (\underline{H}_{CO_2,T°} - \underline{H}_{CO_2,25°})$$
$$+ [\underline{H}_{CO_2,25°} - (\underline{H}_{CO,25°} + 0.5\underline{H}_{O_2,25°})]$$

Substituting the heat of reaction calculated in Ex. 8.7 and heat capacities obtained from the literature,

$$1.88 \int_{298}^{T} (6.50 + .001\,T)dT + \int_{298}^{T} \left(10.34 + .00274\,T - \frac{195{,}500}{T^2}\right)dT$$

$$+ (-67.63)(1000) = 0$$

A trial-and-error solution for T yields $T = 2625°K.*$

When excess reactants or incomplete conversion must be taken into account, the standard heat of reaction obviously applies only to the quantity of material actually reacted. Inlet and out enthalpies for any unreacted materials must be included in the energy balance, however. The procedure is the same as that used to account for the nitrogen in Ex. 8.8.

The assumption of a constant reaction pressure is not unreasonable for most continuous flow reactors. Should it be necessary to determine the specific volume change resulting from a continuous reaction, the composition of the product mixture and the final temperature must first be calculated. For a known reaction pressure, the desired specific volume can then be calculated from the ideal gas law or the compressibility factor equation of state.

Batch reactions are generally carried out at constant volume. The change in pressure can be calculated from a knowledge of the reactor volume, the number of mols of product mixture present, and the temperature of the mixture. Should a liquid or solid phase be present, the pressure calculation will be based on that portion of the product mixture which exists as a gas or vapor, and the corresponding volume will be the reactor volume minus the volume occupied by the other phase or phases.

8.4 Chemical Equilibria

The fact that a reaction may not go to completion because of an approach to equilibrium has already been noted. It follows that the determination of equilibrium conditions is an important aspect of chemical change, because the degree of conversion must be known before either the pertinent mass- or energy-balance calculations can be undertaken. The thermodynamic relationships applicable to chemical equilibria are therefore of considerable importance to the chemical engineer. These relationships and their practical application are treated in the development which follows.

Criterion for equilibrium. Let the hypothetical reaction

$$\alpha A + \beta B \rightleftharpoons \epsilon E$$

in which α, β, and ϵ are the *relative* coefficients in the balanced reaction, typify any reversible chemical reaction. Since the reaction is reversible, equilibrium can be approached from either direction, depending on the quantities of A, B, and E present initially. In any event, the equilibrium system will consist of a mixture of all three components at a particular pressure and temperature.

---

* In general, the integrated equation will not be linear in T and more than one root will exist. Physical restrictions such as the fact that T in degrees Kelvin cannot be negative will make it possible to identify the single root of practical interest.

It was shown in Sec. 6.10 that G_V and G_L must be equal when a vapor phase and a liquid phase are in equilibrium at constant temperature and pressure. Although the derivation will not be presented here, it can also be shown that an equivalent criterion applies to chemical equilibria at constant temperature and pressure, namely,

$$G_{products} = G_{reactants}$$

For the particular reaction under consideration, the equivalent expression is

$$\epsilon \overline{G}_E = \alpha \overline{G}_A + \beta \overline{G}_B \tag{8.9}$$

in which $\overline{G}$, the *partial molal free energy*, denotes the free energy of a component in a mixture and is directly analogous to the partial molal volume considered in Sec. 7.3, that is,

$$\overline{G}_j = \left(\frac{\partial G}{\partial M_j} \right)_{T,P,M_A,M_B,\cdots} \tag{8.10}$$

The analogy also requires that $\overline{G}_j$ and $\underline{G}_j$ be identically equal when j exists as a pure, unmixed substance.

The next step is to replace each of the $\overline{G}$ terms in Eq. (8.9) with equivalent terms amenable to quantitative evaluation. The relationship between $\underline{G}$ and f at constant temperature was developed in Sec. 7.3 and is, for any particular component j,

$$d\underline{G}_j = RT d(\ln f_j) \tag{8.11}$$

This expression can clearly be integrated at constant temperature to obtain the free energy of component j in any general state relative to that in any convenient reference state,

$$\underline{G}_j - \underline{G}_j{}^\circ = RT \ln \left(\frac{f_j}{f_j{}^\circ} \right) \tag{8.12}$$

where G_j is the free energy in any state whatsoever (and f_j is the corresponding fugacity) and the superscript degrees denote reference-state conditions. Since the general state may be one for which j is a component in a mixture, a less restrictive form of Eq. (8.12) is

$$\overline{G}_j - \underline{G}_j{}^\circ = RT \ln \left(\frac{\overline{f}_j}{f_j{}^\circ} \right) \tag{8.13}$$

In accordance with the comment following Eq. (8.10), this expression will reduce to Eq. (8.12) if j is a pure substance rather than a component in a mixture.

The ratio of the fugacity of a particular substance in any general state to its fugacity in the reference state is a dimensionless quantity called the *activity* of the substance and is commonly denoted by the symbol a. Hence, by definition,

$$a_j = \left(\frac{\overline{f}_j}{f_j{}^\circ} \right) \tag{8.14}$$

The quantitative evaluation of a obviously depends on the reference state selected and will be considered in due course. In the meantime, Eq. (8.13) can clearly be written in the form

$$\overline{G}_j = RT \ln a_j + \underline{G}_j{}^\circ \qquad (8.15)$$

If Eq. (8.15) is written for each of the components appearing in Eq. (8.9) and the expressions so obtained are substituted into the latter equation, the result is

$$\epsilon RT \ln a_E + \epsilon \underline{G}_E{}^\circ = \alpha RT \ln a_A + \alpha \underline{G}_A{}^\circ + \beta RT \ln a_B + \beta \underline{G}_B{}^\circ$$

and rearrangement yields

$$RT \ln \frac{(a_E)^\epsilon}{(a_A)^\alpha (a_B)^\beta} = -(\epsilon \underline{G}_E{}^\circ - \alpha \underline{G}_A{}^\circ - \beta \underline{G}_B{}^\circ) \qquad (8.16)$$

Because this equation was derived from Eq. (8.9), which presupposed the existence of equilibrium conditions, the activities appearing in the equation must be those pertaining to the equilibrium mixture. Further, the right-hand side of Eq. (8.16) is equal to the free energy change which would result were the reaction to be carried out with each of the reactants and products in the reference state.

By definition, the ratio of equilibrium activities, each raised to a power equal to the corresponding coefficient in the balanced chemical reaction, is the *equilibrium constant*, K_a. Also by definition, the change in free energy for the reference-state reaction will be denoted by ΔG°. Eq. (8.16) may accordingly be written

$$RT \ln K_a = -\Delta G^\circ \qquad (8.17)$$

and this relationship applies to any chemical system at equilibrium. It is important to remember that temperature has been held constant throughout the derivation leading to this final equation.

Recall that α, β, and ϵ are *relative* coefficients in the balanced chemical reaction. It follows that ΔG° is also a relative quantity and, from Eq. (8.17), that the numerical value of K_a will change as the *absolute* values of the coefficients are changed. As will be demonstrated shortly, this situation presents no problem as long as the same balanced reaction equation is used consistently.

Practical application. The reference state generally used for both activity and ΔG° is the pure, unmixed substance at 25°C and a pressure of 1 atmosphere.* Recall that these conditions correspond to those used earlier for heats of reaction. *Standard free energies of formation* (ΔG°) for various compounds at 25°C are commonly tabulated in the literature along with standard

---

* The standard state for gases is actually the pure substance at $f = 1$ atmosphere rather than $P = 1$ atmosphere. However, the distinction is not critical since $f = P$ for an ideal gas and deviation from ideality is slight at atmospheric pressure.

heats of reaction. They may be combined to obtain $\Delta G°$ for any desired reaction at 25°C in exactly the same way that heats of formation are used to calculate heats of reaction.

EXAMPLE 8.9. Calculate K_a at 25°C for the reaction

$$N_2O \rightleftharpoons NO + \tfrac{1}{2}N_2$$

Solution. The standard free energies of formation for N_2O and NO, obtained from the literature, are 24.82 and 20.72 kcal/mol, respectively. Hence

$$\tfrac{1}{2}N_2 + \tfrac{1}{2}O_2 \rightarrow NO; \qquad \Delta G° = +20.72 \text{ kcal/mol}$$
$$\underline{N_2O \rightarrow N_2 + \tfrac{1}{2}O_2; \qquad \Delta G° = -24.82 \text{ kcal/mol}}$$
$$N_2O \rightarrow NO + \tfrac{1}{2}N_2; \qquad \Delta G° = -\ 4.10 \text{ kcal/mol}$$

Substituting in Eq. (8.17) and solving for K_a,

$$\ln K_a = -\frac{(-4.10)(1000)}{(1.987)(298)} = +0.692$$

$$K_a = 2.00$$

The standard state defined above also makes it possible to express activities in equivalent terms which are readily evaluated. For gases, $f° = 1$ atmosphere and, assuming an ideal solution, $\bar{f}_j = y_j f_j$, y being the mol fraction and f the fugacity of the pure substance. This equality, it may be recalled, is the Lewis-Randall rule developed in Sec. 7.3. Substituting in Eq. (8.14),

$$a_j = \frac{\bar{f}_j}{1} = y_j f_j = y_j \left(\frac{f}{P}\right)_j P \qquad (8.18)$$

For a non-ideal gas, f/P may be obtained from the generalized plot described in Sec. 6.8. For an ideal gas, $f/P = 1$ and Eq. (8.18) reduces to

$$a_j = y_j P = p_j = \left(\frac{N_j}{N_T}\right)P \qquad (8.19)$$

where N_j and N_T are the mols of component j and the mols of total mixture, respectively. Note that P must be in atmospheres in both Eqs. (8.18) and (8.19) since $f°$ was 1 atmosphere and a must be dimensionless.

An alternative simplification for liquids and solids takes cognizance of the fact that the fugacities of liquids and solids are independent of pressure for practical purposes. Again utilizing the development presented in Sec. 7.3, $\bar{f}_j = \gamma_j x_j f_j = \gamma_j x_j f_j°$ since f and $f°$ both refer to the pure liquid or solid and differ only insofar as they refer to different pressures. Therefore

$$a_j = \frac{\gamma_j x_j f_j°}{f_j°} = \gamma_j x_j \qquad (8.20)$$

γ is equal to 1 for an ideal solution, while both γ and x are unity for any pure solid or pure liquid, making the activity unity also.

Eqs. (8.18), (8.19), and (8.20) make it possible to replace the activities in Eq. (8.16) with fugacities or partial pressures, depending on the extent to which simplifying assumptions are applicable. The symbols K_f and K_p are often used to denote the corresponding equilibrium constants. The equivalent constant in terms of molal quantities (N), derived from Eq. (8.19), is particularly useful and will be denoted by K_N.

EXAMPLE 8.10. Write expressions for K_a, K_f, K_p, and K_N for the reaction

$$3A + 2B \rightleftharpoons C$$

in which A is a solid and B and C are gases.

Solution. By definition,

$$K_a = \frac{(a_C)}{(a_A)^3(a_B)^2} \tag{8.21a}$$

For the usual reference states, a_A is unity since A exists as a pure solid at equilibrium. Also, for the two gases, $a = yf$; hence

$$K_f = \frac{y_C f_C}{(1)(y_B f_B)^2} \tag{8.21b}$$

If ideal behavior can be assumed, $yf = yP = p$ and

$$K_p = \frac{p_C}{p_B^2} \tag{8.21c}$$

Finally, letting $p = yP = (N/N_T)P$ and cancelling N_T and P to simplify the expression,

$$K_N = \frac{(N_C)(N_T)}{(N_B)^2(P)} \tag{8.21d}$$

Note that K_a, K_f, K_p, and K_N are numerically identical if the usual reference states and ideal-gas behavior apply.

The composition of an equilibrium mixture must reflect the quantities of each component introduced into the system initially. This fact provides a final relationship which makes it possible to express all mol fractions or mol quantities in terms of a single unknown, whereupon the equilibrium composition can be calculated if the equilibrium constant is known. A typical technique is to let x be the mols of any one component produced or consumed in reaching equilibrium. Application of the mass balance will then yield expressions for each of the pertinent mol fractions or mol quantities in terms of x and the component quantities present initially. The detailed procedure is best presented by example.

EXAMPLE 8.11. Five mols of A, 1 mol of B, and 2 mols of C are placed in a reaction vessel and brought to equilibrium according to the reaction equation given in Ex. 8.10. The equilibrium pressure and temperature are 14.7 psia and 25°C, respectively, and $K_a = 0.93$ at this temperature for the usual standard states. Calculate the quantity of each component present at equilibrium.

Solution. Let x be the mols of C produced in going from the given initial conditions to equilibrium. The balanced reaction equation indicates that $3x$ mols of A and $2x$ mols of B will be consumed during the process. A simple mass balance then shows that there will be $5 - 3x$ mols of A, $1 - 2x$ mols of B, and $2 + x$ mols of C present at equilibrium. N_T, the total mols of *gas* ($B + C$), is therefore $3 - x$. Substituting these values and $P = 1$ atmosphere into the expression for K_N obtained in Ex. 8.10 and remembering that $K_a = K_N$,

$$0.93 = \frac{(2 + x)(3 - x)}{(1 - 2x)^2(1)}$$

from which $x = 1.65$ or -0.65. The first answer can be rejected since it would correspond to a negative number of mols of B present at equilibrium. The second is acceptable, and its negative sign merely indicates that C was consumed rather than produced in the process of reaching equilibrium. This aspect of the solution is noteworthy, for it indicates that the direction of the reaction need not be predicted before the equilibrium calculations are carried out.

Substituting $x = -0.65$ into the mol quantities previously determined, we find that there will be 6.95 mols of A, 2.3 mols of B, and 1.35 mols of C present at equilibrium. It is noteworthy that the quantity of A did not enter into the equilibrium calculations. This is typical of pure liquids and solids, the quantities being immaterial provided only that they are sufficient to insure that they will not be completely consumed before equilibrium is established.

The fact that the equilibrium composition is independent of the absolute coefficients used in balancing a given reaction may now be demonstrated. Changing the reaction given in Ex. 8.10 to

$$6A + 4B \rightleftharpoons 2C$$

will clearly double $\Delta G°$ in accordance with Eq. (8.16) and, from Eq. (8.17), will square K_a. At the same time, however, the exponents on each of the activities in Eq. (8.16) will also be doubled. The equation to be solved for x in Ex. 8.11 would accordingly be

$$(0.93)^2 = \frac{(2 + x)^2(3 - x)^2}{(1 - 2x)^4(1)^2}$$

which is clearly the square of the original equation. The additional roots introduced by the squaring will be found to be extraneous in the same way that the solution $x = 1.65$ was.

Effect of temperature. The free energies of formation obtainable from the literature yield values of K_a at 25°C. The relationship used to convert these values to other temperatures can be derived from Eq. (6.11),

$$dG = -SdT + VdP \qquad (6.11)$$

as follows:

Since Eq. (6.11) applies generally, it may be applied specifically to the reactants or products of a given reaction in the standard state. It may also be divided through by T and the restriction of constant pressure imposed to yield

$$\frac{dG^\circ_{\text{prod}}}{T} = \frac{-S^\circ_{\text{prod}}}{T} dT \qquad \text{and} \qquad \frac{dG^\circ_{\text{reac}}}{T} = \frac{-S^\circ_{\text{reac}}}{T} dT$$

Subtracting the second of these equations from the first,

$$\frac{dG^\circ_{\text{prod}} - dG^\circ_{\text{reac}}}{T} = -\frac{S^\circ_{\text{prod}} - S^\circ_{\text{reac}}}{T} dT$$

or, since the derivative of a difference equals the difference of the derivatives,

$$\frac{d(\Delta G^\circ)}{T} = -\frac{\Delta S^\circ}{T} dT \qquad (8.22)$$

in which ΔS° is the entropy change for the reaction when carried out in the standard state. Finally, let $\dfrac{\Delta G^\circ}{T^2} dT$ be subtracted from both sides of Eq. (8.22). The difference on the left-hand side of the resulting equality will be found to be the derivative of the quotient $\Delta G^\circ / T$; hence

$$d\left(\frac{\Delta G^\circ}{T}\right) = -\left(\frac{\Delta S^\circ}{T} + \frac{\Delta G^\circ}{T^2}\right) dT \qquad (8.23)$$

Now let Eq. (8.17) be differentiated after dividing through by RT:

$$d(\ln K_a) = -\frac{1}{R} d\left(\frac{\Delta G^\circ}{T}\right)$$

or, substituting from Eq. (8.23),

$$d(\ln K_a) = \frac{1}{RT}\left(\Delta S^\circ + \frac{\Delta G^\circ}{T}\right) dT \qquad (8.24)$$

This equation can be used to determine the variation of K_a with temperature, provided the parenthetical term on the right can be evaluated as a function of T. Since $G = H - TS$ by definition, it follows that $G^\circ = H^\circ - TS^\circ$ and, at any particular temperature, $\Delta G^\circ = \Delta H^\circ - T\Delta S^\circ$ and

$$\Delta S^\circ + \frac{\Delta G^\circ}{T} = \frac{\Delta H^\circ}{T}$$

Eq. (8.24) may therefore be written in the final form

$$d(\ln K_a) = \frac{\Delta H^\circ}{RT^2} dT \tag{8.25}$$

The integration of Eq. (8.25) to determine K_a at any temperature when its value at 25°C is known requires that ΔH° be expressed as a function of temperature. The concept of path independence makes it possible to derive the needed relationship, assuming pertinent heat capacities and the heat of reaction at 25°C to be known. At any temperature T,

$$
\begin{aligned}
\Delta H^\circ &= H^\circ_{\text{prod},T} - H^\circ_{\text{reac},T} \\
&= (H_T - H_{25^\circ})_{\text{prod}} + (H_{\text{prod}} - H_{\text{reac}})_{25^\circ} + (H_{25^\circ} - H_T)_{\text{reac}} \\
&= \int_{298}^{T} (MC_p)_{\text{prod}} dT + \Delta H^\circ_{25^\circ} - \int_{298}^{T} (MC_p)_{\text{reac}} \, dT \\
&= \int_{298}^{T} \Delta(MC_p) dT + \Delta H^\circ_{25^\circ} \tag{8.26}
\end{aligned}
$$

where $\Delta(MC_p)$ denotes MC_p for the products minus MC_p for the reactants. The integration of Eq. (8.26) will yield an expression for ΔH° as a function of T, for use in Eq. (8.25). The detailed calculation is illustrated in the following example.

EXAMPLE 8.12. Calculate K_a at 1000°K for the reaction

$$SO_2 + \tfrac{1}{2} O_2 \rightleftharpoons SO_3$$

Solution. The following data may be obtained from the literature: For SO_2, ΔH° and ΔG° of formation at 25°C are -70.94 and -71.68 kcal/mol, respectively; $C_p = 7.116 + .009512 T - 3.511 \times 10^{-6} T^2$ cal/(gm-mol)(K°) with T in °K. For SO_3, the corresponding data are -94.39, -88.59, and $6.077 + .023537 T - .687 \times 10^{-6} T^2$, respectively. For O_2, $C_p = 6.148 + .003102 T - .923 \times 10^{-6} T^2$.

The procedures for calculating K_a and ΔH° for the reaction at 25°C have already been demonstrated, and the calculation will be left as an exercise. The results are $\Delta H^\circ = -23,450$ cal/mol and $\ln K_a = 28.6$. The next step is to calculate $\Delta(MC_p)$:

$$
\begin{aligned}
\Delta(MC_p) &= (6.077 + .023537 T - .687 \times 10^{-6} T^2) \\
&\quad - (7.116 + .009512 - 3.511 \times 10^{-6} T^2) \\
&\quad - (.5)(6.148 + .003102 T - .923 \times 10^{-6} T^2) \\
&= -4.113 + .012474 T + 3.285 \times 10^{-6} T^2
\end{aligned}
$$

This expression, together with the heat of reaction at 25°C, may now be substituted into Eq. (8.26), and the equation can be integrated between 298°K and T°K to obtain

$$\Delta H^\circ = -22,810 - 4.113 T + .00624 T^2 + 1.095 \times 10^{-6} T^3$$

which is the needed expression for ΔH° as a function of temperature.

Substitution of the foregoing expression into Eq. (8.25) makes it possible to integrate the equation between 298°K, where $\ln K_a = 28.6$, and any temperature of interest. An upper limit of 1000°K is indicated for the problem at hand, but a more useful expression can be obtained by integrating with an indefinite upper limit, T. The result is

$$\ln K_a - 28.6 = -39.49 + \frac{11{,}480}{T} - 2.07 \ln \frac{T}{298}$$
$$+ .00314T + .276 \times 10^{-6}T^2$$

from which K_a at any desired temperature can be determined. For $T = 1000°K$, the equation yields $K_a = 4.48$. This value may now be used to determine equilibrium compositions at 1000°K.

Effect of pressure. Once standard states have been agreed upon, $\Delta G°$ at any given temperature is fixed and, in accordance with Eq. (8.17), so is K_a. Thus K_a is independent of the pressure at which equilibrium is established. Pressure may still affect equilibrium compositions, however, as can readily be seen from Eq. (8.21d). With $K_N = K_a$ fixed, an increase in pressure in the example problem must be accompanied by a decrease in N_B or an increase in N_C or N_T. This shift in equilibrium is seen to be consistent with the familiar principle of LeChatelier.

When the same number of mols of gas appear in both sides of a balanced chemical reaction, both pressure and the total number of mols at equilibrium will cancel out of the expression corresponding to Eq. (8.21d). Even so, a sufficiently high pressure may still affect the equilibrium. This should be apparent from Eq. (8.21b) upon recognition of the fact that the fugacities of non-ideal gases vary with pressure.

Effect of excess reactants and inerts. In Ex. 8.11, the quantities of the three components present initially are seen to enter into the equilibrium calculations. This aspect of the calculations takes full account of the effect of a non-stoichiometric reaction mixture, and neither K_a nor the exponents on the activity terms are altered by the presence of excess reactants.

The presence of non-reacting, inert components in the equilibrium mixture has a similar effect. Gaseous inerts must be considered when calculating the total number of mols present at equilibrium, but K_a and the activity exponents are not affected. It is noteworthy that inert components have no effect whatsoever if N_T completely cancels out of the expression equivalent to Eq. (8.21d).

Simultaneous reactions. It may be that more than one reaction can occur when specified reactants are brought together. In such an event the extent to which each reaction proceeds will be characterized by a different unknown variable $(x,y,\ldots)$. Since separate K_a-activity relationships can be written for each reaction, however, there are always as many equations as there are unknowns, and the composition of the equilibrium mixture can be determined by solving the pertinent equations simultaneously.

The value of K_a for a given reaction at the specified equilibrium temperature provides a quick indication of whether the reaction need be considered in the equilibrium calculations: If K_a is large, the reaction may be assumed to go to completion; if it is small, the reaction will take place to a negligible extent only. In either case the reaction need not be considered, although the presence of the reactants or products in the equilibrium mixture is pertinent.

EXAMPLE 8.13. Steam and hot carbon (coke) can react to form hydrogen and either carbon monoxide or carbon dioxide according to the reactions

(1) $\quad C + H_2O \rightleftharpoons CO + H_2$

(2) $\quad C + 2\,H_2O \rightleftharpoons CO_2 + 2\,H_2$

Assuming K_a's to be known for both reactions at the temperature of interest and that ideal-gas conditions prevail, develop the relationships necessary to calculate the composition of the three-component gas mixture at equilibrium.

Solution. The relationships equivalent to Eq. (8.21d) are

$$K_{a_1} = \frac{(N_{CO})(N_{H_2})P}{(N_{H_2O})(N_T)}$$

and

$$K_{a_2} = \frac{(N_{CO_2})(N_{H_2})^2 P}{(N_{H_2O})^2 (N_T)}$$

For a basis of one mol of steam present initially, let x be the mols of CO formed in reaction (1) and y be the mols of CO$_2$ formed in reaction (2). A mass balance shows that the equilibrium mixture will contain $x + 2y$ mols of H$_2$ and $1 - x - 2y$ mols of unreacted H$_2$O in addition to the x mols of CO and y mols of CO$_2$. Adding these quantities together, the total number of mols present at equilibrium is found to be $1 + x + y$. Accordingly,

$$K_{a_1} = \frac{(x)(x + 2y)P}{(1 - x + 2y)(1 + x + y)}$$

$$K_{a_2} = \frac{(y)(x + 2y)^2 P}{(1 - x - 2y)^2 (1 + x + y)}$$

With K_{a_1}, K_{a_2}, and P known, these two equations can be solved simultaneously for x and y. The equilibrium composition can then be determined.

8.5 Summary

The calculation of the composition and energy changes associated with chemical reactions is not particularly difficult once the degree of conversion has been established, and there is little point in summarizing the pertinent techniques. In the final analysis, only a straightforward application of the mass and energy balances is required. The determination of equilibrium conditions is somewhat more involved, and it may be helpful to summarize the pertinent steps in the determination as follows:

   1) Write and balance the pertinent chemical reaction.

   2) Calculate $\Delta H°$ and $\Delta G°$ for the reaction at 25°C by combining the necessary formation reactions and the corresponding heats and free energies of formation, as illustrated in Ex. 8.5.

   3) Substitute the value of $\Delta G°$ so obtained into Eq. (8.17),

$$RT \ln K_a = -\Delta G° \qquad (8.17)$$

and calculate the value of $\ln K_a$ at 25°C.

   4) Calculate $\Delta(MC_p)$ and substitute, along with $\Delta H°_{25°C}$, into Eq. (8.26),

$$\Delta H° = \int_{298}^{T} \Delta(MC_p)dT + \Delta H°_{25°C} \qquad (8.26)$$

Integrate the equation to obtain $\Delta H°$ as a function of T.

   5) Substitute the function obtained in step (4) into Eq. (8.25),

$$d(\ln K_a) = \frac{\Delta H°}{RT^2} dT \qquad (8.25)$$

and integrate between 298°K, where $\ln K_a$ is known from step (3), and $T°K$ to obtain K_a as a function of T.

   6) Substitute the reaction temperature of interest into the result from step (5) to determine K_a at that temperature.

   7) Set up the activity relationship equivalent to Eq. (8.21a), using the coefficients from the balanced reaction equation, and reduce the relationship to a function of mol fractions similar to Eq. (8.21d), as illustrated in Ex. 8.10. Any necessary corrections for non-ideality will be introduced in this step.

   8) Let x be the number of mols of one of the reactants or products present at equilibrium. Using given initial quantities of reactants and products, apply the mass balance to determine the number of mols of each component and the mols of total *gas** at equilibrium in terms of x.

   9) Substitute the latter expressions into the reduced activity relationship obtained in step (7) and solve for x. The equilibrium concentration of each component is then readily determinable, since the quantity of each component is already known as a function of x.

   The fact that any one of the variables in the K_a-activity relationship may be the unknown to be determined should not be overlooked. When the free

---

   * The analogous procedure applicable to multi-component liquid or solid phases lies beyond the scope of the present treatment.

energy data needed to determine K_a are not available in the literature, it may be necessary to measure equilibrium concentrations experimentally. The K_a-activity relationship can then be solved for K_a and, if desired, the result can be converted to a $\Delta G°$. Similarly, the relationship might be solved for the system pressure or the quantity of an inert diluent required to establish a specified equilibrium condition.

REVIEW, STUDY, AND DISCUSSION

8-1. Define internal mol ratio, stoichiometric proportion, theoretical quantity (of a reactant), excess reactant, limiting reactant, percentage excess, percentage conversion, degree of completion, yield, heat of reaction, standard heat of formation, standard heat of reaction, standard heat of combustion, adiabatic reaction temperature, partial molal free energy, activity, equilibrium constant, K_f, K_p, K_N, standard free energy of formation.

8-2. Aniline ($C_6H_5NH_2$) reacts with oxygen to form carbon dioxide, water, and free nitrogen. Write and balance the chemical reaction. List all possible mol ratios indicated by the reaction: 6 mols of carbon per mol of aniline, etc.

8-3. FeS_2 reacts with oxygen to form Fe_2O_3 and SO_2. Calculate the heat of reaction at 25°C. (The standard heat of formation of Fe_2O_3 is -198.5 kcal/mol. See Ex. 8.5 for other pertinent data.)

8-4. The standard heat of combustion of ethyl mercaptan (C_2H_6S) is -448.0 kcal/mol. Calculate the standard heat of formation of this compound.

8-5. Ammonia is to be synthesized from nitrogen and hydrogen. Derive an expression for the heat of reaction as a function of the temperature at which the reaction is carried out. Compare the heat of reaction at 500°C with that at 25°C.

8-6. The standard heats of formation of $H_2O(l)$ and $H_2O(g)$ are -68.32 and -57.80 kcal/mol, respectively. Calculate the standard latent heat of vaporization of water at 25°C.

8-7. Calculate the adiabatic reaction temperature for the combustion of ethyl alcohol (C_2H_5OH) with 25 per cent excess air if the alcohol and air are supplied at 25°C. (Note: the water formed in the reaction will be in the vapor state.)

8-8. The standard free energies of formation at 25°C for NH_3, $HNO_3(g)$, and $H_2O(g)$ are -3.90, -17.57, and -54.64 kcal/mol, respectively. Calculate ln K_a for the vapor-phase oxidation of ammonia to form nitric acid and water at a reaction temperature of 25°C. Calculate K_a for the synthesis of ammonia from nitrogen and hydrogen at 25°C.

8-9. $K_a = 3.16$ for the reaction

$$NO + \tfrac{1}{2} O_2 \rightleftharpoons NO_2$$

at 740°K. Assuming this to be the only reaction which will occur, calculate the equilibrium conditions which will result when equal molal quantities of NO and O_2 are permitted to react to equilibrium at 740°K and atmospheric pressure.

8-10. For the conditions of Prob. 8-9, identify the excess reactant and the limiting reactant. What is the percentage excess of the excess reactant? What is the degree of completion of the reaction? What is the percentage conversion of the oxygen?

8-11. Define the conventional standard states used for gases and for liquids and solids. Show how activities can be converted to partial pressures and mol fractions and list the necessary simplifying assumptions.

8-12. Laboratory data were taken to determine K_a for the reaction

$$SO_3 \rightleftharpoons SO_2 + \tfrac{1}{2} O_2$$

At 1740°F and 2 atm pressure, SO_3 was found to be 62 per cent dissociated. Calculate K_a for these conditions.

8-13. Compound Q dissociates according to the reaction

$$2Q(g) \rightleftharpoons J(g) + 2B(s)$$

and K_a for the dissociation reaction at 25°C is 0.145. It has been suggested that dissociation during storage at 25°C be minimized by storing Q under partial vacuum. What storage pressure will insure an equilibrium gas mixture containing not more than 10 per cent J?

8-14. Using the results from Probs. 8-5 and 8-8, derive an expression for K_a as a function of temperature for the synthesis of ammonia from nitrogen and hydrogen.

8-15. Ammonia is to be synthesized at atmospheric pressure from nitrogen and hydrogen in stoichiometric proportion. At what temperature will the equilibrium conversion be 25 per cent?

8-16. For the temperature obtained in Prob. 8-15, calculate the equilibrium conversion (a) if 20 per cent excess nitrogen is supplied, and (b) if the pressure is increased to 3 atmospheres.

PART III

Chemical Engineering Design and Analysis

The definition of chemical engineering presented in Chap. 1 stated that the chemical engineer is concerned with changes in state, energy content, or composition. Within this area of activity the problems to be faced fall into one of two broad categories. On the one hand it may be necessary to *design* the equipment or process sequence which will effect a desired change. Alternately, it may be necessary to *analyze* the operation of an existing piece of equipment or process to determine the significance of observed results, to explain unanticipated behavior and recommend remedial action, or to predict the consequences of a modified design or technique. It is noteworthy that this breakdown applies equally to work in the field of research, design, development, or any of the other functional fields listed in Chap. 1.

Design and analysis problems differ only in what is known initially and what must be determined. It follows that the same fundamental principles are applicable to problems of either type. These principles were identified qualitatively in Part I, and the intervening chapters have paved the way for the more quantitative examination which follows. This examination will, in turn, prepare the student for the detailed study and application of the pertinent principles in subsequent course work and, ultimately, in professional practice.

CHAPTER 9

Rate Processes

The rate at which change takes place is a critical consideration in chemical engineering. Faced with a problem of either design or analysis, the chemical engineer must establish the quantitative relationships among: the nature of the change, the quantity of material involved, processing time, equipment size, and process operating conditions. This relationship is embodied in the rate concept introduced in Chap. 2, and the practical application of this basic concept to specific processes is considered in this chapter.

The rate processes of primary interest to the chemical engineer are *heat transfer, chemical reaction, mass transfer, and fluid flow*. Such a breakdown obscures the fact that all four processes have significant characteristics in common, and a classification based on mechanism will ultimately be preferable. For introductory purposes, however, it is believed that the successive consideration of each of the major rate processes in turn is most advantageous. Analogies and common characteristics are identified, but the detailed analysis of mechanisms is not attempted.

9.1 *The Generalized Rate Concept*

Rate definition. The general concept of rate was treated in Sec. 2.7, but a brief review is not out of place at this point. The first step in applying the

219

rate concept, it may be recalled, is to define the particular rate of interest. For a batch, or unsteady-state process, the usual definition is

$$\text{Rate} = \frac{d\Gamma}{\Lambda d\theta} \tag{9.1}$$

in which Γ is the property or quantity undergoing change and Λ is a factor such as length, volume, or surface area which characterizes the extent of the system. If $d\Gamma/d\theta$ is inherently negative, it is customary to include a minus sign in the definition so as to make the rate always positive.

If attention is focused on a particular quantity of material flowing through a steady-state process, Eq. (9.1) may also be applied to flow processes. However, it is generally more advantageous to adopt the open-system viewpoint and consider the steady-state change occurring within a system whose location is fixed in space. For this case the rate definition becomes

$$\text{Rate} = \frac{d\gamma}{d\Lambda} \tag{9.2}$$

in which γ, equal to $d\Gamma/d\theta$, is the rate at which the quantity Γ is entering or leaving the system. *

Needless to say, the particular system variables represented by Γ and Λ must be specifically identified before a rate is completely defined. The units for these variables and for the time factor are also pertinent and should be clearly specified.

Rate correlation. The rate correlation provides a quantitative relationship among the rate of change, the physical environment, and the potential or driving force tending to produce the change. The latter may be identified by considering the equilibrium condition, at which the rate of change is zero and the potential must disappear. The general form of the rate correlation is

$$\text{Rate} = K[\phi(\pi)] \tag{9.3}$$

in which π is the potential and K is the rate coefficient, a function of environment. Ideally, K will be independent of π, but this is not always the case. The units of K are clearly dependent on the units specified in the rate definition and those pertaining to the driving force π.

Process application. A differential rate equation results when the rate definition and the rate correlation are combined, i.e.,

$$\frac{d\Gamma}{\Lambda d\theta} = K[\phi(\pi)] \tag{9.4}$$

or
$$\frac{d\gamma}{d\Lambda} = K'[\phi(\pi)] \tag{9.5}$$

---

* An equivalent system of nomenclature will be used throughout this chapter. Capital-letter symbols denote quantities undergoing change, while the corresponding lower-case symbols denote the steady-state rate at which the quantity is entering or leaving the system.

For a given set of environmental conditions the rate coefficient can be evaluated and the rate equation can then be integrated, provided π and Γ or, more rarely, π and θ can be quantitatively related. A mass balance, energy balance, or equation of state will generally provide the needed relationship.

The development of the relationship between π and Γ is often the most difficult aspect of rate calculations. A consistent method of analysis will reduce the likelihood of error. The recommended procedure is to let the temperature, pressure, number of mols, etc., at time θ (or at point x in a flow system) be denoted by T, P, N_A, N_B, . . . , and the corresponding values at time $\theta + d\theta$ (or point $x + dx$) be $T + dT$, $P + dP$, $N_A + dN_A$, $N_B + dN_B$, . . . , without regard for the algebraic sign of the various differentials. The appropriate balance or equation of state may then be written in terms of these values, and it will be found that the algebraic signs take care of themselves. This technique will be illustrated by example in due course.

As was noted in Chap. 2, Eq. (9.4) or (9.5) may be solved for any one of the variables involved, depending on the given information. Specifically, the unknown variable might be the time, system size, or potential needed to effect a desired change, or the extent of the change which will result when time, system size, and potential are known. Thus the same rate equation is applicable to problems of either design or analysis. Both types of calculation will be illustrated in subsequent sections.

9.2 Heat Transfer

Rate definition. For unsteady-state processes, the conventional definition of rate of heat transfer is

$$\text{Rate} = \frac{\delta Q}{A d\theta} \qquad (9.6)$$

in which A is the surface area across which the transfer occurs. Note that the definition of a system is prerequisite to the definition of rate, since Q may be positive or negative and it may be necessary to include a minus sign in the rate definition. The corresponding definition for a steady-state flow process is

$$\text{Rate} = \frac{\delta q}{dA} \qquad (9.7)$$

Rate correlation. For the transfer of heat by either natural or forced *convection*, the rate correlation takes the form

$$\text{Rate} = U(T_h - T_l) \qquad (9.8)$$

where T_h is the temperature of the hot material or stream, T_l is the temperature of the cold, and U is the *overall heat transfer coefficient*. The more significant environmental factors affecting U are the geometry of the system, the extent to which convection is forced rather than natural, and the physical properties of the materials to which, from which, and through which the heat is transferred. Since the latter properties may change with temperature, the rate coefficient for heat transfer is not entirely independent of the corresponding potential. Fortunately, the variation with temperature is not great, and a temperature-independent coefficient can often be assumed without introducing significant inaccuracies into the calculations.

The thermal *radiation* emitted by a body is proportional to the absolute temperature of the body raised to the fourth power. Consequently, when heat is transferred by radiation between two bodies at different temperatures, the appropriate rate correlation is found to be

$$\text{Rate} = h_r(T_h{}^4 - T_l{}^4) \tag{9.9}$$

where the subscripts h and l refer to the hot and cold bodies, respectively. The rate coefficient for radiant heat transfer, h_r, is a complex function of the geometry of the system and the *emissivity* and *absorptivity* of the radiating surfaces.

Heat transfer by conduction is characterized by a third form of rate correlation,

$$\text{Rate} = - k\frac{dT}{dx} \tag{9.10}$$

in which the rate coefficient k is the *thermal conductivity* of the conducting medium and dT/dx is the temperature *gradient* in the direction of transfer. When the conduction is not uni-directional, the spatial gradient must be used and Eq. (9.10) can be written

$$\text{Rate} = - k(\text{grad } T) \tag{9.11}$$

where, by definition,

$$\text{grad } T = \frac{\partial T}{\partial x}i + \frac{\partial T}{\partial y}j + \frac{\partial T}{\partial z}k \tag{9.12}$$

Process application. When the rate definition and rate correlation for unsteady-state, convective heat transfer are equated, the result is

$$\frac{\partial Q}{Ad\theta} = U(T_h - T_l) \tag{9.13}$$

and rearrangement and integration yields

$$\theta = \frac{1}{A}\int_1^2 \frac{\partial Q}{U(T_h - T_l)} \tag{9.14}$$

The integral in this equation can be evaluated, provided the relationships among Q, T_h, and T_l can be established. The application of the energy balance yields the necessary relationships. For a closed system not subject to kinetic energy, potential energy, or work effects, the reduced balance is

$$Q = U_2 - U_1 \tag{9.15}*$$

At time θ, let the hot material be at a temperature T_h and have an internal energy U_h while the cold material is at a temperature T_l and has an internal energy U_l. At time $\theta + d\theta$, let the corresponding temperatures and energies be $T_h + dT_h$, $U_h + dU_h$, $T_l + dT_l$, and $U_l + dU_l$. Also let δQ_l be the heat absorbed by the cold material during the time interval $d\theta$.

If the cold material is taken as the system and Eq. (9.15) is applied over the time interval $d\theta$, the result is

$$\delta Q_l = (U_l + dU_l) - U_l = dU_l$$

or, assuming a constant-volume system and no change of phase,

$$\delta Q_l = dU_l = M_l(C_v)_l dT_l \tag{9.16}$$

The corresponding equation for the hot material as the system is

$$\delta Q_h = dU_h = M_h(C_v)_h dT_h \tag{9.16a}$$

However, since $\delta Q_h = -\delta Q_l$, Eqs. (9.16) and (9.16a) may be combined to yield

$$M_h(C_v)_h dT = -M_l(C_v)_l dT_l \tag{9.17}$$

(This equation might also have been obtained directly by applying the energy balance to a system embracing both hot and cold materials.)

Either Eq. (9.16) or (9.16a) can be used to eliminate δQ from Eq. (9.14), and it remains only to eliminate either T_h or T_l. This may be accomplished by integrating Eq. (9.17) from any time θ_o, at which T_{ho} and T_{lo} are known, to the indefinite time θ. Assuming the heat capacities to be independent of temperature for the sake of simplicity, the result is

$$M_h(C_v)_h(T - T_o)_h = -M_l(C_v)_l(T - T_o)_l \tag{9.17a}$$

This equation may be solved for either T_h or T_l, whereupon the integral in Eq. (9.14) can be expressed in terms of a single unknown and integrated between any desired limits.

A procedure which is completely analogous to that outlined above is applicable to problems requiring the use of the steady-state rate definition or the rate correlation forms for radiant or conductive heat transfer. For the case of unsteady-state conduction, the fact that T varies with both time and position leads to a partial differential equation which cannot be solved

---

* The use of the symbol U to denote both internal energy and the overall heat transfer coefficient is unfortunate but is consistent with conventional usage. Here, confusion can be avoided by noting that U is always subscripted when it refers to internal energy, whereas the unsubscripted symbol always denotes the heat transfer coefficient.

by a simple separation of variables such as was effected in deriving Eq. (9.14). Otherwise, the outlined procedure is generally applicable.

EXAMPLE 9.1. A sheet of copper 1 foot square and 0.25 inches thick is to be cooled from 200°F by immersing it in a shallow pan containing 14 lbs of water at an initial temperature of 70°F. Calculate the temperature of the copper 30 seconds after immersion if the estimated overall heat transfer coefficient is 80 BTU/(hr)(ft²)(F°).

Solution. Letting Q be the heat absorbed by the copper, the differential rate equation is

$$\text{Rate} = -\frac{\delta Q}{A d\theta} = U(T_c - T_w)$$

and the pertinent energy balances are

$$\delta Q = M_c C_c dT_c = -M_w C_w dT_w$$

where the subscripts c and w denote the copper and water. Using a specific gravity of 8.92 for copper and heat capacities of 0.094 and 1.00 BTU/(lb)(F°) for copper and water, respectively, the relationship between T_c and T_w at any time may be obtained as follows:

$$M_c = \frac{(8.92)(62.4)(1)(1)(.25)}{12} = 11.6 \text{ lbs}$$

$$M_c C_c = (11.6)(.094) = 1.09 \text{ BTU/F°}$$

$$\therefore \quad \delta Q = 1.09 dT_c = -(14)(1)dT_w \quad \text{and} \quad dT_w = -.078 dT_c$$

Integrating the latter equation between 200° and $T_c°$ for the copper and between 70° and $T_w°$ for the water,

$$70 - T_w = -.078(200 - T_c)$$

from which $T_w = 85.6 - .078 T_c$ and $T_c - T_w = 1.078 T_c - 85.6$.

Rearranging the rate equation and substituting from the above yields

$$-\int_{200}^{T_c} \frac{dT_c}{1.078 T - 85.6} = \frac{1}{1.078} \ln\left(\frac{130}{1.078 T_c - 85.6}\right) = \frac{UA\theta}{M_c C_c}$$

For $\theta = 30/3600$, $U = 80$, $A = 2$, and $M_c C_c = 1.09$, solution of the above equation yields $T_c = 112°F$. (This answer is based on the assumptions of negligible heat transfer from the edges of the sheet, a uniform temperature in both copper and water, and negligible heat loss to the surroundings. In view of the fact that U is probably known only within plus-or-minus 10 per cent or more, these assumptions are not unreasonable.)

EXAMPLE 9.2. The double-pipe heat exchanger shown schematically in Fig. 9.1 is to be used to cool w pounds per hour of fluid A from T_1 to T_2. w' pounds per hour of fluid B will flow countercurrently through the annulus and be heated from T'_1 to T'_2. Derive an expression giving the length of the exchanger as a function of the flow rates w and w', the heat capacities C and C', the inlet and outlet temperatures, the heat transfer coefficient U, and the inner pipe diameter D.

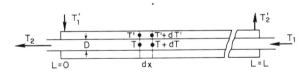

Fig. 9.1   Flow diagram for a double-pipe heat exchanger.

Solution. Letting q be the BTU per hour absorbed by the cold (annular) stream, the rate equation is

$$\text{Rate} = \frac{\delta q}{dA} = \frac{\delta q}{\pi D dx} = U(T - T')$$

For the differential element of the annulus as the system, the general energy balance reduces to

$$H_i - H_o + \delta Q = 0$$

or, in rate form,

$$h_i - h_o + \delta q = 0$$

But $h_i - h_o = w'C'(T'_i - T'_o) = w'C'[T' - (T' + dT')] = -w'C'dT'$, and hence $\delta q = w'C'dT'$. A similar analysis for the inside (hot) stream yields $-wCdT = \delta q_h = -\delta q$. The pertinent relationships are accordingly

$$\delta q = wCdT = w'C'dT'$$

Assuming constant heat capacities and integrating between T_2 and T and between T'_1 and T' (note the two different subscripts),

$$wC(T_2 - T) = w'C'(T_1' - T')$$

from which

$$T - T' = \left(\frac{w'C'}{wC} - 1\right)T' + \left(T_2 - \frac{w'C'}{wC}T'_1\right) = \alpha T' + \beta$$

where α and β, defined by this equation, have been introduced only to conserve notation.

T and δq may now be eliminated from the rate equation,

$$\frac{w'C'dT'}{\pi D dx} = U(\alpha T' + \beta)$$

and, assuming U to be constant, the equation can be integrated upon separation of variables:

$$L = \int_0^L dx = \frac{w'C'}{\pi DU}\int_{T'_1}^{T'_2}\frac{dT'}{\alpha T' + \beta} = \frac{w'C'}{\alpha\pi DU}\ln\left(\frac{\alpha T'_2 + \beta}{\alpha T'_1 + \beta}\right)$$

which is the desired relationship. It is noteworthy that the derivation did not introduce any difficulties with respect to algebraic sign. This will always be the case if the system, q, and inlet and outlet streams are consistently identified.

9.3 Chemical Reaction

Rate definition. The rate of a chemical reaction requires careful definition, for an obvious definition is not necessarily implicit in the reaction equation. For the hypothetical reaction

$$A + 2B \rightleftharpoons 3D + E \qquad (9.18)$$

the rate definition might be based on the rate of disappearance of either A or B or on the rate at which either D or E is produced. The usual practice is to define the rate in terms of a *key reactant*. Should B in Eq. (9.18) be the oxygen in an oxidation reaction, for example, the rate would normally be defined in terms of the change in the number of mols of A, the material being oxidized.

The extensive factor to be included in the rate definition can also vary. The volume of the reacting mixture (not necessarily equal to the volume of the reaction vessel) is generally used when the reaction is homogeneous. For a heterogeneous surface reaction, on the other hand, the interphase surface area might better describe the extent of the system; and for catalyzed reactions the mass or volume of catalyst present might be the most pertinent factor.

For illustrative purposes, we will let the subscript A denote the key reactant and will assume the volume of the reacting mixture to be the pertinent extensive factor. The rate definition for an unsteady-state batch reaction can then be written

$$\text{Rate} = -\frac{dN_A}{V d\theta} \qquad (9.19)$$

and the corresponding definition for a steady-state flow reaction is

$$\text{Rate} = -\frac{dn_A}{dV} \qquad (9.20)$$

Note the necessity for the minus signs, since dN_A and dn_A are inherently negative.

The flow rate n_A of component A at any point in a flow reactor can be related to the feed rate F by defining a variable X_A such that $n_A = X_A F$ and hence, for a given feed rate, $dn_A = F dX_A$. The quotient F/V is commonly called the *space velocity* and is denoted by S. Thus $V/F = 1/S$ and $d(V/F) = dV/F = d(1/S)$ and the rate definition can be expressed in the form

$$\text{Rate} = -\frac{dn_A}{dV} = -\frac{F dX_A}{dV} = -\frac{dX_A}{dV/F} = -\frac{dX_A}{d(1/S)} \qquad (9.21)$$

This form of the rate definition has certain advantages in measuring and correlating rate data for continuous reactions.

Rate correlation. The thermodynamic analysis presented in Chap. 8 showed that, at constant temperature and pressure, the criterion for chemical equilibrium is

$$G_{\text{products}} = G_{\text{reactants}}$$

This implies that the rate correlation for chemical reactions should involve free energy as a driving potential, and the resulting expression might then be converted to one involving activities, fugacities, mol fractions, or concentrations depending on the validity of pertinent simplifying assumptions. In practice, reaction rate data are generally correlated directly in terms of concentrations as driving forces. A typical rate correlation, written for the reversible reaction given in Eq. (9.18), has the form

$$\text{Rate} = k_f(C_A)^a(C_B)^b - k_r(C_D)^d(C_E)^e \qquad (9.22)$$

in which k_f and k_r are the rate coefficients for the forward and reverse reactions, respectively, and C is the concentration of the subscript component.

The exponents a, b, d, and e *may* be equal to the corresponding coefficients in the balanced chemical reaction, but will frequently be different. This is a consequence of the fact that they depend on the reaction *mechanism*, which may involve a considerable departure from the overall reaction as written in Eq. (9.18). Suppose, for example, that the reaction actually takes place in two successive steps,

$$A + B \rightleftharpoons AB + D$$
and
$$AB + B \rightleftharpoons 2D + E$$

The original reaction clearly describes the overall result, but the rate of one of the sub-reactions may be *limiting* and will thereby govern the overall reaction rate. It must be concluded that the coefficients of the overall reaction need not bear any direct relation to the exponents in the rate correlation.

The *order* of a reaction is equal to the sum of the concentration exponents in the rate correlation. Should it be known that $a = b = d = 1$ and $e = 0$ in Eq. (9.22), the forward reaction would be second order ($a + b = 2$) while the reverse reaction would be first order.

In the absence of specific information regarding reaction mechanism or order, the exponents in the rate correlation must be determined experimentally. A typical experiment might involve carrying out the reaction isothermally in a small batch reactor and measuring the composition of the reacting mixture as a function of time. The data would then be subjected to graphical differentiation (see Appendix B) to determine the reaction rate as a graphical function of time and of the concentration of each of the components.

At this point it becomes necessary to adopt a hypothesize-and-test procedure: We might first hypothesize that the reaction rate is dependent only on the concentration of component A (and hence zeroth order with respect to the other components.) In such an event, the rate correlation would reduce to: Rate $= k_f(C_A)^a$, or log (Rate) $=$ log $k_f + a$ log C_A. Accordingly, if a straight line results when Rate is plotted against C_A on log-log paper, the hypothesis is confirmed and the slope of the line gives the reaction order while the intercept yields the value of the rate coefficient. If the plot is non-linear, however, the hypothesis is disproved and an alternative must be investigated, e.g., that the rate depends only on C_B or perhaps on the product $C_A C_B$. Successive hypotheses will thus be made and tested until the proper fit with the experimental data is obtained.

The effect of temperature on reaction rate is generally appreciable and can be accounted for by making the rate coefficient temperature dependent. The dependence is likely to be exponential, in which case the quantitative relationship might be of the form

$$k = Ae^{-E/RT} \qquad (9.23)$$

in which A and E are constants, R is the gas law constant, and T is the absolute temperature. This equation is commonly referred to as the *Arrhenius equation*, and E is called the *energy of activation*. A and E would be evaluated by making an experimental determination of k as a function of temperature and plotting k vs. $1/T$ on semi-log paper.

At equilibrium, the forward and reverse reaction rates must be equal, since the net rate is zero. Setting the rate equal to zero in Eq. (9.22) and rearranging yields

$$\frac{k_f}{k_r} = \frac{(C_D)^d(C_E)^e}{(C_A)^a(C_B)^b} \qquad (9.24)$$

The right-hand side of this equation is seen to resemble the equilibrium-constant expressions encountered in Chap. 8, and suggests that equilibrium data might be used to determine one rate coefficient when the other is known. Eq. (9.24) also makes it clear that k_r must be zero if the reaction is to proceed to completion. Here again, equilibrium data can be helpful. If K_a is large, the reaction may be considered to go to completion for practical purposes and k_r may be assumed to be zero. Such reactions are called *irreversible*.

Process application. Combining Eqs. (9.19) and (9.22) yields the differential rate equation for a batch reaction,

$$-\frac{dN_A}{Vd\theta} = k_f(C_A)^a(C_B)^b - k_r(C_D)^d(C_E)^e \qquad (9.25)$$

in which k_f, k_r, and the exponents a, b, d, and e are presumed to be known. N_A, C_A, C_B, C_D, and C_E must now be related to permit integration of Eq. (9.25). In the completely general case both a mass balance and an equation of state will be pertinent. The calculations presented in Ex. 9.3 are typical.

EXAMPLE 9.3. N_{A_o} mols of A and N_{B_o} mols of B are fed to a batch reactor in which they react according to Eq. (9.18). Express N_A, C_A, C_B, C_D, and C_E as functions of a single unknown in preparation for the integration of Eq. (9.25).

Solution. Let x be the mols of A which have reacted up to time θ. At that time, then, $N_A = N_{A_o} - x$ (and $dN_A = -dx$), $N_B = N_{B_o} - 2x$, $N_D = 3x$, and $N_E = x$. If V is constant, as is usually the case in batch reactions, each N may be divided by V to obtain the corresponding concentration as a function of x. The case of a varying volume, for which the equation of state becomes pertinent, is more commonly encountered in flow reactions and will be considered in Ex. 9.4.

For a steady-state flow reaction, Eq. (9.25) becomes

$$-\frac{dn_A}{dV} = k_f(C_A)^a(C_B)^b - k_r(C_D)^d(C_E)^e \qquad (9.26)$$

The analysis leading to the integration of this equation parallels that illustrated in Ex. 9.3 with one important modification: Since mol *rates* rather than mol quantities are involved, any concentration C must be expressed in mols *per unit time* divided by volume *per unit time*, i.e., $C = n/v$, where v is the volumetric flow rate at the point for which n is the mol flow rate. The flowing volume may vary from point-to-point in the reactor and should not be confused with the reactor volume V, which is constant.

One of two limiting cases is normally assumed in designing or analyzing a flow reactor. In the first it is assumed that the materials in the reactor are perfectly mixed and that the composition of the reacting mixture is everywhere the same. It follows that, for steady-state conditions, the reaction rate is constant. Further, the composition of the product stream leaving the reactor must be the same as the composition within the reactor. This is an important point, for it means that the reaction rate at any given temperature is uniquely determined by a specified product composition.

The other limiting case is that for which the composition of the reacting mixture varies continuously in the direction of flow and all products and reactants are assumed to move always forward, with no back-mixing. The fact that composition varies from point to point means that the rate will also vary, from a maximum value at the inlet to a minimum at the outlet. The average rate will obviously be greater than that for the case of perfect mixing, where the rate is constant at the outlet value, and the assumption of no back-mixing accordingly corresponds to a minimum reactor volume for a desired conversion or a maximum conversion for a given reactor volume.

EXAMPLE 9.4. Compound C is to be produced in a 50 cubic foot steady-state flow reactor operated at 120°F and a pressure of 3 atmospheres, according to the irreversible, homogeneous, gas-phase reaction

$$A + B \rightarrow C$$

The reaction is first order with respect to A, and k is known to be equal to 26.0 hr^{-1} at 120°F. A will be fed in 20 per cent excess, and 90 per cent conversion of B is desired. Calculate the mols of C which will be produced per hour assuming (a) no back-mixing, and (b) perfect mixing.

Solution. The pertinent rate equation is

$$\text{Rate} = -\frac{dn_A}{dV} = kC_A$$

and, at any point in the reactor, $C_A = n_A/v$. Assuming the ideal gas law to be applicable at 3 atmospheres, $v = n_T RT/P$, where n_T, equal to $n_A + n_B + n_C$, is the total number of mols passing the point per unit time. Integration of the rate equation therefore requires the development of a relationship among n_A, n_B, and n_C. This may be obtained by making a mass balance in conjunction with the given reaction equation, which indicates that $-dn_A = -dn_B = dn_C$.

For x mols/hr of B and $1.2x$ mols/hr of A fed to the reactor, the mass-balance equations can be integrated between the reactor inlet and any point to obtain

$$1.2x - n_A = x - n_B = n_C - 0$$

from which $n_B = n_A - .2x$ and $n_C = 1.2x - n_A$, and hence $n_T = n_A + x$. Then

$$dV = -\frac{dn_A}{kC_A} = -\frac{v\,dn_A}{kn_A} = -\frac{n_T RT\,dn_A}{Pkn_A} = -\frac{(n_A + x)RT\,dn_A}{Pkn_A}$$

The last expression can be integrated between $n_A = 1.2x$ at the inlet and $n_A = .3x$ at the outlet (where $n_B = n_A - .2x = .1x$ for 90 per cent conversion of B). Thus

$$V = -\frac{RT}{Pk}\left[.3x - 1.2x + x \ln\left(\frac{.3x}{1.2x}\right)\right]$$

$$= +\frac{RT}{Pk}(.9 + \ln 4)x = \frac{2.29RT}{Pk}x$$

Substituting $V = 50$, $R = .73$, $T = 580$, $P = 3$, and $k = 26.0$ yields $x = 4.02$ mols/hr and $.9x = 3.62$ mols/hr of C produced.

For the case of perfect mixing, the rate will be constant and based on the outlet concentration. At the outlet, $n_A = .3x$ and $n_T = n_A + x = 1.3x$; hence $C_A = n_A/v = n_A P/n_T RT = .3P/1.3RT = .231P/RT$. Then

$$dV = -\frac{dn_A}{kC_A} = -\frac{RT\,dn_A}{.231\,Pk}$$

and

$$V = -\frac{RT}{.231\,Pk}(.3x - 1.2x)$$

Substituting known values and solving for x yields $x = 2.36$ mols/hr and $.9x = 2.12$ mols/hr of C produced.

Reaction rate calculations become more complicated when simultaneous or successive reactions must be considered, but only to the extent that the rate equations for all pertinent reactions must be solved simultaneously. A departure from isothermal conditions is a more troublesome problem, for it necessitates the simultaneous consideration of an energy rate equation and a reaction rate equation containing a variable rate coefficient. It is significant that the principles here presented can be readily extended to cover even that eventuality.

9.4 Mass Transfer

Rate definition. The *diffusional* or *mass-transfer* operations are, by definition, those in which phase compositions are changed by the transfer of mass from one phase to another. The rate of change is usually expressed in terms of the number of mols of a given component in one of the phases, while the pertinent extensive factor is the interfacial area between the two phases. Thus the appropriate rate definitions for unsteady-state and steady-state processes are

$$\text{Rate} = \frac{dN_A}{A\,d\theta} \tag{9.27}$$

and

$$\text{Rate} = \frac{dn_A}{dA} \tag{9.28}$$

respectively. Here again, dN_A or dn_A can be either positive or negative, depending on the phase selected as a reference, and it may be necessary to introduce a minus sign into either definition.

Rate correlation. Fugacity was identified as the appropriate driving force for mass transfer processes in the course of developing the concept of wet- and dry-bulb thermometry in Sec. 7.5. The mathematical form of the rate correlation is therefore

$$\text{Rate} = K(\bar{f}_A' - \bar{f}_A'') \tag{9.29}$$

in which K is the overall mass transfer coefficient and $\bar{f}_A'$ and $\bar{f}_A''$ are the fugacities of component A in the two phases of interest. Note that $\bar{f}_A'$ must be the greater of the two fugacities if the rate is to be positive in accordance with the rate definition. Since an erroneous assumption regarding the direction of transfer will reverse the sign of both the rate definition and the rate correlation, the ultimate rate equation will be correct in any event.

In correlating mass transfer data it is customary to assume that the resistance to the transfer is concentrated in a thin film, or *boundary layer*, of fluid* on each side of the interface and that the interface itself offers no resistance, that is, that equilibrium exists at the interface. If there is to be no accumulation of mass within the boundary layers, the rate of transfer through each layer must be equal to the overall rate; hence

$$\text{Rate} = K(\bar{f}_A{}' - \bar{f}_A{}'') \tag{9.29}$$
$$= k'(\bar{f}_A{}' - \bar{f}_{A_i}) \tag{9.29a}$$
$$= k''(\bar{f}_{A_i} - \bar{f}_A{}'') \tag{9.29b}$$

in which k' and k'' are the mass transfer coefficients associated with the respective boundary-layer resistances and $\bar{f}_{Ai}$ is the fugacity at the interface.

An algebraic rearrangement and combination of the above equation yields

$$\frac{\text{Rate}}{k'} + \frac{\text{Rate}}{k''} = (\bar{f}_A{}' - \bar{f}_{A_i}) + (\bar{f}_{A_i} - \bar{f}_A{}'') = \bar{f}_A{}' - \bar{f}_A{}'' = \frac{\text{Rate}}{K}$$

from which it can be seen that

$$\frac{1}{K} = \frac{1}{k'} + \frac{1}{k''} \tag{9.30}$$

This relationship, stating in effect that resistances in series are additive, has many applications. A similar equation can be written for heat transfer processes and, since each term represents a resistance to transfer, additional resistances such as the resistance of the tube wall separating two fluids can be included as necessary.

The fact that fugacities are not amenable to direct measurement is usually circumvented by relating fugacity to partial pressure, mol fraction, or concentration. The pertinent relationships are $\bar{f}_A = y_A f_A = y_A P = p_A$ for gases and $\bar{f}_A = x_A f_A = x_A p^*_A$ for liquids. These relationships, strictly applicable only when the assumptions presented in Sec. 7.3 are valid, are generally used even when the underlying assumptions are not entirely valid, with deviations from ideality being absorbed into the mass transfer coefficient.

The use of the foregoing relationships in conjunction with Eqs. (9.29) gives

$$\text{Rate} = K(y_A P - x_A p^*_A) \tag{9.31}$$
$$= k'(y_A P - y_{A_i} P) = k'P(y_A - y_{A_i}) \tag{9.31a}$$
$$= k''(x_{A_i} p^*_A - x_A p^*_A) = k''p^*_A(x_{A_i} - x_A) \tag{9.31b}$$

---

* The introductory development presented herein will be restricted to a consideration of vapor-liquid systems for the sake of simplicity. The analysis is generally applicable to other systems, however.

considering k' to apply to the vapor film and k'' to the liquid. The values of the coefficients in Eqs. (9.29) differ from those in Eqs. (9.31) to the extent that the latter reflect any deviations from ideality.

The driving force across the liquid film is frequently expressed in terms of concentrations rather than in terms of mol fractions. Since $x_A = N_A/N_T$ and $N_T = V\rho'$, where ρ' is the density in mols per unit volume, $x_A = N_A/V\rho' = C_A/\rho'$. Substituting into Eq. (9.31b) and factoring out $1/\rho'$ (assumed to be constant) yields

$$\text{Rate} = \frac{k''p^*_A}{\rho'}(C_{A_i} - C_A) \tag{9.32}$$

The common practice is to let $k''p^*_A/\rho' = k_L$ by definition, whereupon Eq. (9.32) reduces to

$$\text{Rate} = k_L(C_{A_i} - C_A) \tag{9.33}$$

The subscript L calls attention to the fact that k_L is associated with the liquid film and must be used in combination with a driving force expressed as a concentration difference. The usual units for k_L are mols/(ft²)(hr)(mols/ft³). Similarly, Eq. (9.31a) is generally written

$$\text{Rate} = k_G(y_A P - y_{A_i} P) = k_G P(y_A - y_{A_i}) \tag{9.34}$$

and the usual units for k_G are mols/(ft²)(hr)(atm).

Either K_G or K_L may be used as the overall mass transfer coefficient, depending on the units associated with the overall driving force. When K_G is used, it is generally convenient to introduce a new variable y^*_A such that $y^*_A P = x_A p^*_A$. This is merely a statement of Raoult's law, and it can be seen that y^*_A is the mol fraction which would be present in the vapor phase were the vapor to be in equilibrium with a liquid in which the mol fraction of A was x_A. Substituting $y^*_A P$ for $x_A p^*_A$ in Eq. (9.31) yields

$$\text{Rate} = K_G(y_A P - y^*_A P) = K_G P(y_A - y^*_A) \tag{9.35}$$

The analogous expression for a driving force expressed in concentration units is

$$\text{Rate} = K_L(C^*_A - C_A) \tag{9.36}$$

where C^*_A is the concentration which would be present in the liquid phase were the liquid to be in equilibrium with a vapor in which the mol fraction of A was y_A.

The relationships between $y^*_A P$ and C_A and between $y_A P$ and C^*_A are shown graphically in Fig. 9.2, in which the curve $a - b$ is the equilibrium curve. It is customary to assume that a straight line of slope m is a satisfactory approximation to the curve between a and b, whereupon

$$y_A P - y^*_A P = m(C^*_A - C_A) \tag{9.37}$$

A comparison of this equation with Eqs. (9.35) and (9.36) shows that

$$K_L = mK_G \qquad (9.38)$$

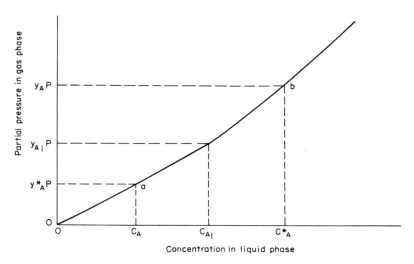

Fig. 9.2   Significance of $y^*_A P$ and C^*_A.

Further, Eq. (9.30) may now be written in either of two final forms:

$$\frac{1}{K_G} = \frac{1}{k_G} + \frac{m}{k_L} \qquad (9.39)$$

$$\frac{1}{K_L} = \frac{1}{mk_G} + \frac{1}{k_L} \qquad (9.40)$$

The correlations and auxiliary relationships presented so far pertain to the transfer of mass to or from the interface due to *turbulence* within the boundary layer. Turbulence refers to the swirls or *eddies* of flow which carry mass into and out of the boundary layer. In the absence of turbulence mass may be transferred by *molecular diffusion*. This situation is analogous to that in which heat is transferred by conduction, whereas *eddy diffusion* is analogous to heat transfer by convection. The pertinent rate correlation for molecular diffusion is

$$\text{Rate} = -D_m \frac{dC_A}{dx} \qquad (9.41)$$

in which the rate coefficient D_m is called the *molecular diffusivity*, and the gradient dC_A/dx is measured in the direction of transfer. The more general form of the correlation, equivalent to Eq. (9.11) for conductive heat transfer, is

$$\text{Rate} = -D_m(\text{grad } C_A) \qquad (9.42)$$

There is one further aspect of mass transfer phenomena which should be noted. Consider a two-component system for the sake of simplicity: If a concentration or partial pressure difference exists within a phase for component A, an equal but opposite driving force must exist for component B. Thus when A is transferred in one direction, B will be transferred in the opposite direction. The rates of transfer will be found to be equal, and this phenomenon is known as *equimolal counter-diffusion*.

The effect of equimolal counter-diffusion may be cancelled by bulk flow which exactly compensates for the expected transfer of component B. Consider, for example, the humidification of air by the mass transfer of water from an adjoining liquid surface. The fact that water vapor moves through the gas film adjacent to the surface implies the existence of a partial pressure difference, and the concept of equimolal counter-diffusion requires that air be transferred in the opposite direction at an equal rate. The fact that air does not cross the interface can be accounted for by considering the entire vapor-air mixture to be moving away from the interface toward the main gas phase at such a rate that the *net* flow of air through the boundary layer is zero.

When the net rate of transfer of component B is zero, the transfer of component A is called *diffusion through a stagnant layer*. Since the bulk flow described above carries A as well as B away from the interface, the rate of transfer due to bulk flow and that due to the usual mass-transfer driving force must be added to obtain the net rate of transfer of component A. It is customary to incorporate both effects into a single rate coefficient, and the numerical value of the rate coefficient for diffusion through a stagnant layer will accordingly differ from that for equimolal counter-diffusion.

In the completely general case, the actual mass transfer conditions may lie anywhere in between the two extremes of equimolal counter-diffusion and diffusion through a stagnant layer. The rate for equimolal counter-diffusion can be multiplied by a *relative-velocity factor*, ϕ, to correct for the extent to which the entire phase moves away from the interface. ϕ will be equal to one for the case of equimolal counter-diffusion, and it is normally incorporated directly into the rate coefficient for the case of diffusion through a stagnant layer.

Process application. For the most part the mass transfer processes of practical interest in chemical engineering occur under steady-state conditions, and the pertinent rate equation for the overall transfer is therefore

$$\frac{dn_A}{dA} = K_G P(y_A - y^*_A) \tag{9.43}$$

or
$$\frac{dn_A}{dA} = K_L(C^*_A - C_A) \tag{9.44}$$

The manipulation of either equation to permit integration parallels the development for heat transfer processes in Sec. 9.2, the only significant difference being the use of a differential mass balance instead of a differential energy balance. Humidification in a wetted-wall column will be considered by way of illustration.

In a wetted wall column, as the name implies, the liquid flows down the wall of the column in a thin film while the gas normally flows upward through the center. The fact that the liquid film is thin makes it possible to assume an interfacial contact area equal to the inside area of the column wall. Thus $A = \pi D z$ and $dA = \pi D \, dz$, where z is the column height.

A schematic flow diagram for a wetted-wall column is shown in Fig. 9.3, in which V is the vapor rate in mols per unit time, L is the liquid rate in the

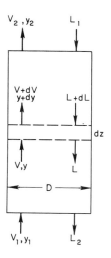

Fig. 9.3   Schematic flow diagram for a wetted-wall humidification column.

same units, and y is the mol fraction water in the vapor phase and corresponds to y_A in the rate equation. Except for the difference in orientation, the similarity to the heat exchanger schematic shown in Fig. 9.1 should be immediately apparent. Note particularly that the variables at height z are L, V, and y, whereas the corresponding values at height $z + dz$ are $L + dL$, $V + dV$, and $y + dy$. This analysis follows the recommendations given in Sec. 9.1, and the fact that the flow is countercurrent will take care of itself.

The problem now is to relate n_A to y_A to permit the integration of Eq. (9.43), the choice of this equation over Eq. (9.44) being dictated by the fact that there is no concentration difference in the liquid phase in this case. Under steady-state conditions, the general mass-rate balance equation reduces to $m_i = m_o$, or, making a water balance around the differential element of height dz as the system,

$$Vy + (L + dL) = [(V + dV)(y + dy)] + L$$

or

$$dn_A = dL = Vdy + ydV + dydV \tag{9.45}$$

The principles of calculus permit the elimination of the second-order differential, and the remaining terms on the right-hand side of Eq. (9.45) can be combined to obtain

$$dn_A = dL = d(Vy) \tag{9.46}$$

With $d(Vy)$ substituted for dn_A and $\pi D dz$ substituted for dA, Eq. (9.43) can be rearranged and integrated to obtain

$$\pi D \int_0^z dz = \pi Dz = \frac{1}{P}\int_{y_1}^{y_2} \frac{d(Vy)}{K_G(y^* - y)} \tag{9.47}$$

Since the liquid phase is pure water, y^* depends only on the vapor pressure p^*, which in turn depends on the water temperature. Prob. 7-15 correctly suggested conditions under which the water temperature (and hence y^*) might be held constant. The final integration of Eq. (9.47) would also appear to require that V be expressed as a function of y. In this particular case, however, it has been found that both V and K_G vary with y but that the quotient V/K_G is essentially constant. Eq. (9.47) can therefore be written

$$\pi Dz = \frac{V}{K_G P}\int_{y_1}^{y_2} \frac{dy}{y^* - y} \tag{9.48}$$

and integrated to obtain the desired final relationship

$$\pi Dz = \frac{V}{K_G P}\ln\left(\frac{y^* - y_1}{y^* - y_2}\right) \tag{9.49}$$

For the more general case in which a relationship between V and y is needed, a total-mass balance will be pertinent:

$$V + (L + dL) = (V + dV) + L$$

which reduces to $dL = dV$. This may be combined with Eq. (9.46) to obtain $dV = d(Vy)$, and integration of this relationship from the bottom of the column to height z yields

$$V - V_1 = Vy - V_1 y_1$$

from which

$$V = \frac{V_1(1 - y_1)}{1 - y}$$

$$Vy = \frac{V_1(1 - y_1)y}{1 - y}$$

and

$$d(Vy) = \frac{V_1(1 - y_1)}{(1 - y)^2}dy \tag{9.50}$$

In more complicated applications where the compositions of both phases are changing, it is frequently advantageous to convert mol fractions to mol ratios. This is particularly true when both phases contain an *inert* component which is not transferred. The rate at which the inert components flow through the system is everywhere the same, and the advantage of expressing concentrations in mols per mol of inert material should be obvious.

In many situations of practical interest physical measurement of the interfacial area between phases is impracticable or even impossible. This difficulty is surmounted by letting $dA = adV = aSdz$, where a is the interfacial area per unit volume, V is the effective tower volume, and S is the cross-sectional area of the tower. a may then be transferred to the right-hand side of Eq. (9.43) or (9.44) and the product K_Ga or K_La may be treated as a lumped coefficient to be evaluated experimentally. Eq. (9.48) might therefore be written

$$z = \frac{V}{K_GaSP} \int_{y_1}^{y_2} \frac{dy}{y^* - y} \tag{9.51}$$

The concept of a *transfer unit* is frequently used as an alternative approach to mass transfer calculations comparable to the above example. The integral in Eq. (9.51) is an effective measure of the difficulty of the proposed transfer, for it is the ratio of the change to be effected (the integral of dy) to the available driving force. By definition, the numerical value of the integral is equal to the *number of transfer units*, N_{TU}, required for the specified change; or,

$$N_{\text{TU}} = \int_{y_1}^{y_2} \frac{dy}{y^* - y} \tag{9.52}$$

More transfer units will obviously be required if the transfer is made more difficult either by extending the limits of the integration or by providing a smaller driving force.

The quotient V/K_GaSP in Eq. (9.51) has the dimensions of length, where length in this case clearly implies height. Since this quotient is multiplied by the number of transfer units to obtain the total height of the column, it is considered to define the *height of a transfer unit*, abbreviated HTU. It can be seen that the height of a transfer unit reflects the characteristics of the process equipment, and experimental mass transfer data are often correlated directly in terms of HTU values rather than in terms of rate coefficients. HTU values for many systems of interest are reported as functions of gas and liquid rates and system geometry.

The definitions of the HTU and N_{TU} presented here are not directly applicable to all mass transfer operations. Modified definitions are required to permit the use of K_L instead of K_G and to provide for the effect of bulk flow away from the interface in the case of diffusion through a stagnant layer.

The basic concept is the same in all applications, however. As a matter of fact, it is also applicable to heat transfer processes and even has some advantages over the more conventional coefficient approach.

EXAMPLE 9.5. Air having an initial dew point of 36°F is to be fed to a wetted-wall column 3 inches in diameter at a rate of 130 pounds per hour and is to emerge with a relative humidity of 43.5 per cent at 80°F. The humidification is to be carried out adiabatically at atmospheric pressure, with a constant water temperature of 64°F. Laboratory tests carried out under similar conditions indicate the height of a transfer unit, as used in Eq. (9.51), to be 13.3 feet. (a) What height column will be needed for the process? (b) Calculate the value of K_G for the given conditions.

Solution. For a dew point of 36°F the psychrometric chart in Appendix C-7 gives $H = 0.007$, from which $y_1 = .007/1.007 = 0.00695$. At 80°F, $p^* = 0.5067$ psia, $p_2 = (.435)(.5067) = 0.2205$, and $y_2 = .2205/14.7 = 0.015$. At 64°F, $p^* = 0.2949$ psia and $y^* = .2949/14.7 = 0.02005$. Integrating Eq. (9.52) and substituting the foregoing values,

$$N_{TU} = \ln\left(\frac{.02005 - .00695}{.02005 - .015}\right) = \ln\left(\frac{.0131}{.00505}\right)$$

$$= \ln 2.6 = 0.956$$

$$z = (N_{TU})(HTU) = (.956)(13.3) = 12.7 \text{ ft}$$

For (b), $V = 130/29 = 4.48$ mols/hr; $S = \pi D^2/4 = \pi(.25)^2/4 = 0.0491$ ft^2; $a = \pi Dz/\pi(D^2/4)z = 4/D = 4/.25 = 16$ ft^2/ft^3; hence

$$HTU = 13.3 = \frac{V}{K_G a SP} = \frac{4.48}{K_G(16)(.0491)(1)}$$

from which $K_G = 0.429$ mols/(ft^2)(hr)(atm).

The equilibrium stage method. In many mass transfer processes two phases are brought together for a short time and then separated. The techniques already presented in this section could be applied to such processes, but the *equilibrium stage* method is more widely used. In this method the first step is to calculate the phase compositions which would have resulted had equilibrium been reached in the time during which the phases were in contact. An empirical *stage efficiency* factor is then applied to provide for the fact that true equilibrium was not in fact achieved.

A typical definition of stage efficiency is

$$E_m = \frac{y_o - y_i}{y^*_o - y_i}(100) \tag{9.53}$$

in which y_i and y_o are the actual mol fractions of the more volatile component in the entering and leaving vapor, and y^*_o is the mol fraction which would result were the effluent vapor to be in equilibrium with the effluent liquid.

The particular efficiency defined by Eq. (9.53) is called the *Murphree gas efficiency*. In the usual application, either y_o or y_i is known initially, and the equilibrium calculations yield a value for y^*_o. A knowledge of the stage efficiency then permits the calculation of y_i or y_o, whichever is unknown. The corresponding mol fraction for the liquid phase can then be determined via a mass balance calculation.

EXAMPLE 9.6. Refer to Fig. 7.1 in Sec. 7.3 and assume the abscissa to be mol per cent A instead of weight per cent. Equal mol quantities of a saturated vapor analyzing 60 per cent B (the more volatile component) and a saturated liquid analyzing 50 per cent B are subjected to a single-stage contact at 385°. The molal latent heats of A and B are equal, and the contact is adiabatic. Calculate the mol fraction B in the effluent vapor and liquid streams for an anticipated Murphree gas efficiency of 80 per cent.

Solution. The equilibrium phase compositions at 385°, obtained from Fig. 7.1, are 68.5 per cent B in the vapor and 35 per cent B in the liquid. Substituting into Eq. (9.53),

$$E_m = 80 = \frac{y_o - .60}{.685 - .60}(100)$$

from which $y_o = 0.668$. x_o may now be determined by making an $M_i = M_o$ mass balance for component B:

$$V_i y_i + L_i x_i = V_o y_o + L_o x_o$$

The fact that the molal heats of vaporization are equal now becomes pertinent, for it means that the vaporization of a given quantity of B must be accompanied by the condensation of an equal quantity of A if the energy balance is to be satisfied (assuming sensible heat effects to be negligible), and hence that V and L will be constant. For a basis of one mol of vapor and one mol of liquid fed to the stage, then,

$$(1)(.60) + (1)(.50) = (1)(.668) + (1)(x_o)$$

from which $x_o = 0.432$. The effluent compositions are thus found to be 66.8 per cent B in the vapor and 43.2 per cent B in the liquid.

9.5 *Flow of Confined Fluids*

Fluid flow processes involve the bulk transport or movement of fluids relative to a bounding surface. The present treatment is restricted to fluids flowing through confining ducts, but in the completely general case the bounding surface may be the surface of an object around which the fluid passes instead of the surface of the duct. The fact that the movement is relative is also significant, for in many applications the bounding surface is also in motion with respect to a fixed reference point. In the limiting case the fluid itself may be at rest while the bounding surface moves through it. A solid object sinking in water is an obvious example of the latter situation and is considered to be a fluid flow process as here defined. Such processes are considered separately in Sec. 9.6.

The pertinent rate in the flow of confined fluids is simply the mass rate at which the fluid crosses the boundaries of a system or is accumulated within a system. While it is possible to begin the development by defining rates analogous to those presented in the earlier sections of this chapter, an approach based on the direct application of the mass balance will be more advantageous in this case. It is shown in due course that the results of the latter approach are not inconsistent with the more generalized approach used previously.

The mass-rate balance. Applied over a differential time increment and subject to the restriction that no mass is converted to energy, the general mass balance presented in Sec. 2.3 can be written

$$\delta M_i - \delta M_o = dM_s \tag{9.54}$$

in which dM_s is the change of mass within the system. A rate equation is obtained by dividing through by $d\theta$,

$$\frac{\delta M_i}{d\theta} - \frac{\delta M_o}{d\theta} = \frac{dM_s}{d\theta} \tag{9.55}$$

This equation clearly shows that, in the completely general case, fluid flow processes involve three separate and distinct rates—the rate of flow into the system, the rate of flow out of the system, and the rate of accumulation within the system. Only for a steady-state system does the right-hand side of Eq. (9.55) vanish, whereupon we might write

$$\text{Rate} = \frac{\delta M_i}{d\theta} = \frac{\delta M_o}{d\theta} \tag{9.56}$$

Except for a missing extensive factor, Eq. (9.56) is analogous to the rate definitions used previously. The pertinent extensive factor is the cross-sectional area normal to the direction of flow. Unfortunately the areas at the inlet and outlet may be different, and it is not feasible to incorporate a generalized extensive factor into Eq. (9.56). Still, it may be helpful to recognize that the rate of flow at any one point can be defined by

$$\text{Rate} = \frac{\delta M}{S d\theta} \tag{9.57}$$

as long as S represents the cross-sectional area at that point. The rate defined by Eq. (9.57) is called the *mass velocity* and is commonly represented by the symbol G.

A point-rate might also be defined in terms of the flowing volume rather than the flowing mass,

$$\text{Rate} = \frac{\delta V}{S d\theta} \tag{9.58}$$

The rate so defined is identically equal to the *mean linear velocity*, u. Since $M = \rho V$ and $\delta M = \rho \delta V$, it can be seen that the relationship between G and u is simply

$$G = u\rho \tag{9.59}$$

Eqs. (9.57) and (9.59) may be combined to obtain

$$\frac{\delta M}{d\theta} = GS = u\rho S \tag{9.60}$$

and substitution into Eq. (9.55) yields

$$(u\rho S)_i - (u\rho S)_o = \frac{dM_s}{d\theta} = \frac{d(\rho V)_s}{d\theta} \tag{9.61}$$

Eq. (9.61) is an alternative mathematical statement of the Law of Conservation of Mass and is often called the *equation of continuity* or simply the *continuity equation*. For a steady-state process it may be written

$$u\rho S = \text{a constant} \tag{9.62}$$

This relationship has obvious significance when the flowing fluid is compressible (variable ρ) or when the duct is not of uniform cross-sectional area.

EXAMPLE 9.7. Steam at 25 psia and 400°F flows into a nozzle having inlet and outlet cross-sectional areas of 3 and 0.5 square inches, respectively, and discharges at atmospheric pressure. Assuming the flow to be adiabatic and reversible, calculate the linear velocity at the nozzle exit for an inlet velocity of 20 feet per second.

Solution. The continuity equation will be applicable and may be written

$$u_o = \frac{u_i \rho_i S_i}{\rho_o S_o} = \frac{(20)(\rho_i)(3)}{(\rho_o)(0.5)}$$

At 25 psia and 400°F the Steam Tables give $V_i = 1/\rho_i = 20.30$ ft³/lb. Since an adiabatic, reversible process is also isentropic, the outlet conditions are defined by $P = 14.7$ psia and $S_o = S_i = 1.8160$ BTU/(lb)(°R), the latter value being obtained from the Steam Tables for the given inlet conditions. For $P = 14.7$ and $S = 1.8160$, the Steam Tables give $V_o = 1/\rho_o = 30.60$ ft³/lb, and the solution is readily completed:

$$u_o = \frac{(20)(30.60)(3)}{(20.30)(.5)} = 181 \text{ ft/sec}$$

Rate correlation. The relationship between point rate and an appropriate driving force is most readily derived by applying the general energy balance and the second law statement to an incremental length of duct as a system. For steady-state conditions and a basis of a unit mass of fluid flowing, the energy balance may be written

$$-d\underline{H} - \frac{udu}{g_c} - \frac{gdz}{g_c} + \delta Q - \delta \underline{W} = 0 \tag{9.63}$$

It is shown in Sec. 6.2 that $d\underline{H} = Td\underline{S} + \underline{V}dP$. Further, the second law statement can be solved for δQ to obtain $\delta Q = Td\underline{S} - \delta \underline{lw}$. Using these relationships to eliminate $d\underline{H}$ and δQ from Eq. (9.63),

$$-Td\underline{S} - \underline{V}dP - \frac{udu}{g_c} - \frac{gdz}{g_c} + Td\underline{S} - \delta \underline{lw} - \delta \underline{W} = 0 \tag{9.64}$$

Cancellation of $Td\underline{S}$ and rearrangement yields

$$\underline{V}dP + \frac{udu}{g_c} + \frac{gdz}{g_c} = -\delta \underline{W} - \delta \underline{lw} \tag{9.65}$$

This equation is often referred to as the *mechanical energy balance.*

The work term in Eq. (9.65) provides for flow through a pump or compressor, where work is done on the system, or through a turbine or expansion engine whereby the system does work. For flow through a simple duct or pipe the $\delta \underline{W}$ term drops out and the equation reduces to

$$\frac{dP}{\rho} + \frac{udu}{g_c} + \frac{gdz}{g_c} = -\delta \underline{lw} \tag{9.66}$$

in which $\underline{V}$ has been replaced with its equivalent, $1/\rho$. The lost work term in this equation accounts for the energy expended as a consequence of fluid friction. For the ideal case of frictionless flow, $\delta \underline{lw}$ is zero and

$$\frac{dP}{\rho} + \frac{udu}{g_c} + \frac{gdz}{g_c} = 0 \tag{9.67}$$

This form of the mechanical energy balance is known as the *Bernoulli equation.*

An alternative derivation of Eq. (9.66) provides insight into the significance of the lost work term. The usual forces acting on a fluid flow system are those due to fluid pressure, gravitational force, and the force associated with fluid friction, and any net force must result in acceleration of the fluid in accordance with Newton's law. The derivation is accomplished by writing a force balance around an element of fluid δM flowing in the positive x direction through an incremental length dx of a circular duct having a diameter D and a cross-sectional area S:

Let P, z, and u be the pressure, elevation, and velocity, respectively, at point x, with corresponding values of $P + dP$, $z + dz$, and $u + du$ at point $x + dx$, dx being positive in the direction of flow. For these conditions, the net force due to fluid pressure acting on δM will be, in the direction of flow, $[P - (P + dP)]S = -SdP$. The total gravitational force will be $\delta Mg/g_c$, but only the component in the direction of flow is pertinent. This is readily shown to be $(\delta Mg/g_c)(-dz/dx)$. The force associated with fluid friction may be expressed as the product of a *shear stress*, force per unit area, and the area of the duct wall over which it is applied. Letting the shear stress be denoted by τ_s, the corresponding force is accordingly $\tau_s(\pi Ddx)$. Since this force opposes the flow, the force in the direction of flow is $-\tau_s(\pi Ddx)$.

The three forces in the direction of flow may now be summed and substituted into Newton's law to obtain their relationship to fluid acceleration:

$$-SdP - \frac{\delta Mg}{g_c}\left(\frac{dz}{dx}\right) - \tau_s(\pi Ddx) = \frac{\delta Ma}{g_c} = \frac{\delta M}{g_c}\left(\frac{du}{d\theta}\right)$$

Now let $\rho Sdx = \rho\delta V = \delta M$ be substituted into the equation,

$$-SdP - \frac{\rho Sg}{g_c}dz - \tau_s(\pi Ddx) = \frac{\rho Sdxdu}{g_cd\theta} = \frac{\rho Sudu}{g_c}$$

and the equation divided through by $\rho S = \rho\pi D^2/4$ and rearranged to obtain

$$\frac{dP}{\rho} + \frac{udu}{g_c} + \frac{gdz}{g_c} = -\frac{4\tau_sdx}{\rho D} \tag{9.68}$$

This equation is seen to be comparable to Eq. (9.66), and the comparison indicates that $\delta \underline{lw} = 4\tau_sdx/\rho D$.

All terms in the mechanical energy balance and its reduced forms, including Eq. (9.68), have the dimensions FL/M, the corresponding units in the English system being ft-lb$_f$ per lb$_m$. These units are commonly reduced to feet even though the cancellation of lb$_f$ with lb$_m$ is not strictly proper, and this procedure gives rise to the use of *feet of head* or simply *head* as a basic unit of energy in fluid flow calculations. Specific reference may be made to the pressure head, velocity head, static head (due to elevation), or friction head. The student will do well to keep the true significance of the term head and its pseudo-dimension of length firmly in mind.

The left-hand side of Eq. (9.68) can be considered to represent the driving potential for fluid flow, whereas the right-hand side accounts for the resistance to flow. A rate correlation form analogous to those encountered earlier in the chapter can be obtained by multiplying Eq. (9.68) through by $-\rho Du/4\tau_sdx$, whereupon

$$\text{Rate} = u = \left(\frac{\rho Du}{4\tau_sdx}\right)\left(-\frac{dP}{\rho} - \frac{udu}{g_c} - \frac{gdz}{g_c}\right)$$
$$= \beta\left(-\frac{dP}{\rho} - \frac{udu}{g_c} - \frac{gdz}{g_c}\right) \tag{9.69}$$

in which $\beta = \rho Du/4\tau_sdx$ might be considered to be the rate coefficient for fluid flow. It would appear that the coefficient has been made to depend on the rate by the introduction of u into the numerator. Actually, the shear stress τ_s is itself a complex function of fluid velocity, and the inclusion of an additional velocity term in the rate coefficient merely changes the form of the coefficient-rate relationship which already existed. It is also noteworthy that the driving force in Eq. (9.69) includes a function of the rate u.

The shear stress in Eq. (9.69) or (9.68) can be evaluated from experimental data and may be presented as a graphical function of fluid properties, system geometry, and flow rate. A somewhat more common technique is to define a *friction factor, f*:

$$f = \frac{2g_c D \delta \underline{l} w}{u^2 dx} = \frac{8g_c \tau_s}{\rho u^2} \tag{9.70}$$

from which

$$\delta \underline{l} w = \frac{f u^2 dx}{2g_c D} \tag{9.71}$$

This equation can be used to eliminate $\delta \underline{l} w$ from Eq. (9.66) if desired. Experimental data provide the basis for a graphical relationship between f and the pertinent environmental factors—fluid properties, system geometry, and flow rate. It should be emphasized that the definition of friction factor given by Eq. (9.70) is not universal. A factor equal to $f/4$ is often used, and friction-factor plots presented in the literature must be used with care to insure that they are properly interpreted.

Process application. The differential rate equation for fluid flow through confining ducts is given by Eq. (9.69) or its equivalent in terms of a friction factor. The presence of the rate itself in both the rate coefficient and the driving force complicates the process application somewhat but does not lead to insurmountable difficulties. At worst, a trial-and-error solution will be necessary.

EXAMPLE 9.8. Water is to be pumped through 200 feet of 1-inch pipe into an elevated tank at a rate of 25 gpm. The outlet end of the pipe is open to the atmosphere and is 40 feet above the inlet. What pressure must be provided at the inlet end of the pipe?

Solution. For the pipe as the system, the continuity equation shows that u will be the same at all points since ρ and S do not change. Eq. (9.69) can therefore be integrated following a separation of variables:

$$\frac{4\tau_s u dx}{\rho D u} = -\frac{dP}{\rho} - \frac{u du}{g_c} - \frac{g dz}{g_c}$$

and

$$\frac{4\tau_s L}{\rho D} = -\frac{P_o - P_i}{\rho} - \frac{g}{g_c}(z_o - z_i)$$

This may be solved for P_i to obtain

$$P_i = P_o + \frac{\rho g}{g_c}(z_o - z_i) + \frac{4\tau_s L}{D}$$

The detailed procedure for evaluating τ_s lies beyond the scope of the present treatment. Suffice it to say that both f and τ_s can be determined when u, D, the surface roughness of the pipe, and the fluid density and viscosity are known. The use of a suitable graphical correlation yields $f = 0.022$ and $\tau_s = 0.56$ lb_f/ft^2. The above equation can now be solved for P_i, with a check of the units disclosing that both P_i and P_o must be expressed in lb_f/ft^2:

$$P_i = (14.7)(144) + (62.4)(40) + \frac{(4)(.56)(200)}{(1/12)}$$

$$= 9990 \ lb_f/ft^2 \text{ or } 69.3 \text{ psia}$$

9.6 Flow around Immersed Objects

Rate definition. The rate definition for flow around immersed objects differs from that pertaining to flow through ducts in only two respects. First, it is important to remember that the point rate u refers to the *relative* velocity of the fluid with respect to the immersed object. Second, it will usually be convenient to express the rate in terms of the *superficial velocity* u_o, defined as the relative velocity at which the fluid would be moving were the cross-sectional area not partially blocked by the immersed object. For the case of an unconfined fluid, u_o is called the *free stream velocity* and denotes the relative velocity of the fluid at a distance from the object such that local velocity perturbations due to the presence of the object need not be considered.

Rate correlation. The rate correlation for flow around immersed objects may take either of two forms, depending on whether or not the object is freely suspended in the fluid or is independently supported. For the case of free suspension the object will be subject to a buoyant force as well as to gravitational force and the force associated with fluid friction. The latter force, called the *drag force*, is only partially attributable to the *skin friction* or shear stress resulting from flow along a surface of the object. The other contributing factor is the fact that the fluid is diverted as it flows around the object, and it is well known that a streamlined object presents less resistance to flow than does a bluff object. The resistance to flow associated with the shape of the object is called *form drag*. Thus the drag force includes both skin friction and form drag.

Newton's law may be applied to a solid object of mass M falling freely with respect to a surrounding fluid to obtain the relationship

$$Mg - \frac{\rho_f Mg}{\rho_s} - g_c F_D = Ma = M\frac{du}{d\theta} \tag{9.72}$$

in which ρ_s and ρ_f are the densities of the solid object and of the fluid, respectively, and F_D is the drag force. The first term in Eq. (9.72) represents the gravitational force. The second term represents the buoyant force, the volume of fluid displaced by the object being equal to M/ρ_s, the volume of the object. As written, Eq. (9.72) applies only when the object is *falling* with respect to the fluid. Application to a rising object requires that the sign on F_D be reversed since the drag force always opposes the direction of motion.

In most applications steady-state conditions will prevail and Eq. (9.72) can be reduced to

$$Mg - \frac{\rho_f Mg}{\rho_s} - g_c F_D = 0 \qquad (9.73)$$

The equivalent rate correlation form, analogous to Eq. (9.69) for flow through ducts, is

$$\text{Rate} = u_o = \frac{u_o}{g_c F_D}\left(Mg - \frac{\rho_f Mg}{\rho_s}\right) \qquad (9.74)$$

The drag force F_D is a non-linear function of the density and viscosity of the fluid, the size and shape of the object, the proximity of other objects or duct walls, and the relative velocity. It is usually correlated graphically in terms of a drag coefficient C_D which is analogous to the friction factor pertinent to flow through ducts. The relationship between F_D and C_D is

$$F_D = \frac{C_D u_o^2 \rho A_p}{2g_c} \qquad (9.75)$$

in which A_p is the projected area of the object, normal to the direction of flow.

The elimination of the buoyant force term from Eq. (9.72) makes the equation applicable to the case of fluid flow around an object which is independently supported. However, this situation is most likely to be encountered when the fluid is flowing through a fixed bed composed of a large number of similar objects each of which is supported by those below it or by a retaining screen or grid across the bottom of the bed. Eq. (9.69) rather than a modified form of Eq. (9.72) is commonly used as the rate correlation for such applications. A modified definition of f is used, and the relationship between f and the environmental factors which affect it will, of course, be different than that for the case of flow through an unobstructed passage.

Process application. The application of Eq. (9.74) parallels that of Eq. (9.69) and need not be discussed in detail. The case of steady-state flow through a fixed bed of supported objects is also amenable to a straightforward analysis similar to that illustrated in Ex. 9.8, the only real difference being in the steps and techniques used to determine the proper value for the modified friction factor. This determination, as has already been noted, does not lie within the scope of the present treatment.

EXAMPLE 9.9. For $0.001 \leq uD \leq 0.01$, the drag force acting on spherical particles settling in water can be correlated by the equation

$F_D = 0.00035(uD)^{1.365}$, where F_D is in lb_f, u is the settling velocity in ft/sec, and D is the particle diameter in inches. Calculate the settling velocity for a particle of alumina (sp. gr. = 4.0) 0.012 inches in diameter.

Solution. Cancelling g/g_c and substituting $\rho_f/\rho_s = 1/4$, Eq. (9.73) can be written

$$F_D = 0.00035(uD)^{1.365} = M - .25M = .75M$$

Then

$$M = \rho_s V = \rho_s \frac{\pi D^3}{6} = \frac{(4)(62.4)(\pi)(.012/12)^3}{6}$$

$$= 1.307 \times 10^{-7} \text{ lbs}$$

$$(uD)^{1.365} = \frac{(.75)(1.307)(10^{-7})}{.00035} = 0.00028$$

from which $uD = 0.0025$ and $u = .0025/.012 = 0.208$ ft/sec.

One of the more important applications of the relationships for flow through a bed of solid particles is to the operation of filtration. A consideration of the unsteady-state aspect of batch filtration should be informative. When a liquid-solid mixture or *slurry* is fed to a batch filtration process, the filtrate flowing out of the process leaves behind an ever-increasing quantity of solid material which offers resistance to flow just as the permanent filter medium does. Thus resistance to flow increases gradually as the process continues. The rate of filtration will accordingly fall unless the driving force is increased in proportion to the increased resistance. In any event the resistance to flow will clearly depend on the quantity of solids collected as well as on such variables as particle size and shape, fluid viscosity, and the *void space* or *porosity* of the cake, that is, the interstitial volume not occupied by solid material.

The rate at which fluid flows through a filter quite frequently falls in the range where it can be expressed as a linear function of the driving force. Further, driving forces other than an applied pressure difference can usually be neglected. For these conditions the rate equation for filtration can be written

$$u_o = \frac{dV}{Sd\theta} = K\left(-\frac{dP}{dL}\right) \tag{9.75}$$

in which V is the volume of filtrate collected, L is the equivalent thickness of the cake of solid material which has been deposited, and K is the rate coefficient and depends on the physical properties of the cake and of the fluid.

The pressure drop in Eq. (9.75) is an independent variable, but L and V must be related before the equation can be integrated. A mass balance will yield the necessary relationship when the porosity of the cake and the solids content of the slurry feed are known. Eq. (9.75) can then be integrated to determine either filter area, filtration time for a given filtrate volume, or the volume of filtrate which can be collected in a given time.

The foregoing analysis has been oversimplified in three important respects. First, it assumes a constant pressure drop, and this need not be the case. Second, it neglects the resistance of the permanent filter medium and feed and discharge lines. And third, it assumes K to be a constant, whereas filter cakes are often compressible and cake porosity may change as filtration proceeds. The general rate concept embodied in Eq. (9.75) is applicable even when one or more of these assumptions is invalid, although the detailed calculations will be considerably more complicated.

9.7 Conclusion

We can sympathize fully if the student finds himself somewhat overwhelmed by the concentrated exposure to the rate processes which this chapter provides. Let it again be emphasized that the treatment is basically an introductory survey, even though quantitative relationships have been freely used. Perhaps the most significant conclusion to be drawn is that all design and analysis problems require the judicious application of but a few fundamental principles. If the student is diligent in his attempt to master these principles in subsequent courses, he will have little trouble with their application when the time comes.

The problem of evaluating the rate coefficient to be used in a given rate correlation has been ignored in this introductory treatment. When detailed attention is given this aspect of rate calculations in subsequent studies it v.ill be found that the marked similarity of all rate processes, here emphasized only with respect to the development of the appropriate rate equation, also extends in large part to the evaluation of the rate coefficients. The rate coefficient for convective heat transfer, that for mass transfer by eddy diffusion, and the friction factor used in fluid flow are shown to be closely related, for example. Thus recognition of the characteristics which all rate processes have in common is an important first step toward the ultimate goal of full understanding. The student who would like to have a succinct summary of these characteristics for review purposes need only turn back to Sec. 9.1.

The problems which follow are intended to fix basic principles even more firmly in mind and should also serve to convince the student that even the limited knowledge he has accumulated up to this point has quantitative usefulness. These problems have been tailored to make them consistent with this limited knowledge, but in all other respects they are wholly typical of the problems the practicing chemical engineer is expected to solve.

REVIEW, STUDY, AND DISCUSSION

9-1. Define or discuss the significance of each of the following terms: rate, extensive factor, rate correlation, rate coefficient, thermal conductivity, gradient, key reactant, space velocity, reaction mechanism, reaction order, energy of activation, irreversible reaction, diffusional or mass transfer operation, boundary layer, turbulence, eddy, molecular diffusion, eddy diffusion, molecular diffusivity, equimolal counter-diffusion, diffusion through a stagnant layer, K_G, K_L, k_G, k_L, relative velocity factor, HTU, N_{TU}, equilibrium stage, stage efficiency, mass velocity, mean linear velocity, shear stress, head, friction factor, superficial velocity, free stream velocity, drag force, skin friction, form drag, drag coefficient, slurry, void space or porosity.

9-2. Write and discuss the significance of the following equations: the Arrhenius equation, the mechanical energy balance, the Bernoulli equation, the continuity equation, Newton's second law of motion.

9-3. Refer to Ex. 9.1 in Sec. 9.2. How long would it take to cool the copper sheet to the same final temperature if the sheet were only 0.125 inches thick?

9-4. 100 gallons of water, initially at 60°F, are to be heated to 180°F in a jacketed vessel having an effective heat transfer surface of 23.6 ft². The heat will be supplied by steam condensing at a constant temperature of 230°F in the jacket, and the overall heat transfer coefficient is estimated to be 250 BTU/(ft²)(hr)(F°). Sufficient agitation will be provided to permit the assumption of a uniform water temperature at all times. How long will it take to heat the water to the desired final temperature?

9-5. At what rate (gal/hr) can water be heated in the vessel described in Prob. 9-4 if water is fed continuously at 60°F and removed at 180°F? (Note: The temperature of the water in the vessel will also be 180°F.) At what rate must steam be supplied to the vessel jacket?

9-6. Refer to Fig. 9.1 in Sec. 9.2. Calculate the required exchanger length when $D = 1$ in., $T_1' = 70°F$, $T_1 = 150°F$, $T_2 = 90°F$, $w = 1000$ lbs/hr, $w' = 1500$ lbs/hr, $C = C' = 1.0$ BTU/(lb)(F°), and $U = 150$ BTU/(ft²)(hr)(F°).

9-7. Derive an expression equivalent to Eq. (9.17) for the case of two streams flowing through a double-pipe heat exchanger in the same direction. Using the conditions (except T_2) and calculated exchanger length from Prob. 9-6, calculate the outlet temperatures of the two streams if the flow were to be made parallel instead of countercurrent.

9-8. The reaction $2A + B \rightarrow A_2B$ is known to be first order with respect to B. For rate $= -dN_B/Vd\theta$ by definition, the rate constant has been determined to be 0.2 reciprocal minutes. Assuming the volume of the reacting mass to remain constant, how long will it take to convert 95 per cent of the B in a batch reactor if the initial concentration of B is one mol per cubic foot? If it takes 5 minutes per batch to fill and empty the reactor, how many batches can be processed per hour? How big should the reactor be if A_2B is to be produced at a rate of 40 mols per hour under these conditions?

9-9. Refer to Ex. 9.4 in Sec. 9.3. For the case of no back-mixing, what percentage conversion will be obtained in the reactor if both A and B are fed at a rate of 4.02 mols per hour? Since feeding excess A improves conversion, why shouldn't a large percentage of excess A be recommended for the operation of this reactor?

9-10. The heat transferred in a double-pipe heat exchanger must pass through a fluid film at the inside surface, the wall of the tube, and a fluid film at the outside surface. Let h_i, h_o, T_i and T_o be the inside and outside film coefficients and surface temperatures, respectively, at a point where the inside and outside fluid temperatures are T and T', also respectively.

a) Write separate rate equations for the transfer through each film and through the tube wall. (Note that the areas associated with each transfer are all different.)

b) Derive an expression similar to Eq. (9.30) in Sec. 9.4 relating the overall coefficient U to the film coefficients and the thermal conductivity and thickness of the tube wall.

9-11. Write the differential rate equation for steady-state convective heat transfer, substitute $mCdT$ for δq and πDdx for dA, and derive an expression analogous to Eq. (9.51) in Sec. 9.4. Define an HTU and N_{TU} for heat transfer on the basis of the expression derived.

9-12. Refer to Ex. 9.5 in Sec. 9.4. Assuming K_G to be proportional to the air velocity raised to the 0.8 power, calculate the temperature and per cent humidity of the outlet air for an air rate twice the design rate. (Note that the outlet wet-bulb temperature must be 64°F if the humidification is to be adiabatic.)

9-13. Refer to Fig. 7.1 in Sec. 7.3 and assume the abscissa to be mol per cent A instead of weight per cent. A saturated vapor analyzing 55 per cent B and a saturated liquid analyzing 40 per cent B are contacted in a single stage. The liquid/vapor ratio in both the feed and effluent streams is 0.8 mols per mol, and the effluent liquid is found to contain 0.33 mol fraction B. Calculate the Murphree gas efficiency of the stage.

9-14. An incompressible fluid flows through a pipe of diameter D_1 with a mean linear velocity u_1. A restriction in the line has a diameter D_2. Derive an expression relating the velocity through the restriction, u_2, to u_1, D_1, and D_2.

9-15. An ideal gas flows isothermally through a pipe of uniform cross-section. The gas enters at 30 psig and 80°F with a linear velocity of 10 feet per second and leaves at a lower pressure because of friction. Derive an expression relating the velocity at any point to the pressure at that point.

9-16. A large tank is being drained by a siphon which discharges at atmospheric pressure as shown in Fig. P9.16. Using the mechanical energy

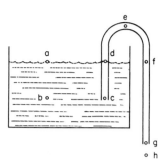

Fig. P9.16

balance, compare the relative magnitudes of the pressure, velocity, and static heads at points a through h. What variables will determine the rate of discharge through the siphon? Is there any limitation on the elevation of point e?

9-17. Refer to Prob. 9-14. Integrate the Bernoulli equation between points 1 and 2 assuming the pipe to be horizontal. Substitute the answer from Prob. 9-14 into the integrated expression and solve for u_1 as a function of P_1, P_2, D_1, and D_2. On the basis of the resulting expression, suggest a practical method for experimentally determining the flow rate in the pipe.

9-18. Water drains from a cylindrical tank at a rate which depends on the level z (in feet) in the tank, the rate correlation being $CFM = 0.51(z)^{0.57}$. The tank is 6 feet in diameter and 6 feet high. (a) How long will it take for the level in the tank to fall from 4 feet to 2 feet? (b) With the tank still draining, water is pumped in at a rate of 1.3 CFM. How long will it take to raise the level from 2 to 4 feet? What maximum level may be attained with this same feed rate?

9-19. Refer to Ex. 9.8 in Sec. 9.5. The inlet to the piping system is to be 10 feet below the surface of a large, open reservoir. Because the pressure at this point will not be 69.3 psia, a pump is to be installed in the line. Integrate the mechanical energy balance between a point at the surface of the reservoir and the outlet end of the piping system. Assuming the friction associated with the conditions at the pipe inlet to be equal to $0.45u^2/2g_c$, calculate the head which must be developed by the pump.

9-20. Refer to Ex. 9.9 in Sec. 9.6. (a) Calculate the diameter of a particle of quartz (sp. gr. $= 2.65$) which will settle at the same velocity as was calculated for the alumina particle. (b) At what velocity will the alumina particle "settle" in a centrifugal force field six times stronger than the gravitational force field?

9-21. When the pressure drop across the filter cake is constant, Eq. (9.75) can be rearranged to obtain

$$\theta = \int_0^V \frac{L\,dV}{KA(-\Delta P)}$$

in which L, the thickness of the cake, depends on V, the volume of filtrate collected. Assuming the volume of filtrate which is retained within the cake to be negligible, prove that

$$L = \frac{Vx}{(1-x)(1-\epsilon)A}$$

where x is the volume fraction solids in the feed slurry and ϵ is the void fraction in the cake (that is, the fraction of the bulk volume of the cake which is actually occupied by solid particles is equal to $1 - \epsilon$). Use this expression to eliminate L from the rearranged form of Eq. (9.75) given above and complete the integration to obtain an expression for θ as a function of V, K, A, ΔP, x, and ϵ.

9-22. A filter having a filtering area of 24 square feet is to be used to filter a slurry containing 5 per cent solids by volume. Laboratory tests have indicated that a void fraction of 0.35 is to be expected in the cake and that $K = 1.64 \times 10^{-9}$ ft^4/(lb$_f$)(sec). If the pressure drop across the cake is to be held constant at 30 psi, how long will it take to collect 12 cubic feet of filtrate? What will be the thickness of the cake at this time? How much longer would it take to double the thickness of the cake?

CHAPTER 10

Chemical Engineering Economics

Of all the many symbols used in chemical engineering calculations probably none is more important, in the final analysis, than the dollar sign. With but few exceptions economic decisions are involved in every aspect of the chemical engineer's concern for change. If he finds that economic factors need not be considered directly in the course of solving a given practical problem, it is only because someone else has already considered them prior to formulating the problem statement. The clear implication is that the importance of economic factors varies directly with the scope of the problem. If the prospective chemical engineer looks forward to a career of any real challenge and opportunity, an understanding of fundamental economic principles is essential.

Mathematical statements of the laws of conservation of mass and energy were presented in Chap. 2. With tongue only slightly in cheek, we might propose an analogous statement to be known as the law of conservation of money

$$\$_i - \$_o = \$_2 - \$_1 \tag{10.1}$$

In most chemical engineering applications the first term in this economic balance represents the revenue from the sale of a product, the second term is the total cost of producing that product, and the unsteady-state terms on the right-hand side of the equation represent the profit (or loss) associated with the operation. Like the mass and energy balances it parallels, the economic balance must be applied over a specified time interval. An annual basis is most frequently used, although a per-pound-of-product basis is sometimes advantageous.

Generally, though not invariably, the economic balance is solved for the profit or loss appearing on the right-hand side of the equation, and non-engineering market specialists are called upon to supply the data needed to evaluate the in, or revenue, term. Thus the chemical engineer is likely to be concerned primarily with the cost term in Eq. (10.1), and cost estimation is a major aspect of chemical engineering activity. The determination of the costs associated with a proposed venture is frequently referred to as a *feasibility study*, since the results indicate whether or not the venture is economically feasible.

The feasibility of a proposed venture is sometimes demonstrated in terms of a resultant reduction in net cost rather than in terms of profit as such. Contemplated changes to an existing process may affect neither production rate nor the dollar value of the product, but they must still be examined for economic justification. The comparative net costs of various alternatives provide a basis for decision by management in such cases, and the pertinent cost estimates are often prepared by the chemical engineer.

10.1 Chemical Engineering Costs

The list of items to be considered in making a cost estimate is an imposing one, whether the estimate be part of a large-scale feasibility study or merely the basis for a direct cost comparison. A complete listing is hardly necessary for introductory purposes, but a consideration of pertinent cost *categories* and the more frequently encountered costs included in each should be informative. For the most part the order of presentation coincides with the order in which the categories are considered in the preparation of an actual cost estimate. The latter will be treated separately in Sec. 10.2.

Fixed capital investment. Whatever the scale of a venture, funds must be made available at the outset for the purchase or construction of facilities. The amount of money which must be expended for non-recurring costs such as the initial cost of process equipment is called the *fixed capital investment*, commonly abbreviated F.C.I. The magnitude of the F.C.I. has a direct bearing on subsequent operating cost and profit calculations, but it may also constitute an independent criterion of feasibility: An otherwise attractive venture may have to be abandoned if a company cannot raise the capital to cover the necessary F.C.I.

The first step in estimating F.C.I. is usually to determine the cost of the major pieces of process equipment—the reaction vessels, fractionating columns, heat exchangers, pumps, compressors, storage vessels, and other items normally shown on the process flow diagram. The total cost of such equipment is called the *capital equipment cost*. Although accounting practices differ from company to company, piping, instrumentation, and similar auxiliaries are not usually considered to be items of capital equipment. The cost of such items is, however, properly included in the total F.C.I. and is often a significant fraction of the final figure.

For the most part, the capital equipment cost is based on costs as purchased and does not include the cost of design engineering work, structural framework, and equipment installation. These costs must therefore be added as separate items of F.C.I. Other items to be added would be the cost of site purchase and preparation, the cost of process and service buildings, and the construction contractor's fee.

If the feasibility study pertains to a complete plant which is to be largely self-sufficient, the F.C.I. also includes cost of any necessary utilities plants. In an alternative situation, the F.C.I. includes the cost of providing connecting piping and power lines when the plant is to be tied in with existing facilities. The boundary around the area allocated to the new plant is commonly referred to as the *battery limit*, and the cost of tie-in facilities is called the *outside-battery-limit* or OBL cost.

Finally, since all possible eventualities cannot be anticipated, some money must be set aside to cover contingencies. The amount allocated for this purpose varies with the degree of uncertainty associated with the cost estimation, but must be included as part of the F.C.I. in any event.

Total capital investment. In the long run all operating expenses are offset by sales revenue. When a plant is started up or goes *on stream* for the first time, however, there is no sales revenue until after a product inventory has been built up. In the meantime, money must be available to meet initial operating expenses such as payrolls and the cost of raw materials in inventory, in process, and already converted to finished product. The funds allocated for this purpose constitute the *working capital* of the enterprise. Since the expense of producing a given quantity of product always precedes the sale of that same quantity, the availability of working capital is a continuing necessity. Working capital is therefore added to fixed capital investment to obtain the *total capital investment* associated with the enterprise.

Operating cost. In contrast to the total capital investment which is based on non-recurring expenses, *operating* cost refers to those costs which recur on a regular or intermittent but predictable basis. Since the magnitude of such costs varies directly with the time interval over which they accrue, a suitable time period must be defined for accounting purposes. As noted previously, the usual practice is to express operating costs on an annual basis.

Operating costs are often classified for accounting purposes as being either direct or indirect. *Direct* operating costs, as the adjective implies, are those which are directly associated with the operation of the process and include such items as the cost of raw materials and operating labor. *Indirect* costs, on the other hand, are those which, although still properly assignable to the process, are more remote. Administrative overhead and sales expense are typical examples.

For practical purposes, a breakdown of operating costs into fixed and variable costs is somewhat more advantageous. Here again the adjectives are largely self-explanatory, *fixed* costs being those which are independent of the rate of production, whereas *variable* costs usually vary directly with production rate. The distinction is shown graphically in Fig. 10.1, in which sales revenue is also represented as being directly proportional to production

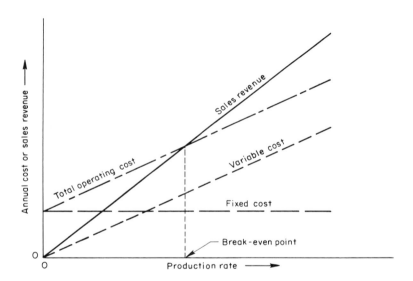

Fig. 10.1 Effect of production rate on sales revenue and on fixed, variable, and total operating costs for a typical chemical process.

rate. It can be seen that there is a minimum rate of production below which operation is unprofitable because of continuing fixed costs. This rate is called the *break-even point*.

The major components of variable cost are the cost of raw materials, the cost of operating and supervisory labor including fringe benefits (more formally known as *payroll overhead* or *burden*), the cost of operating supplies such as catalysts and other chemicals which do not enter into the final product, and the cost of utilities—water, electricity, steam, fuel, and perhaps air. Maintenance and repair costs may be either variable or fixed, depending on the nature of the process and the company's accounting procedures. *Royalties* or *license fees* stemming from the use of processes or equipment under patent protection may also be either variable or fixed, depending on the terms of the royalty agreement.

Fixed operating costs are, strictly speaking, directly related to the amount of money tied up in the fixed capital investment. Some of them, such as insurance, property taxes, and interest paid on the F.C.I., represent a fixed percentage of F.C.I. on an annual basis. Others may be calculated as a percentage of F.C.I. as a matter of convenience. Typical of the items in the latter category are maintenance expense, if not treated as a variable cost, and *depreciation*, the money set aside for the purchase of new equipment when the original equipment wears out.

Certain costs are often treated as fixed costs based on F.C.I. to facilitate cost estimation, even though they actually depend on a variety of other factors. Among such are works overhead, administrative overhead, and sales expense. *Works overhead* refers to the cost of control laboratory and plant office operation, plant protection, and similar items. Administrative overhead, on the other hand, pertains to the cost of executive supervision and general administration, and usually includes the cost of research and development as well.

It should be emphasized that the cost categories listed in this section are not inflexible and that actual practice varies from company to company and even from project to project. The important thing is to insure that no costs are overlooked when a cost estimate is prepared.

10.2 Cost-Estimating Methods

The preparation of a detailed, precise cost estimate for an extensive project can easily require hundreds of man-hours of work over and above the time and effort expended on technical design calculations. The engineering method described in Chap. 3 is ideally suited to such a situation, for it provides a continuous indication of the ultimate feasibility of the project, and the investigation can be dropped at any point if the prognosis is not sufficiently encouraging. In practice, then, not one but several successive cost estimates are prepared in the course of making a feasibility study. The methods commonly used in preparing such estimates are described in this section.

Preliminary estimates. The first estimate of the order of magnitude of the necessary capital investment and probable operating cost is usually made as soon as it has been decided to consider the manufacture of a given product. The initial decision may specify only a tentative production rate and production process, but even this meager information is a sufficient basis for a preliminary cost estimate. Past experience within the company and within the industry as a whole is the sole source of the data used in preparing such estimates.

Unless the proposed process is absolutely new, cost-capacity data based on past experience can be used directly in preparing a preliminary estimate. For example, industry-wide data show that the fixed capital investment needed for a butadiene plant is approximated by the relationship

$$\text{F.C.I.} = 1.21(\text{PR})^{0.66} \times 10^6 \qquad (10.2)*$$

where PR is the production rate in thousands of tons per year and F.C.I. is in dollars. Similar relationships, with exponents ranging from 0.3 to 1.0, have been established for other products. In the absence of a specific relationship, an exponent of 0.6 is generally assumed, this rule-of-thumb being known as the *six-tenths rule*. The cost of a single existing plant of whatever capacity can then be used to determine the constant in a cost-capacity equation similar to Eq. (10.2). When the process is new and no previous data are available, it is necessary to select as a basis for cost estimation an established process believed to be similar to that under consideration.

As for operating cost, an estimate of probable yields will permit the calculation of raw materials costs, but past experience is the only basis for estimating other variable costs at this point. Fixed costs, on the other hand, can be predicted on the basis of the estimated F.C.I. For example, depreciation might be estimated at 10 per cent of the F.C.I. Typical percentages for other fixed costs are 5 per cent for maintenance, 2 per cent for local taxes, 1 per cent for administrative overhead, and 1 per cent for insurance.

Because of the considerable guesswork involved, preliminary estimates may be in error by as much as 100 per cent. Even so, they can hardly be considered useless, for they establish the order of magnitude of the actual cost and this can be an important piece of information when a project is just getting under way.

Intermediate estimates. A major improvement in the precision of the preliminary estimate becomes possible as soon as mass and energy balance calculations have been completed and the sizes or capacities of major pieces of process equipment have been determined. At this point a reasonably satisfactory estimate of capital equipment cost can be prepared and used as a basis for estimating other F.C.I. items. At the same time, the utilities requirements indicated by the energy balance calculations lead to an improved estimate of variable operating costs. The preliminary estimate of labor costs can also be refined, since some indication of the degree of complexity of the process is now available.

* Berk, J. M., and Haselbarth, J. E., *Chemical Engineering*, 68, No. 6, 182 (1961).

The determination of capital equipment cost involves the application of separate cost correlations, some of which are considered in the next chapter, to each piece of process equipment. These correlations assume standard features and materials of construction, but the results can be corrected to allow for such things as extra thickness for high-pressure service or special materials for corrosive conditions. For example, the base correlation for heat exchanger costs provides an estimate of the cost of an exchanger for low-pressure, non-corrosive service. This cost might be multiplied by a factor of 1.2 to allow for high-pressure design, and the result might be multiplied by 2.5 to provide for stainless steel construction.

The fact that costs change with time must also be taken into account. Any one of several *cost indexes* which reflect such changes might be used, but the *Engineering News-Record* (ENR) Index for general construction costs and the *Marshall and Stevens* (M&S) Index for equipment costs are most popular. As an illustration of the application of such indexes, consider a fractionating column which cost $55,000 in 1955 when the M&S Index was 191. The estimated cost of the same column in December, 1960, when the M&S Index was 238, would have been

$$55,000 \left(\frac{238}{191}\right) = \$68,500$$

The current M&S Index is published regularly in *Chemical Engineering* magazine, with annual averages since 1913 summarized in the first March issue of every year.

Once the capital equipment cost has been determined, the simplest and quickest procedure for estimating the cost of other F.C.I. items is to multiply the capital equipment cost by a single factor based on general experience. The usual factors are 3.10 for a solids process plant, 4.74 for a fluid process, and 3.63 for a plant in which both solids and fluids will be processed. Fixed operating costs are then estimated as percentages of F.C.I. just as they are in preliminary estimates.

When the technical design calculations are sufficiently far along to provide the necessary data and information, a slightly more detailed cost estimating procedure becomes possible. For one thing, actual cost quotations might be obtained from prospective suppliers of any items of equipment which will have unusual features. Perhaps more significant is the fact that the overall factors listed in the preceding paragraph can be broken down into component factors specifically pertinent to the proposed operation. Thus the costs of equipment installation, piping, insulation, instrumentation, buildings, and similar items of F.C.I. would be separately estimated as percentages of the capital equipment cost.

The cost of instrumentation, for example, is generally from 2 to 20 per cent or so of the capital equipment cost, and the percentage selected from within this range by the cost estimator reflects the extent to which the use of automatic controls is indicated by the design calculations. Other typical ranges of percentage of capital equipment cost are 5 to 30 per cent for installation, 30 to 80 per cent for piping (for a fluid process), 0 to 100 per cent or more for buildings, 20 to 65 per cent for engineering and construction, and 10 to 65 per cent for contingencies. The results of the technical design calculations provide the basis for selecting the specific percentage to be used for each category.

Final estimates. Ultimately, each of the items included in the F.C.I. may be covered by firm bids and the only estimate still necessary in this area will be for contingencies. This status is reached only after the technical calculations have been completed and a detailed layout of all facilities, including piping and electrical wiring, is available. It is noteworthy that construction will often be well along before the last few estimates are replaced by firm bids.

Operating costs, on the other hand, are never definite until after the fact. Unforeseen difficulties may make it necessary to add an additional operator to each shift; or perhaps additional maintenance costs will be incurred. In the final analysis, the cost estimator's job is not complete until the plant is on stream and turning out a product which meets specifications. Until that point is reached, he will be continually improving the precision of his intermediate estimate as more and more data and information become available. Thus the original feasibility study gradually gives way to what might be called a mopping-up operation, but the methods of cost estimation outlined herein continue to be pertinent.

Although the foregoing treatment repeatedly refers to the design and construction of an entire plant, it should not be inferred that the methods described are not equally appropriate for small-scale projects. As a piece of equipment gradually wears out and maintenance costs rise, for example, a cost comparison will be made to determine whether or not it should be replaced with a new unit. Such a comparison should clearly include a consideration of operating costs as well as the installed cost of the new unit, and detailed cost calculations may be required.

10.3 Economic Analyses

A cost estimate is not an end in itself but only a means to an end: It provides the basis for a decision to follow one of two or more alternative courses of action. Other factors often have an important bearing on such a decision, but we are here concerned only with the cost factor. The interpretation of a direct cost comparison is, of course, straightforward. The results of a feasibility study, on the other hand, present the cost of only one alternative—that of proceeding with the venture. Some criterion of feasibility is accordingly needed if a logical decision is to be reached. Some of the more widely used criteria are presented in this section.

Profit, return, and payout time. When a proposed venture will turn out a product which is already on the market, the price at which the product can be sold will be known at the outset of the feasibility study. In such a case a knowledge of the proposed production rate can be used immediately to calculate gross sales revenue. In making the calculation, allowance must be made for the fact that even though most chemical plants are operated on a 24-hour basis, they must be shut down from time to time for routine and emergency maintenance. That fraction of the year during which the plant is actually on stream and producing a saleable product is called the *service factor*. The term *stream day* is also often used to distinguish between days of actual operation and calendar days.

The term *gross profit* means different things to different companies, but it refers generally to the difference between gross sales revenue and operating cost. Depending on company policy, depreciation and interest on borrowed money may or may not be included as items of operating cost in calculating gross profit. When they are not, they will enter into the calculation of *net profit*, the profit remaining after all costs have been taken into consideration and state and Federal income taxes have been deducted. The latter is a most significant deduction, for the Federal tax rate in recent years has been 52 per cent of the gross profit remaining after all costs have been deducted.

Perhaps the most popular criterion of feasibility is that based on the *rate of return* on the original investment, equal to the annual net profit divided by the total capital investment. If desired, the fact that depreciation charges gradually reduce F.C.I. can be taken into account by using an *average* rate of return based on the average capital investment over the life of the plant. In either case the calculated rate of return can be compared with the *minimum acceptable return* established as a matter of company policy, to determine feasibility. A typical figure for minimum acceptable return for average-risk projects might be 15 per cent of capital investment, with a higher minimum being specified for projects of greater risk.

An alternative criterion of feasibility is the *payout time*, equal to the fixed capital investment divided by either gross or net annual profit depending on company policy. It can be seen that payout time is simply the time needed to recover the capital investment. The maximum acceptable payout time is usually between two and five years, the actual figure reflecting both the minimum acceptable return and the anticipated life of the plant.

Many companies follow the practice of deducting from gross or net profit a "cost" equivalent to the minimum acceptable return, thereby obtaining a corrected profit figure which is directly indicative of the relative attractiveness of the proposed venture. This practice is particularly advantageous when a choice must be made from among several alternatives, for the alternative having the highest rate of return or the lowest payout time is not necessarily the most attractive. In contrast, a comparison of the profits remaining after deduction of the minimum acceptable return is almost invariably a suitable basis for a decision.

The foregoing criteria of feasibility presuppose a knowledge of the price at which the product can be sold. When a new product is to be introduced for the first time it may be preferable to solve the economic balance for the minimum practicable selling price rather than for profit or return as such. The procedure in such a case is to calculate the annual operating cost and the annual profit equivalent to the minimum acceptable return before taxes. In accordance with Eq. (10.1), the sum of these two figures must be equal to the minimum acceptable annual sales revenue, and the latter can be converted to a unit sales price by dividing by the annual production rate. A market survey can then be made to determine whether the product can be sold at that price and in the quantity proposed for production, and the feasibility of the venture will be directly indicated by the results of the survey.

The economic balance as a design equation. From the mathematical viewpoint, the job of the design engineer is to establish values for a number of design variables by solving an equal number of equations simultaneously. More often than not, he will find that the application of all pertinent technical relationships such as the mass balance, the laws of thermodynamics, and the rate equation still leaves an indeterminate system. If so, the missing equation is almost certain to be an economic balance. The clear implication is that economic analyses are likely to be an integral part of all but the simplest of design calculations.

With but few exceptions, the sole economic objective of the designer is to minimize cost, and he need not be directly concerned with the revenue and profit terms in the economic balance. Again from the mathematical viewpoint, this suggests differentiating a cost equation and setting the first derivative equal to zero so as to locate the minimum point. Such a procedure is in fact possible in some cases, but for the most part the equation will be too complex and unwieldy. The alternative is to use a trial-and-error approach which is wholly analogous to that used in purely technical calculations: The designer will try various combinations of the pertinent design variables, calculate the corresponding cost for each combination, and select for his final design the combination for which the cost is lowest.

The engineering method described in Chap. 3 is particularly appropriate in design work, for good engineering judgment can materially reduce the extent of the calculations leading to an optimum design. Having first established the *relative* cost of all pertinent items by rough, order-of-magnitude approximations and estimates, the designer can usually pinpoint one or more items which contribute most to the total cost. Process changes which will reduce these major costs should then be investigated. Even though such changes normally increase other costs, the increase is likely to be proportionately smaller and a net reduction in cost will result.

10.4 Conclusion

It is not necessary that the chemical engineer be a full-fledged accountant or economist, but it is generally essential that he have a working familiarity with the fundamentals of cost accounting and the economic principles upon which they are based. The material presented in this chapter should make the student aware of the importance of economics in the field of chemical engineering—and in engineering in general—and should also acquaint him with some of the more important aspects of cost estimation. It should be emphasized that the methods described, although they are indicative of general practice, are not purported to be directly applicable to all situations. Many alternative techniques could be investigated, but the present treatment should suffice for introductory purposes.

As was noted in Chap. 2, the full impact of economics as an aspect of change cannot really be appreciated until the student has a fairly strong technical background. This being the case, the further study of economics is best deferred until the technical aspects of change have been subjected to a thorough examination. In the meantime it can only be hoped that the student will not lose sight of the ultimate importance of economic factors in chemical engineering design and analysis.

REVIEW, STUDY, AND DISCUSSION

10-1. Define the following terms: feasibility study, fixed capital investment, capital equipment, battery limit, OBL cost, on stream, working capital, total capital investment, operating cost, direct cost, indirect cost, fixed cost, variable cost, break-even point, payroll overhead or burden, royalty or license fee, depreciation, works overhead, six-tenths rule, service factor, stream day, gross profit, net profit, rate of return on investment, minimum acceptable return, average rate of return, payout time.

10-2. An 80-ton-per-day chemical plant was constructed in 1955 at a fixed capital investment of $10,000,000. Estimate the cost of a similar plant in 1960 if the capacity of the new plant is 100 tons per day.

10-3. Estimate the fixed operating cost for the new plant described in Prob. 10-2.

10-4. A heat exchanger having a heat-transfer surface area of 4,000 square feet will cost $22,500. Estimate the cost of a 2,000-square-foot exchanger and compare the two costs on a dollars-per-square-foot basis. Would there be any advantage in using two smaller exchangers in parallel instead of a single large unit? Explain.

10-5. Assuming the chemical plant described in Prob. 10-2 to be a fluid process plant, estimate the cost of the capital equipment for the new plant.

10-6. Assuming the cost given in Prob. 10-4 to be the cost as delivered, estimate the cost of installation, connecting piping, building, engineering and construction, and contingencies. Justify the estimate in each category to the best of your ability. Estimate the fixed operating cost to be associated with the operation of the exchanger.

10-7. The new plant described in Prob. 10-2 is expected to yield a gross profit of $1,000,000 per year less depreciation charges. If depreciation is to be 10 per cent per year, calculate the net profit after taxes for a 52 per cent tax rate. What is the rate of return on the capital investment? What is the payout time based on gross profit? Calculate the profit remaining after a minimum acceptable return of 15 per cent of the capital investment has been deducted from the net profit.

10-8. Two alternatives to the venture described in Prob. 10-7 are to be considered. The first, a moderate addition to the older plant, will require an investment of $280,000 and is expected to yield a gross profit of $350,000. The second, a new facility closely tied in with the existing plant, will require an investment of $850,000 and is expected to yield a gross profit of $770,000. Compare the relative attractiveness of all three alternatives on the basis of net profit, rate of return on capital investment, payout time, and profit remaining after the minimum acceptable return has been deducted. Which alternative appears to be most attractive?

10-9. A two-component mixture, available as a saturated vapor at 250 psia, is to be separated into its components. One component is to be delivered at 400 psia, the other at 70 psia, and the optimum operating pressure for the separation process is to be determined. A fractionating column will be used for the separation, but auxiliary heat exchangers and a product compressor will also be needed. Low-pressure operation will permit the use of a smaller fractionating column. Describe in reasonable detail a logical procedure for determining the optimum operating pressure.

CHAPTER 11

Chemical Process Equipment

A descriptive, largely qualitative treatment of the more important types of equipment currently used in chemical processing may seem out of place in a text which stresses fundamentals, especially when a sudden research break-through might lead to radically new techniques. The validity of such an objection notwithstanding, the inclusion of some purely descriptive material is believed to be desirable. For one thing, the characteristic features of a particular piece of equipment invariably reflect the influence of one or more of the fundamental aspects of change, including the economic aspect considered in the last chapter. The descriptive material will accordingly help to bridge the gap between the theoretical and practical sides of engineering.

It will also provide the student with a working vocabulary of chemical engineering terms. This should eliminate a major cause of confusion and bewilderment in the overall learning process. Perhaps more important, it will prepare the student for meaningful outside reading of the periodical literature as urged in Chap. 3. Such reading is certain to be a most fruitful supplement to formal classroom instruction.

Chemical process equipment can be broadly classified into five categories:

1) Equipment associated with the bulk transport of material from one location to another.

2) Equipment in which material undergoes a change of temperature or phase.

3) Equipment in which material undergoes chemical reaction.

4) Equipment in which phases are separated by mechanical means.

5) Equipment in which mass is transferred from one phase to another.
It will be convenient to consider each of these categories separately, even though some overlapping exists. The fact that the above classification parallels that used in discussing rate process theory in Chap. 9 suggests that review, at the appropriate point, of pertinent sections of the latter chapter would be advantageous.

11.1 Fluid Flow

A large majority of the bulk transport problems to be faced by the chemical engineer involve the movement of gases and liquids, with the transportation of solids being encountered much less frequently. It may also be noted that the design and analysis of solids-handling equipment such as conveyor belts and automatic feed hoppers generally falls to the mechanical engineer. There is little reason to consider such devices in the present discussion, which will accordingly be confined to the flow of fluids.

The principles of fluid flow are of fundamental importance in chemical engineering. They are obviously pertinent whenever a fluid is conveyed in a pipe or other conduit from one piece of process equipment to another but they must also be considered in the design of the equipment itself, and the problems arising in this area of application can be extremely complex. The latter will be examined in due course.

Flow through conduits. The most commonly used conduit for process fluids is steel pipe, available in 24 *nominal sizes* (approximate inside diameter) ranging from $\frac{1}{8}$ to 30 inches. Various wall thicknesses or *schedule numbers* are also available, Schedule 40 being used for most applications. The pertinent dimensions of the standard sizes of both pipe and tubing may be obtained from Perry's Handbook or a similar reference source.

Fittings such as those shown in Fig. 11.1 are used to join two or more pieces of pipe, to change the direction or diameter of a pipeline, or to close off the end of a pipe. Although Fig.11.1 shows only threaded or screwed fittings, flanged and welded fittings are also widely used. Either a coupling or a union may be used to join two pieces of pipe of equal size, but a coupled joint can be assembled or disassembled only by turning one of the pipes. When this is impossible or undesirable, the use of a union with its separate nut is indicated.

The design or analysis of a piping system involves the direct application of the continuity equation and the mechanical energy balance presented in

Sec. 9.5. In the completely general case an economic balance will also be pertinent: For a given mass rate of flow, the continuity equation requires that the use of a smaller—and less expensive—pipe be reflected in a higher linear velocity. The increased velocity must result in greater frictional

Fig. 11.1   Pipe fittings in common use. Top row, left to right: union, coupling, plug, cap. Middle row: 90-degree elbow (ell), street elbow, reducing coupling, bushing. Bottom row: nipple, close nipple, tee.

resistance in accordance with the rate relationship and, finally, the mechanical energy balance indicates that additional work input is required to overcome this increased resistance. This means an increase in the cost of pumping or compression which can be compared with the saving made possible by the use of a smaller pipe size. A typical cost-vs-diameter curve was presented in Fig. 2.7, Sec. 2.12. Two order-of-magnitude figures for optimum velocity are 5 ft/sec for water and 40 ft/sec for air or steam, and these figures are often used in making quick estimates of piping size.

The lost work associated with flow through a straight length of pipe is directly proportional to the length of the flow path, but the friction generated in fittings must also be taken into account. The usual practice is to express this resistance in terms of an equivalent length of straight pipe, expressed as a number of pipe diameters. For example, the equivalent length of a standard elbow is approximately 30 pipe diameters. In a 2-inch pipe this corresponds to 5 feet of pipe, and this length (plus the equivalent length of any other fittings) would be added to the actual length of straight-run piping to obtain the total equivalent length to be used in evaluating the lost work term in the mechanical energy balance.

When fluid flows from one pipe into a larger or smaller one, the expansion or contraction of the flow cross-section causes turbulence which is dissipated as lost work. The relationship generally used to provide for this situation is

$$\mathrm{lw}_{e,c} = K \frac{u^2}{2g_c} \tag{11.1}$$

where $\mathrm{lw}_{e,c}$ is the lost work due to the expansion or contraction, u is the fluid velocity in the smaller pipe, and K is a resistance coefficient lying between 0 and 1.0, with the actual value depending on the direction of flow and the ratio of the diameter of the smaller pipe to that of the larger. In the limiting case, Eq. (11.1) can be applied to flow into or out of a large tank by evaluating K at a diameter ratio equal to zero.

Flow measurement and control. If a plant or process is to operate satisfactorily, it is imperative that the operators have a knowledge of pertinent flow rates. Recently developed flow meters make it possible to measure the mass rate of flow directly, but the use of velocity or volumetric flow meters is somewhat more common. In *positive displacement* meters, the reading on a dial or other indicator is directly proportional to the volume of fluid processed, and instantaneous rates can be calculated only by graphically differentiating the data obtained from several successive readings. Velocity meters, on the other hand, indicate or record instantaneous rates, and the integration of a rate-time relationship is necessary to determine the accumulative flow. In either case the density of the flowing fluid is pertinent if the mass rate of flow is to be calculated.

One fairly obvious method of determining linear velocity is to measure the pressure drop across a portion of the flow system and substitute the measured value into the rate equation, whereupon the equation might be solved for velocity. As a more practicable alternative, a significant pressure drop over a short distance can be induced by installing, at some point in the line, a plate through which a hole or *orifice* has been drilled. Since the orifice opening is somewhat smaller than the cross-sectional area of the pipe in which it is installed, the fluid accelerates in accordance with the continuity equation, and the velocity change produces an equivalent change in pressure in accordance with the mechanical energy balance. Since the orifice-to-pipe diameter ratio is a completely independent variable, orifice meters can be designed to yield a pressure drop in any desired range.

Some of the kinetic energy developed in the orifice is recovered when the fluid decelerates as it leaves the restriction, but the conversion of useful energy to lost work is still significant. Much of the loss can be attributed to the abrupt change in cross-section and can therefore be reduced by making the change more gradual. Meters embodying this feature are called *Venturi* meters. Since a simple orifice plate is considerably less expensive than a Venturi, it might be necessary to make an economic balance to determine whether the greater efficiency of a Venturi would justify the additional cost.

Both the orifice meter and the Venturi require the use of auxiliary equipment to measure the pressure drop, which must then be converted to obtain the flow rate. A popular alternative device, the *rotameter*, is a self-contained, direct-reading instrument consisting essentially of a small solid object or *float* inside a vertical, tapered tube with the wide end at the top. As fluid flows upward through the tube the float takes a position such that the drag force, buoyant force, and gravitational force acting on it are in balance. An increase in flow rate temporarily increases the drag force and the float moves upward. Because of the taper, this makes a greater cross-sectional area available for flow, thereby reducing the linear velocity around the float and the drag force on the float. At some point the forces again become balanced and the float comes to rest. The position of the float is therefore directly related to the rate of flow, and the tube can be calibrated to show flow rate as a function of float position.

The rate of flow through a given piping system is readily controlled by opening or closing a valve in the line. If the change of resistance with valve setting is expressed in terms of a corresponding change in equivalent length, the mechanical energy balance clearly shows the cause-and-effect relationship pertaining to flow control: Assuming the applied pressure, velocity, and static heads to be constant, lw must also be constant. But lw depends on both velocity and equivalent length; hence an increase in equivalent length due to valve action must result in a corresponding decrease in velocity.

Compression and expansion. A consideration of the mechanical energy balance makes it apparent that the pressure of a flowing stream can be readily increased by using a *pump* (liquid flow) or a *compressor* (gas or vapor flow) to supply energy in the form of work. Conversely, the pressure will decrease if the stream supplies work to the surroundings. The equivalent of the compressor in such cases is an *expansion engine* or *turbo-expander*.

Applied to a compressor or pump as the system, the mechanical energy balance may be written

$$-W = \frac{P_o - P_i}{\rho} \qquad (11.2)$$

in which P_i is the inlet or *suction* pressure and P_o is the outlet or *discharge* pressure. This reduced form of the energy balance takes cognizance of the

fact that kinetic and potential energy changes across pumps and compressors
are usually negligible. Lost work, on the other hand, is not, and the absence
of an lw term in Eq. (11.2) requires that W be interpreted as the *net* work
actually delivered to the fluid between the suction and discharge points.
This net work may be divided by a *mechanical efficiency* factor to obtain the
quantity of work which must be delivered to the drive-shaft of the compressor
or pump. A similar procedure is applicable to expanders, the only difference
being that the efficiency factor is a multiplier rather than a divisor. Depending on equipment type and operating conditions, mechanical efficiencies
can range all the way from 0 to 90 per cent or so.

As an aid to flowsheet analysis, the two common symbols used to portray
pumps and compressors are shown in Fig. 11.2. These symbols are used

Fig. 11.2 Flowsheet symbols for pumps and compressors.

somewhat interchangeably even though they imply different mechanical
features. The mechanical details of pumps and compressors are best left
for future study.

As an alternative to the use of an expansion engine or turbo-expander, it
should also be possible to lower the pressure of a flowing fluid—that is, to
move to a lower energy level—without doing work in accordance with the
second law of thermodynamics. This can be accomplished directly by merely
restricting the flow so as to increase frictional resistance or lost work. A
simple *expansion* or *throttling* valve in the line suffices for this purpose. For
liquids, pressure reduction is almost invariably obtained by means of a
throttling valve, since the small volume change accompanying pressure reduction makes an expansion engine impracticable. An economic comparison
is frequently necessary when a gas is to be expanded, with the cost of installing
the expander being compared to the dollar value of the energy which can
be recovered.

The symbols shown in Fig. 11.3 are commonly used to indicate throttling
valves on process flowsheets. Since these same symbols may be used in detailed flow diagrams to represent valves used for control and cut-off as well
as for throttling, care must be exercised in flowsheet analysis.

Cost correlations. A rough estimate of the cost of a simple piping system
can be obtained by determining the length of the system and multiplying
the answer by a cost-per-foot figure which includes an allowance for valves

and fittings. For a more precise estimate, the number and types of valves and fittings must be determined, whereupon the total cost of such items can be obtained by summing unit costs. The cost of installing a piping system is roughly proportional to the number of joints in the system.

Fig. 11.3   Flowsheet symbols for valves.

Compressor costs depend on a number of factors, but a reasonable estimate can be based on the *brake horsepower* delivered to the driveshaft. Cost correlations for pumps, on the other hand, are based on throughput and delivered head as separate considerations. Unless special features are involved, pumps are not particularly expensive. The delivered cost of a large compressor, however, can be as much as several hundred thousand dollars.

Pumps and compressors may be driven by electric motors or by steam- or gas-driven turbines. The cost of the driver can be estimated from a knowledge of the horsepower required and must be added to the cost of the pump or compressor to obtain the cost of the complete installation.

Mixing of fluids. As was noted in Chap. 2, mixing is inherently a spontaneous process, and should therefore be readily achieved. Even so, special equipment is necessary when the heat of mixing is appreciable, when solids or extremely viscous liquids must be processed, when partial immiscibility is encountered, or when complete homogeneity is essential. If the mixture is only a physical dispersion rather than a true solution, for example, one phase may tend to settle out unless continuous agitation is provided. The time factor must also be considered, and some agitation or stirring to hasten the mixing process is desirable even in simple cases.

The design of mixing equipment is a rather specialized area of chemical engineering. Mixing theory is rapidly being strengthened, but it is not likely to replace empiricism and the judgment gained by experience for some time to come. This is particularly true in the design of equipment for special applications such as the formulation of solid rocket propellants. At the other extreme, a simple pipe tee or wye may be all that is required to bring two fluids together and permit them to be thoroughly mixed by the turbulence associated with flow as they move on to the next process unit.

The average chemical engineer's knowledge of fluid flow principles should provide an adequate basis for the solution of the latter problem. Similarly, a knowledge of the fundamental principles of heat transfer should enable the average engineer to design a cooling system to remove heat of solution. The specialist is normally consulted regarding other details of a mixing system, however, for even the height-to-diameter ratio of the mixing vessel can have a significant effect on the efficiency of mixing.

The objective of a mixing process need not necessarily be a change in composition. For example, hot water might be obtained by the direct addition of steam to a cold-water feed stream. The pertinence of the energy balance to such a process is obvious, since the steam rate and the outlet water temperature are directly related. When the mixing process involves heat of solution, the use of the energy balance is similarly called for, either to determine the outlet temperature which will result from adiabatic mixing or to calculate the heat which must be removed to obtain a predetermined outlet temperature. The principles discussed in Chaps. 6 and 7 are applicable in such cases.

11.2 Heat Transfer

Heating and cooling. In most applications, process streams are heated or cooled by the transfer of heat from or to other process streams or auxiliary streams made available for this express purpose. The two streams involved in the transfer are separately confined and no fluid mixing occurs. Despite the fact that heat flows in one direction only, the term *heat exchange* is commonly applied to the unit operation of heat transfer under such conditions.

One of the simplest types of heat exchange equipment is the *double-pipe* exchanger consisting of two concentric pipes of suitable length with one fluid flowing through the center pipe and the other through the annular space between the two pipes. Other exchanger designs involve the use of flat, parallel plates or coiled tubing. The *shell-and-tube* exchanger, on the other hand, departs from the double-pipe idea only in that it may have hundreds of inner pipes or tubes enclosed in a single outer pipe or shell. In the simplest design of such units the tube-side fluid enters a header at one end of the exchanger, flows through the tubes in parallel, and is withdrawn from a second header at the other end. More frequently, baffles are installed in the headers to direct the fluid back and forth through the unit. Exchangers embodying this feature are called *multi-pass* exchangers. The variety of flow arrangements which may be obtained by merely changing baffles is a notable feature of shell-and-tube units and accounts in part for their widespread use.

If both fluids to be processed in a heat exchanger enter at the same end of the unit and flow in the same direction to the outlet, an interesting consequence of the second law of thermodynamics is encountered: The temperatures of the two streams will approach each other but could become equal only if the exchanger were infinitely long. In no event can they actually cross one another. This limitation can be circumvented by prescribing *counter-current* flow, in which case the outlet temperature of either stream might be made to approach the inlet temperature of the other without a second law violation. It is only necessary that the temperature of the hot stream at any point be greater than that of the cold stream at the same point. True counter-current flow is unattainable in many exchanger designs, but it is generally approached as closely as possible.

From the fluid flow standpoint, each of the fluids passing through a heat exchanger can be considered independently of the other, with the principles already discussed being applicable to each. In particular, simple heating and cooling do not involve changes in stream composition or total mass, and any equipment specified for these purposes can be disregarded when making a mass balance around a process.

The application of the energy balance to a typical heating-cooling problem was demonstrated in Sec. 9.2, and a review of Exs. 9.1 and 9.2 is suggested at this point. Recall that the solutions to these problems involved the assumption of negligible heat loss to the surroundings; that is, the heat given up by the hot stream was considered to be completely recovered in the cold stream. This assumption is not unreasonable in most applications but may be inappropriate when process temperatures are well above or below *ambient* temperature (the temperature of the surroundings) or when the equipment will not be well insulated.

In the detailed design of a heat exchanger, it would be necessary to determine the desired inlet and outlet temperatures, pipe or tube diameters, and perhaps even one or both flow rates before the calculations illustrated in Ex. 9.2 could be undertaken. Economic considerations play a major role in the specification of these design parameters. The cost of the equipment itself, the dollar value of the energy which might be recovered, the cost of supplying auxiliary streams when necessary, and even the pumping costs associated with the pressure drop through the exchanger must all be taken into account. Needless to say, the detailed design problem is not a simple one.

Vaporization and condensation. The foregoing characteristics of simple heating and cooling are, generally speaking, equally pertinent to heat transfer processes involving a change of phase. The only significant difference is the fact that the coefficient in the rate correlation may change appreciably, for it is a function of variables which need not be considered in simple heating and cooling. This aspect lies outside the scope of the present treatment, but the omission is not critical. For practical purposes the same fundamental principles are applicable to all processes in which heat is transferred from one stream to another, whether a phase change results or not.

Vaporization and condensation may also be effected without any transfer of heat to or from the stream being processed. A liquid can be readily vaporized by permitting it to expand adiabatically to a pressure below its saturation pressure, and this operation is called *flash vaporization* or simply *flashing*.

Conversely, condensation will occur when a vapor is compressed to a pressure greater than its saturation pressure.

Partial rather than complete vaporization or condensation is often prescribed to obtain a separable mixture of two phases. In such cases a combination of mass balance, energy balance, and vapor-liquid equilibrium calculations must be carried out to determine the composition and state of each of the phases. All of the fundamental relationships pertinent to the calculations were introduced in Chaps. 4 through 7, but their application in combination is best deferred for subsequent study.

Typical flowsheet symbols for heat exchangers are shown in Fig. 11.4. Like those used for pumps and compressors, the symbols are somewhat inter-

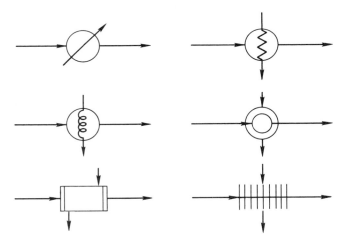

Fig. 11.4   Flowsheet symbols for heat exchangers.

changeable even though some correspondence between specific symbols and specific exchanger designs is evident. Except on detailed diagrams where all streams are shown, the arrows portraying the flow of auxiliary streams such as air, steam, or cooling water may have no apparent source or destination and may not even be labelled. It should also be noted that simple boxes or rectangles, appropriately labelled "vaporizer", "partial condenser", or "aftercooler", etc., are not infrequently used in lieu of the symbols shown in Fig. 11.4.

Evaporation, crystallization, and drying. Because partial vaporization usually involves the transfer of heat, it qualifies as a heat transfer operation. In many cases, however, phase separation is effected at the same time and in the same equipment. To the extent that the separation depends primarily on the transfer of heat to the system, such processes can be conveniently discussed at this point. Those separations which are essentially fluid flow or mass transfer operations are treated later in the chapter.

When a solution is concentrated by vaporization of a portion of the solvent, the operation is called *evaporation*. In principle, the operation could be continued until only a solid residue remained, but the practical aspects of the problem change with the appearance of a solid phase. It is for this reason that the term evaporation is commonly applied only to concentration to the point of saturation. That stage of vaporization during which solid crystals precipitate and grow is called *crystallization*. Finally, the solvent still remaining when crystallization is complete may be removed by *drying*. Needless to say, the lines of demarcation separating these three operations are not particularly sharp.

A simple tank equipped with heating coils can be used for evaporation, but the heat-transfer coefficient associated with such a design is not particularly high unless considerable agitation is provided. A more common alternative is to provide for recirculation of the liquid through an external pipe loop. One typical design, that of a *forced-circulation* evaporator, is shown schematically in Fig. 11.5. The heating element is essentially a shell-and-tube

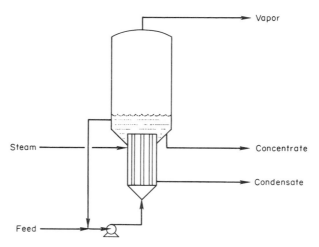

Fig. 11.5   Schematic diagram of a forced-circulation evaporator.

heat exchanger with steam condensing in the shell. The recirculation rate in such a unit is generally several times greater than the fresh feed rate.

The use of recirculation or agitation in evaporation correctly implies that the heat-transfer coefficient increases with liquid velocity past the heat transfer surface. Another example of the role of economics in chemical engineering is immediately encountered: The higher heat transfer coefficient obtained with higher liquid velocity reduces the capital cost of the evaporator, since less heat transfer surface is needed. But high velocity can be achieved only at the expense of increased lost work and a consequent higher pumping cost. Thus an economic evaluation is necessary just as it is when a pipe line or heat exchanger is to be sized.

It might also be noted that the recovery of the latent heat in the vapor leaving the top of the evaporator is desirable from the economic standpoint. *Multiple-effect* evaporators effect a partial recovery by using the vapor from one effect to supply heat to the next, in lieu of steam. The necessary temperature driving-force for heat transfer is provided by running each successive effect at a lower pressure, thereby reducing the boiling point to a temperature below that of the vapor leaving the preceding effect. Here again, an economic balance is necessary to determine whether the energy recovered in a multiple-effect system will compensate for the cost of additional capital equipment.

Crystallization is often an integral part of the phenomena occurring inside an evaporator. A slurry of crystals and *mother liquor* is withdrawn from the bottom of the unit and it is only necessary that the mixture be fluid enough to flow readily. In other applications special equipment may be required to insure proper crystal growth to a desired ultimate size or structure. An alternative to evaporative crystallization is possible when the solute becomes less soluble as the temperature is lowered. In such cases crystallization can be effected by cooling rather than heating the feed solution. In any event the design of crystallization equipment is primarily dependent on the application of the principles of heat transfer plus the consideration of any necessary special requirements. The latter need not be detailed here.

Drying can be similarly analyzed in terms of the pertinent principles of heat transfer if certain restrictions are imposed. First, the rate at which liquid diffuses to the surface of the wet solid may be the controlling rate when very little liquid is present, in which case heat transfer plays a subordinate role. During the initial stages of drying when the solid is thoroughly wet with liquid, however, the heat transfer rate is of primary importance. Second, the drying may be accomplished by exposing the wet solid to a stream of hot, dry gas. Here heat and mass transfer occur simultaneously, and both must be considered in analyzing the process. The mass transfer aspects of drying are discussed briefly in Sec. 11.5.

Only in rare cases is crystallization followed directly by drying. The latter operation is economical only when the amount of liquid to be removed is small, whereas the effluent from a crystallizer generally includes an appreciable quantity of mother liquor. This can be largely removed by inserting a filtration operation or its equivalent between the crystallizing and drying steps. The intermediate operations commonly used do not involve heat transfer and are considered separately in Sec. 11.4.

Flowsheet symbols for evaporators, crystallizers, and driers range all the way from simple squares or rectangles to detailed pictorial sketches similar to Fig. 11.5. There is little point in portraying typical symbols under the circumstances, but they are almost always labelled in any event. The same observation applies to all the other operations to be discussed in the remainder of the chapter. Customarily, the stream shown leaving the bottom of a unit is the heavier or more dense phase, while the lighter or less dense phase is shown going off at or near the top. It is also customary to indicate co-current or countercurrent flow by drawing stream arrows in the appropriate directions.

Cost correlations. The cost of heat exchange equipment is conventionally correlated as a function of the heat transfer surface area provided. As indicated by the solution to Prob. 10-4, the cost per square foot of surface area decreases with size. When the separation of phases is also involved, as it is in the case of evaporation, crystallization, or drying, the pertinent cost correlations are somewhat more complex and will not be presented here.

11.3 Chemical Reaction

The equipment in which chemical reactions are carried out varies all the way from a simple open tank to a complicated unit which provides for agitation, intimate contact with a catalyst, unusual conditions of pressure and temperature, the suppression of undesirable side reactions, the continuous removal of a solid product, and the dissipation of the heat of reaction. This wide range of design features, coupled with an equally wide range of operating conditions, makes generalization difficult. Even so, there are some aspects of reactor design which can be profitably examined in this introductory treatment. Of all the many types of chemical process equipment, chemical reactors probably represent the epitome of the interrelationships among theoretical, practical, and economic considerations.

An early step in the design of any chemical reactor is the application of the pertinent rate equation as illustrated in Sec. 9.3. But the rate coefficient cannot be evaluated until a reaction temperature has been selected, and economics immediately enters the picture: The increased cost associated with operation at elevated temperatures must be balanced against the effect of temperature on reaction rate. Further, raising the temperature to increase the rate of reaction will, more often than not, affect the equilibrium unfavorably. Thus the cost of separating product from unreacted material and reprocessing and recycling the latter must also be considered in making the overall cost comparison. In the completely general case the effect of operating pressure is subject to a similar economic analysis.

The selection of a particular reactor type may also be prerequisite to the specification of tentative operating conditions, since different conditions may be preferable depending on whether the operation is to be batch or continuous. In the latter case, a further choice must be made between two reactor types. A *stirred-pot* reactor, as the name implies, is agitated or stirred so as to maintain a uniform composition throughout the reacting mass, and the reaction conditions closely approach the case of perfect mixing discussed in Sec. 9.3. In a *tubular* or *differential flow* reactor, on the other hand, the composition varies continuously along the length of the reactor and back-mixing is minimized. The complete absence of back-mixing is often called *plug flow*.

Basic design features. Batch reactors are used advantageously for small-scale operations or when exceptionally close control of reaction conditions is essential. A stirred-pot reactor is also suitable for such conditions since the reaction rate is constant and constant operating conditions are easily maintained. The continuous operation permitted by a stirred-pot reactor is an added advantage, but a batch reactor of the same size will usually process more material per unit of time.

The design features of batch and stirred-pot reactors are quite similar, the basic unit being a simple vessel, usually closed, fitted with the necessary feed and discharge openings. Reaction rate, throughput, and the nature of any catalyst used dictate the size of the vessel, but special considerations may dictate its shape. If heat of reaction is to be supplied or removed, a double-walled or *jacketed* vessel may be used, with a heating or cooling medium being circulated through the jacket. Alternately, the heating or cooling medium can be circulated through one or more coils of tubing placed inside the vessel. Agitation is readily provided by a motor-driven agitator.

A tubular reactor has a greater capacity per unit volume of reactor than either a batch or stirred-pot reactor, as was shown in Sec. 9.3. It follows that this type of reactor is likely to be a first choice unless the unique characteristics of one of the other types are pertinent. For example, the fact that reaction rate varies along the length of a tubular reactor means that the rate of heat liberation from an exothermic reaction will also vary, and the use of a stirred-pot reactor may be indicated if isothermal operation is desirable.

Plug flow through a tubular reactor is promoted by making the reactor long and narrow, and the reaction "vessel" may actually be only a suitable length of pipe. This design is particularly advantageous when an endothermic reaction is to be carried out at high temperature, because the pipe can be run through a direct-fired heater or furnace which will supply the heat of reaction and maintain the desired temperature. In such a case the diameter of the reaction tube will obviously depend on fluid flow and heat transfer considerations as well as on the pertinent reaction kinetics.

Catalyzed reactions. Many chemical reactions of industrial importance require the presence of a catalyst which accelerates the desired reaction preferentially and thereby suppresses the formation of undesirable by-products. Intimate contact between reactants and catalyst is essential in such cases, and special design features may be needed to insure this condition. If, as is sometimes the case, the reactants and the catalyst can co-exist in a single-phase, homogeneous mixture, intimate contact is assured. Unfortunately, it then becomes necessary to separate the catalyst from the mixture when the reaction is complete.

A more challenging situation arises when two or more phases are involved, a typical example being the reaction of components of a gas or vapor phase on the surface of a solid catalyst. One solution to this problem is to pass the reacting mixture through a vessel containing a bed of catalyst pellets. Theoretically, the catalyst is left unchanged by the reaction it catalyzes and a *fixed-bed* reactor might be operated indefinitely. In practice, however, the gradual *deactivation* of the catalyst is likely to be caused by contaminants in the feed stream or by the accumulation of a reaction product on the catalyst surface. For the most part *spent* catalyst can be processed or *regenerated* to restore its activity. Since the reactor must be taken off stream during regeneration, continuous operation requires the use of two or more reactors operated in a cyclic fashion with one being regenerated while the others are on stream.

The flow through fixed-bed reactors approximates plug flow, although considerable back-mixing may occur. When a closer approach to perfect mixing is desired, the use of a *fluidized-bed* reactor may be called for. In this design the reactant vapor flows upward through the reactor and small catalyst particles are partially suspended in the vapor stream. The result is a bed of solid particles which exhibits many of the characteristics of a fluid, and the continuous motion of the bed provides the desired mixing action. The mobility of the catalyst also makes it possible to withdraw spent catalyst continuously, regenerate it in a separate piece of equipment, and return regenerated catalyst to the reactor. The heat of reaction in a fluidized-bed reactor is often supplied or removed by withdrawing the spent catalyst at one temperature and returning regenerated catalyst at a higher or lower one.

Reactor costs. One of the simplest techniques for estimating the cost of a chemical reactor is to calculate the total weight of the reaction vessel and apply a cost correlation based on weight. The cost of special features may then be calculated separately and added to the base cost. It is noteworthy that the cost of the catalyst initially charged to a fixed- or fluidized-bed reactor can be a significant item of capital investment. In the petroleum industry, for example, catalysts containing platinum are widely used in an operation called reforming. The initial catalyst inventory in a large reformer may represent an investment of as much as a million dollars or more.

11.4 Mechanical Separation

The recovery, in relatively pure form, of one or more components from a multi-component mixture or solution is a major problem in chemical engineering. Many different approaches to the problem are possible, but close inspection reveals that they are based on common fundamental principles. The consideration of these principles can be facilitated by distinguishing between those separational methods which involve the diffusion of a component or components from one phase to another and those which do not. The diffusional, or *mass transfer*, operations are characterized by a more or less continuous change in phase composition and are discussed in Sec. 11.5. The present discussion is confined to those operations in which phase compositions are constant and the problem reduces to that of separating the phases by mechanical means.

The mechanical mixture to be separated almost invariably consists of particles, drops, or bubbles of one (or more) phase, called the *dispersed* phase, suspended in another called the *continuous* phase. If no solid phase is present, the separation may be effected by inducing coalescence of the dispersed phase and a complete separation by mechanical means is theoretically possible. The complete separation of two or more solid phases is also feasible. On the other hand, a pure solid phase cannot be completely recovered from a fluid-solid mixture by purely mechanical means, although a solid-free fluid phase can be recovered. Thus the separation of fluid and solid phases generally involves the removal of some or most of the fluid to leave a more concentrated fluid-solid mixture. A complete separation may ultimately be effected by a mass transfer or diffusional operation.

Both the rate of separation and the degree to which separation is complete vary widely with process conditions and the type of equipment used. Fortunately, almost all mechanical separations are based on the practical application of one of two fundamental mechanisms. On the one hand, a separation can be effected by exploiting the relative motion of the dispersed phase with respect to the continuous phase. Alternately, the separation involves the use of a medium or device which is permeable to one phase but not to the other. These two mechanisms and the equipment in which they are utilized are discussed separately in the paragraphs to follow.

Separation based on relative motion. The force balance applicable to a solid particle or liquid drop falling freely through a fluid medium was developed in Sec. 9.6 and was found to be

$$Mg - \frac{\rho_f Mg}{\rho_s} - g_c F_D = M \frac{du}{d\theta} \qquad (9.72)$$

where the drag force, F_D, is a function of velocity. The fact that the velocity is relative rather than absolute makes possible the design of systems in which the dispersed and continuous phases have absolute velocities in opposite directions. Such systems effect separation on a continuous basis, and it is only necessary that the absolute upward velocity of the continuous phase be less than the settling velocity of the dispersed phase. The settling velocity can accordingly be used in the continuity equation to calculate the minimum cross-sectional area for a separator of a given capacity. The height of the unit can then be specified so as to provide for effective disengagement despite localized velocity disturbances, a size distribution in the dispersed phase, and the variation of dispersed-phase concentration with position in the separator.

A simple change of sign for the drag force in Eq. (9.72) makes the foregoing analysis equally applicable to systems in which the dispersed phase rises rather than settles in the continuous fluid phase. Thus the principle of relative motion is utilized directly in *entrainment separators* to remove solid particles or liquid droplets from gases, in *de-aerators* to separate gas bubbles from a liquid, in *settlers* or *thickeners* to recover clear liquid from a liquid-solid mixture or *slurry*, and in *decanters* to separate one liquid phase from another. In general, these separations are carried out on a continuous basis, but batch processes are also practicable in some applications.

The principle also provides a basis for the separation of a dispersed solid phase from another of different particle size or density. An auxiliary fluid, introduced for the express purpose, provides the necessary continuous phase. If the density of the fluid lies between those of the two solid phases, a *sink-or-float* separation results. The restriction on fluid density may be removed by utilizing the difference in rates at which the two solid phases settle in a fluid of lower density: In an operation called *classification*, the fluid moves upward through the unit to carry the smaller or lighter particles overhead while the larger or heavier particles sink to the bottom. The cross-sectional area of the classifier is such that the absolute upward velocity of the fluid is bracketed by the relative settling velocities of the two solid phases being separated.

Simple gravity separators become impracticable when settling velocities are inordinately low. This situation arises when the densities of the dispersed and continuous phases are approximately equal or when the dispersed phase elements are extremely small. A variety of modified techniques is available for use in such circumstances. For the most part they involve the substitution of a stronger, artificial force for gravitational force, or the agglomeration of the small particles, drops, or bubbles into larger ones that have increased settling velocities. A brief listing of the more common techniques and their characteristics should be informative:

Centrifugal force is utilized in several separational operations. The term centrifugal separator generally refers to a motor-driven device in which a centrifugal force many times stronger than the gravitational force is developed. Such devices are not normally used for gas streams, but other devices employing centrifugal force frequently are. Air classifiers may be equipped with fans which create a centrifugal force field to supplement gravitational force. In *cyclone separators*, often used to remove entrained solids or liquids from gas streams, the feed stream enters the cyclone tangentially to create a swirling flow pattern. The resulting centrifugal force throws the particles to the periphery of the unit where they can fall to the bottom, while the gas flows upward in a central core.

Electrostatic and magnetic force fields are also used to supplement or replace gravitational force. Entrained solids or liquids may be removed from a gas stream in an *electrostatic* or *Cottrell precipitator* in which the particles are given an electrical charge and then collected at an oppositely-charged electrode. *Electrostatic separators* make use of the same principle to separate solids having different electrical conductivities. Similarly, a *magnetic separator* might be used to separate two solids having different magnetic properties.

When a liquid-solid separation is difficult because the solid particles are extremely small, *flocculation* may be effective. This process may involve the addition of an electrolyte to the slurry to neutralize the electrical charges which are often carried by small particles and act to oppose agglomeration. Alternately, the small particles might be induced to adhere to larger particles introduced as a flocculating agent.

An equivalent approach is applicable to gas-solid or gas-liquid separations. As the gas stream flows upward through a falling shower of liquid, the solid particles or liquid droplets impinge on the larger liquid drops and are carried down with them. This operation is often called *scrubbing*. Similarly, de-aeration can be facilitated by contacting the gas-liquid mixture with larger gas bubbles supplied from an external source.

As an alternative to increasing bubble size in de-aeration, it may be practicable to decrease the distance the bubbles must travel before they reach the surface of the liquid and become disengaged. One technique is to use a spray nozzle in combination with a gravity separator. The small droplets created by the nozzle facilitate disengagement because the gas need only travel to the surface of the drop, and the separator provides the residence time needed to complete the separation.

The applicability of the sink-or-float method of separating solids can sometimes be extended by a *flotation* operation. Solid particles having a density greater than that of the fluid are made to float by inducing small air bubbles to adhere to them, thereby reducing the effective density. Various flotation agents are used to promote froth formation and to make the bubbles adhere selectively to only one of the two solid phases to be separated.

Ultimately, the decision to use a particular method of separation depends on an economic comparison. Among the variables which must be considered are the physical properties of the system, the quantity of material to be processed, and the degree of separation desired. The comparison is made even more difficult by the fact that separational methods based on permeability or diffusion may also be practicable for a given application. Fortunately, several rough guides may be used to reduce the scope of the problem. These will be covered in the subsequent study of the unit operations.

Separation based on permeability. Despite the wide applicability of the principle of relative motion, there are many instances in which the techniques already described are inappropriate. A widely-used alternative solution to the problem of effecting a mechanical separation involves passing the mixture through a medium or device which will permit the passage of one phase while holding up the other. A simple strainer exemplifies the general method and is in fact often used to remove small amounts of solids from a fluid stream. The unit operation of *filtration* embraces this and most similar separational methods; the major exception to this is the sizing of solid particles by *screening*.

Among the filter media in common use are woven screens or cloth, tangled mats of metallic or non-metallic fibers, solid but porous metallic or ceramic disks, and packed beds of settled solid particles. The separation may be effected by making the openings or pore spaces in the medium smaller than the solid particles to be separated. Filtration by impingement is also feasible and is used to remove liquid drops from a gas stream, or fine particles from gases or liquids, even when penetration is theoretically possible. For example, wire-mesh *de-misters* are frequently used to remove entrained droplets from a wet gas stream. The droplets impinge on the filter medium and coalesce to form drops which are too large to be re-entrained by the gas stream.

Filtration is inherently a batch operation. The *bag filter* in a vacuum cleaner must be emptied from time to time; the *dust filter* in a forced-air heating system must be replaced periodically; and industrial *filter presses* are shut down for cake removal at regular intervals. This is not to imply that continuous or semi-continuous operation is impossible. The rotary vacuum filter described in Chap. 1 is an excellent example of a filtering operation which is essentially continuous. A dust filter may also be operated continuously by *scrubbing* away the accumulated solids with a liquid wash stream. Further, any batch process operated on a cyclic basis has the characteristics of a steady-state operation since there is no accumulation of mass within the system from cycle to cycle.

It was pointed out in Sec. 9.6 that the rate of filtration decreases as solids accumulate on the filter medium, and this phenomenon has an interesting economic consequence: At first glance, it suggests that frequent removal of the accumulated solids is desirable if throughput is to be maximized. But filtration must be stopped while the cake is being removed; hence, frequent removal means less time for actual filtering. There should be—and is—an optimum time at which filtration should be stopped and the cake removed.

Filters generally leave a significantly smaller quantity of liquid with the solid residue than do gravity settlers or thickeners. If desired, even this liquid can be largely removed by displacement with air or another liquid as an integral part of the filtration process. On the other hand, large volumes of slurry can usually be handled more economically in thickeners than in filters. In view of these comparative advantages, it is not surprising that the two processes are used in tandem in many applications, a thickener being used to provide a more concentrated feed slurry for the filter. This pre-concentration reduces the size of the filter required, but a cost comparison is often necessary to determine whether the reduced filter size results in a savings sufficient to cover the cost of the thickener.

Except for the motive power required to operate some types of filters, the only energy associated with filtration is that needed to force the fluid through the unit. In *gravity filters* the necessary driving force is provided by static head. Alternately, the feed may be supplied to the filter under pressure, or the filtrate can be removed under vacuum. *Centrifugal filters*, as the name implies, depend on centrifugal force rather than gravitational or pressure force as a driving potential.

11.5 Diffusional Separation

When methods of separation were first considered in Chap. 2, it was pointed out that *phase* separation is the usual technique but that *component* separation is the ultimate objective. The two concepts are completely compatible only when the components to be separated exist in different phases. In many instances it is necessary to effect the desired component distribution between or among phases before the separation of the phases themselves becomes appropriate. It may be recalled from Sec. 9.4 that the diffusional or mass transfer operations are, by definition, those in which phase compositions are changed by the transfer of mass from one phase to another.

The overall mass transfer process actually involves three separate steps. First, two non-equilibrium streams are brought together so as to permit the transfer of mass between them. Second, mass is transferred, thereby changing compositions in the direction of equilibrium. And, finally, the resulting product streams are separated by mechanical means. Although mass transfer is involved only in the middle step, it is usually convenient to treat all three steps as integral parts of the overall mass transfer operation.

Partial vaporization or condensation, evaporation, crystallization, and some drying operations are not normally considered to be mass transfer processes for several reasons, even though they clearly involve the transfer of mass from one phase to another. Perhaps the most obvious basis for this distinction is the fact that the first of the three steps listed above does not apply to these operations. Furthermore, they depend to a considerable extent on the transfer of heat to or from the surroundings, whereas any heat effects associated with other mass transfer processes are a consequence of, rather than a cause of, the transfer of mass.

Mass transfer processes. All diffusional operations are based on common fundamental principles, but practical design methods differ depending on the nature of the phases involved. When mass is to be transferred between two immiscible phases, the two phases are brought into direct contact with each other. Transfer between miscible phases is also practicable, but the phases must be kept separate to prevent random mixing. A porous membrane or diaphragm which is more permeable to one component than to another is normally used in such cases. The resulting operation differs from filtration only to the extent that it is carried out on a molecular scale rather than on a macroscopic scale, and no external driving force is required.

When one component of a solid mixture is selectively dissolved in a suitable solvent, the operation is called *leaching* or *solvent extraction*. The resulting mixture of solution and undissolved solid is then separated into an *extract* phase and a *raffinate* phase. The former is the solvent-rich phase and is normally a pure solution. The raffinate, on the other hand, is a mechanical mixture of undissolved solid and unrecovered solution. These same terms are also used in liquid-liquid extraction in which one component of a liquid solution is selectively transferred to a solvent introduced for the purpose.

The foregoing concepts are readily extended to *drying* if the wet solid is considered to be a single phase. Exposure to a dry gas stream results in the transfer of the liquid component into the gas phase. Only rarely will either the dry gas fed to the drier or the dry solid produced be absolutely free of the liquid component. "Dry" is used in a relative sense in drying, and care must be exercised to avoid misinterpretation. The term *bone-dry* is frequently used to denote composition on a moisture-free basis.

In both drying and solid-fluid extraction, mass is transferred from the solid to the fluid phase. Transfer in the opposite direction is also practicable in an operation known as *adsorption*. In *physical adsorption* the transfer is due to an intermolecular attraction between the solid *adsorbent* and the adsorbed component or *adsorbate*. *Chemisorption* denotes an adsorption process in which the adsorbent and adsorbate combine in a chemical reaction which can be reversed. In either case, the subsequent recovery of the adsorbate from the solid surface is commonly called *desorption* rather than drying or extraction, even though a solid-to-gas transfer is involved.

A special case of adsorption is that in which mass is transferred from fluid to solid and from solid to fluid simultaneously. The transfer normally involves only ions rather than complete, uncharged molecules and is appropriately known as *ion exchange*. The exchange of either anions or cations is possible, depending on the properties of the solid ion exchange *resin* used, and anion and cation exchange may be used in combination to effect a complete separation if desired. Continuous or semi-continuous operation necessitates the periodic *regeneration* of the exchange resin.

The gas-liquid operation which is analogous to extraction is called *absorption*. A multi-component gas mixture is brought into contact with a liquid *absorbent* and the selective transfer of one or more components from the gas to the liquid phase results. In the operation of *stripping*, also called desorption, the transfer is in the other direction. In both absorption and stripping the adjectives *rich* and *lean* may be applied either to the gas or to the liquid to indicate the relative concentration of the component being absorbed. Absorption and stripping are often used together, the rich liquid leaving the absorber being stripped to recover the absorbed component. The resulting lean liquid may then be recirculated to the absorber.

When the vapor content of a gas stream is increased by bringing the gas into contact with a pure liquid rather than a liquid solution, the operation is known as *humidification*. In *de-humidification* the same contact results in a decrease in the vapor content of the gas. While the latter is obviously a separational process, the former is not. Instead, it is generally prescribed to effect cooling by converting sensible heat into latent heat of vaporization. It is also a natural complement to drying, since the gas stream used for drying is automatically humidified as it picks up material from the drying solid. From a fundamental standpoint, humidification and de-humidification can be considered to be special cases of stripping and absorption.

In absorption and stripping an auxiliary stream is introduced into the operation for the express purpose of providing a second phase. When the second phase is created by partially vaporizing or condensing the process fluid itself the operation is called *distillation*. Distillation also differs from absorption and stripping in that it involves the transfer of mass in both directions simultaneously, with the more volatile component vaporizing and passing from the liquid to the vapor phase while the less volatile component condenses. The resulting vapor, enriched in one component and depleted in another, is called the *distillate* product. The liquid effluent is the bottom product or simply the *bottoms*. The term *reflux* denotes that portion of either the distillate or bottoms which is condensed or vaporized and returned for contacting with the feed stream.

Separations effected by bringing immiscible phases into direct contact are much more common than are those which make use of semi-permeable membranes. Only two operations of the latter type will be mentioned here. A partial separation of the components of a gaseous mixture can be obtained by *gaseous diffusion* to the extent that the components diffuse through a membrane at different rates, depending on their respective molecular weights. Similarly, it may be possible to separate two solutes in a liquid solution by *dialysis*, with the rate of diffusion depending on molecular size rather than molecular weight. Rates of separation are low in both gaseous diffusion and dialysis, and these operations are not widely used in industrial process plants.

Mass transfer equipment. The efficiency of mass transfer operations depends in large part on the amount of interphase contact area provided and the duration of the contact. One means of providing adequate contact time and area for vapor-liquid systems is to distribute the liquid over a solid surface as was done in the wetted-wall column described in Sec.9.4. A substantial increase in surface may be obtained by filling the column with solid pellets and letting the gas and liquid flow countercurrently through the interstitial spaces. The increased contact area is obtained only at the expense of higher pressure drop, but *packed columns* are widely used in vapor-liquid mass transfer operations.

In another popular contacting method the vapor is bubbled through the liquid to produce a froth having a high interfacial contact area. One design in common use consists of a horizontal *perforated plate* or *sieve tray*. Liquid flows horizontally across the tray while the vapor bubbles up through the holes. The vapor rate must be high enough to prevent weepage of liquid through the holes.

Liquid-liquid and liquid-solid mass transfer devices range from packed columns used for unsteady-state adsorption to agitated vessels in which mass transfer and phase separation are effected simultaneously. Only a limited separation is possible under the latter conditions, since vigorous agitation and good separation are inherently incompatible. It might therefore be more economical to provide separate vessels for contacting and separating.

The advantages of countercurrent flow were discussed when heat transfer was considered earlier in the chapter, and it was noted that a substantial temperature cross is possible; that is, the outlet temperature of the cold stream may be higher than that of the hot stream. The same observation applies to countercurrent mass transfer operations. In a packed column, for example, the concentration of the transferred component in the effluent vapor can be considerably higher than that which corresponds to equilibrium with the effluent liquid. Unfortunately, true countercurrent operation is not generally feasible in many types of mass transfer equipment. For example, sieve trays are essentially cross-flow devices, while the use of a mixing unit and a separating unit in series obviously corresponds to co-current or parallel flow.

As was indicated in Sec. 9.4, those operations in which mass transfer is limited by an approach to equilibrium are called *equilibrium stage* operations. It is significant that the limitations on mass transfer embodied in the equilibrium stage concept apply to single stages only. When a number of stages are used in series, the process is more nearly analogous to that occurring in a packed column, particularly if the two phases being treated flow from stage to stage countercurrently. Although multi-stage mass transfer operations are normally considered to be "unit" operations, they clearly involve a combination of units as far as any fundamental analysis is concerned. Their further consideration will accordingly be deferred to Chap. 13.

Equipment costs. Like that used for chemical reactions, the equipment in which mass transfer operations are carried out embraces many different design variations. One solution to the problem of cost estimation is to use the same technique as was used for chemical reactors: The cost of the basic vessel or column can be estimated on the basis of its weight, and the cost of additional special features can be calculated separately and added to the base cost. Alternately, a cost-per-stage correlation might be used to estimate the cost of multi-stage equipment. This technique is commonly applied to both packed and tray-type columns, for example, with the cost per tray or per foot of packed height being correlated as a function of tower diameter.

11.6 Materials of Construction

All the many items of process equipment described in this chapter have an important feature in common: They must be constructed of materials which will withstand chemical attack as well as mechanical stress. Design details dictated by the latter requirement may be left to the mechanical engineer, but only the chemical engineer can fully assess the chemical properties of materials. In addition to specifying operational design features, then, the chemical engineer must also select, from an imposing list of possible choices, the materials best suited for use in the construction of process equipment. The problem is all the more formidable when, as is often the case, properties such as density, heat capacity, melting point, thermal or electrical conductivity, or nuclear cross-section must be considered along with chemical stability.

Steel and its alloys have been used extensively in process equipment in the past and are still preferred in most applications. Other well-established materials are aluminum, magnesium, copper, lead, tin, and zinc and their alloys; and non-metallic materials such as glass, graphite, and ceramics. In recent years, however, an impressive number of less-familiar materials have been put to use in either the pure or alloyed state. Typical examples are silicon, titanium, hafnium, zirconium, tantalum, beryllium, niobium, and even boron. The chemical engineer must have a working familiarity with such materials even though their relatively high cost prevents their wide-spread use.

An ever-increasing number of polymers and plastic resins are also available for use and cannot be overlooked. Among the more common formulations are phenol-formaldehyde resins, polyamides, co-polymers of vinyl and vinylidene chloride, and polymethyl methacrylate, each of which is probably better known by tradename: Bakelite, Nylon, Saran, and Lucite or Plexiglass. Other materials in the polymer-plastic category are polystyrene, polyethylene, polypropylene, polyformaldehyde, and various polyesters, silicones, synthetic rubbers, and epoxy resins, to mention but a few.

Finally, the chemical engineer must be aware of the many possibilities for using two or more materials in combination, or for giving a particular base material a special surface treatment to improve chemical stability. The so-called tin can, for example, is actually made of tin-coated steel and galvanized iron is steel coated with zinc. Tanks, reaction vessels, and pipe may be lined with lead, glass, baked-on or cured-in-place resins, or any one of a number of other metallic, ceramic, polymeric, or plastic materials. Alternately, a base metal such as steel might be subjected to oxidation under carefully controlled conditions so as to produce an adherent oxide film on its surface to protect it from further oxidation.

If two or more materials are equally satisfactory from the process standpoint, a cost comparison becomes pertinent. It is significant that the comparison cannot be based on the purchased cost alone, for other factors may have a direct bearing. As an example, consider steel pipe vs. pipe made of polyethylene or a similar plastic material. The latter has the advantage of chemical inertness, light weight, and low cost; but steel pipe might still be the logical choice for an overhead piping system because it will span greater distances without sagging, thus fewer supports will be needed. Similarly, the higher first cost of one material as compared to another may be more than offset by a longer service life and reduced maintenance costs.

New processing techniques involving abnormal operating conditions are continually extending the scope of the problem of materials selection. Unheard of only a short time ago, processes carried out near absolute zero or at temperatures up to several thousand degrees Fahrenheit are now almost commonplace. At the same time, pressures may range from a thousand atmospheres or more all the way down to almost total vacuum, where many solid materials will literally boil away. Clearly the problem of handling an extremely corrosive substance under such conditions is a formidable one. The almost limitless array of available materials, material combinations, and surface treatments, coupled with the diverse factors which affect true cost, makes the job of specifying materials all the more difficult.

11.7 Conclusion

The theoretical side of chemical engineering is being continually strengthened and expanded, but it is the ability to put theory to practical use which is the ultimate measure of a chemical engineer's proficiency. As was stated at the outset, one of the purposes of this chapter is to bridge the gap between the theoretical and practical sides of engineering. This can only be done by citing examples of present-day engineering practice, and it is hoped that the student will not infer that he is entering a field in which all major problems have already been solved. The conversion of new research findings into working processes and equipment is a never-ending responsibility of the engineer.

While a familiarity with current chemical engineering practice is a distinct asset to the student, there is little reason to be concerned with details at this point. The student who feels that he still does not understand distillation, for example, need not be alarmed: Several weeks will be devoted to this important topic in due time. Thus the present chapter, like those which have preceded it, is intended more to familiarize than to teach. It is, so to speak, only a first approximation of the problem.

On the other hand, many technical terms have been introduced and defined in this chapter, and the student should incorporate them into his own vocabulary as soon as possible. For the most part their assimilation will be presupposed in the remainder of this text and in subsequent courses. Thus the student should be prepared to interpret such statements as "The rich liquid leaving the absorber is steam-stripped to recover the absorbent." Repeated reference to the present chapter is recommended as necessary until all new terms are readily interpreted.

REVIEW, STUDY, AND DISCUSSION

11-1. Define each of the following terms: nominal pipe size, schedule number, equivalent length of fittings, lost work of expansion or contraction, mechanical efficiency, brake horsepower, countercurrent and parallel flow, ambient conditions, mother liquor, plug flow, catalyst deactivation, spent catalyst, regeneration, mass transfer, dispersed phase, continuous phase, slurry, extract phase, raffinate phase, bone-dry, adsorbent, adsorbate, exchange resin, absorbent, rich gas, lean liquid, distillate product, bottoms, reflux, equilibrium stage.

11-2. Briefly describe the major characteristics of each of the following operations or pieces of equipment: pipe nipple, coupling, union, street elbow, reducer, bushing; positive displacement meter, orifice, Venturi, rotameter, pump, compressor, turbo-expander, throttling process; double-pipe, shell-and-tube, and multi-pass heat exchangers; flash vaporization, evaporation, crystallization, drying; forced-circulation and multiple-effect evaporators; stirred-pot, tubular, differential flow, jacketed, fixed-bed, and fluidized-bed reactors; entrainment separator, de-aerator, thickener, decanter, sink-or-float separation, classification, cyclone separator, Cottrell precipitator, electrostatic separation, magnetic separation, flocculation, scrubbing, flotation, filtration, screening, de-mister, bag filter, dust filter, filter press, gravity filter, centrifugal filter, leaching, adsorption, chemisorption, desorption, ion exchange, humidification, distillation, gaseous diffusion, dialysis, packed column, sieve tray, extraction, absorption, stripping.

11-3. The heat required for a process operation is to be supplied by the condensation of 6,000 pounds per hour of steam at 240°F. Specify a suitable diameter for the steam supply line and for the condensate return line.

11-4. The resistance coefficient at the entrance to the condensate return line in Prob. 11-3 is 0.5. Estimate the pressure drop associated with the flow through the entrance.

11-5. Refer to Prob. 9-19. Calculate the pressure at the suction side of the pump. If the pump has a mechanical efficiency of 40 per cent and is driven by an electric motor having an efficiency of 90 per cent, how many kilowatts of electricity must be supplied to the motor? Calculate the annual cost of electricity if the unit cost is 0.9 cents per kw-hr and the pump is expected to have a service factor of 0.95.

11-6. A shell-and-tube heat exchanger is to provide 2300 square feet of heat transfer surface. It is to be constructed from 1-inch brass tubing (unlike pipe, tubing is specified according to outside diameter) with water to flow through the tubes. Specify a suitable number of tubes, the number of tube passes, and the number of tubes per pass.

11-7. Cooling water, available at 60°F, is to be used to cool 20,000 lb/hr of a process stream from 150°F to 75°F. The specific heat of the process stream is 0.85. Estimate the cooling water flow rate in gallons per minute.

11-8. A fixed-bed catalytic reaction system is to be used to process 120,000 lb/hr of feed with a space velocity of 0.5 pounds of feed per hour per pound of catalyst. 0.7 per cent of the feed is converted to coke which is deposited on the surface of the catalyst. The coke build-up deactivates the catalyst, and it is estimated that an accumulation of 1.5 per cent of the weight of the catalyst can be tolerated before the spent catalyst is regenerated. The regeneration process reduces the coke level to 0.5 per cent of the weight of the catalyst and takes 8 hours, during which time feed cannot be processed. Specify the minimum number of fixed-bed reactors of uniform size which will permit continuous operation.

11-9. A state highway department uses either sand or salt on icy roads during the winter, depending on specific conditions. A load of salt has been dumped into the sand storage bin by mistake. Specify several different methods for separating the two materials and compare the advantages and disadvantages of each. What solution to the problem would you recommend?

11-10. Refer to Prob. 9-21. For any particular set of operating conditions, the relationship between filtering time and volume of filtrate collected may be written $\theta_f = cV^2$, where c is a constant. Because the filter must be dumped periodically, however, the *effective* rate of filtration is $r = V/(\theta_f + \theta_d)$, where θ_d is the dumping time. Combine these two equations to eliminate V and obtain an expression for r as a function of θ_f and θ_d. Prove that r will be a maximum when θ_f equals θ_d.

11-11. The dew point of a mixture of air and water vapor is to be reduced to $-17.3°C$ by a silica gel adsorption process. The mixture is initially saturated at 30°C and atmospheric pressure, and is to be processed at a rate of 2,000 mols per hour. It is estimated that the silica gel will adsorb water up to 30 per cent of the weight of the dry gel and that subsequent desorption will yield a gel containing 5 per cent water on a dry basis. What additional information is needed before the quantity of silica gel which will be required can be calculated? Supply this information yourself on the basis of assumptions which you consider to be reasonably realistic and calculate the weight of silica gel required. Briefly summarize the reasoning behind any necessary assumptions.

11-12. A feed stream analyzing 45 per cent A and 55 per cent B is to be separated by distillation in a sieve tray column, with component A to be recovered and component B to be discarded. What factors should be considered in specifying the purity of the two product streams? Be as specific as you can on the basis of the available information.

CHAPTER 12

Mass Balance Calculations

The various aspects of change have, for the most part, been treated separately up to this point. In contrast, practical problems in either design or analysis are more likely to be comprehensive and to require the consideration of several aspects simultaneously. Unfortunately, comprehensive problems based on more than one of the fundamental aspects of change are best deferred until these aspects have been covered more thoroughly in subsequent course work. What is needed, then, is a simple vehicle for practice in problem analysis, because the ability to recognize pertinent relationships and to visualize a route from problem statement to solution is of critical importance to the chemical engineer. As it happens, the mass balance is ideally suited for this purpose.

The basic simplicity of the general mass balance equation presented in Chap. 2

$$M_i - M_o = M_2 - M_1 + M_c \qquad (12.1)$$

is attested by the fact that its repeated use in the intervening chapters has presumably occasioned little difficulty. In the final analysis, the application of the mass balance *is* straightforward, for it involves only the substitution of known quantities for all terms but one and solving for the one unknown. Thus any difficulty in mass balance problems must lie in the determination of the appropriate numerical values for the known quantities. This aspect of the overall problem is amenable to a logical approach, but if the student expects to be given a check-list which will obviate the need for independent thinking, he is due to be disappointed. Mass balance problems can be classified only to a limited degree, and the possible variations within each classification are almost without limit. The intelligent student will concentrate on the underlying principles to be presented in this chapter and not on the specific problems used by way of illustration.

12.1 The Mass Balance Matrix

Except for the simplest and most straightforward problems, the first step in attacking any mass balance problem should be the preparation of a block flow diagram showing all process units and flowing streams. Since the use of a specific example will facilitate the discussion to follow, let us consider a process involving three separate components, A, B, C, and suppose the process flow diagram shown in Fig. 12.1. The process is to be steady state

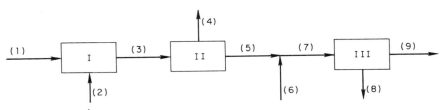

Fig. 12.1 Hypothetical box flow diagram.

and will not involve nuclear reactions; hence, Eq. (12.1) reduces to

$$M_i = M_o \tag{12.2}$$

In the completely general case the solution of the mass balance problem represented by this hypothetical process requires the specification of the quantity of A, B, and C in each of the nine streams shown in Fig. 12.1. Thus a total of 27 quantities are to be specified by one means or another. Some of these must obviously be fixed by the problem statement, but there are always a number of unknowns to be determined and, presumably, an equal number of equations to be solved for them. The fact that Eq. (12.2) must be satisfied both as it applies to the overall process and as it applies to individual components entering and leaving specific pieces of process equipment is an effective starting point in developing the necessary equations.

It was emphasized in Chap. 2 that a separate mass balance can be written for each component involved in a given process. A total-mass balance might also be appropriate, but the number of *independent* balances can never exceed the number of components—three in this case. It should also be clear that balances can be written around each of the three boxes representing process units in Fig. 12.1, and that a fourth balance can be made around the mixing point at which stream (6) is introduced. Here again, however, the number of independent balances is limited and only four independent systems are possible in the present case.

In accordance with the foregoing, a little thought should make it clear that a four-unit process involving three components can give rise to as many as 12 independent mass balance equations. It can therefore be anticipated that the mass balance problem pertaining to such a process will involve an equal number of unknowns. Needless to say, the prospect of solving 12 equations simultaneously is not a pleasant one. Before simplifying the picture, however, let us temporarily complicate it even further:

Suppose the problem statement includes the information that stream (7) analyzes 10 per cent A. By itself this information does not eliminate any of the contemplated unknowns. Rather, it permits the use of an additional equation, namely,

$$\frac{\text{lbs of } (B + C)}{\text{lbs of } A} = \frac{90}{10}$$

in stream (7). Were the percentage figures for all three components given, three such *ratio equations* could be written—e.g., B/A, C/A, and C/B. Other ratios are equally possible, but the number of independent relationships is again restricted, this time to the number of percentage figures given. Even so, it is clear that many more than 12 equations might be applicable to this rather simple process.

The significant point of the foregoing is that one of the primary qualifications for handling mass balance problems is the ability to recognize all of the many quantitative relationships which are applicable. The information provided by percentage analyses is particularly noteworthy in this respect, for the equations to be obtained from such information are all too often overlooked by beginning engineers.

Although other methods are usually preferable, a problem such as that cited here can in fact be solved by the method of simultaneous equations. The following example is presented by way of illustration:

EXAMPLE 12.1. Determine the quantity of each component in each stream of the flow diagram shown in Fig. 12.2.

Solution. The quantities entering at the bottom-left of Fig. 12.2 are readily determined to be 360 lbs of P, 150 lbs of Q, and 90 lbs of R; hence, seven quantities remain to be determined. These have been identified by the letters a through g in Fig. 12.2, a being the pounds of P in the stream entering the

unit at the top and so forth. These seven unknowns are readily matched
with three component balances and four ratio equations:

$$(1) \ a + 360 = e \qquad\qquad (4) \ a = (90/10)b$$
$$(2) \ c + 150 = f \qquad\qquad (5) \ c = (86/14)d$$
$$(3) \ b + d + 90 = g \qquad\quad (6) \ f = (20/65)e$$
$$(7) \ g = (15/65)e$$

The simultaneous solution of seven equations could be a laborious task, but
it can be seen here that the nature of the equations is such that a solution

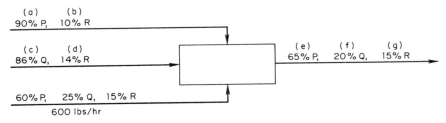

Fig. 12.2   Flow diagram for Example 12.1.

can be effected without too much difficulty. Note that the equations presuppose a steady-state process. Were any mass accumulating within the
system during the operation, additional information would be required before
the problem could be solved.

A procedure such as that used in the foregoing example will always lead
to a solution to the problem, provided only that none of the pertinent equations are overlooked. But we have repeatedly emphasized that the good
engineer not only gets the answer but does so in the shortest time and with a
minimum of effort. This, then, is the real challenge of mass balance problems.
The suggestions which follow should be of help to the student in meeting
this challenge.

12.2 The Unit Balance for Physical Change

Because individual process units are the building blocks for complete
processes, the ability to make a mass balance around a single unit is an
essential attribute. We shall therefore concern ourselves first with this type
of problem, and leave multi-unit processes for later consideration. It will
also be convenient to restrict the initial analysis to processes involving physical change only, with chemical change to be treated in a subsequent section.

Preliminary analysis. The preparation of a simple block flow diagram
showing all available quantitative information has already been recom-

mended as the first step in solving any mass balance problem. Even "obvious" information, such as the fact that air consists of 21 per cent oxygen and 79 per cent nitrogen, should be meticulously shown on the diagram. It is equally advantageous to indicate all components known or expected to be present in each stream even when quantities or percentages are not known initially. This practice not only affords protection against oversight but also indicates the most direct method of solution in many instances, since the stream quantities remaining to be determined can be readily identified. In the latter regard, it is important to take note of the component or components *not* present in any given stream, as will be seen shortly.

As a final preparatory step, the process should be identified as being either batch or steady state so that those terms in the general mass balance equation which are not pertinent can be eliminated. Note that it is occasionally feasible to treat even a batch process on a steady-state basis. As an example, consider a batch filter: Slurry is fed into the unit and the solids build up on the filter medium while the filtrate is continuously removed. After a time the slurry feed is stopped while the accumulated solids are removed, whereupon a new cycle can be started. Although this is quite clearly a batch process, each cycle has the characteristics of a steady-state operation since there is no net accumulation of mass within the system.

Mass balance systems. The mass balance relationship given by Eq. (12.1) is meaningful only if the system around which the equation is to be applied has been defined. Since only single-unit processes are to be considered for the time being, the system of interest will be obvious. The solution to the problem represented by Fig. 12.1, on the other hand, would require the successive consideration of several different systems. In all cases the system selected should be clearly identified before Eq. (12.1) is applied. This procedure is followed in the present chapter even though there can be no confusion when only a single unit is involved, and the student should adopt the same practice so as to form the habit.

Actually, the decision to examine only single units for the present is not as restrictive as it may seem. Consider the process shown in Fig. 12.1: If desired, the mixing point and unit III can readily be combined to yield a single system by merely drawing a new box around the combination as shown in Fig. 12.3. The new box can then be treated as a single unit, and the broken lines in Fig. 12.3 can be completely disregarded. This follows directly from the fact that the mass balance pertains only to streams crossing the boundary of the system of interest and takes no cognizance whatsoever of streams flowing *within* the system. In other words, *all* mass balances are made around single-unit systems in the final analysis. The only consideration being deferred in the present treatment, then, is the selection of the particular portion of a given process flow diagram which should be boxed in and thereupon treated as a unit. This aspect of the problem is covered in Chaps. 13 and 14.

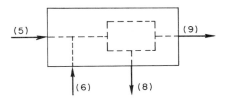

Fig. 12.3　Schematic conversion of a complex process into a single-unit system.

Basis of calculation. With but few exceptions, the quantity of mass entering, leaving, or being accumulated within a given system will vary depending on the time interval over which the mass balance is applied. A suitable time interval must therefore be selected as the *basis* for any mass balance calculations and should be clearly stated at the outset. Once a basis has been specified, it may be convenient to drop time units out of the calculations, thereby simplifying the problem of checking unit consistency. Thus 2,500 pounds per hour could be treated more simply as 2,500 pounds once a basis of one hour's operation has been specified. For the sake of clarity, it is recommended that the time basis be restated when reporting the answer or answers to a problem.

The time interval used as a basis for a given solution need not be explicit. Instead, it is frequently more convenient to base the calculations on an arbitrary quantity of material at some point in the process. Thus a suitable basis might be simply "100 pounds of feed", for example, and it would not be necessary to state further that this amount of material enters in, say, 7.42 minutes, as long as all other mass quantities used in the solution are consistent with the stated basis.

The judicious selection of a basis is often an important factor in simplifying the solution to a problem. There are no hard-and-fast rules governing the selection, but one guiding principle can be offered as a temporary substitute for experience: The most advantageous basis is generally that which makes the most quantitative information immediately usable. The following three cases illustrate the application of the principle.

1) A coal analyzing 75% C, 3% H_2, 8% O_2, 2% S, 1% N_2, and 11% ash is to be burned in a furnace and the composition of the resulting stack gas is to be determined. Since steady-state operation is clearly implied, the gas *composition* does not depend on either time or the amount of coal burned, and the choice of a basis can be completely arbitrary. In this case, a logical

basis is 100 pounds of coal burned, since the given percentages can be immediately expressed in pounds without intervening calculation.

2) Suppose the same coal is to be burned and we wish to determine the
rate at which coal should be supplied in order to produce 10,000 SCF of
stack gas per hour. One might now be tempted to use a basis of one hour or
the equivalent basis of 10,000 SCF of stack gas, but a basis of 100 pounds
of coal burned is again preferable. The advantages of this basis are unchanged
from the first example, and once the quantity of gas produced by 100 pounds
of coal has been determined, it is a simple matter to scale the 100 pounds
up or down to obtain the quantity corresponding to 10,000 SCF of stack gas.

3) If the stack gas analysis is known and the coal composition is to be
determined, on the other hand, a more convenient basis would be 100 cubic
feet of stack gas. Note the switch to a volumetric basis in keeping with the
convention of stating gas analyses in volume per cent. As a matter of fact,
if ideal-gas behavior can be assumed, a basis of 100 *mols* of stack gas is even
more advantageous. Since mol per cent equals volume per cent for ideal
gases, the latter basis permits the immediate determination of the mol quantities of each component in the stack gas.

The most convenient basis is not always apparent from the problem statement. Given partial analyses of both coal and stack gas, for example, we
might elect to start the problem at either end. Secondary considerations
usually make one choice preferable to the other, however, and only rarely
does the engineer find it necessary to be completely arbitrary about his
selection of a basis.

The importance of using the same basis throughout a set of calculations
cannot be overemphasized, even though it should be obvious. Several different systems may be examined in the course of solving a comprehensive
problem, however, and it follows that the selection of a basis generally
precedes the selection of a system. The basis can also be reflected in the
figures entered on the block flow diagram if desired. In any event, both a
basis and a system must be specified before quantitative mass balance calculations are undertaken.

Quantitative calculations. Despite the diversity of possible mass balance
problems, it is possible to set forth a sequence of steps which generally result
in the most direct solution to a problem. Even so, the suggested procedure
does not eliminate the need for judgment and common sense. Alternative
procedures may be more advantageous in any particular case, and, like the
rule for selecting a basis, the following list is presented only as a temporary
substitute for experience. A few of the more commonly used alternatives are
demonstrated in the course of solving sample problems.

Step 1: Prepare a block flow diagram, select a basis for the calculations,
and enter all available quantitative information on the diagram. Complete

the qualitative mass balance by also showing all components expected to be present in each stream. For multi-unit processes, a particular system should also be specified before quantitative calculations are undertaken.

Step 2: Inspect the flow diagram to see if there are any components for which quantities are known in all streams but one. The mass balance may be immediately applied to any such components to determine the quantity present in the remaining stream. Unless the calculations are accompanied by units and labels which make it obvious, the particular component being balanced should be clearly identified.

Step 3: When pertinent stream analyses are known, make immediate use of the information obtained in Step 2 to determine quantities of other components to the fullest extent possible. This step may make it possible to apply the mass balance to a second component, as outlined in Step 2, and so on.

Step 4: When the preceding two steps are not applicable or have been completed without the problem having been solved, introduce an algebraic unknown. As is the case in selecting a basis, the unknown should be defined so as to make the most information immediately available, albeit in terms of the unknown. Such a procedure automatically obviates the need for solving a set of simultaneous equations in many cases. Like the basis and the system, the quantity represented by the unknown should be clearly stated.

Step 5: Return to steps 2 and 3, this time treating all functions of the unknown as if they were known. The resulting mass balances make it possible to express still other quantities in terms of the same unknown. In most cases, it is found that one of the balances can be solved for the unknown, whereupon the solution can be readily completed. Otherwise, recourse to additional unknowns and the solution of simultaneous equations is necessary.

Although only component balances are referred to in the above steps, it is well to keep a sharp eye open for possible applications of a total-mass balance. This is particularly true when it becomes necessary to resort to simultaneous equations, because the calculations are usually simplified if the total-mass balance is used as one of the equations. A subsequent example illustrates this point.

The following illustrative examples demonstrate the efficacy of the recommended procedure. Given information is shown on the flow diagrams in Fig. 12.4, and the problem in each case is to determine the quantity of each component in each stream.

EXAMPLE 12.2, Fig. 12.4(a). Step 1: Basis—100 lbs entering at left, or 79 lbs of A and 21 lbs of B. System—the process unit. All stream components are already shown on the flow diagram.

Step 2: B is unknown in only one stream, and a B balance yields 21 lbs of B leaving at right.

Step 3: $(21)(40/60) = 14$ lbs of A leaving at right.

Step 2: A is now unknown in only one stream, and an A balance yields $79 - 14 = 65$ lbs of A leaving at bottom.

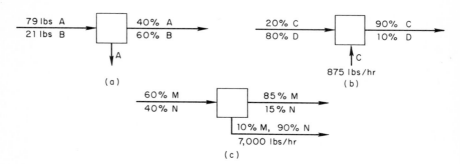

Fig. 12.4   Block flow diagrams for sample problems.

An alternative to the calculation made in Step 3 would be $21/.60 = 35$ total lbs leaving at right. Then, using a total mass balance, $79 + 21 - 35 = 65$ lbs leaving at bottom.

EXAMPLE 12.3, Fig. 12.4(b). Step 1: Basis—875 lbs of C entering at bottom. System—the process unit. All stream components are already shown on the diagram.

Step 2: Not immediately applicable in this example.

Step 4: Let x be the lbs of C entering at left. Since D and C are in 80/20 ratio in the entering stream, there will be $4x$ lbs of D entering at left.

Step 2: A D balance yields $4x$ lbs of D leaving at right.

Step 3: $(4x)(90/10) = 36x$ lbs of C leaving at right.

Step 2: From a C balance, $x + 875 = 36x$, and x is found to be 25 lbs of C entering at left. The rest of the solution is straightforward.

EXAMPLE 12.4, Fig. 12.4(c). Step 1: Basis—1 hour, or 7,000 lbs out at bottom. System—the process unit. All stream components are already shown on the diagram.

Step 2: Not immediately applicable in this example.

Step 4: Let x be the lbs of N leaving at right; hence, $(x)(85/15) = 5.66x$ lbs of M leave at right.

Step 2: An M balance yields $700 + 5.66x$ lbs of M entering at left. An N balance is also possible, and yields $6300 + x$ lbs of N entering at left.

Step 3: $(700 + 5.66x)(40/60) = 467 + 3.78x$ lbs of N entering at left; hence $467 + 3.78x = 6300 + x$, from which $x = 2100$ lbs N out at right, and the solution is readily completed.

EXAMPLE 12.5. Repeat Ex. 12.1 using the recommended step technique.

Step 1: Basis—1 hour, or 600 lbs entering at bottom, equal to 360 lbs of P, 150 lbs of Q, and 90 lbs of R. System—the process unit. All stream components are already shown in Fig. 12.2.

Step 2: Not immediately applicable in this example.

Step 4: Let x be the total lbs leaving at right; hence, $0.65x$ lbs of P, $0.20x$ lbs of Q and $0.15x$ lbs of R leave.

Step 2: From a P balance, $0.65x - 360$ lbs of P enter at top; and, from a Q balance, $0.20x - 150$ lbs of Q enter at the top.

Step 3: $(0.65x - 360)(10/90) = 0.0722x - 40$ lbs of R enter at the top. Also, $(0.20x - 150)(14/86) = 0.0326x - 24.4$ lbs of R enter at left.

Step 2: An R balance may now be written and solved for x:

$$(.0722x - 40) + (.0326x - 24.4) + 90 = .15x$$

from which $x = 566$ lbs, total mass leaving at right. The solution is now easily completed.

Some alternative techniques. The details of the foregoing solutions were intentionally varied to emphasize the flexibility of the recommended procedure. In Ex. 12.4, x was used to represent a component, while in Ex. 12.5 it represented a total stream. Similarly, a ratio equation was solved for x in Ex. 12.4, whereas mass balances were solved directly in the other examples. The important point is that *any* logical method of attack will always lead to a solution.

An alternative approach to problems such as Ex. 12.3 is preferred by many engineers. Any component which is present in only one entering stream and only one leaving stream is commonly called a *tie substance*, since it effectively ties the two streams together. When a tie substance is present but is of unknown quantity, the selection of a basis which temporarily fixes the quantity can be an effective move toward a quick solution. An alternative solution to Ex. 12.3 employing this technique should be informative:

Basis—100 lbs of total mass entering at left, or 20 lbs of C and 80 lbs of D, the tie substance. Note that the 875 figure must be disregarded for the time being since it is not consistent with the arbitrary basis, but a D balance yields 80 lbs of D leaving at right and hence $(80)(90/10) = 720$ lbs of C leaving at right. A C balance then gives $720 - 20 = 700$ lbs of C entering at bottom.

Now, since 875 lbs of C actually enter at the bottom, it is clear that all figures must be scaled up by a factor of $875/700 = 1.25$; hence $(1.25)(20) = 25$ lbs of C actually entering at left, which is the same answer as was obtained by the original method.

In the effort to demonstrate the basic simplicity of mass balance calculations, we have perhaps understated the case for simultaneous equations. Many engineers would automatically make use of two simultaneous equations in Ex. 12.4, and of three in Ex. 12.5. The former example is used to demonstrate this alternative technique:

Let x be the total lbs in at left and y be the total lbs out at right. From a total-mass balance, $x = 7{,}000 + y$; and an M balance yields $0.60x = 700 + 0.85y$. Multiplying the total-mass balance through by 0.85 and solving simultaneously,

$$\begin{array}{r} 0.85x = 5950 + 0.85y \\ 0.60x = 700 + 0.85y \\ \hline 0.25x = 5250 \end{array}$$

from which $x = 21{,}000$ and $y = 21{,}000 - 7{,}000 = 14{,}000$. Note how the simplicity of the total-mass balance makes its use preferable to a second component balance.

It can be seen that the foregoing method of solution is no more complicated than was the original method, and many engineers will contend that it is actually simpler. In any event, it is safe to state that the use of two or more unknowns in a solution is hardly something to be avoided except as a last resort. If a direct solution is not readily apparent, don't hesitate to introduce as many unknowns as appear to be necessary. The odds are that any resulting simultaneous equations can be solved in no more time than it would take to seek out a more direct method.

Only ratio equations and total-mass or component-mass balance equations are utilized in the solution of the foregoing examples, but other relationships are frequently pertinent. For the most part these relationships reflect the characteristic features of process equipment, and some of the more common examples are cited below. A more general relationship, all too often overlooked by beginning engineers, accounts for the fact that the whole must be equal to the sum of its parts. The use of a *summation equation* is most likely to be called for when the percentage analysis of a given multi-component stream is partially or totally unknown. This is demonstrated in Ex. 12.8 in the next section.

Pertinent process characteristics. The fact that information pertinent to the solution of a problem may be given only by implication rather than directly was emphasized in Chap. 3. Mass balance problems provide an excellent illustration of this important point: Characteristic features of specific items of process equipment may have a direct bearing on the mass balance problem, and they are not usually stated explicitly. Thus the chemical engineer must be able to deduce pertinent mass balance relationships from a knowledge of equipment design features. The observations which follow should prepare the student for the particular cases most likely to be encountered and should also alert him to the need for similar deductions in other applications.

A common source of fluid will often be connected to more than one process unit by a piping system having an appropriate number of branches. In such cases it should be recognized that the composition of the fluid stream is the same at all points, and a knowledge of composition at any point is all that is needed to determine the composition at all points. A mass balance around the point or points where the flow splits is still pertinent, however, since the inflow must be equal to the sum of the flows in the various branch outlets. Thus an unknown outlet rate can frequently be determined by difference. These observations should be wholly obvious, yet many a beginning student has been completely baffled by a simple mass balance problem only because they were overlooked.

It should also be apparent that the presence of an intermediate storage or surge tank across a flow line can be completely ignored under steady-state conditions. This is true even if the tank has multiple outlets, for in such cases the branch-line analysis discussed above will suffice. When unsteady-state conditions prevail, on the other hand, it may be necessary to make a balance around the tank itself.

Fluid mixing operations are commonly indicated on flow diagrams by the shaft-and-propeller symbol introduced in Chap. 1. In the absence of chemical reaction, mixing equipment can also be identified by the presence of two or more inlet streams and, usually, a single outlet. When more than one is indicated, all outlet streams may be assumed to have identical compositions, and the same composition must exist within the mixing vessel itself. It is noteworthy that the same observation applies to agitated vessels of any kind, including stirred-pot chemical reactors: Unless a phase separation is effected simultaneously, all outlet streams leaving such vessels have the same composition. It might also be noted that temperatures and other intensive properties are also identical. This observation is frequently overlooked by beginning engineers attempting to fix pertinent conditions at all points on a complex flow diagram.

The compositions of the two phases produced by partial vaporization or condensation must satisfy the equilibrium requirement. This fact often provides needed mass balance information which, at first glance, appears to be missing from a given flow diagram. The same observation applies to a single equilibrium stage in mass transfer operations, although it may be necessary to correct the calculated equilibrium compositions for the stage efficiency. Note, however, that the equilibrium restriction does not apply to multi-stage operations viewed as a single process.

From the standpoint of the mass balance, phase separation by mechanical means is essentially the reverse of the problem of mixing. The composition of each phase must be known, and equilibrium or solubility calculations are frequently needed to establish compositions. In the absence of mass transfer between phases, *phase* compositions do not depend on the degree of separation. A knowledge of the quantity of each phase present in any multi-phase stream thus permits the determination of the overall composition, since the compositions of the component phases are presumed to be known. In a separation which yields a liquid and a liquid-solid mixture, for example, the liquid which accompanies the solid will have the same composition as the other liquid—and both will be saturated with respect to the solid. This is another point which is often overlooked by beginning engineers, and the student will do well to take careful note of it.

It was pointed out in Sec. 11.4 that any batch process operated on a cyclic basis has the characteristics of a steady-state operation, since there is no accumulation of mass within the system from cycle to cycle. Typical examples of this situation are the periodic removal of filter cake from a batch filter, the intermittent removal of cinders and ashes from a coal-fired furnace, and the alternating on-stream and regenerating cycles used in fixed-bed adsorption and chemical reaction. In such processes it is often necessary to account for the retention of small amounts of other components along with the major component being accumulated. For example, the void space in a fixed-bed reactor will obviously be filled with a mixture of reactants and reaction products when the reactor is taken off-stream for regeneration.

As a more specific example, the quantity of filtrate retained in an accumulation of filter cake is often calculated from a knowledge of the porosity of the cake, assuming that the interstitial volume not occupied by solid material is filled with filtrate. Some filters permit the partial draining of the cake, however, and it may be necessary to make an assumption regarding the amount of filtrate retained. As was noted above in general terms, any liquid retained with the solid will be saturated with the solid and will have the same composition as the pure filtrate recovered from the operation.

The mass transfer operations involve both mixing and separation. The application of the mass balance to each of the latter operations has already been considered, and it is a simple matter to combine the pertinent principles to effect the solution of an overall process which includes both. As was the case with separation alone, a knowledge of phase compositions is prerequisite to the completion of the mass balance. Equilibrium or solubility calculations are accordingly pertinent.

The foregoing is hardly a complete list of the cases in which an awareness of the operating characteristics of items of process equipment provides pertinent mass balance information. Even so, it should suffice to convince the student of the importance of subjecting all processes to a careful and logical analysis to insure that implied information is not overlooked.

12.3 The Unit Balance for Chemical Change

With but slight modification, the mass balance principles discussed in the preceding section are directly applicable to problems involving chemical rather than purely physical change. These modifications have already been presented in Secs. 2.3 and 8.1 and only a brief summary need be given here: (1) The general mass balance as given by Eq. (12.1) applies to elements, but not to the chemical compounds associated with chemical reactions; (2) reaction coefficients denote *mol* quantities; (3) the application of a total-mass balance does not permit the use of mol units as a general rule; and (4) simultaneous or consecutive reactions may be added together to obtain a single overall reaction only after pertinent yield factors have been introduced. If the significance of these restrictions is not immediately clear, the pertinent parts of Secs. 2.3 and 8.1 should be reviewed at this point.

One of the first steps in solving a mass balance problem involving chemical reaction should be to write and balance the pertinent reaction or reactions when these are known. The coefficients in front of each reactant and product then provide a complete mass balance relationship, albeit on an arbitrary basis. This basis is easily scaled up or down depending on the quantities given in any particular problem. The internal ratios discussed in Sec. 8.1— e.g., two mols of oxygen per mol of H_2SO_4—will be of considerable help in effecting the scale-up and identifying all pertinent relationships.

The complete mass balance relationship provided by a balanced chemical reaction can also be exploited when the introduction of an algebraic unknown appears to be desirable or necessary: Letting the unknown denote the quantity of one component reacted or produced makes it immediately possible to express all other reactants and products in terms of the same unknown, and the solution of numerous simultaneous equations may be avoided. Note that fractional functions of the unknown can be eliminated by assigning the unknown to a reactant or product for which the coefficient in the balanced reaction equation is unity. Other reactants and products are then expressable as simple, whole-number multiples of the unknown.

Despite the pertinence of modification (1) at the beginning of this section, it is often advantageous to use a modified form of the general mass balance equation rather than to apply the usual form of the equation only to elements. For any particular component, the modified form may be written

$$M_{in} + M_{produced} - M_{consumed} = M_{out} \qquad (12.3)$$

where the second and third terms denote the quantity of that component produced by or consumed in chemical reaction. These terms may be evaluated from a knowledge of the balanced reaction equation or equations, whereupon the in-out balance may be completed. Ex. 12.9 illustrates this technique as well as the effectiveness of assigning an unknown to a reactant or product as suggested in the preceding paragraph.

Except for the foregoing comments, identical procedures of solution are applicable to problems involving either chemical or physical change. All of the discussion of the preceding section pertaining to the selection of a basis, looking for tie substances, and making use of algebraic unknowns as necessary, etc., is equally applicable when the change is chemical rather than physical. This is demonstrated in the solutions to the sample problems which follow.

EXAMPLE 12.6. Propane (C_3H_8) is to be burned with 25 per cent excess air to form carbon dioxide and water vapor. Calculate the composition of the stack gas leaving the furnace and the quantity of gas (SCF) which will be produced per ton of propane burned.

Solution. This example has already been solved as Ex. 8.3 in Sec. 8.1. It is suggested that the student make use of the techniques presented in this chapter to work out his own solution for comparison with that presented earlier.

EXAMPLE 12.7. Producer gas is made by burning coke with insufficient air so as to promote the formation of CO rather than CO_2. A producer gas containing CO and CO_2 in a mol ratio of 7:1 is to be produced from a coke analyzing 90 per cent carbon and 10 per cent ash. The ash will leave the gas producer as a solid residue containing 3 per cent unburned carbon. How much gas (SCF) will be obtained per ton of coke fed?

Solution. Basis—2000 lbs of coke fed. (Note that a mol basis is impracticable because the molecular weight of ash is indeterminate.) System—the gas producer. The pertinent block flow diagram is given in Fig. 12.5.

The coke contains 200 lbs of ash, and an immediate ash balance is indicated to find the carbon lost in the residue:

$$(200)(3/97) = 6.2 \text{ lbs C in residue}$$

$$\frac{1800 - 6.2}{12} = 149.5 \text{ mols C react}$$

Taking cognizance of internal ratios, we see that the producer gas must contain 149.5 mols of (CO + CO_2). For a 7:1 ratio, then, $149.5/8 = 18.7$ mols of CO_2, leaving 130.8 mols of CO.

The same internal ratio principle then permits the determination of the oxygen content of the gas:

$$18.7 + \frac{130.8}{2} = 84.1 \text{ mols of } O_2$$

and, from an oxygen balance, this amount must have come in with the air. Hence $(84.1)(79/21) = 316$ mols of N_2 in and out. The total quantity of producer gas is therefore $316 + 18.7 + 130.8 = 466$ mols, and

$$(466)(359) = 167,000 \text{ SCF gas/ton coke fed}$$

EXAMPLE 12.8. If steam is introduced into the gas producer of Ex. 12.7, a *water gas* containing free hydrogen as well as CO, CO_2, and N_2 will result.

Using the coke and residue analyses from Ex. 12.7, calculate the air-to-steam ratio which will yield a water gas analyzing 25 per cent CO and 10 per cent H_2. (Assume the gas contains no free oxygen or undecomposed steam.)

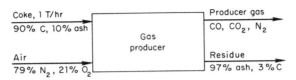

Fig. 12.5 Block flow diagram for Example 12.7.

Solution. Basis—The basis used in Ex. 12.7 might be used here, but, since the air-steam ratio is independent of the quantity of coke actually burned, a basis of 100 mols of carbon burned is entirely suitable and will simplify the numerical calculations somewhat. System—the gas producer. The preparation of a block flow diagram is left to the student.

From a carbon balance, the water gas will contain 100 mols of $(CO + CO_2)$. The elements remaining to be balanced are H_2, N_2, and O_2, none of which can be balanced directly. The use of an algebraic unknown is therefore indicated. Letting x be the mols of steam fed would appear to be advantageous since it will permit the immediate determination of the mols of H_2, CO, and total water gas as functions of x:

From a hydrogen balance, x mols in $= x$ mols out; then $x/.10 = 10x$ mols of water gas, and $(10x)(.25) = 2.5x$ mols of CO. A carbon balance then gives $100 - 2.5x$ mols of CO_2, and the oxygen accounted for in the gas is thus

$$(100 - 2.5x) + \frac{2.5x}{2} = 100 - 1.25x \text{ mols}$$

Of this amount, $0.5x$ mols came from the steam; hence the difference, or $100 - 1.75x$, must have come from the air. Multiplying by 79/21 yields $376 - 6.59x$ mols of N_2 in and out.

All possible balances have now been made without obtaining an equation which can be solved for x. As was suggested earlier, a summation equation may be appropriate in such a case. Here, the total mols of water gas must equal the sum of the constituent mols, or,

$$10x = x + 2.5x + (100 - 2.5x) + (376 - 6.59x)$$

from which $x = 30.5$ mols of steam; and

$$\frac{376 - (6.59)(30.5)}{.79} = 221.5 \text{ mols of air}$$

$$\therefore 221.5/30.5 = 7.26 \text{ mols air/mol steam}$$

EXAMPLE 12.9. An aqueous solution of ethylene glycol (EG) analyzing 50 mol per cent EG is produced from ethylene, air, and water; the overall reaction is

$$C_2H_4 + \tfrac{1}{2} O_2 + H_2O \rightarrow (CH_2OH)_2$$

When 400 per cent excess air and the stoichiometric quantity of water are used, the process yields an off gas analyzing 5 per cent CO_2 on a dry basis, presumed to be formed by the side reaction

$$C_2H_4 + 3 O_2 \rightarrow 2 CO_2 + 2 H_2O$$

The off gas also contains 0.02 mols of water per mol of dry gas. Calculate the percentage conversion of ethylene and the percentage yield of EG.

Solution. Basis—100 mols ethylene fed. System—the overall process. On the basis of the given information, 200 mols of oxygen, 752 mols of nitrogen, and 100 mols of water will enter the process along with the ethylene. Confirmation of these figures and the preparation of a flow diagram for the process is left to the student.

A nitrogen balance gives 752 mols of N_2 in the off gas, but no other balances are immediately feasible. In accordance with the recommendation made earlier in this section, let x be the mols of oxygen in the first reaction. Then the reaction also involves $2x$ mols of C_2H_4, $2x$ mols of H_2O, and $2x$ mols of EG. Additional balances still being impracticable, let y be the mols of C_2H_4 in the second reaction, which then also involves $3y$ mols of O_2, $2y$ mols of CO_2, and $2y$ mols of H_2O. The total dry off gas may now be obtained from a CO_2 ratio equation, $2y/.05 = 40y$ mols of dry gas, and the water accompanying the off gas is $(40y)(.02) = 0.8y$ mols. Further, the 50 per cent solution will contain the $2x$ mols of EG and hence $2x$ mols of H_2O. Eq. (12.3) may now be written for the water:

$$100 + 2y - 2x = 2x + 0.8y \qquad \text{or} \qquad x = 25 + 0.3y$$

A summation equation will provide the needed second relationship between x and y. Applying Eq. (12.3) successively to the ethylene and to the oxygen,

$$100 + 0 - (2x + y) = \text{mols } C_2H_4 \text{ in off gas}$$

$$200 + 0 - (x + 3y) = \text{mols } O_2 \text{ in off gas}$$

Since the $40y$ mols of dry off gas is the sum of the N_2, CO_2, O_2, and unreacted C_2H_4,

$$40y = 752 + 2y + (200 - x - 3y) + (100 - 2x - y)$$

from which $x = 350.7 - 14y$

Simultaneous solution of the two equations for x as a function of y yields $x = 31.8$ and $y = 22.8$. Thus of 100 mols of C_2H_4 fed, 86.4 mols $(2x + y)$ are converted in one reaction or the other while 63.6 mols $(2x)$ are converted to EG. Total conversion is therefore 86.4 per cent, but the yield of EG is only 63.6 per cent.

It was stated earlier that there are no hard-and-fast rules governing the selection of a basis. Clearly the same conclusion applies to the selection of a method of attack, whether the problem is purely physical or involves both physical and chemical change. It can only be suggested that the student experiment with various possibilities until he finds those which are most to his liking.

12.4 Nuclear Reactions

Although neither mass nor energy is conserved in processes involving nuclear reactions, the Einstein relationship, $E = Mc^2$, may be readily combined with the two conventional laws of conservation. Substitution of the velocity of light into the equation followed by the necessary unit conversions yields an energy-mass equivalence of 3.87×10^{13} BTU of energy created for every pound of mass destroyed. By comparison, it would be necessary to burn approximately 1.4 million tons of coal to obtain the same quantity of energy. Alternately, a typical home heating system rated at 100,000 BTU per hour could be operated continuously for almost 100 years on the energy equivalent to a mass of one gram.

It can readily be seen that the quantity of mass destroyed in a nuclear power reactor, for example, can safely be neglected in any calculations pertaining solely to the application of the mass balance. It is, however, necessary to determine the quantity accurately when energy balance calculations are also pertinent.

12.5 The Unsteady State—Process Control

It has been noted that many unsteady-state processes can be conveniently analyzed on a steady-state basis by making a judicious selection of a basis. This follows from the fact that mass cannot be indefinitely accumulated within or removed from a system, and, ultimately, mass in must equal mass out. Even "true" steady-state processes may be subject to variation over short periods of time. A feed rate of 6,000 pounds per hour, for example, is not likely to mean that 100 pounds enter the system during each minute of each hour but rather that the *average* rate is 100 pounds per minute. In general, deviations from an average input rate will produce an equivalent deviation in output rate only after a time lag which may range from a few seconds to several hours. During this period the operation is actually unsteady-state, but such fluctuations can be ignored when only average rates are of interest.

There are occasions when the chemical engineer must concern himself with instantaneous rather than average rates, most notably when designing or analyzing process control systems. The general mass balance can be converted to an instantaneous rate form for use in such situations by writing it in differential form and dividing through by an infinitesimal increment of time. The result, presented earlier in Sec. 2.7, is

$$m_i - m_o = \frac{dM_s}{d\theta} \tag{12.4}$$

in which m_i and m_o denote the instantaneous *rates* at which mass is entering and leaving the system and M_s is the mass within the system. Ex. 12.10 is a typical application of this form of the mass balance and is, in fact, a practical example of the calculations leading to the design and analysis of process control systems.

EXAMPLE 12.10. Water flows into an open tank at the top and out through a valve at the bottom, the effluent rate being directly proportional to the liquid level in the tank. At a time when the liquid level is such that the output and input rates are both equal to m_1, the input rate is suddenly changed to a new value m_2 and is held constant at this value. Determine the variation of the output rate with time following the change in input rate.

Solution. Since $m = \rho v$, $M_s = \rho V_s = \rho S z$, and $dM_s = \rho dV_s = \rho S dz$, Eq. (12.4) can be written

$$\rho v_2 - \rho v_o = \rho S \frac{dz}{d\theta} \tag{12.5}$$

where v_2 is the new, constant volumetric input rate, v_o is the time-dependent volumetric output rate, S is the cross-sectional area of the tank, and z is the liquid level. Also, v_o can be expressed as a driving force over a resistance, $v_o = z/R$, where the proportionality constant has been absorbed into R. Then $z = Rv_o$ and $dz = Rdv_o$. Substituting this expression into Eq. (12.5) and cancelling ρ,

$$v_2 - v_o = RS \frac{dv_o}{d\theta} \tag{12.6}$$

The product RS will be found to have the dimensions of time and is called the *time constant* of the system,* to be denoted by T. Eq. (12.6) may therefore be written

$$\frac{dv_o}{d\theta} + \frac{1}{T} v_o = \frac{1}{T} v_2 \tag{12.7}$$

and the solution to this differential equation is

$$v_o = v_2 + Ce^{-\theta/T} \tag{12.8}$$

---

* Electrical, thermal, and mechanical systems may also be characterized by one or more time constants. In electrical circuits, the time constant is the product of a resistance and a capacitance. By analogy, the cross-sectional area S in Ex. 12.10 can be considered to be the *capacitance* of the hydraulic system.

where C is a constant of integration. It may be evaluated from the fact that $v_o = v_1$ at $\theta = 0$:

$$v_1 = v_2 + Ce^0 \qquad \text{or} \qquad C = v_1 - v_2$$

and the final form of Eq. (12.8) is

$$v_o = v_2 + (v_1 - v_2)e^{-\theta/T} \tag{12.9}$$

This is the desired expression for the *response* of the system, i.e., the variation of output rate with time as a result of the change in input rate. Fig. 12.6 shows the response as a graphical function of time, for $v_2 > v_1$.

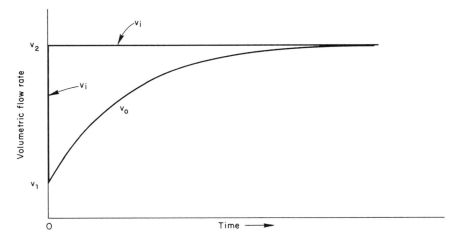

Fig. 12.6   Graphical representation of solution to Example 12.10. This response is typical of any system characterized by a single time constant.

It is noteworthy that the foregoing solution is primarily concerned with the change in output rate rather than with the accumulation of mass within the system as such. This is typical of process control calculations, but it should be clear that the calculations involve the direct application of the unsteady-state mass balance nevertheless.

12.6 Conclusion

The basic principles underlying the application of the mass balance to any given system have all been set forth in this chapter. The two remaining chapters will be concerned with the application of these principles, but we repeat the earlier observation that the possible variations in application are almost limitless. The student who truly understands the *principles* rather than specific applications, and is prepared to apply them meticulously, need never fear the outcome.

Unfortunately, any complex mass balance problem provides innumerable opportunities for mistakes, any one of which can completely nullify the rest of the solution. There is no real substitute for experience when it comes to analyzing comprehensive problems, but experience is gained only through practice, and an awareness of some of the more common pitfalls should help during the practice stage of the learning process. Some of the more common errors in solving mass balance problems are

1) the failure to take all pertinent given information into account;

2) the failure to recognize information given by implication only;

3) the use of unwarranted assumptions;

4) carelessness in setting up the mass balance, with the result that one or more streams are overlooked;

5) an unwitting switch from one basis to another in mid-problem;

6) the combination of simultaneous or consecutive chemical reactions without regard for pertinent yield data;

7) the failure to check unit conversions; and

8) carelessness in numerical computation, particularly with respect to decimal point location.

Corresponding preventive steps should be obvious and need not be listed. In any event, it is quite likely that most students will gain a full appreciation for the importance of careful and logical work only after they have suffered the consequences of their mistakes a few times, for "Once burned, twice careful". Since the completion of one or more mass balances is almost invariably prerequisite to calculations pertaining to the other aspects of change, the student can expect to put the mass balance to early use in subsequent courses in chemical engineering. The problems which follow should provide a medium for the development of skill and confidence. At the same time, the student should gain valuable experience in the important area of problem analysis and thereby improve his ability to reason logically and independently.

REVIEW, STUDY, AND DISCUSSION

12-1. Define system, basis, ratio equation, summation equation, tie substance, water gas, time constant, capacitance, system response.

12-2. Refer to Fig. 12.4(c), Sec. 12.2. Assign algebraic unknowns to the pounds of M entering at left, the pounds of M leaving at right, the pounds of N entering at left, and the pounds of N leaving at right, the total mass entering at left, and the total mass leaving at right. Relate these unknowns with as many mass-balance, ratio, and summation equations as you can identify. (At least 11 are possible.) Show that all but six of these equations are derivable from the others and cannot be considered to be independent equations.

12-3. A slurry consisting of an insoluble solid suspended in water analyzes 12 per cent solids by weight. It is to be fed to an evaporator at a rate of 10,000 lbs per hour and water will be removed by evaporation to concentrate the slurry to 25 per cent solids by weight. How much water (lb/hr) must be evaporated?

12-4. A moist solid contains 16 per cent water by weight and is to be dried to reduce the moisture content to 4 per cent. A drier capable of removing 200 lbs of water per hour is available for use. At what rate can the moist solid be fed to this drier?

12-5. A solid analyzes 70 per cent soluble material and 30 per cent insolubles. The soluble material is to be extracted by contact with a suitable solvent. The insoluble residue will be removed from the bottom of the contacting unit and will be accompanied by an equal quantity of saturated solution analyzing 40 per cent solubles and 60 per cent solvent. The rest of the solution, also saturated, will be withdrawn as a separate stream. The fresh solvent stream fed to the unit will contain 10 per cent soluble material. Complete the mass balance around the contacting unit for a feed rate of 1250 lbs of solid (soluble plus insoluble) per hour.

12-6. A brine slurry containing 10 lbs of solid NaCl per 100 lbs of saturated brine is fed to a continuous thickener at a rate of 1780 lbs per hour to produce an underflow analyzing 65 per cent solid NaCl. How many pounds per hour of overflow are produced? How much total salt (lb/hr) leaves the thickener in the underflow? (The solubility of NaCl in water at the temperature of operation is 225 gms per 1000 gms of water.)

12-7. Refer to Fig. 7.1 in Sec. 7.3. A vapor stream analyzing 50 per cent A and 50 per cent B is to be cooled from 500° to 400° in a partial condenser, with the resulting liquid then to be separated from the remaining vapor. The feed rate will be 3,000 lbs per hour. Assuming equilibrium is attained in the condenser, complete the mass balance using Fig. 7.1 only to determine liquid and vapor compositions. Repeat the problem using the inverse-lever-arm principle.

12-8. Refer to Fig. 7.1 in Sec. 7.3. A saturated vapor analyzing 20 per cent A is to be separated in a continuous, one-stage distillation process. The product streams will be a saturated liquid analyzing 36 per cent A and a saturated vapor of lower concentration. Assuming equilibrium will be maintained, at what temperature should the process be carried out? What will be the composition of the vapor product stream?

12-9. The vapor product from Prob. 12-8 will be condensed to a saturated liquid in a heat exchanger and 50 per cent of the condensate will be returned to the distillation process as reflux, the other 50 per cent being withdrawn as product. Draw a schematic flow diagram for the distillation unit and heat exchanger and calculate the pounds of A, pounds of B, and total pounds in each stream for a basis of 100 lbs of saturated vapor fed to the distillation process. (Suggestion: Combine the distillation unit and the exchanger into a single system for the initial mass balance calculations.)

12-10. Calculate the overall composition and quantity of the mixture produced by mixing the reflux and feed streams of Prob. 12-9. Show that this composition can be obtained graphically by using the inverse-lever-arm principle on Fig. 7.1. Show that the quantities of the two outlet streams may then also be found graphically.

12-11. Repeat Prob. 12-9 for a stage efficiency, as defined by Eq. (9.53) in Sec. 9.4, of 80 per cent.

12-12. A feed stream enters a fractionating column at a rate of 200,000 lbs per hour and is separated into an overhead product and a bottoms product. The feed analyzes 83.5 per cent n-pentane (nC_5), 15 per cent iso-pentane (iC_5), 1.0 per cent material heavier than pentane (HTP), and 0.5 per cent material lighter than pentane (LTP). Most of the iC_5 and all the LTP leave in the overhead product, which also analyzes 1.0 per cent nC_5 but contains no HTP. The bottoms product analyzes 3.0 per cent iC_5. All percentages are in weight per cent. Complete the mass balance around the column.

12-13. A limestone analyzing 95 per cent $CaCO_3$ and 5 per cent inert material is to be heated in a kiln to drive off pure gaseous CO_2 and yield CaO as a solid product. The CaO product stream will be 90 per cent pure, the impurities consisting of the inert material plus undecomposed $CaCO_3$. How much limestone must be fed to the unit to yield 100 tons of the impure CaO product? What fraction of the $CaCO_3$ fed will pass through the kiln without reacting? How many SCF of CO_2 will be evolved?

12-14. The flue gas from a combustion process analyzes 79 per cent nitrogen and 21 per cent CO_2 and is to be contacted with NH_4OH to produce $(NH_4)_2CO_3$. The nitrogen will pass through the reactor unchanged, and will be removed in a waste gas stream containing 4 per cent CO_2. How many SCF of flue gas must be fed to the reactor to produce one ton of ammonium carbonate?

12-15. Methane (CH_4) is burned with air and the resulting stack gas is found to analyze 0.9 per cent CO and 4.5 per cent O_2 on a dry basis. Complete the mass balance. What percentage of excess air is being supplied to the furnace? What is the dew point of the stack gas at atmospheric pressure?

12-16. Mono-chlorbenzene (C_6H_5Cl) is to be produced by reacting benzene (C_6H_6) with chlorine. It is estimated that only 83 per cent of the chlorine reacting will enter the desired reaction, the other 17 per cent entering a side reaction to yield di-chlorbenzene ($C_6H_4Cl_2$). HCl is formed as a byproduct in both reactions. Complete the mass balance for the production of 50,000 lbs of C_6H_5Cl per day.

12-17. 2,000 mols of hydrogen per hour are supplied to a reactor in a stream which also analyzes 10 per cent inert material and 3 per cent reaction product. The reaction consumes 500 mols of hydrogen per hour, and the effluent gas stream containing the unreacted hydrogen, all the inert material, and 54 per cent reaction product is to be reprocessed to recover the product and provide the hydrogen stream which is fed to the reactor.

A makeup stream analyzing 99 per cent hydrogen and 1 per cent inert material is to be fed to the reprocessing unit to provide the hydrogen consumed in the reaction, while 99.65 per cent of the reaction product entering the reprocessing unit is to be recovered as a pure substance. The remainder will be lost in a separate out-going stream which will also contain H_2 and inert material in the same ratio as they are found in the effluent stream from the reactor, the purpose of this stream being to remove the inert material introduced with the makeup hydrogen. The reprocessing unit does not involve any chemical reaction. Determine the composition and quantity of all streams entering and leaving the reprocessing unit.

12-18. Molten sulfur is burned with dry air to produce SO_2, the air rate being adjusted so that the gas mixture leaving the burner analyzes 9 per cent SO_2. The gas mixture passes directly into a catalytic converter where the SO_2 is oxidized to SO_3 with 97 per cent conversion. Complete the mass balance around the burner for a sulfur feed rate of 100 tons per day. What percentage of excess air is supplied to the burner? What is the analysis of the gas leaving the converter?

12-19. The velocity of light is 186,300 miles per second. Substitute this value into the Einstein equation and prove that one pound of mass is equivalent to 3.87×10^{13} BTU of energy.

12-20. Refer to Ex. 12.10. The water leaving the tank in that example enters the top of a second open tank having a cross-sectional area S_b, and flows out through a valve at the bottom of the second tank at a volumetric rate v_b equal to z_b/R_b. Derive an equation similar to Eq. (12.6) relating v_b, θ, T_b, and v_o. Derive a differential equation relating v_b and its rate of change to v_2, the input rate to the first tank, by combining the first derived equation with Eq. (12.6) to eliminate v_o as a variable. (Note: $dv_o/d\theta$ should also be eliminated.)

CHAPTER 13

Multi-Stage Operations

It has been repeatedly stated that the chemical engineer is primarily concerned with the changes in state, energy content, or composition which
attend the conversion of given raw materials into a desired product or products. The latter conversion is clearly the ultimate goal and almost invariably
necessitates the use of two or more operations or processes in combination.
It follows that the chemical engineer must have complete familiarity with
the characteristics of all the unit changes and with the fundamental principles applicable thereto.

Although such familiarity is essential, it is not a sufficient qualification by
itself. Operations and processes used in combination are often mutually
inter-dependent, and this inter-relationship must be considered both in the
synthesis of complex processes by the proper combination of a number of
unit changes and in the analysis of these processes in terms of their component
units. Since process synthesis and analysis are the very essence of chemical
engineering, the interaction between and among unit changes merits specific
consideration. Such consideration is, in part, the purpose of the remainder
of this text.

Unfortunately, a much broader and more detailed understanding of fundamental principles is prerequisite to any intensive study of either process
design or analysis. As a consequence the treatment to follow must be somewhat cursory, and it will not be practicable to investigate all of the funda-

mental aspects of change from the viewpoint of a complex process. Instead, only the application of the mass balance will be considered in detail. The basis for this decision was presented earlier in the introduction to Chap. 12, and a review of the latter should help to give proper perspective to the material which follows.

Perhaps the simplest case in which two or more unit changes are used in combination is that in which the component unit changes are essentially identical. As was noted in Chap. 11, the use of several equilibrium stages in series is frequently advantageous. Since each stage in the series has the same characteristics, the equilibrium stage operations constitute a convenient starting point for the discussion of multi-unit processes. The most important equilibrium stage operations being solvent extraction, absorption, stripping, and distillation, it will be worthwhile to consider each of these operations in turn.

13.1 Solvent Extraction

A review of the operating characteristics of a single stage is desirable as an introduction to multi-stage extraction. Only solvent extraction is considered, but the principles are equally applicable to liquid-liquid extraction. For the sake of simplicity, the analysis is also restricted to a binary system. Thus the operation involves the introduction of a solvent in which one component of the feed stream dissolves preferentially while the other remains undissolved for practical purposes.

Basic mass balance analysis. A single-stage extraction unit is shown schematically in Fig. 13.1. The quantitative data accompanying the diagram

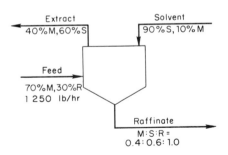

Fig. 13.1 Schematic flow diagram for a single-stage extraction operation.

are those given in Prob. 12-5, with the symbols M, R, and S denoting the soluble material, insoluble residue, and pure solvent, respectively. It should be worthwhile to complete the mass balance by way of review:

For a basis of one hour, the feed contains 375 lbs of R and 875 lbs of M. R being a tie substance, the raffinate must contain 375 lbs of R and hence 150 lbs of M and 225 lbs of S for a total of 750 lbs. Let x be the pounds of impure solvent fed. A total-mass balance permits the determination of the quantity of extract as a function of x, and the result will be found to be $(500 + x)$ lbs. Either M or S may then be balanced to solve for x. Using an S balance,

$$0.90x = 225 + 0.60(500 + x)$$

from which $x = 1750$ lbs of solvent containing 175 lbs of M and 1575 lbs of S. The extract stream thus totals 2250 lbs and contains 900 lbs of M and 1350 lbs of S.

Multi-stage calculations. Each stage of the two-stage extraction unit shown in Fig. 13.2 closely resembles the single stage already considered, and

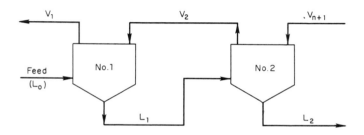

Fig. 13.2   Schematic flow diagram for a two-stage, countercurrent extraction operation.

additional stages could readily be added if desired. The letter symbols shown in the figure are those commonly used in both extraction and distillation. Strictly speaking, L and V denote the liquid and vapor streams encountered in distillation, but they are often used for the raffinate and extract phases in extraction as well. *The subscripts assigned to these symbols always refer to the stage in which the stream originates.* The use of $n + 1$ as a subscript for the solvent feed makes the notation independent of the number of stages involved.

Since the quantity of liquid accompanying the undissolved solid in the raffinate depends only on the effectiveness of the physical separation in each stage, it is reasonable to assume that the solid residue leaving each stage carries with it the same *quantity* of liquid. The *composition* of the liquid, on the other hand, will differ from stage to stage. In this regard it is essential to recognize the fact that the liquid leaving the bottom of any stage will have the same composition as the overflow liquid leaving the top of the same stage, as was emphasized in general terms in Sec. 12.2.

To facilitate the subsequent comparison of the single- and two-stage operations, let the composition and quantity of the feed and solvent streams entering the latter be the same as before. Since R is still a tie substance in the two-stage process, both L_1 and L_2 must contain 375 lbs of R and 375 lbs of solution, but the compositions of the solutions are yet to be determined. In any event, L_2 totals 750 lbs and a total-mass balance around the entire process yields $V_1 = 2250$ lbs. A total-mass balance may then be made around either stage to obtain $V_2 = 1750$ lbs. (It is assumed that the student will confirm these results to his own satisfaction.) The initial use of a total-mass balance around the entire process is noteworthy, for this technique is almost always advantageous.

When the compositions and quantities of both streams at either end of a multi-stage operation are known—in this case either V_{n+1} and L_2, or the feed and V_1—the mass balance calculations can be completed by starting at the end for which data are available and proceeding through the process stage by stage. This situation frequently arises in distillation and will be exemplified in due course. In the present case, with only V_{n+1} and the feed stream completely specified, an alternative procedure is required. Since, by implication, a direct solution would be possible if the composition of V_1 were known, it is logical to make it known in terms of an algebraic unknown. Such a procedure, it will be recalled, is recommended as a general technique in Sec. 12.2.

Accordingly, let x be the pounds of S in V_1. The ratio of S to total solution is therefore $x/2250$, and the same ratio must apply to the liquid in stream L_1; hence, L_1 must contain $(375)(x/2250) = 0.1667x$ lbs of S. Thus the total quantity of S entering unit No. 2 is $(.1667x + 1575)$ lbs. Finally, since V_2 and the liquid in L_2 have the same composition, this quantity of S is distributed proportionately between 1750 lbs of V_2 and 375 lbs of liquid in L_2. The quantity of S in L_2 is thus $(.1667x + 1575)(375/2125)$, equal to $0.0294x + 278$. An S balance around the entire process may now be solved for x:

$$1575 = (0.0294x + 278) + x$$

yielding $x = 1260$ lbs. The mass balance is readily completed to show that V_1 contains 990 lbs of M plus 1260 lbs of S; L_1 contains 210 lbs of S, 165 lbs of M, and 375 lbs of R; L_2 contains 315 lbs of S, 60 lbs of M, and 375 lbs of R; and V_2 contains 1470 lbs of S and 280 lbs of M.

Before comparing these results with those obtained in the single-stage process, it should be informative to examine an alternative method of solution. First, note that ratios were repeatedly used in the foregoing calculations. The calculations might therefore be simplified by letting x be the pounds of S per pound of solution in V_1—and, note, in the liquid portion of L_1 as well.

Similarly, let y be the pounds of S per pound of solution in V_2 and L_2. Separate S balances can then be written around each of the two units to obtain two equations to be solved simultaneously:

$$\text{No. 1:} \qquad 1750x = (2250 + 375)y$$

$$\text{No. 2:} \qquad 1575 + 375x = (1750 + 375)y$$

The remainder of the solution is straightforward.

Advantages of multi-stage operation. What was accomplished by adding a second stage to the extraction process? First, note that the quantity of soluble material lost in the raffinate was reduced from 150 pounds to 60 pounds. The corresponding percentage recovery of soluble material, i.e., the percentage of soluble material in the feed which is not lost to the raffinate, was increased from 83 to 93 per cent. Further, the concentration of soluble material in the extract was increased from 40 to 44 per cent. Since the recovery of the solute from the extract solution is necessary to complete the separation, the increased concentration should permit a more economical recovery operation.

A second basis for comparison is the quantity of solvent required. The foregoing calculations were based on the same quantity fed to both processes, but an alternative possibility would be to use the two-stage unit to obtain the same percentage recovery or the same extract concentration provided by a single stage, in which case less solvent would be needed in the two-stage process. The latter advantage is particularly pertinent when the extract is a saturated solution in any event. (As a matter of fact, Prob. 12-5 states that the extract is saturated at 40 per cent soluble material. This limitation is disregarded in the above calculations so as to make the example more informative.)

The use of additional stages further improves either percentage recovery, extract concentration, or solvent consumption. The gain per stage decreases with the number of stages, however. An economic comparison is accordingly indicated, with the cost of each additional stage being compared with the value of the material lost in the raffinate, the cost of recovering the solvent, and the cost of the solvent. In separations which are particularly difficult, the use of 20 or more stages is not uncommon.

Theoretically, the mass balance calculations for any number of stages can be carried out by either of the techniques illustrated for the two-stage process. If a separate algebraic unknown is used for the effluent liquid concentration from each stage, the number of simultaneous equations to be solved will obviously equal the number of stages. Stage-to-stage calculations using a single unknown are no less laborious. Fortunately, the drudgery of repetitive calculations can be materially reduced by resorting to graphical methods. The basic features of the latter are considered in a subsequent section.

Problems involving process analysis, in which the number of stages is known, are probably less frequently encountered than are those involving process synthesis, in which the ultimate separation is specified and the number of stages is to be determined. Depending on the information given, a trial-and-error procedure may be necessary in either case, a number of stages being assumed so that calculated stream compositions may be checked against those specified. Here again effective use may be made of graphical methods. It should also be remembered that the calculations as illustrated here pertain only to the number of equilibrium or *ideal* stages. A stage efficiency factor is commonly used to relate the number of ideal stages to the number of actual stages available or required. Efficiency factors equivalent to the Murphree gas efficiency defined in Sec. 9.4 might also be used.

13.2 Absorption and Stripping

The above discussion of multi-stage extraction operations is readily extended to absorption and stripping. The only significant difference is the fact that a gas phase is present in the latter, whereas extraction pertains to solids and liquids. From the standpoint of the mass balance there is no difference whatsoever, and the techniques already presented for use in extraction problems are generally applicable to absorption and stripping. Unlike extraction, however, absorption and stripping usually involve the transfer of significant quantities of energy from one phase to the other. Isothermal operation is therefore likely to be the exception rather than the rule, and due recognition must be given the effect of temperature changes on equilibrium conditions.

The foregoing correctly implies that absorption and stripping problems may require the simultaneous application of a mass balance and an energy balance around each stage. Simplifying assumptions or approximations are often made to reduce the complexity of the problem. Alternately, use may be made of graphical methods similar to those used in extraction, but which also provide for a consideration of energy effects. Some typical techniques are outlined in the subsequent discussion of distillation and graphical methods.

Although Fig. 13.2 implies a horizontal arrangement of successive extraction stages, vertical systems are also feasible, particularly when phase densities differ substantially. This condition is obviously met when one of the phases is gaseous, and absorption and stripping operations are almost invariably carried out in either plate or packed columns. Packed columns are not considered to be stage-type devices, since concentrations vary continuously throughout the column, but plate columns definitely involve stage-wise contacting, and the concept of an ideal plate or tray is wholly equivalent to that of an ideal or equilibrium stage. If Fig. 13.2 is turned on end, it will

be seen that it is directly comparable to the stripping column shown schematically in Fig. 13.3. Note that the trays in tray columns are conventionally
numbered from the top down.

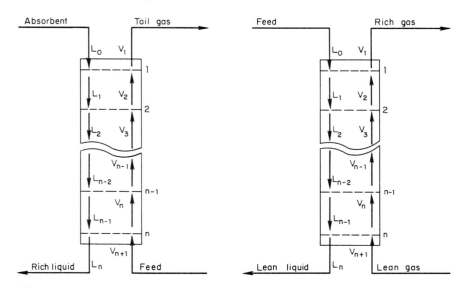

Fig. 13.3   Schematic flow diagrams for absorption (left) and stripping operations.

Fig. 13.3 makes it clear that an absorption or stripping operation is readily
treated as an integral unit, even though it consists of a number of unit stages.
Both total-mass and component balances can be made around the entire
column, even in the absence of information pertaining to the number of
stages or stream compositions within the column. The synthesis or analysis
of a complex process sequence in which extraction, absorption, or stripping
is only one of many operations is usually expedited by giving initial consideration only to the overall aspects of the multi-stage operation. Internal details
are then treated separately in subsequent calculations. As is demonstrated
in the preceding section, an overall total-mass or component balance can
be an effective first step in such calculations.

Stage-to-stage calculations. In solvent extraction, the liquid portion of
the raffinate leaving such equilibrium stage has the same composition as the
extract solution leaving the same stage. The equivalent condition in absorption and stripping is that the liquid and vapor streams leaving any given
stage will be in equilibrium with each other. Assuming pertinent equilibrium
data to be available, absorption and stripping problems can be solved by
making successive mass balances around each stage in turn, just as was done
for the case of solvent extraction. However, it is usually preferable to use

an alternative technique: The total-mass and component balances around a system embracing the first through ith plates in Fig. 13.3 are

$$L_o + V_{i+1} = L_i + V_1 \qquad (13.1)$$

$$L_o x_o + V_{i+1} y_{i+1} = L_i x_i + V_1 y_1 \qquad (13.2)$$

Successively setting i equal to 1, 2, . . . n will yield $2n$ independent equations which are comparable to those which would be obtained by writing balances around each of the n stages separately. The general technique is illustrated in Ex. 13.1.

The need for considering Eqs. (13.1) and (13.2) simultaneously may be avoided by expressing compositions in mols of solute (the transferred component) per mol of solvent or per mol of inert (insoluble) gas. Eq. (13.2) then takes the form

$$L'X_o + V'Y_{i+1} = L'X_i + V'Y_1 \qquad (13.3)$$

in which X and Y are the mol ratios as defined above, and L' and V' denote the solute-free liquid and solute-free gas, respectively. No subscripts are necessary on the latter two terms because they are constant throughout the column. A more useful form of Eq. (13.3) is

$$Y_{i+1} = \frac{L'}{V'} X_i - \left(\frac{L'}{V'} X_o - Y_1\right) \qquad (13.4)$$

and, assuming L'/V', X_o, and Y_1 to be known, this equation gives Y_{i+1} as a function of X_i. Since the equilibrium data give X_i as a function of Y_i, Eq. (13.4) and the equilibrium data may be used alternately to determine compositions for one stage after another, starting with the first stage at the top of the column. Should it be desirable or necessary to start the calculations at the bottom of the column, an equation analogous to Eq. (13.4) is readily derivable.

EXAMPLE 13.1. The CO_2 content of a gas stream is to be reduced from 10 per cent to 1 per cent by countercurrent, stagewise contact with a triethanolamine (TEA) solution. As an initial approximation the operation may be assumed to take place isothermally at 25°C, and the pertinent equilibrium data are given in Fig. 13.4. How many equilibrium stages are required if the lean TEA solution fed to the column contains 0.0526 mols of CO_2 per mol of TEA and the feed ratio is to be 0.25 mols of TEA per mol of feed gas?

Solution. Basis: 100 mols of feed gas, corresponding to 25 mols of TEA. $Y_1 = 1/99 = 0.0101$ mols of CO_2 per mol of inert gas: $Y_{n+1} = 10/90 = 0.111$ mols of CO_2 per mol of inert gas; $V' = (100)(.90) = 90$ mols of inert gas; $X_o = 0.0526$ mols CO_2 per mol of solvent; and $L' = 25$ mols of solute-free solvent. Hence $L'/V' = 25/90 = 0.278$, and $(L'/V')X_o - Y_1 = (.278)(.0526) - .0101 = 0.0045$. Eq. (13.4) may therefore be written

$$Y_{i+1} = 0.278X_i - 0.0045 \qquad (13.5)$$

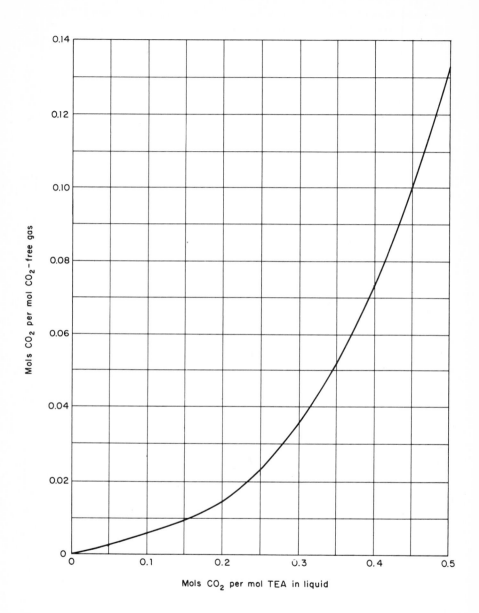

Fig. 13.4   Equilibrium data for CO_2 over a 0.5 normal triethanolamine (TEA) solution at 25°C and atmospheric pressure. (Prepared from data in Perry's *Chemical Engineers' Handbook*

Although an overall mass balance to determine X_n is not immediately pertinent in this problem, it is noteworthy that Eq. (13.5) can be converted into an overall CO_2 balance by setting i equal to n, as can be seen from Fig. 13.3. Thus

$$Y_{n+1} = 0.111 = 0.278X_n - 0.0045$$

from which $X_n = 0.415$ mols of CO_2 per mol of CO_2-free, rich TEA leaving the column.

For $Y_1 = 0.0101$, the equilibrium data give $X_1 = 0.152$. Substituting this value into Eq. (13.5) with $i = 1$ yields

$$Y_2 = (.278)(.152) - 0.0045 = 0.0378$$

Returning to the equilibrium data, we find that $X_2 = 0.312$. For $i = 2$, Eq. (13.5) gives

$$Y_3 = (.278)(.312) - 0.0045 = 0.0822$$

The equilibrium data then give $X_3 = 0.413$ and, for $i = 3$, Eq. (13.5) gives

$$Y_4 = (.278)(.413) - 0.0045 = 0.1105$$

Since Y_4 and Y_{n+1} are equal for practical purposes, it can be seen that $n = 3$, and three equilibrium stages will be required for the specified separation.

A trial-and-error procedure is necessary when the separation which can be effected in a given number of equilibrium stages is to be determined. If, for example, a value for any unknown stream composition is assumed, calculations parallel to those carried out in Ex. 13.1 can be made to determine the corresponding number of equilibrium stages. This procedure is then repeated, using different assumed values, until the calculated number of stages agrees with the number given. The method is illustrated in Ex. 13.2.

13.3 Distillation

It is suggested in Sec. 11.5 that distillation differs from absorption and stripping only to the extent that the auxiliary absorbent or stripping medium is replaced by a liquid or vapor obtained by partial condensation or vaporization of the process fluid itself. The schematic flow diagrams shown in Fig. 13.3, with appropriate changes in nomenclature, accordingly depict distillation as well as absorption or stripping. A more common practice is to include the overhead condenser or the bottom *reboiler* in the diagram as shown in Fig. 13.5. Column internals, not shown in this figure, are similar to those shown in Fig. 13.3.

When vapor reflux is returned to the bottom of a distillation column as shown in the right-hand sketch of Fig. 13.5 the operation is called stripping, even though it does not involve the use of an auxiliary stripping medium. The term *rectification*, rather than absorption, is used to describe the operation depicted in the left-hand sketch. Note that rectification requires a vapor feed, while the feed to a stripping column is a liquid.

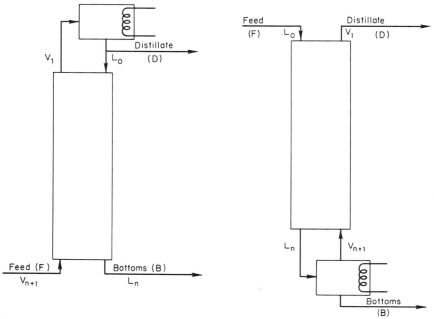

Fig. 13.5 Schematic flow diagrams for the two distillation operations: rectification (left), and stripping.

Close inspection of the reboiler and condenser in Fig. 13.5 reveals a significant difference in stream routing. The vapor leaving the top of a rectifier is usually completely condensed, and a portion of the condensate is returned to the column as *reflux*. Reboilers, on the other hand, normally effect only a partial vaporization, with all of the vapor produced being returned to the column while the residual liquid is withdrawn as a bottom product. Some separation is thus effected in the reboiler, which may be considered to act as an additional ideal stage in the overall separation. Partial condensation is also possible, as is total vaporization, but neither of these alternatives is widely used.

Distillation calculations. Like absorption and stripping, distillation involves simultaneous mass and heat transfer. Fortunately, the latent heat of vaporization per mol is essentially independent of concentration for many systems of practical interest. In the absence of other energy effects, this means that the heat used to vaporize any part of the liquid must come from the condensation of an equal quantity (mols) of vapor. As a consequence neither the liquid nor the vapor rate, in mol units, changes from plate to plate in the distillation column. This condition is called *equimolal* or *constant molal overflow* and permits a greatly simplified approach to column design or analysis.

Mass balance calculations pertaining to distillation can be carried out analytically in a plate-to-plate sequence similar to the procedure used in absorption or extraction. If the assumption of constant molal overflow is pertinent, a component balance around a system embracing the overhead condenser and the first i plates in a rectifying column can be written

$$y_{i+1} = \frac{L}{V} x_i + \frac{D}{V} x_D \qquad (13.6)$$

The derivation of this equation parallels that of Eq. (13.4) and will be left as an exercise for the student, as will the derivation of the equivalent equation representing a balance around the reboiler and bottom plates of a stripping column. Note that V and L do not need plate subscripts since they are the same for all plates under the conditions of constant molal overflow. It should also be noted that x and y, when used without subscripts to denote a particular component, conventionally refer to the more volatile component.

Equilibrium data are pertinent to distillation calculations, just as they are in absorption and stripping operations, and the data may be initially available in any of the forms described in Sec. 7.3. Whatever the initial form, it is usually advantageous to prepare an x-y plot for direct use in the calculations. Enthalpy data is also needed when the assumption of constant molal overflow is not applicable.

EXAMPLE 13.2. An ethanol-water mixture analyzing 20 mol per cent ethanol and available as a saturated vapor is to be rectified at atmospheric pressure in a plate column equipped with a total condenser as shown in Fig. 13.5, left. Constant molal overflow may be assumed, and pertinent equilibrium data are given by the x-y diagram of Fig. 13.6. The bottom product is to contain not more than 7.5 mol per cent ethanol. What distillate product composition can be obtained in a column which provides the equivalent of four ideal plates?

Solution. Basis: 100 mols of feed, or 20 mols of ethanol and 80 mols of water. Since the given data are not sufficient to permit the immediate determination of the product stream quantities, a trial-and-error procedure is indicated. As a first trial, let $x_D = 0.70$. Using this value, a total-mass balance and an ethanol balance may be solved simultaneously to obtain the quantity of distillate and bottoms:

Total mass: $\qquad F = 100 = \quad B \ + \ D$

Ethanol: $\qquad 0.20F = \quad 20 = .075B + .70D$

Solution of these equations yields $D = 20$ and $B = 80$. The assumption of constant molal overflow then requires that

$$L_o = L_1 = \ldots = L_n = B = 80$$

and, for a saturated vapor feed,

$$F = V_{n+1} = V_n = \ldots = V_2 = V_1 = 100$$

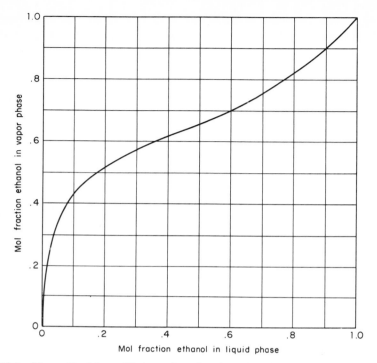

Fig. 13.6 Vapor-liquid equilibrium data for the ethanol-water system at atmospheric pressure.

Note that the mass balance around the condenser is automatically satisfied, that is, $V_1 = L_o + D$. The ratio L_o/D, equal to 4.0 in this case, is called the *external reflux ratio* and is an important variable in distillation. The *internal reflux ratio*, L/V, is also significant. It is constant for constant molal overflow but may vary appreciably under other conditions. Here, $L/V = 0.80$, constant.

The substitution of known values for L, V, D, and x_D into Eq. (13.6) yields

$$y_{i+1} = 0.80x_i + 0.14 \tag{13.7}$$

The given equilibrium data and Eq. (13.7) may now be used alternately to determine compositions for one plate after another just as was done in Ex. 13.1. The results of the calculations are given in the following table, and should be confirmed by the student. Note that $x_D = x_o = y_1$.

i	y_i	x_i
0	—	0.70
1	0.70	0.605
2	0.624	0.42
3	0.476	0.145
4	0.256	0.03

Since $x_4 = x_B$ is less than the 0.075 specified, the foregoing solution is acceptable at first glance. However, a more realistic interpretation of the problem statement would be that the maximum value of x_D is desired. Further, $x_B = 0.03$ is not consistent with the value of 0.075 used in the initial overall mass balance. A second trial solution using a higher assumed value of x_D is indicated, and the trial-and-error process must be repeated until x_B comes out at 0.075. It will be found that this condition is satisfied for $x_D = 0.73$, and the maximum possible concentration of ethanol in the distillate product is therefore 73 mol per cent.

Effect of tray efficiency. Suppose the problem in Ex. 13.2 were the determination of the number of trays or plates needed to yield $x_D = 0.70$ and $x_B = 0.075$. The calculations made in the first trial solution to the original problem are wholly applicable and the tabulated summary clearly shows that three trays are not sufficient, while a fourth tray oversteps the desired value of x_B. Since an efficiency factor has yet to be applied, the specification of a fractional ideal plate is not unrealistic. The fraction is usually estimated by linear interpolation. In this case,

$$\frac{.145 - .075}{.145 - .03} = 0.565$$

and 3.6 ideal plates would be specified.

Murphree efficiencies similar to the gas efficiency defined in Sec. 9.4 are readily incorporated into the procedures illustrated in Exs. 13.1 and 13.2. Each value of x obtained from the equilibrium plot need only be corrected, by an appropriate efficiency calculation, to an actual value before proceeding to the next mass balance calculation. A trial-and-error procedure would be necessary were a Murphree *gas* efficiency to be introduced into the foregoing solutions, but the use of an efficiency expressed in terms of *liquid* mol fractions permits a direct analytical solution. Alternately, the calculations might be started at the bottom of the column so that y rather than x is obtained from the equilibrium plot.

An *overall efficiency* is frequently used in lieu of an efficiency which must be applied to each plate in turn. By definition, the overall efficiency is the ratio of the number of ideal plates to the number of actual plates. For 3.6 ideal plates, an overall efficiency of 80 per cent would therefore dictate the use of $3.6/.80 = 4.5$ actual plates. A fractional actual plate being impracticable, this would be rounded upward to five.

Energy effects. Two separate mass balances should be pertinent in any binary system, but one is automatically satisfied by the assumption of constant molal overflow. When the assumption is not justified, analytical computation becomes extremely laborious. Not only must the second mass balance be applied to each tray, but an energy balance is also pertinent. Further, restrictions arising out of the fact that all enthalpies must be those of saturated liquids and saturated vapors must be considered along with the usual equilibrium restriction. When it is realized that many systems of practical interest involve more than two components, the potential complexity of distillation calculations is quite apparent. Problems requiring the simultaneous application of both mass and energy balances lie outside the scope of the present treatment. However, a fairly straightforward graphical procedure may be used to solve problems for binary systems even when energy effects must be considered. This procedure is demonstrated in the next section.

Fractionation. It should be apparent from Fig. 13.5 that the bottoms from a rectifying column might be fed to a stripping column, with the distillate leaving the stripper constituting the feed for the rectifier. This is frequently done, and the resulting combination of a rectifying column atop a stripping column is called a *fractionating* column, with the feed being introduced into the side of the column as shown in Fig. 13.7. The location of the

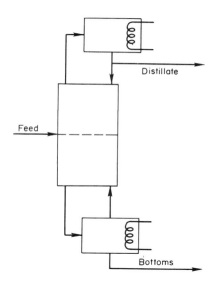

Fig. 13.7   Schematic flow diagram for a fractionating column.

feed plate is an important design variable which depends on both the composition and condition of the feed stream. As a general rule the feed plate is located at a point where the compositions of the internal streams are close to that of the feed. A saturated vapor feed, for example, would normally be introduced at a point where the composition of the saturated vapor flowing inside the column is the same as the feed composition.

Because of the changes occurring at the feed plate, only by coincidence will the same internal reflux ratio be found in both the rectifying and stripping sections of a complete fractionating column. It is therefore necessary to use different equations in each section, but the mass balance calculations are otherwise identical to those already exemplified. Provision for more than one feed stream, or for the removal of a *side-stream* product at any point in the column, is also possible. Each section of column, between any two adjacent points at which feed is introduced or product is removed, must be analyzed separately under such conditions, since a different reflux ratio exists in each section.

The design and analysis of complete fractionating columns, with or without multiple feed streams or side-product streams, is outside the scope of this text. It is significant, however, that the calculations pertinent to such columns are for the most part identical to those presented in this section. The student who understands the mass balance principles illustrated in Exs. 13.1 and 13.2 should have little difficulty when he encounters more complex problems later on.

13.4 Graphical Methods

The equilibrium stage operations are particularly amenable to graphical analysis. This is indeed fortunate, for the prospect of designing, say, a 50-plate fractionating column by numerical computation is not very inviting. High-speed automatic computers are ideally suited for repetitive calculations, however, and many multi-stage problems are in fact already being solved by machine. Even so, there is little doubt that graphical methods will continue to play an important role in chemical engineering, and a brief introductory treatment at this point is not out of place. At the very least it should suffice to convince the student of the efficacy of graphical techniques.

McCabe-Thiele method. Applicable to binary distillation problems whenever the assumption of constant molal overflow is permissible is a fairly simple graphical method commonly called the *McCabe-Thiele* method. To illustrate its use, suppose an ethanol-water feed stream analyzing 20 mol per cent ethanol is to be rectified to produce a distillate product analyzing 60 mol per cent ethanol and a bottoms product analyzing 7.5 mol per cent ethanol. The necessary number of ideal plates is to be determined.

The first step is to complete the overall mass balance as was done in Ex. 13.2, and for a basis of 100 mols of feed it will be found that $D = 23.8$ and $B = 76.2$. Thus $L = 76.2$, $V = 100$, and substitution of known values into Eq. (13.6) yields

$$y_{i+1} = 0.762x_i + 0.143 \qquad (13.8)$$

This is the equation of a straight line called the *operating line*, and it can be plotted directly on the same x-y coordinates as are used for the equilibrium curve. The result is shown in Fig. 13.8, and it is only necessary to remember that the equilibrium curve is a plot of y_i vs. x_i, whereas the operating line is a plot of y_{i+1} vs. x_i. These two plots provide the basis for a graphical solution as follows:

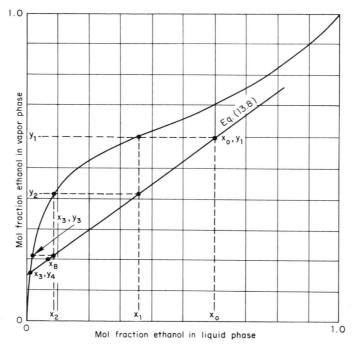

Fig. 13.8   Graphical solution to illustrative distillation problem (McCabe-Thiele method).

For $i = 0$, the point (x_o, y_1) lies on the operating line and can be located from the known value of $x_D = 0.60 = x_o$. The point (x_1, y_1) must then lie on the equilibrium curve and also on the horizontal line $y = y_1$; hence, the point can be located at the point of intersection of these two lines. Now let $i = 1$: The point (x_1, y_2) must lie on the operating line as well as on the vertical line $x = x_1$. Since x_1 is known from the previous step, the latter line can be drawn and the point (x_1, y_2) located at its point of intersection with the operating line. This fixes y_2 and a new horizontal line, and so on until the point x_B is reached.

To summarize, the graphical procedure involves plotting the equilibrium and operating lines and merely stepping off alternate horizontal and vertical line segments between them to determine the conditions on each plate. Each pair of horizontal and vertical lines corresponds to an ideal plate, and the required number of plates can be determined by counting the number of "steps" when the graphical construction has been completed. In this case two plates are not sufficient, three are too many, and a linear interpolation by inspection indicates that approximately 2.3 theoretical plates will be required for the specified separation.

The McCabe-Thiele method has obvious advantages when many plates are required for a separation. The graphical construction also gives a clear picture of the effect of a change in the internal reflux ratio, L/V, which is also the slope of the operating line: The line must go through the point $y_1 = x_o = x_D$ in any event; hence, changing L/V merely pivots the line about that point. Decreasing L/V swings the line closer to the equilibrium line, thereby shortening the line segments and reducing the separation per plate. This would appear to suggest that L/V should be maximized so as to minimize the number of plates required for a given separation. But as L/V increases, the quantity of distillate product decreases. Economics must therefore be considered in determining optimum operating conditions. In the limiting case, L/V becomes unity and D goes to zero. This condition, called *total reflux*, is sometimes prescribed in experimental studies of column operation.

The McCabe-Thiele method can also be used in stripping column and fractionator design or analysis. In the latter application separate operating lines must be drawn for the rectifying and stripping sections of the column, since L/V changes at the feed plate. The switch from one line to the other is made at the point the feed stream is to be introduced into the column. Additional operating lines will similarly be required for the case of multiple feed streams or side-product streams.

The Ponchon-Savarit method. A second graphical method, the *Ponchon-Savarit* method, can be advantageously used when constant molal overflow cannot be assumed and the McCabe-Thiele method is inappropriate. The construction is made on an enthalpy-concentration diagram similar to that introduced in Sec. 7.7, where it was also shown that adiabatic mixing (or separation) is characterized by straight lines on the diagram. The isotherms shown on the H_2SO_4-H_2O diagram in Sec. 7.7 are not normally shown on Ponchon plots. Instead, only the loci of all saturated vapor and saturated liquid points are drawn. It is the fact that vapor and liquid enthalpies are thus taken into account that frees the Ponchon-Savarit method from the restriction of constant molal overflow.

A Ponchon diagram for the ethanol-water system at atmospheric pressure is presented in Fig. 13.9. The heavy horizontal lines crossing the diagram are the two saturation lines, and the x and y points determined in the foregoing McCabe-Thiele problem solution have been plotted on these lines. The dashed lines connect points which are related by equilibrium and are called equilibrium *tie lines*. The solid, sloped lines, on the other hand, connect points which are related by the mass balance, Eq. (13.8). It is significant

that these lines, when extended, all meet at a common point. That this is
no coincidence can be demonstrated as follows:

A total-mass balance written around the overhead condenser and the top i
plates in the column is

$$V_{i+1} = D + L_i$$

or $$D = V_{i+1} - L_i \qquad (13.9)$$

If i is successively set equal to 0, 1, . . . n, it can be seen that

$$D = V_1 - L_o = V_2 - L_1 = \ldots = V_{n+1} - L_n = F - B$$

In other words, the quantities of liquid and vapor *passing each other* at any
point in the column differ by a fixed amount to be symbolized by Δ. Assuming the column to be operated adiabatically, then, Δ must lie on a straight
line drawn through each pair of points in accordance with the principles
presented in Sec. 7.7. Thus all the lines must have a common intersection
at the delta point as shown in Fig. 13.9.

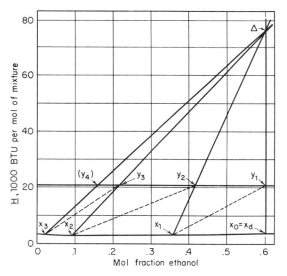

Fig. 13.9 Ponchon-Savarit solution to illustrative distillation problem.

Application of the inverse-lever-arm principle to the line $\overline{\Delta\text{-}y_1\text{-}x_o}$ discloses
a significant relationship between the location of the delta point and the
external reflux ratio, L_o/D. Using values from Fig. 13.9,

$$\frac{H_\Delta - H_{y_1}}{H_{y_1} - H_{x_o}} = \frac{76,300 - 20,800}{20,800 - 3,500} = \frac{55,500}{17,300} = 3.2$$

It is no coincidence that L_o/D is also equal to 3.2. Since $V_1 = L_o + D =
L_o + \Delta$, the inverse-lever-arm principle requires that the ratio of the line

lengths $\overline{\Delta\text{-}V_1}$ (that is, $\overline{\Delta\text{-}y_1}$) and $\overline{L_o\text{-}V_1}$ (that is, $\overline{x_o\text{-}y_1}$) must be equal to L_o/Δ. But Δ and D are numerically equal in quantity; hence L_o/Δ equals L_o/D and the above calculations are substantiated.

The points shown in Fig. 13.9 were borrowed from the McCabe-Thiele problem solution as an expedient in demonstrating the relationships among them, but they might have been determined independently by the following graphical procedure: x_o and y_1 are known and can be plotted on the saturated liquid and saturated vapor lines, respectively. The delta point is next located by the inverse-lever-arm method, using the known value of L_o/D. y_1 being known, x_1 can be obtained from an x-y equilibrium diagram or its equivalent and is plotted on the saturated liquid line. A straight line is next drawn between x_1 and Δ, and the intersection of this line with the saturated vapor line establishes y_2. The equilibrium diagram then gives x_2, etc.

It has been stated that Δ and D are numerically equal in quantity, but the graphical construction clearly shows a significant difference in their enthalpies. This difference is directly attributable to the heat removed in the overhead condenser and is, in fact, identically equal to the condenser heat duty in BTU per mol of distillate product. Application of the steady-state energy balance around the condenser yields

$$V_1 H_1 - (L_o h_o + D h_D) + Q = 0$$

(The use of H for vapor enthalpies and h for liquid enthalpies, both on a per-unit-mass basis, is conventional in distillation calculations.) Let $Q_D = Q/D$ be the heat absorbed per mol of D. Substituting in the energy balance and rearranging,

$$V_1 = H_1 L_o h_o + D(h_D - Q_D)$$

or, since D and Δ are equal in quantity,

$$V_1 H_1 = L_o h_o + \Delta(h_D - Q_D) \qquad (13.10)$$

In accordance with the principles developed in Sec. 7.7, then, the ordinate of the delta point must be $(h_D - Q_D)$. Since Q_D is inherently negative in accordance with the usual thermodynamic definition of Q, $-Q_D = h_\Delta - h_D = h_\Delta - h_o$, and the condenser duty per mol of D is seen to be equal to the vertical distance between Δ and $x_o = x_D$. In the sample problem, the condenser duty is thus $76,300 - 3,500 = 72,800$ BTU per mol of distillate product.

When the Ponchon-Savarit method is applied to a stripping column, the delta point is found to lie below the saturated liquid line but to be aligned vertically with x_B. The enthalpy difference between x_B and the delta point is the reboiler duty per mol of bottom product. The graphical construction for a complete fractionating column requires the use of separate delta points for the rectifying and stripping sections of the column, with the construction shifting from one delta point to the other at the feed point. A mass balance can be written around the feed plate in the column to show that the feed point on the diagram must lie on a straight line connecting the two delta points.

Like the McCabe-Thiele method, the Ponchon-Savarit construction can be used to analyze the effect of changing the reflux ratio. As L_o/D increases, the delta point moves upward and goes to infinity when D becomes zero at total reflux. The construction lines to the delta point are therefore parallel, vertical lines, and it can readily be seen that this condition corresponds to the minimum number of plates for a given separation. Conversely, if the delta point is lowered until a construction line and an equilibrium tie line coincide, the need for an infinite number of plates is indicated. This condition is called *minimum reflux*. The equivalent relationship on a McCabe-Thiele diagram would be that corresponding to the operating line intersecting the equilibrium curve at the point $x = x_B$. In some applications minimum reflux corresponds to an operating line which is tangent to the equilibrium curve.

Three-component methods. Extraction, absorption, and stripping would appear to require graphical methods different from the foregoing, since a third component must be taken into account. Actually, a method directly analogous to the McCabe-Thiele method can be applied to such three-component operations by plotting compositions in terms of mol ratios rather than mol fractions. Eq. (13.5) can readily be plotted on the mol-ratio equilibrium diagram of Fig. 13.4 for example, and Ex. 13.1 might then be solved graphically by the McCabe-Thiele technique.

An alternative procedure is to use a triangular diagram such as that shown in Fig. 13.10, this diagram having been prepared for the graphical solution of the extraction problem already solved analytically in Sec. 13.1. The coordinates of any point on the diagram give the mass fractions of solvent S and soluble material M, the insoluble residue R being determined by difference from unity. Thus the origin of the diagram corresponds to pure R, the outer 45° line to pure liquid solution (zero per cent R) of whatever composition, and the inner 45° line to all mixtures containing 50 per cent R and 50 per cent liquid solution.

A trial-and-error procedure is necessary whenever the separation which can be effected by a given number of stages is to be determined. (This is also true of the McCabe-Thiele and Ponchon-Savarit methods.) In the example cited in Sec. 13.1, the compositions of F and V_{n+1} were given, and x_F and y_{n+1} can be located on the diagram as shown. If the composition of V_1 is assumed, an overall mass balance can be solved for L_2, and y_1 and x_2 may also be located on the diagram. Then, since passing streams differ by a fixed amount just as they do in distillation, the lines $\overline{x_2\text{-}y_{n+1}}$ and $\overline{y_1\text{-}x_F}$ can be extended to locate a delta point at the point of intersection. The graphical solution then proceeds as follows:

L_2 is a mixture of pure R and pure liquid solution of composition y_2; hence, y_2 must lie on a line through the origin and x_2. The intersection of this line with the overflow locus thus fixes y_2. A line through Δ and y_2 can then be extended to intersect the underflow locus at x_1, etc. If the value of y_1 given by the graphical construction does not check the value originally assumed, the trial-and-error solution must be repeated using a new assumed value. The solution is complete when the assumed and derived values of y_1 are in agreement.

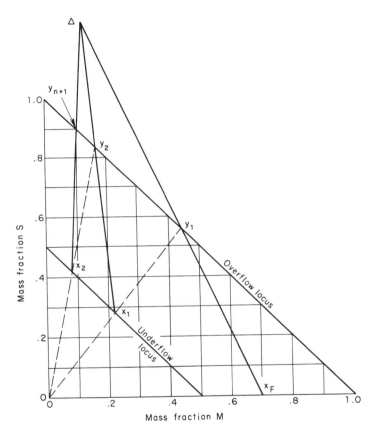

Fig. 13.10   Graphical solution to two-stage extraction problem.

It is interesting to note that a graphical solution to the overall mass balance is also possible. For the above example, the mass balance equation is

$$F + V_{n+1} = L_2 + V_1 = \Sigma$$

where Σ represents either summation, just as Δ was used to represent a difference. In accordance with the mass balance equation, Σ must lie on a straight line connecting x_F and y_{n+1}, and the inverse-lever-arm principle can be applied to determine its exact location. Then, once y_1 has been assumed and plotted on the diagram, x_2 must lie on a straight line through y_1 and the Σ point. Since x_2 also lies on the underflow locus, it can immediately be located at the point of intersection of the y_1-Σ line and the underflow locus.

The same scale need not be used on both the ordinate and abscissa of right-triangular diagrams. In Fig. 13.10, for example, that portion of the diagram to the right of x_F is not used and need not have been shown. The abscissa scale could then be expanded to spread out the diagram and increase the accuracy of the graphical construction. On other occasions the use of an equilateral rather than a right triangle may be advantageous. The graphical relationships outlined above are not changed by either of these modifications.

13.5 Conclusion

The analytical mass balance calculations discussed in the first part of this chapter do not involve any new principles in addition to those presented in Chap. 12. A review of the example problems should make this immediately apparent, for it will be seen that each problem was solved by the judicious application of pertinent balance, ratio, and summation equations, together with the introduction of algebraic unknowns as necessary, just as was done in the preceding chapter. If the new examples seem to be more difficult, then, it is only because multi-unit rather than single-unit systems have been considered. Once a particular system has been selected from among several possibilities, however, the calculations are identical to those outlined in Chap. 12.

In the final analysis, only two alternatives need be considered in selecting the system about which to make total-mass and component balances: An overall balance around the entire process is likely to be an advantageous first step, and it will then be necessary to make balances around individual units or combinations of units. In general, the latter systems should be selected so as to have a maximum number of known streams, and a minimum number of unknown streams, crossing the system boundary. This precept was consistently followed here, balances having been made around the top of a column where D, L_o, and V_1 were already known, for example.

Except for the foregoing observation, a generalized approach which will work in all conceivable situations cannot be set forth. Even experienced engineers may try and err before the most effective route to a solution is identified, and the student can hardly expect to be any more perspicacious. Even so, the experience gained by practice will be of considerable help in due time. In the meanwhile it can only be stated that there is no substitute for a logical analysis coupled with careful numerical computation.

Although the principles underlying the typical graphical methods considered in the latter part of the chapter are few and relatively straightforward, the student who does not completely understand them need not be dismayed. Our purpose was not so much to teach these methods as it was to convince the student that they are logical and effective. True understanding will come when the subject is encountered again in subsequent course work. Meanwhile, the problems to follow, even if solved by rote, should prove interesting and informative.

REVIEW, STUDY, AND DISCUSSION

13-1. Define extraction, raffinate, extract, L_o, V_{n+1}, L_n, ideal or equilibrium stage, absorption, stripping, x_i, y_{n+1}, X_o, Y_1, distillation, rectification, reboiler, reflux, equimolal or constant molal overflow, theoretical plate, external reflux ratio, internal reflux ratio, Murphree gas efficiency, overall efficiency, fractionation, side-stream product, McCabe-Thiele method, operating line, total reflux, Ponchon-Savarit method, equilibrium tie line, Δ, delta point, H_{n+1}, h_F, minimum reflux, underflow, overflow, Σ point.

13-2. Vegetable oil is to be recovered from 4,000 lbs per hour of a vegetable mash by countercurrent extraction with 7,000 lbs per hour of a solvent. The mash analyzes 55 per cent oil, and it is estimated that the fresh solvent fed to the process will contain 4 per cent oil. The underflow stream leaving the bottom of each contacting unit will retain 0.9 lbs of solution per lb of oil-free mash. How many ideal stages will be required if 5 per cent of the total oil entering the process will leave in the raffinate product?

13-3. What percentage of the total oil fed will be lost to the raffinate if the conditions described in Prob. 13-2 are applied to a single-stage unit? To a two-stage unit? To a three-stage unit? Compare the results and estimate the percentage loss for a four-stage unit.

13-4. The results obtained with the three-stage unit of Prob. 13-3 are to be compared with those that might be obtained with a single stage. Using the mash feed rate and composition, fresh solvent composition, and bottoms solution-to-mash ratio given in Prob. 13-2, calculate:

a) the percentage loss and mass fraction oil in the extract product if the solvent feed rate to the single unit is 7,000 lbs per hour.

b) the solvent feed rate and mass fraction oil in the extract product if the single unit is to have the same percentage loss as the three-stage unit.

c) the percentage loss and solvent feed rate if the single unit is to yield the same concentration of oil in the extract product as will the three-stage unit.

Compare the above results with those obtained in Prob. 13-3.

13-5. Derive an equation similar to Eq. (13.4), but which gives X_{j-1} as a function of Y_j, by making a component balance around the bottom j plates of the absorption column shown in Fig. 13.3. Use the equation to confirm the solution to Ex. 13.1.

13-6. For the conditions given in Ex. 13.1, what value of L'/V' will permit the use of only two theoretical plates? What is the corresponding feed ratio in mols of lean solution per mol of feed gas?

13-7. Derive an equation similar to Eq. (13.6), but which gives x_{j-1} as a function of y_j, by making a component balance around the reboiler and bottom j plates of the stripping column shown in Fig. 13.5.

13-8. A saturated liquid analyzing 20 mol per cent ethanol and 80 mol per cent water is to be distilled in a stripping column to remove 77 per cent of the water. Constant molal overflow may be assumed. How many actual plates will be needed in the stripping column if not more than 8 per cent of the ethanol is to be lost in the bottoms and the overall efficiency of the column will be 70 per cent?

13-9. Repeat Prob. 13-8 with a Murphree gas efficiency of 70 per cent applied to each plate in the column instead of an overall efficiency of 70 per cent. What is the overall efficiency for these new conditions?

13-10. Let L, V, L', and V' denote the liquid and vapor rates in the rectifying and stripping sections, respectively, of a fractionating column. Prove that the straight line represented by Eq. (13.6) and that represented by the solution to Prob. 13-7 intersect at $x = x_F$ when $V = V'$ and $L' = L + F$. (The latter conditions correspond to a saturated liquid feed.)

13-11. On the basis of the relationships between V and V', and L and L', given in Prob. 13-10 for a saturated liquid feed, deduce corresponding relationships for a saturated vapor feed. Prove that the lines referred to in Prob. 13-10 intersect at $y = y_F$ for this condition.

13-12. Prepare a graphical solution to Ex. 13.2, to confirm the analytical solution. (The data in Appendix C-4 should be used to prepare an accurate equilibrium plot for this problem and those which follow.)

13-13. Prepare a graphical solution to Prob. 13-8.

13-14. Prepare a graphical solution to Ex. 13.1. How many stages will be needed to reduce the CO_2 content of the gas stream from 11 per cent to 0.25 per cent if all other conditions specified in Ex. 13.1 remain the same?

13-15. A saturated liquid feed (see Prob. 13-10) analyzing 40 mol per cent ethanol and 60 mol per cent water is to be fractionated to obtain a distillate product analyzing 75 mol per cent ethanol and a bottoms product analyzing 1.0 mol per cent ethanol. It is proposed to operate the rectifying section at $L/V = 0.80$.

a) Derive the equation of the operating line for the rectifying section, or upper operating line [see Eq. (13.8)].

b) Calculate L'/V' and derive the equation for the operating line in the stripping section, or lower operating line (see Prob. 13-7).

c) Plot the two operating lines on an equilibrium diagram and determine the number of theoretical plates needed for the separation. At what point in the column should the feed be introduced?

13-16. Prepare a graphical solution to Prob. 13-8 using the Ponchon-Savarit method. How much heat, in BTU per mol of bottom product, must be supplied to the reboiler?

13-17. Determine the number of theoretical plates needed for the separation specified in Prob. 13-15 by the Ponchon-Savarit method. Calculate the condenser and reboiler heat duties.

13-18. Prepare a graphical solution to Prob. 13-2 using a right-triangular diagram. Use the Σ-point method to solve the overall mass balance.

13-19. Using a trial-and-error graphical method, calculate the percentage loss for the four-stage unit referred to in Prob. 13-3 and compare the result with your original estimate.

CHAPTER 14

Mass Balance Techniques for Complex Processes

The application of the mass balance to multi-unit systems was demonstrated in the last chapter, where it was shown that the combination of several stages into a single system is a necessary adjunct to the consideration of systems which bound only a single unit or stage. When a number of different unit operations and processes are assembled in series or parallel to form a complex, integrated chemical process, the same technique applies: Mass balances may be written not only around each of the individual component steps in the process but also around combinations ranging from two adjacent units to an entire plant. The first step in analyzing complex processes, then, is to identify the system or systems which may be most advantageously investigated. Once this has been done, the techniques presented in Chap. 12 are directly applicable. It is this first step which is of primary concern in the present chapter, although the methods used to complete the mass balance (once a system has been selected) will also be reviewed.

14.1 Simplifying the Flow Diagram

Flow diagrams are prepared for a variety of purposes and may accordingly range from a simple block diagram which shows only major processing units and process streams to a detailed diagram which may show all valves, process instrumentation, all auxiliary streams such as cooling water and fuel gas, and even lines which are used only during start-up or shutdown. With practice, the student should gain the ability to eliminate mentally those parts of a complex flow diagram which need not be considered in making the initial mass balance calculations. Meanwhile it would be advisable to redraw the diagram in simplified form. As a matter of fact, this technique is recommended whenever two or more process units are to be treated as a single system. Mistakes are far less likely to occur when the system boundary and all streams crossing it are clearly visible.

Through-flow units. The simplification of a complex flow diagram for mass balance purposes should not stop with the elimination of such features as process instrumentation and lines used only during start-up or shutdown. Most flow diagrams will include a number of units through which mass flows without undergoing any change in either quantity or composition. Heat exchangers, pumps and compressors, valves, unbranched piping systems, and hold-up or storage tanks—assuming steady-state operation—obviously fall into this category. Such units need not be considered in making mass balance calculations and should not be shown in the simplified diagram. The fractionating column shown in Fig. 13.7 (Sec. 13.3) provides a good example of the simplification which can often be achieved by this practice: A mass balance around the column alone must be written $F + L_o + V_{n+1} = V_1 + L_n$; but if the system boundary is extended to include reboiler and condenser, this reduces $F = B + D$.

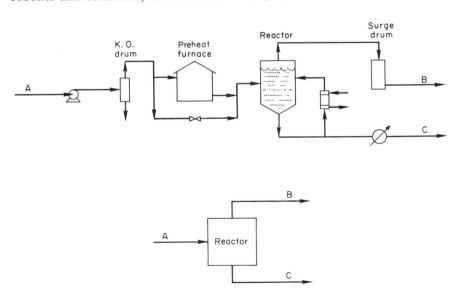

Fig. 14.1 Complex flow diagram and equivalent simplified system for mass balance purposes.

Ultimately, it will be necessary to determine the quantity of cooling water needed for the condenser and the quantity of steam or other heating medium needed for the reboiler. Both quantities depend on energy requirements, and it is noteworthy that the latter cannot be determined until the compositions and quantities of the pertinent process streams have been established. Thus there is little to be gained by showing reboilers and condensers on a flow diagram to be used as a basis for an initial analysis.

The engineering method discussed in Chap. 3 will sometimes provide the basis for temporarily relegating a piece of process equipment into the through-flow category. For example, the gas stream leaving a compressor may be routed through a knock-out drum to effect removal of small amounts of liquid produced in the compression process. The fact that a few pounds of liquid are thus recovered from hundreds or even thousands of pounds of total throughput clearly suggests disregarding the separation as a first approximation. When it comes down to the design of the drum itself, of course, these few pounds become a major factor.

A typical reduction of a complex flow diagram into a much simpler equivalent which is entirely satisfactory for an initial mass balance analysis is shown in Fig. 14.1.

Identical units in parallel. It is not often that two or more identical pieces of equipment are used in parallel, since a single unit having the same total capacity is always less expensive. In the absence of exact data, the relative cost can be estimated from the six-tenths rule introduced in Sec. 10.2: The cost of two half-size units will be exactly twice the cost of one of them, whereas the approximate cost of a single, full-size unit would be only $2^{0.6} = 1.516$ times as much as a half-size unit.

Despite the foregoing, circumstances occasionally dictate the use of identical units in parallel. The design of a single, mammoth piece of equipment may be impractical; or multiple units may be specified to improve operating flexibility. For example, plant operation could be continued, albeit at reduced capacity, in the event of a breakdown. Process control might also be simplified if only one small unit need be run at variable capacity while others run at full capacity only. Finally, multiple units may be prescribed to permit the quasi-continuous operation of batch processes. At least one unit can then be in operation at all times while others are being filled, emptied, heated up, or regenerated.

It should be apparent that identical units in parallel can be combined into a single system as far as the initial mass balance calculations are concerned. Once compositions and total flow rates have been determined, the combined inlet and outlet streams can easily be split up into the appropriate number of sub-streams. Detailed design calculations may then be completed.

Series combinations. The use of two or more equilibrium stages in series was considered in Chap. 13, but there are many other situations in which a series sequence of process units having similar characteristics is advantageous. Multiple-effect evaporation, described in Sec. 11.2, is one example; or practical limitations on the height of fractionating columns may dictate the use of two or more separate columns. A typical example of the latter situation is shown in the flow diagram for the pentane isomerization process presented in Sec. 1.5 (Fig.1.4). Heat exchangers are also often used in series, particularly when one stream is to exchange heat with several other streams successively.

Other series combinations which are frequently encountered involve units whose functions are complementary rather than supplementary. Whenever a separation is effected by introducing an auxiliary solvent into the process, the solute must be recovered from the extract to complete the separation. Thus extraction will usually be accompanied by a solvent recovery operation. Similarly, the rich liquid produced in an absorption operation will often be stripped immediately to separate the absorbent and absorbate. In all such cases the consequences of treating the entire two-step operation as a single system should be investigated.

The fact that stream compositions and quantities are not identical in most series sequences makes an overall mass balance around the entire series somewhat less informative than is the case with parallel units. Nevertheless, such a balance will automatically eliminate several intra-series streams from consideration and may therefore be advantageous as an initial step. Separate mass balances around each of the elements in the series will obviously be required to complete the analysis.

On some occasions it may even be advantageous to combine dissimilar units into a single system. For example, the operations of thickening and filtration both effect the removal of a liquid phase from a liquid-solid mixture. When these two processes are used in series, as they often are, it is usually the overall separation which is of primary importance. A system embracing both units will make it possible to disregard the underflow stream leaving the thickener and entering the filter, while the filtrate and the thickener overflow streams, being identical in composition, can be viewed as a single stream.

14.2 Selecting a System

Only rarely will the elimination of extraneous streams and process units reduce a complex flow diagram to a single unit as was the case in Fig. 14.1. Even the simplified diagram may still be quite complex and permit the selection of any one of several systems for an initial mass balance application. Depending on the order in which various systems are successively selected, the mass balance calculations can be either relatively straightforward or almost impossibly complicated. Experience and judgment are the only real guides to the analysis of complex processes, but experience can only be gained by practice. The observations which follow should help to point the way during the practice stage.

It was argued in Sec. 3.3 that the analysis of a complex problem should logically start with a consideration of the information to be determined and proceed backwards toward given information. The general desirability of this procedure notwithstanding, the reverse procedure is more likely to be effective in mass balance problems. This is particularly true when the problem is to determine *all* unknown compositions and quantities, as is usually the case in practice, for there is no clear indication of which of the several unknowns should be tackled first.

The obvious alternative is to start with given information, and the nature and extent of such information will be a major consideration in selecting a system about which to make an initial mass balance. The clear implication is that the system should be selected so as to minimize the number of unknown streams crossing its boundary. Hopefully, it will be possible to define a system for which only one entering or leaving stream is unknown. The ensuing mass balance calculations will then eliminate this unknown, whereupon additional information becomes available for the solution of the remainder of the problem.

The general effectiveness of an overall mass balance around the entire process was presumably demonstrated in the last chapter. This possibility should always be investigated at the outset and, if not immediately practicable, kept in mind as the calculations proceed. An alternative approach is to give first consideration to those individual process units for which one or more stream compositions or quantities are known. If a balance around a given unit involves too many unknowns to be fruitful, the boundary of the initial system can be successively extended to encompass adjacent process units until, hopefully, the boundary cuts across a new stream which makes additional information available.

When all likely systems have been investigated without a logical selection being indicated, it is probable that the use of one or more algebraic unknowns is necessary. The most effective technique in such cases, as was suggested in Chap. 12, will usually be to define the unknown so as to make it possible to express a maximum number of other compositions or quantities in terms of the same unknown. The analysis then proceeds as outlined above, but with all functions of the unknown now being treated as if they were known. Hopefully, the analysis will yield an equation which can be solved for the unknown. If not, it may be necessary to define a second unknown and repeat the entire process.

The application of the procedure outlined above will be demonstrated in the sample problems to be presented later in the chapter.

14.3 Special Techniques

Recycle operations. As was noted in the first chapter, the efficient use of material frequently depends on a *recycle* operation in which a stream separated out at one point in the process sequence is returned to the process at another point upstream for reprocessing. Typical examples are the re-use of auxiliary materials such as solvents or absorbents and the recycle of un-reacted materials back through a chemical reactor. Another common application, to be considered shortly, occurs in drying operations.

Recycle operations are notoriously troublesome for beginning chemical engineers, but they need not be. The first step in solving mass balance problems involving recycle should almost invariably be an overall mass balance around the entire process—that is, around a system which encompasses the recycle stream itself, its point of origin, the point at which it is returned to the process, and all process units between these two points. Since the recycle stream does not cross the boundary of such a system, its composition and quantity are not pertinent in the initial calculations.

The recycle stream may be introduced into subsequent calculations by defining a new system whose boundary cuts across the stream. Additional data pertaining to the stream itself or to one or more of the process units involved will be needed at this time, and the nature of these data will generally suggest a logical system. The most likely prospects are the points at which the recycle stream is separated from or returned to the main process stream, one or more of the process units past which the stream is recycled, or a combination of a process unit and the separation or feedback point. The examples which follow will illustrate the general technique.

EXAMPLE 14.1. An air drier is to remove 500 lbs of water per hour from a solids stream. Over-rapid drying is to be avoided, and it is proposed to raise the humidity of the air entering the drier by recycling moist air from the drier discharge as shown in Fig. 14.2. Pertinent humidities in pounds of

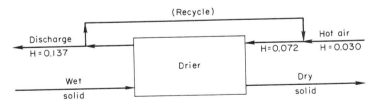

Fig. 14.2   Flow diagram for Example 14.1.

water per pound of dry air are shown on the diagram. What fraction of the air leaving the drier should be recycled?

Solution. A mass balance around the entire process, made in accordance with the general recommendation above, shows that each pound of dry air fed picks up $0.137 - 0.030 = 0.107$ lbs of water. Hence $500/.107 = 4670$ lbs/hr of dry air will be needed, and the overall mass balance can be completed directly if desired. Note that the presence of the recycle stream has no bearing whatsoever on the overall balance.

A balance around the mixing point will now fix the quantity of recycle, but a balance around the drier itself is simpler if it is recognized that the drier effluent, the recycle stream, and the moist air discharged from the process all have the same composition. Thus the air stream flowing through the drier will pick up $0.137 - 0.072 = 0.065$ lbs of water per pound of dry air, and $500/.065 = 7700$ lbs/hr of dry air must flow through the drier itself.

A balance around either the mixing or separation point will complete the problem. For the latter, $7700 - 4670 = 3030$ lbs of dry air recycled, and the fraction recycled is $3030/7700 = 0.394$. The complete composition and quantity for each stream may now be determined if desired.

EXAMPLE 14.2. An ammonia synthesis plant is to produce 1500 mols of ammonia per hour from a stoichiometric mixture of nitrogen and hydrogen in accordance with the process flow diagram given in Fig. 14.3. Pilot plant

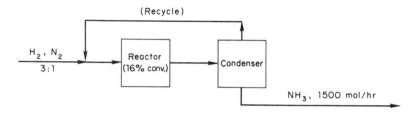

Fig. 14.3 Flow diagram for Example 14.2.

data indicate that a conversion of 16 per cent may be expected in the reactor. Determine the composition and quantity of each stream involved in the process.

Solution. The pertinent chemical reaction is

$$N_2 + 3 H_2 \rightarrow 2 NH_3$$

from which it is apparent that 1500 mols of ammonia will require a feed stream containing 750 mols of nitrogen and 2250 mols of hydrogen. This completes the overall mass balance, and it will again be noted that neither the given percentage conversion nor the presence of the recycle stream entered into the calculation.

The flow diagram makes it clear that the overall conversion is actually 100 per cent, for all unreacted materials are recycled ad infinitum until they finally react. On the other hand, only a portion of the feed to the reactor,

16 per cent in this case, is converted in each pass through the reactor. In the presence of recycle, conversion data conventionally refer to the *conversion per pass.*

The proposed process clearly converts 750 mols of nitrogen and 2250 mols of hydrogen into ammonia each hour. In view of the given conversion data, these quantities must represent 16 per cent of the total feed stream entering the reactor. The reactor feed must therefore contain $750/.16 = 4690$ mols/hr of nitrogen and, correspondingly, 14,070 mols/hr of hydrogen. The quantity and composition of the recycle stream can now be determined by making a mass balance around the mixing point, and the total quantity of recycle will be found to be 15,760 mols/hr.

It is not normally feasible to effect a complete separation of reaction product from unreacted materials. Some of the product may also be present in the recycle stream, but this does not affect the foregoing computation. Suppose, for example, that it is expected that the recycle stream will contain 2.0 per cent ammonia. Then $(15,760)\left(\dfrac{.02}{.98}\right) = 322$ mols per hr of ammonia recycled. This quantity is present everywhere in the recycle loop and may, if desired, be envisioned as a fixed group of inert molecules which is merely superimposed on the other process quantities. The completed mass balance for this amended example is shown in Fig. 14.4. Note that the

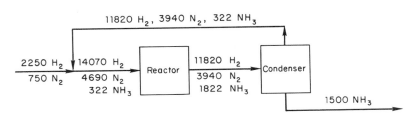

Fig. 14.4   Completed mass balance for Example 14.2, as amended.

reactor effluent contains both the recycle ammonia and the 1500 mols/hr of ammonia formed in the reactor.

It will be well to summarize the foregoing techniques, because it is generally applicable to chemical reactions involving recycle and is the simplest method of attack by far: First, complete a mass balance around the entire process to establish product and fresh feed quantities. Second, apply given conversion data to the product rate to determine the total feed to the reactor—fresh feed plus recycle. Third, make a balance around the mixing point to obtain the recycle rate and composition. Fourth, determine the quantity of product present in the recycle stream. And finally, complete the determination of the compositions and quantities of all other streams.

By-pass operations. In some situations it may be advantageous to pass only part of a process stream through an operation or process while the rest is by-passed around the unit. In Fig. 14.1, for example, a by-pass line around the pre-heat furnace is indicated. For the most part, by-pass is used for purposes of process control, during start-up or shutdown, or as an expedient when the by-passed unit is not fully operative.

In control applications the by-pass rate is varied as necessary to maintain desired conditions in the combined outlet stream. Thus a temperature-sensing device in the reactor feed stream of Fig. 14.1 might be used to actuate the valve in the by-pass line around the furnace. Should the temperature rise or fall from the desired level, more or less material would be automatically diverted to the by-pass to restore proper operating conditions.

The mass balance calculations associated with by-pass operations are similar to those used for recycle. Assuming the nature of the problem to be such that by-pass cannot be disregarded as it was in Fig. 14.1, an overall balance around a system which encompasses the entire by-pass stream and a balance around the by-passed unit only will normally be pertinent. It should not be necessary to illustrate the calculations by example since they are less involved than are the equivalent recycle calculations already exemplified.

Purge operations. One of the problems attending total recycle—that is, the recirculation of everything but the pure product of a reaction—is the possible accumulation of inert materials or reaction by-products within the system. Even though substantial concentrations of such components may not be harmful, it should be clear that their accumulation cannot continue indefinitely. A *purge* or *bleed* stream is sometimes incorporated into the process design to provide for the removal of extraneous components.

Purge streams are normally small and can often be disregarded while making an initial mass balance to establish approximate quantities. In any event, the purge rate varies directly with the rate at which the extraneous material is fed to or produced within the process and inversely with the concentration of the component in the stream being purged. Since the latter concentration is generally highest after the desired product stream has been separated out of the reactor effluent, it is usually a portion of the recycle stream which is purged. The relationship is demonstrated in Ex. 14.3, which also serves to re-emphasize the general approach to recycle problems.

EXAMPLE 14.3. The process shown in Fig. 14.5 is to be used to produce 985 mols per hour of compound A_2B by the reaction

$$2A + B \rightarrow A_2B$$

The feed to the process will be a mixture of A, B, and an inert impurity C in a mol ratio of 2 to 1 to 0.01. A per-pass conversion of 25 per cent is anticipated, and unreacted materials will be recycled back to the reactor feed after purging to remove C from the system. It is estimated that a concentration of 20 per cent C can be tolerated in the recycle stream, which will also contain 5 per cent A_2B. Determine the composition and quantity of all streams involved in the process.

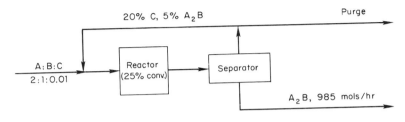

Fig. 14.5 Flow diagram for Example 14.3.

Solution. Component C constitutes a tie substance for the overall mass balance, but its quantity is unknown. It will be denoted by x in accordance with the technique suggested in Chap. 12. The fresh feed stream thus contains x mols of C, $100x$ mols of B, and $200x$ mols of A. From a C balance, then, the purge stream must total $x/.20 = 5x$ mols, of which x mols will be C and $(5x)(.05) = 0.25x$ mols will be A_2B, leaving $3.75x$ mols of A and B. Since A and B are fed and react in the same two-to-one ratio, unreacted quantities will be present in this same ratio; hence the purge stream will contain $2.50x$ mols of A and $1.25x$ mols of B.

Either an A or a B balance can now be solved for x (a total-mass balance is impossible since molecular weights are not given). Applying the "in + produced − consumed = out" relationship (Sec. 12.3) to component B,

$$100x + 0 - (985 + 0.25x) = 1.25x; \qquad x = 10$$

the chemical reaction indicating that $985 + 0.25x$ mols of B will be consumed in the course of producing 985 mols of A_2B product plus the $0.25x$ mols of A_2B lost in the purge stream. Completion of the overall mass balance is straightforward from this point.

It is now known that the reaction produces $985 + (.25)(10) = 987.5$ mols of A_2B per hour. For 25 per cent conversion per pass, the reactor feed stream must contain $987.5/.25 = 3950$ mols of B and twice as much A. Quantities of A and B in the recycle stream can accordingly be determined by making a balance around the mixing point, whereupon the corresponding quantities of C and A_2B can be obtained from the known analysis of the recycle and purge streams. Finally, A_2B and C balances may be written as necessary to complete the solution. It will be worthwhile for the student to finish the calculations and satisfy himself that all mass balances check out.

A study of the foregoing example will make it clear that purging would be uneconomical if the feed stream contained a large quantity of *C* or if only small amounts of *C* could be tolerated in the recycle stream. (Actually, the allowable concentration is most likely to be set by the permissible concentration in the reactor feed stream.) Either of these conditions would make it necessary to discard inordinately large quantities of *A*, *B*, and A_2B in the purge stream. As is so often the case, an economic analysis is indicated, with the value of the discarded material to be compared with the cost of installing recovery and reprocessing facilities.

14.4 Complex Process Sequences

It has already been stated that experience and judgment are the best guides to the analysis of a complex process, but that experience can only be gained by practice. The two examples which follow may help the student find the way in the meantime. Although instruction by example leaves much to be desired, the almost limitless variety of problem situations leaves no other choice. The student who is content merely to confirm proffered solutions will gain little or nothing of lasting value. If, on the other hand, he will concentrate on *why* the calculations are made in a particular order and not on *what* the order is, he should find himself better prepared to devise his own courses of action in the future.

EXAMPLE 14.4. The process shown in Fig. 14.6 is to produce 400 tons per day of 63 per cent nitric acid, the pertinent chemical reactions being

$$\left.\begin{array}{l} CH_4 + H_2O \rightarrow CO + 3\,H_2 \\ CH_4 + 2\,H_2O \rightarrow CO_2 + 4\,H_2 \end{array}\right\} \text{(reforming reactions)}$$

$$N_2 + 3\,H_2 \rightarrow 2\,NH_3 \qquad \text{(NH}_3\text{ conversion)}$$

$$NH_3 + 2\,O_2 \rightarrow HNO_3 + H_2O \quad \text{(HNO}_3\text{ oxidation)}$$

95 per cent of the methane fed enters the second reforming reaction and 5 per cent enters the first. Only nitrogen, hydrogen, and recycle ammonia will enter the converter, and 22 per cent conversion is anticipated. Pure ammonia will leave the condenser and be completely oxidized to nitric acid, with the air also supplying the nitrogen for the ammonia conversion as shown in the flow diagram. The ammonia converter is to operate with a recycle ratio of 7.5 mols of recycle per mol of NH_3 product leaving the condenser. Determine the composition and quantity of all process streams.

Solution. One day's operation will be used as a basis for the calculations. A quick check reveals that an overall mass balance is temporarily impracticable, since only one of the seven inlet and outlet streams is completely specified. It will be noted, however, that carbon is an unspecified tie substance. This suggests the use of an algebraic unknown—say x mols (ton-mols in this case) of CH_4 fed. This choice will also permit a breakdown of the two reforming reactions in terms of x.

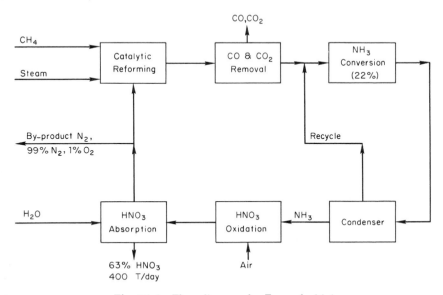

Fig. 14.6   Flow diagram for Example 14.4.

An alternative approach would be to try first to fix as many quantities as directly as possible. The chemical reactions provide obvious relationships, and the known quantity of acid constitutes a suitable starting point. Suppose we try this approach: The molecular weight of HNO_3 being 63, $(400)(.63)/63 = 4$ (ton)mols of HNO_3 produced. The oxidation reaction therefore consumes 4 mols of NH_3 and 8 mols of O_2 and produces 4 mols of H_2O. The NH_3 all comes from the conversion reaction which, accordingly, must consume 2 mols of N_2 and 6 mols of H_2. In turn, the H_2 comes from the two reforming reactions. The given percentage split between these two reactions should be pertinent at this point, and again the use of an unknown is indicated.

To avoid decimal fractions, let x be the mols of CH_4 entering the first reforming reaction, corresponding to $19x$ mols entering the second. The total hydrogen produced is therefore $3x + (4)(19x) = 79x$, and, since all the hydrogen produced is used to make NH_3, $79x = 6$ and $x = 0.076$. It follows immediately that the first reaction yields 0.076 mols of CO while the second yields $(19)(.076) = 1.444$ mols of CO_2. Further, the total steam requirement is $0.076 + (2)(1.444) = 2.964$ mols.

An overall H_2 balance might now be made to determine the quantity of water fed to the absorber, but a more direct approach is possible if it is recognized that the absorption is strictly a physical process. The acid product contains $(400)(.37) = 148$ tons of water, of which 4 mols or 72 tons come from the HNO_3 oxidation reaction, leaving 76 tons to be supplied by the water feed stream.

Two streams—the by-product nitrogen and the oxidation air—remain to be determined, and, not surprisingly, two balances have yet to be made—oxygen and nitrogen. Simultaneous equations might be used, but we shall take the alternative route using a single unknown: Let x mols of O_2 and $99x$ mols of N_2 leave the process in the by-product stream. Since an additional 2 mols of N_2 were converted to ammonia, the total N_2 supplied by the air is $99x + 2$ mols, and the corresponding oxygen is $(99x + 2)\left(\dfrac{21}{79}\right) = 26.3x + 0.532$ mols. Of this amount, x mols leave in the by-product stream and 8 mols enter the oxidation reaction and are consumed.

It would appear that an oxygen balance which can be solved for x has been developed, but we have overlooked the fact that some oxygen accompanies the 2 mols of N_2 fed to the reforming process. Since we are told that only H_2, N_2, and NH_3 enter the converter, this oxygen must leave the process with the CO and CO_2, and, in all probability, converts some CO to CO_2. The amount involved is $(2)(1/99) = 0.0202$ mols, and the complete oxygen balance can therefore be written $26.3x + 0.532 = x + 8 + 0.0202$, from which $x = 0.296$. The oxygen and nitrogen balances may now be completed.

The determination of the recycle stream is the only major problem remaining. For 4 mols of NH_3 product and a recycle ratio of 7.5, the recycle stream must total 30 mols. Further, the 2 mols of N_2 which react represent 22 per cent of the reactor feed for 22 per cent conversion. Thus the reactor feed contains $2/.22 = 9.1$ mols of N_2 and, correspondingly, 27.3 mols of H_2. Of these amounts, 2 mols of N_2 and 6 mols of H_2 come from the fresh feed; hence the recycle must be 7.1 mols of N_2, 21.3 mols of H_2, and, by difference from 30, 1.6 mols of NH_3.

The remainder of the solution is left as an exercise for the student. It is routine and involves only the application of the mass balance to each process unit in turn until all stream quantities and compositions are determined.

EXAMPLE 14.5. Benzene (B) is to be chlorinated to produce chlorobenzene (CB) and by-product di-chlorobenzene (DCB), the pertinent reactions being

$$C_6H_6 + Cl_2 \rightarrow C_6H_5Cl + HCl$$

$$C_6H_6 + 2\ Cl_2 \rightarrow C_6H_4Cl_2 + 2\ HCl$$

The reactor effluent will be separated into a liquid and a vapor phase, and the vapor phase will be scrubbed with the benzene feed to recover unreacted chlorine, leaving pure HCl to be water-absorbed to produce 18 per cent acid.

The liquid phase will be cooled and two-thirds of the cooled product stream will be recirculated back to the reactor to provide temperature control. The other third will be fractionated to recover unreacted benzene and chlorine which will also be returned to the reactor. The factionator bottoms will be further fractionated to obtain 2,500 lbs per hour of CB product and a secondary stream of DCB product. The complete flow diagram and pertinent stream compositions are shown in Fig. 14.7. For what per-pass conversion of chlorine to chlorobenzene should the reactor be designed?

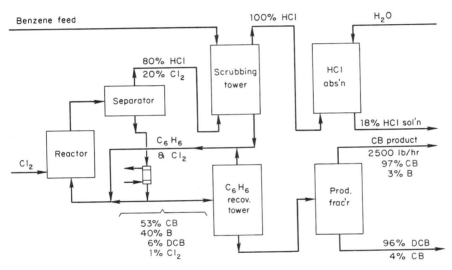

Fig. 14.7   Flow diagram for Example 14.5.

Solution. Since the desired information is the mols of chlorine converted to CB per mol of chlorine entering the reactor, both mol quantities must be determined. A preliminary analysis of the problem suggests that the mols converted can be obtained from an overall mass balance once the quantity of DCB product is known, but the two recycle streams make the calculation of the chlorine feed rate somewhat more difficult. Further, an immediate overall mass balance is seen to be impracticable, yet the CB product stream is the only known quantity. A system whose boundary cuts this stream is therefore indicated.

A balance around the product fractionator will involve too many unknowns to be fruitful, but the addition of the adjacent recovery tower to the system, as suggested in Sec. 14.2, makes the DCB a tie substance for two streams for which compositions are known. A mass balance around this system should be solvable and will yield the quantity of DCB product as well as the composition and quantity of the recycle stream leaving the top of the benzene recovery tower.

With the quantities of CB and DCB produced thus determined, we can work back through the chemical reactions to find the mols of chlorine and benzene consumed and the mols of HCl produced. The latter will permit a balance around the scrubber, thereby fixing the chlorine content of the scrubber bottoms, and finally, since the initial balance fixed the feed to the benzene tower, the rate of product recirculation is also fixed by the two-to-one recycle ratio. The problem analysis is accordingly completed and quantitative calculations can be undertaken.

A basis of one hour is perhaps most obvious but is not essential since percentage conversion depends only on relative rather than absolute flow rates. An arbitrary basis—or an algebraic unknown—will also be needed to make the balance involving DCB as an unspecified tie substance. We shall therefore use a basis of 100 lbs of feed entering the benzene tower, since this will fix a substantial number of other quantities immediately, but it should be noted that many other selections would be equally satisfactory. In any event, the use of weight percentages makes a weight basis preferable to a mol basis.

Balances can now be made around the fractionator train to determine all quantities and compositions, but the alert student will have already realized that they are unnecessary for the particular problem at hand: The selected basis immediately puts 1 lb of chlorine in the overhead stream leaving the benzene tower and also fixes the total quantities of CB and DCB produced by the chemical reactions. When these quantities, in mol units, are checked through the reactions it will be found that the reactions consume 0.553 mols of chlorine and produce an equal mol quantity of HCl. The recycle stream leaving the bottom of the scrubber therefore contains $(.553)(20/80) = 0.1382$ mols of chlorine, or 9.83 lbs.

A consideration of the entire process as a system makes it clear that 0.553 mols or 39.3 lbs of chlorine must be supplied as fresh feed. The total quantity of chlorine entering the reactor is therefore $39.3 + 9.83 + 2 + 1 = 52.1$ lbs, of which 0.471 mols or 33.4 lbs are converted to chlorobenzene. The percentage conversion will be found to be 64 per cent.

Details of the foregoing solution have been intentionally omitted, and it will be worthwhile for the student to confirm the results and to complete the mass balance calculations for the entire process. The *per-pass* conversion of benzene to chlorobenzene should be found to be 23 per cent, and the scale-up factor from the arbitrary basis to the specified production rate is 46.0.

14.5 Conclusion

The two examples just presented provide a fitting conclusion to the consideration of the role of the mass balance in chemical engineering. The repeated use of the techniques described in Chap. 12 should be evident and, with practice, the student will come to use them himself almost without conscious thought. It is significant that alternative techniques may be equally effective, and exclusive dependence on any one method of solution should be avoided in favor of experimentation to set pertinent principles firmly in mind.

The mass balance is only one of the fundamental aspects of change, even though its completion is generally prerequisite to the quantitative consideration of the others. As complicated as mass balance problems may appear to the student at this time, they are but a sample of what lies ahead when all aspects of change must be considered in combination. The skill in problem analysis gained in working such problems can be expected to be an asset of inestimable value throughout one's engineering career. In the final analysis it is this skill which is most essential to success in the field of engineering. Let the student develop it as quickly as he can.

REVIEW, STUDY, AND DISCUSSION

14-1. The flow diagram shown in Fig. 14.8 depicts a process for making ether from ethyl alcohol. Prepare simplified diagrams (a) for use in making

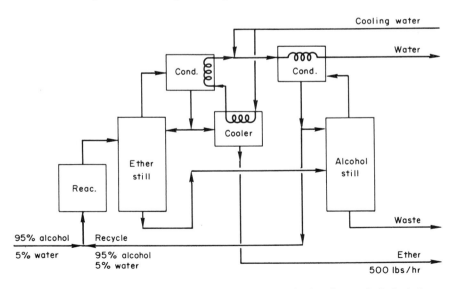

Fig. 14.8 Block flow diagram for the production of ether from ethyl alcohol.

an initial overall mass balance around the process, and (b) to show only the reactor and a separation system as separate units.

14-2. 3,470 lbs per hour of a slurry containing 20 per cent by weight of insoluble solids is fed to a thickener and concentrated to 20 per cent solids by volume. The underflow is sent directly to a rotary vacuum filter in which 670 lbs per hour of filtrate are removed. The filter cake is then dried to yield a product containing 2 per cent moisture by weight. Draw a flow diagram for the entire process and calculate the pounds of final product produced per hour. The specific gravity of the solids is 2.5.

14-3. Phthalic anhydride ($C_8H_4O_3$) is produced by the air oxidation of naphthalene ($C_{10}H_8$), the primary reaction being

$$C_{10}H_8 + 4.5\ O_2 \rightarrow C_8H_4O_3 + 2\ CO_2 + 2\ H_2O$$

Air and naphthalene in a mol ratio of 120:1 are fed to a vaporizer in which 1 per cent of the naphthalene is lost as a nonvolatile tar. The air and vaporized feed then pass to a converter where the above reaction takes place with a 74.6 per cent yield. Maleic anhydride is produced as a byproduct,

$$C_{10}H_8 + 9\ O_2 \rightarrow C_4H_2O_3 + 6\ CO_2 + 3\ H_2O$$

with a yield of 10.9 per cent, while the remainder of the naphthalene feed is completely oxidized to CO_2 and H_2O. The reactor effluent is condensed to recover a crude product stream analyzing 97 mol per cent phthalic anhydride and 3 per cent maleic anhydride. 1 per cent of the phthalic anhydride produced in the reactor is lost to the off gas leaving the condenser.

Calculate the composition of the off gas leaving the condenser.

14-4. A hydrogen recovery process is to supply 2500 mols per hour of hydrogen to a chemical reactor which consumes 20 per cent of this quantity, the balance being returned to the recovery process in a stream which will also contain reaction product in a concentration of 54 per cent. The return stream will be condensed to recover the reaction product with an estimated recovery of 96 per cent, and the necessary makeup hydrogen will then be added to the vapor stream leaving the condenser.

The reactor feed stream will also contain 10 per cent nitrogen, due to the fact that nitrogen enters the process with the makeup hydrogen, the composition of the makeup stream being 99 per cent hydrogen and 1 per cent nitrogen. This nitrogen passes through the reactor unchanged and returns to the recovery process in the return stream. It is to be removed from the system by continually discarding a small portion of the vapor stream leaving the condenser, before the makeup hydrogen is added.

Calculate the concentration of the reaction product in the reactor feed stream.

14-5. Normal butane (nC$_4$) is to be isomerized to produce iso-butane (iC$_4$),

$$CH_3-CH_2-CH_2-CH_3 \longrightarrow CH_2-CH\begin{array}{c} ^{CH_3} \\ _{CH_3} \end{array}$$

A feed stream analyzing 88 per cent nC$_4$ and 12 per cent iC$_4$ will be pre-fractionated to produce a bottoms product analyzing 93 per cent nC$_4$ and 7 per cent iC$_4$. This stream will enter the isomerization reactor where a per-pass conversion of 37 per cent is predicted. The reactor effluent will be recycled back to the fractionator, from which a distillate product stream analyzing 96 per cent iC$_4$ and 4 per cent nC$_4$ will be withdrawn.

Calculate the reactor feed rate and the composition of the reactor effluent stream for a product rate of 30,000 lbs per hour.

14-6. The chemical reaction occurring in the process shown in Fig. 14.7 is

$$2\ C_2H_5OH \rightarrow C_2H_5OC_2H_5 + H_2O$$

and 18 per cent conversion is obtained in the reactor. Calculate the composition and quantity of the feed stream to the alcohol still if the waste stream analyzes 99.0 mol per cent water and 1.0 per cent alcohol.

14-7. The raffinate product from a solvent extraction process is to be dried to remove the residual solvent. The feed stream to the drier contains 0.3 lbs of solvent per lb of solids, and the dried product will analyze 0.5 weight per cent solvent. The drying is to be accomplished by circulating air in the following closed cycle:

The air leaving the drier will be 90 per cent saturated with solvent at 80°C and 735 mm Hg. A blower will raise the pressure to 747 mm Hg, after which the stream will be cooled to 40°C to condense and recover the solvent. The condenser effluent vapor, saturated with solvent at 40°C and 745 mm Hg, will be heated to 100°C and returned to the drier. The vapor pressure of the solvent is given by the relationship

$$\log p^* = 7.89 - \frac{1965}{T}$$

for p^* in mm Hg and T in °K.

Because the operation is carried out below atmospheric pressure, it is estimated that 200 SCFH of fresh air will enter the drier through leaks. Steady-state operation will be maintained by venting a portion of the vapor leaving the condenser.

Calculate the composition and quantity of all streams for a feed rate of 12,000 lbs/hr of solvent and solids to the drier.

14-8. Under carefully controlled conditions propane (C_3H_8) can be oxidized with air to form 0.6 mols of acetaldehyde (C_2H_4O), 0.6 mols of methanol (CH_3OH), 0.6 mols of formaldehyde (CH_2O), and 0.6 mols of CO_2 and CO (combined), for each mol of propane reacting. In one process air is added to a reactor feed stream analyzing 45 per cent N_2, 45 per cent C_3H_8, 5 per cent CO, and 5 per cent CO_2, and the combined stream, analyzing 3.6 per cent O_2, is pre-heated before it enters the reactor. The reactor effluent is condensed to recover all the organic products of the reaction in a liquid mixture and to remove the water formed in the reactions as a separate stream.

The non-condensibles—propane, nitrogen, CO, and CO_2—leave the condenser in a third stream. A portion of this stream is processed to remove all the CO, CO_2, and N_2 contained in it, while the remainder bypasses the processing unit. Fresh propane is then added to the recombined streams to form the reactor feed stream mentioned earlier.

Determine the composition and quantity of all streams involved in the process for a plant which produces 2,000 lbs of acetaldehyde per hour.

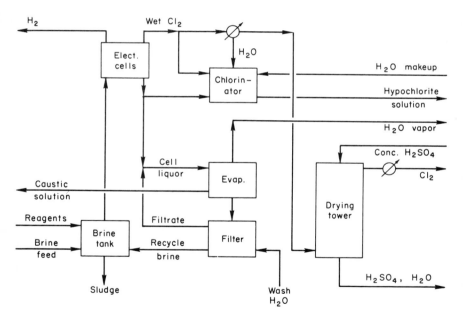

Fig. 14.9 Block flow diagram for an electrochemical plant producing hypochlorite solution, caustic solution, hydrogen, and chlorine from an NaCl brine.

14-9. An electrochemical plant produces 50 per cent caustic, sodium hypochlorite solution, hydrogen, and liquid chlorine from a sodium chloride brine as shown in the block flow diagram of Fig. 14.9. The raw brine feed analyzes 1.0 per cent inert material which is removed in the brine tank by the addition of a negligible quantity of reagents, the inert material being precipitated for removal as a sludge. The brine then flows to the electrolytic cells where the electrochemical reaction is

$$2\ NaCl + 2\ H_2O \rightarrow 2\ NaOH + Cl_2 + H_2$$

The hydrogen and chlorine leaving the cell are saturated with water vapor at 178°F and 735 mm Hg. Spent brine and caustic (NaOH) leave the cell in the cell liquor.

Some cell liquor and wet chlorine is fed to the chlorinator to produce sodium hypochlorite,

$$2\ NaOH + Cl_2 \rightarrow NaOCl + NaCl + H_2O$$

The remaining cell liquor is concentrated by evaporation to produce the 50 per cent caustic solution. The slurry leaving the bottom of the evaporator consists of 5 lbs of solution per lb of solid NaCl and is filtered to remove the NaCl. The filter cake is water-washed to remove entrapped NaOH and is then slurried with additional water to form a brine solution which is recycled to the brine tank. The filtrate, diluted by the wash water, is recycled to the evaporator feed.

The wet chlorine not used in the chlorinator is cooled to 58°F to condense out most of the water vapor, and then dried to less than 300 ppm water in the drying tower by countercurrent contact with 98 per cent sulfuric acid. Spent acid analyzing 45 per cent H_2SO_4 leaves the bottom of the tower as shown in Fig. 14.9.

The hypochlorite product analyzes 8 per cent NaOCl*, and the brine tank sludge contains one lb of brine per lb of inert solids. Other known compositions are given in the following table.

Stream	% NaOH	% NaCl	% H₂O
Brine feed	0	26	73
Cell liquor	11.9	13.4	74.7
Caustic solution	50	1.6	48.4
Filtrate	35	3.0	62
Recycle brine	0	26.5	73.5

Calculate the quantity and composition of all streams for a plant which produces 25T/day of hypochlorite solution and 20T/day of caustic solution.

* Plus some NaCl, but no NaOH or Cl_2.

14-10. 200 tons per day of soda ash (Na_2CO_3) are produced by the Solvay process, described as follows:

Limestone ($CaCO_3$) containing 3 per cent moisture and a few per cent inert material is calcined in a kiln,

$$CaCO_3 \rightarrow CaO + CO_2$$

and the solid CaO product leaving the bottom of the kiln analyzes 95 per cent CaO and 5 per cent unburned $CaCO_3$ plus inerts. Heat for the calcination is obtained by burning coke (100 per cent carbon) with 10 per cent excess air,

$$C + O_2 \rightarrow CO_2$$

1 ton of coke being fed for every 6 tons of limestone.

The CaO product leaving the kiln is slaked with water,

$$CaO + H_2O \rightarrow Ca(OH)_2$$

and the resulting calcium hydroxide solution is fed to a still where it reacts with ammonium chloride,

$$Ca(OH)_2 + 2\,NH_4Cl \rightarrow 2\,NH_3 + CaCl_2 + 2\,H_2O$$

Calcium chloride, unreacted calcium hydroxide, and water are removed from the bottom of the still, the unburned $CaCO_3$ and inert material already having been separated out in the slaker.

The ammonia from the still passes to an ammonia tower where it is absorbed by countercurrent contact with a sodium chloride solution,

$$NH_3 + H_2O \rightarrow NH_4OH$$

and the rich liquor is fed to the top of a carbonation tower. The CO_2-rich gas produced in the kiln is fed to the bottom of the same tower and the resulting reaction is

$$NH_4OH + CO_2 + NaCl \rightarrow NH_4Cl + NaHCO_3$$

Unreacted NH_4OH and CO_2, plus the O_2 and N_2 present in the kiln off gas, leave the top of the carbonation tower and are fed to the bottom of the ammonia tower where the NH_4OH is recovered. The CO_2, N_2, and O_2 are discharged from the top of the latter tower.

The NH_4Cl and $NaHCO_3$ solution leaving the bottom of the carbonation tower is filtered to obtain an NH_4Cl solution which is recycled to the still. The moist bicarbonate cake, containing 20 per cent water, is then calcined to produce a dry Na_2CO_3 product,

$$2\,NaHCO_3 \rightarrow Na_2CO_3 + CO_2 + H_2O$$

What is the composition and quantity (cubic feet at 200°F and 1 atmosphere) of CO_2 and H_2O leaving the calciner per day? How many tons of limestone are required per day? What percentage excess $Ca(OH)_2$ is fed to the still?

14-11. A urea synthesis plant is to use the Pechiney-Grace process. This process can operate with total recycle of unreacted ammonia and carbon dioxide

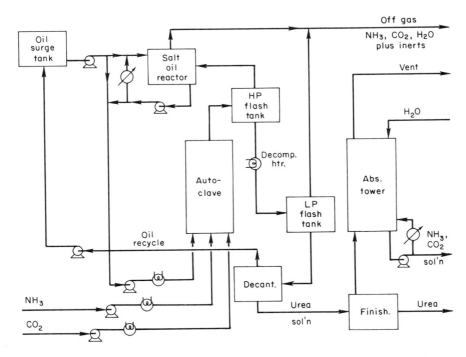

Fig. 14.10 Block flow diagram for the production of urea by the Pechiney-Grace process (courtesy of the Foster Wheeler Corporation).

or as a partial recycle process as shown in Fig. 14.10. A unique feature of the process is the circulation of a stream of light paraffin oil which serves as a heat-transfer medium, but does not enter into the chemical reaction. Proposed operating conditions are as follows: *

CO_2 (99 per cent pure) and NH_3 (3 per cent excess) will be fed to the autoclave at 3000 psig and may be assumed to be completely converted to ammonia carbamate (AC),

$$2 NH_3 + CO_2 \rightarrow NH_2COONH_4$$

Approximately 45 per cent of the AC thus formed will decompose to urea and water,

$$NH_2COONH_4 \rightarrow H_2NCONH_2 + H_2O$$

before the product stream leaves the autoclave. Up to 50 per cent of the remaining AC can then be decomposed to NH_3 and CO_2 (reverse of the

---

* General process description obtained from the Foster Wheeler Corporation.

first reaction above) in the high-pressure flash tank. The decomposition products will be fed to the salt oil reactor where they recombine to form AC with an estimated 95% conversion of CO_2. A slurry of AC in oil will be recycled to the autoclave as shown in the flow diagram. Unreacted CO_2 and NH_3 in the salt oil reactor will pass off overhead with the inert gases introduced into the process with the CO_2. For the total recycle process substantially all of the AC is decomposed and sent to the salt oil reactor for recycle to the autoclave.

The liquid stream leaving the high-pressure flash tank will contain the urea, water, oil, and undecomposed AC, and will go through a decomposer heater in which the remaining AC will also be decomposed to CO_2 and NH_3, with the decomposition products to be separated in the low-pressure flash tank. The oil and aqueous urea solution will then be separated by decantation, the oil being recycled while the urea solution goes to the finishing section for concentration and purification. It is expected that approximately 3 per cent of the urea sent to the finishing section will be hydrolyzed back to NH_3 and CO_2 which will be recovered in the absorber.

Calculate the quantity of CO_2 and NH_3 required, the quantity of CO_2 and NH_3 recovered in the absorber, and the quantity and composition of the off gas for a plant producing an 81 per cent urea solution which, after finishing, yields 13 tons/hr of urea. Conditions in the high-pressure flash tank are to be adjusted so as to provide just enough NH_3 in the off gas (plus that in the absorber effluent) to produce 10 tons per day of $(NH_4)_2SO_4$ in another section of the plant.

Epilogue to a Prologue

A logical test of the effectiveness of most textbooks is the extent to which they provide the student with new knowledge or skills which he can apply with confidence. It is not likely that the present text would score very high on such a test. Indeed, in all probability the text has left the student with a distinct feeling of inadequacy in all but a very few of the areas of subject matter treated. While it can hardly be claimed that such a result is desirable, it is for the most part a necessary consequence of the true purpose of the book: to provide the student with an introductory familiarity with, rather than a working knowledge of, the fundamentals of chemical engineering. This familiarity is the foundation upon which subsequent study will build, and the ease with which subject matter is mastered in this study is the only true measure of the effectiveness of the present text.

What can the student look forward to in subsequent study? The fundamental aspects of change presented here will, of course, be reviewed and subjected to a more detailed analysis. Quantitative thermodynamic relationships here presented with only superficial justification will be derived formally, and numerous supporting, auxiliary, and special-case relationships will be presented. Theoretical and empirical bases for the evaluation of rate coefficients will be developed, with due consideration being given the *mechanisms* by which changes in state, energy content, or composition are effected. The unsteady state and transient effects will be examined as a prelude to the meaningful study of process dynamics and control. And, as the student gains knowledge and skill, the exercise-type problems presented here will give way to more comprehensive problems in which two or more aspects of change must be considered simultaneously. Special analytical, numerical, and graphical techniques pertinent to the solution of such problems will also be investigated.

Ultimately, the student can expect to apply his knowledge of all aspects of change, including the omni-present economic aspect, to the design and analysis of complex process sequences similar to those presented towards the end of Chap. 14. For the most part this will involve the systematic study of each component element of the process sequence in turn, but the fact that the conditions in any one process unit invariably depend upon or influence conditions elsewhere in the process cannot be disregarded. Ideally, all operations and processes in a complex sequence should be considered simultaneously. This area of engineering activity, formally referred to as *systems analysis* or *systems engineering*, provides the ultimate test of the chemical engineer's ability.

It can be expected that systems analysis will be a formidable task. Fortunately, it is a task which is made to order for machine computation, and digital and analog computers having the necessary capacity and versatility are rapidly being developed. Even so, it is significant that systems analysis does not require the application of new principles and techniques so much as it extends the application of those already known. Despite the growing use of automatic computation, neither the fundamantal principles underlying all change nor the chemical engineer who can apply them with judgment will ever become obsolescent.

The study of chemical engineering is only a prologue which sets the stage for a successful and satisfying professional career. Similarly, this text is only a prologue to the study of chemical engineering. If it has set the stage for such study, it has accomplished its purpose.

APPENDIX A

Slide-Rule Techniques

All new slide rules are accompanied by instruction booklets, but in our experience few students read past the use of the C and D scales for multiplication and division, and by the time they encounter more complicated problems, the booklet has long since been mislaid. We will therefore devote a few pages to slide-rule techniques with the expectation that the student will make it a point to put what he learns to immediate and repeated use. It will be assumed that the student is already familiar with simple C- and D-scale multiplication and division.

Consecutive multiplication and division. *First problem:* $(2)(3)(4)/5$. The multiplication of 2 by 3 is straightforward, but multiplication of the product by 4 requires resetting the slide—and this not only takes time but also increases the potential error. The resetting can be avoided by making division by 5 the next step, to be followed by the multiplication of the quotient by 4. Hence the first rule: Alternate multiplication and division as much as possible to avoid unnecessary resetting of the slide. (Note the advantage of assembling as many numbers as possible into a single combination, as illustrated in Sec. 4.3, before starting the calculation.)

Second problem: $(2)(4)(7)/5$. 2 can be multiplied by 4 and the product divided by 5 as before, but this time the 7 is off the end of the rule and a slide resetting is indicated. It can be avoided by first multiplying 2 by 7, then dividing by 5, and finally multiplying by 4. This technique exemplifies

369

the second rule: The desired operations should not necessarily be carried out in the indicated order, but rather in an order which will best serve efficient slide-rule manipulation. Any operation, other than the final step in a calculation, which will leave the slide extended well beyond the end of the rule or the hairline positioned near the end of the rule is likely to lead to a resetting and should be avoided by changing the order of calculation if possible.

Third problem: (6)(6)(6). Alternate multiplication and division is not possible this time unless it is recognized that multiplication by 6 is the same as dividing by $\frac{1}{6}$ or 1667 (note that the decimal point can be disregarded since the decimal point of the answer should already have been determined separately). Do the problem this way, first multiplying and then dividing. Now, with the slide and the hairline both in the final position, note that 6 on the CI scale appears under the hairline and that dividing by 6 on the latter scale is the same as dividing by $\frac{1}{6}$ on the C scale. A check of other points will show that CI-scale numbers are reciprocals of the corresponding C-scale numbers, and can accordingly be used to convert a C-scale multiplication into a CI-scale division or a C-scale division into a CI-scale multiplication.

Let's check the use of the CI scale again by calculating $1/(8)(8)$: Perform the first division in the usual manner and finish by multiplying by 8 on the CI scale, since multiplication by the reciprocal of 8 is equivalent to dividing by 8. It can be seen that the use of the CI scale greatly extends the applicability of the rule regarding alternate multiplication and division.

Fourth problem: (6)(6)(6)(6). First multiplying and then making a CI-scale division takes care of the first three 6's, but the C-scale 6 needed for the final multiplication is off the end of the rule. Note, however, that the relationship between any pair of C- and D-scale numbers is duplicated by the CF and DF scales, the only difference being that the latter scales have the index in the middle rather than at the ends. Thus when numbers are off the end of the rule on the C scale they can often be picked up on the CF scale, with the answer, 1296 in this case, to be read from the DF scale.

It has already been suggested that efficient slide-rule operation will keep the hairline in the center portion of the rule. The free use of the folded (CF and DF) scales will often be advantageous in this respect. The division $11/9$ on the C and D scales puts the slide way out to the left, for example, but very little slide-pushing is required to carry out the division on the CF and DF scales. (Alternately, the problem could be converted to a D- and CI-scale multiplication.)

Fifth problem: (6)(6)(6)(6)(6). The first four 6's can be handled as outlined above to obtain 1296 on the DF scale. Since the last operation was a straightforward multiplication, a reciprocal division should logically follow—and the CIF scale is provided for that express purpose, for it is a reciprocal CF scale just as the CI scale is a reciprocal C scale. One note of caution: The CIF scale can only be used in conjunction with the DF scale, and the CI scale only with the D scale. Only when the C or CF scales are in use can the switch be made from D to DF or vice versa.

In summary, any random combination of numbers can be expeditiously handled by making use of the C, D, CI, CF, DF, and CIF scales as the occasion warrants. As a final example, consider the unit conversion problem introduced in Sec. 4.3,

$$\frac{(2.54)^2(12)^2(60)(60)}{453.6}$$

This problem might be handled in a variety of ways, but we will present one which demonstrates the use of all the different scales: 254 times 254 using C and D scales; divide by 4536 on C scale; multiply by 6 on CF scale; divide by 12 on CIF scale; multiply by 6 on C scale; and, finally, divide by 12 on the CI scale. The student who can follow this sequence and come up with an answer of 737 or 738 is well on his way to getting full use out of his slide rule.

One final observation: There is no point in using the slide rule for calculations which can readily be done mentally. The foregoing example is unrealistic in this respect, because no alert engineer would resort to his slide rule to multiply 12 times 12 or 6 times 6. Instead, he would mentally reduce the problem to $(254)^2(144)(36)/4536$, thereby saving slide-rule time and reducing the possibility of error. Simple divisions should also be done mentally, for the same reasons.

Repetitive division. The successive division of several different numbers by the same divisor is frequently required in chemical engineering. Resetting the slide and hairline for each division can be avoided by either of two alternatives: First, the C-scale index can be set over the reciprocal of the divisor on the D scale, whereupon the various quotients can be obtained by merely shifting the hairline to each dividend on the C scale in turn; that is, division has been replaced by reciprocal multiplication. Alternately, set the hairline over the *divisor* on the D scale, and successively divide by each *dividend* on the C scale. This inverts the quotient, but the normal D-scale answer is to be disregarded. Instead, the answer to the desired division can be read on the C scale, directly above the D-scale index. Only the slide need be moved for successive divisions using this technique. The student should confirm the operation to his own satisfaction.

Multiplication and division by π. The D and DF scales are so aligned that setting the hairline over any number on the D scale puts the product of π times the number under the hairline on the DF scale. Conversely, any

DF-scale number can be divided by π by reading the D-scale number directly below it. Note that the habitual use of the DF, CF, and CIF scales in other calculations will make it possible to introduce π into a computation without an additional slide-rule setting.

Squares and square roots. To square a number, set the hairline over the number on the D scale and read the square under the hairline on the A scale. The reverse procedure is used to obtain square roots, but care is necessary because either of two A-scale settings may be used to represent the same combination of digits in the radicand. This is because the square roots of 3 and 30, for example, are not the same. A little common sense—and a mental approximation, if necessary—is all that is needed to insure the use of the correct A-scale setting. Most rules also have a K scale for determining cubes and cube roots, but the chemical engineer will find that he has little use for it.

When squaring is required as part of a more extensive calculation, it will usually be more convenient to perform the operation as a straightforward multiplication as was done in squaring 254 earlier. Square roots, on the other hand, are obtained via the A and D scales first, after which the rule need merely be turned over to permit the execution of the other operations in the usual manner.

Base-10 logarithms. When the hairline is set over any number on the C or D scale, depending on whether the L scale is on the slide or on the rule proper, the mantissa of the common (base-10) logarithm of the number will be found under the hairline on the L scale. The characteristic must be determined separately in accordance with the rule presumed to be already familiar to the student. Antilogs can be obtained by reversing the procedure. Actually, the engineer will make only infrequent use of the log scale on his slide rule, since most problems requiring the use of logarithms can be solved much more quickly with the log-log scales.

The log-log scales. The primary log-log scale relationship is simple enough: When the hairline is set over any number on the LL scale, the natural (base-e) logarithm of the number will be found under the hairline on the D scale, subject to the determination of the decimal point location. It will be noted that there are several LL scales, and hence several LL-scale numbers for each D-scale number. The difference in logs is one of decimal point only, and most modern rules indicate the proper decimal point opposite each LL scale at the end of the rule. Thus the natural logarithms of 1.03, 1.344, and 19.3 are 0.0296, 0.296, and 2.96, respectively. Conversely, antilogs may be determined by setting the hairline over the log on the D scale and checking its decimal point to determine whether the answer should be read from the LL1, LL2, or LL3 scale.

The LL0 scales are similarly used to obtain natural logs of numbers less than one. Since the use of such scales varies from rule to rule, a detailed procedure will not be specified. Note, however, that the logarithm of any number is equal to the negative log of its reciprocal; hence the use of the LL0 scales can always be confirmed by obtaining the log of the reciprocal of the number using the LL and D scales.

The log-log scales on most rules range from 1.01 to 20,000 and from 0.00005 to 0.99. An approximation based on the series expansion of a natural logarithm provides a ready means for evaluating the logarithms of numbers between 0.99 and 1.01: For small values of x, the natural log of $1 \pm x$ is equal to $\pm x$ for practical purposes. For example, the natural log of 1.003 is approximately 0.003, and that of 0.9972 is approximately -0.0028. The error is greater the greater the value of x, of course; but even for $x = 0.01$ the actual log, 0.00995, differs from the approximation by only 0.5 per cent.

Two methods may be used to determine the natural log of numbers greater than 20,000 or less than 0.00005. One technique is to determine the base-10 log and multiply by 2.303. A more accurate alternative is to factor out powers of 10 and add the logs of the factors to obtain the desired natural log. For example, $53,500 = 5.35 \times 10^4$; therefore ln $53,500 =$ ln $5.35 + 4(\ln 10) = 1.677 + 4(2.303) = 1.677 + 9.212 = 10.889$. The log of 10 to the base e, 2.303, should be committed to memory in view of its frequent use.

Fractional powers and roots. The log-log scales are particularly well suited for calculations involving fractional powers and roots, and such calculations will frequently be required in chemical engineering. Consider the problem of raising 3.6 to the 1.69 power, this calculation involving the determination of the logarithm of 3.6, multiplication of the log by 1.69, and the determination of the antilog of the result. With a log-log slide rule, the first step locates the desired logarithm on the D scale, where it can be subjected to direct C-scale multiplication by 1.69. The product is also found on the D scale, and it is only necessary to set the hairline over the product to obtain the final answer of 8.7 on the LL3 scale.

Fractional roots are similarly handled, with a C- and D-scale division replacing the multiplication used with powers. In either case the decimal point of the product or quotient must be noted since it will indicate which of the several LL scales will give the final answer. For example, the 6.09 root of 3.6 is 1.234 and not 8.2. It is suggested that the student check this result and, while he is at it, decide for himself what root of 3.6 *will* give an answer of 8.2.

The procedures for using the log-log scales, and perhaps other scales as well, tend to become hazy when they are not used for some time. When a refresher is in order, the recommended procedure is to make a trial run on a problem for which the answer is already known. The square root of 0.64, for example, is 0.8. If this answer is obtained when the log-log scales are used to take the 2.0 root of 0.64, or if 0.64 is obtained when 0.8 is raised to the 0.5 power, one can be sure that the slide-rule procedure is correct and can move on with confidence to the particular problem at hand.

Several worked-out examples might be presented at this point, but it is doubtful that they would be of much help. Instead, the matter of practice is left entirely up to the student. The suggestion made in the preceding paragraph is all he needs to check himself out on every aspect of slide-rule operation.

APPENDIX B

Graphical Techniques

Semi-log and log-log plots. One of the more troublesome aspects of graphical representation to the beginning chemical engineer is the extensive use of semi-log and log-log plots. This use is occasioned by the fact that most chemical engineering correlations involve exponentials and therefore yield straight lines when plotted on semi-log or log-log paper. The advantage of any straight-line plot, of course, lies in the ease of interpolation and extrapolation.

The equation $y = mx + b$, for example, yields a straight line when y is plotted against x on regular rectangular co-ordinate paper. Suppose, however, that the equation to be plotted is $y = Ae^{mx}$: Taking the natural log of both sides yields $\ln y = mx + \ln A$, and it can be seen that this form of the equation will also lead to a straight line if $\ln y$ is plotted against x. Or, if both sides of the equation are divided by 2.303 to obtain base-10 logs, $\log y = m'x + \log A$, where $m' = m/2.303$. Again, a straight line will result if $\log y$ is plotted against x.

As a third possibility, consider the equation $y = Ax^m$. Taking the log of both sides as before yields $\log y = m(\log x) + \log A$, and this will give a straight line if $\log y$ is plotted against $\log x$. Note particularly that both the $\log y$ vs. x and the $\log y$ vs. $\log x$ lines can be plotted on regular rectangular coordinate paper, and the only disadvantage is that it will be necessary to calculate the respective logs before each point can be plotted. Conversely, the use of antilogs will be required whenever points are read from the graph.

375

To circumvent this disadvantage, the usual practice is to use semi-log or log-log coordinate paper on which a logarithmic scale is used for one or both coordinates. In other words, the conversion noted above is built into the scale and need not be effected separately. This is a significant point, for it means that plotting y vs. x on log-log paper, for example, will give the same straight line as would be obtained by plotting $\log y$ vs. $\log x$ on rectangular coordinate paper. This relationship should be kept in mind, for semi-log or log-log paper having the desired range or scale will not always be available and it may be necessary or preferable to use regular graph paper instead.

The foregoing observation is even more important when it comes to the determination of slopes. To obtain the slope of the straight line $y = mx + b$ from its graphical representation, it is only necessary to read two (x, y) points and to calculate the slope from the well-known relationship $m = (y_2 - y_1)/(x_2 - x_1)$; or, using the difference symbol introduced in Sec. 2.4, $m = \Delta y/\Delta x$. By analogy, then, if $\log y$ is plotted against x on regular rectangular coordinate paper, the slope must be given by $\Delta(\log y)/\Delta x$, and for a plot of $\log y$ vs. $\log x$ it follows that the slope will be equal to $\Delta(\log y)/\Delta(\log x)$.

Now consider the use of semi-log or log-log paper. Because, as noted above, plotting y vs. x on semi-log paper is directly equivalent to plotting $\log y$ vs. x on rectangular coordinate paper, it follows that the slope of the line must be the same in either case and hence $m = \Delta(\log y)/\Delta x$ for the semi-log plot of y vs. x just as it does for the equivalent plot of $\log y$ vs. x. Hence it will always be necessary to calculate *log y* before the slope of a straight line plotted on semi-log paper can be determined, even though y can be plotted directly as a function of x on such paper.

By the same argument, the slope of a straight line on log-log paper is given by $\Delta(\log y)/\Delta(\log x)$. The calculation can be simplified, incidentally, if it is recognized that $\Delta(\log y) = \log y_2 - \log y_1 = \log (y_2/y_1)$. The same relationship applies to $\Delta(\log x)$, obviously, but the student should take care to see that neither relationship is misused: $(\log X)/(\log Y)$ does not equal $\log (X/Y)$, nor does it equal $\log X - \log Y$.

The student will almost certainly face situations in which he is unsure of the true relationship or slope indicated by a plot on semi-log or log-log paper. Any doubt can be dispelled immediately by considering the equivalent plot on rectangular coordinate paper.

Graphical integration. Even the most extensive table of integrals cannot cover all the integrands which will be encountered by the chemical engineer. Further, the analytical integration of even a simple integrand such as $y\,dx$ is possible only if y can be expressed as an analytical function of x, and the available relationship will often be tabular or graphical instead. Graphical integration circumvents all such limitations and is therefore an essential item in the chemical engineer's bag of tricks.

From the graphical standpoint, the integral of a simple function such as TdS is identically equal to the area between the T-vs.-S curve and the S axis. Conversely, the integral of SdT is equal to the area between the same curve and the T axis. The sides of the area are, of course, fixed by the limits of integration. This same graphical relationship applies to *any* combination of variables, no matter how complex. Data will be needed to permit plotting the necessary curve, but this is the only restriction on the method. To evaluate the integral of TdS, for example, T must be a known function of S, the independent variable in this case.

In the completely general case, let the term *independent variable* denote the variable or combination of variables following the "d operator" in the integrand. In accordance with the restriction noted above, everything else appearing in the integrand must be a known function of the independent variable. The general rule for graphical integration may accordingly be stated as follows: Plot the function vs. the independent variable, *using the latter as abscissa*. The desired integral is the area bounded by the resulting curve, the abscissa, and the limits of integration. Note that the function may include the independent variable itself. By way of illustration, consider the integral $\int_a^b \dfrac{T(\log P)}{V} \, d(PV)$: The independent variable, by definition, is the product PV, and the function is $\dfrac{T(\log P)}{V}$. Graphical integration can be accomplished by plotting the latter vs. PV as the abscissa and determining the area bounded by the curve, the abscissa, and the two limits $PV = a$ and $PV = b$.

Of the several methods available for the actual determination of the pertinent area, we strongly recommend one for general use and will not even mention other possibilities. The method is based on the fact that any area can be considered to be the product of a length times an appropriate width or height. The area of a circle of diameter D, for example, is identically equal to that of a rectangle of length D and height $\pi D/4$. The pertinence of this concept to graphical integration is best brought out by example:

Consider the curve a-b in Fig. B.1. By definition, $\int_{x_1}^{x_2} y\,dx$ equals the area bounded by the curve, the x axis, and the two vertical lines corresponding to the limits $x = x_1$ and $x = x_2$. Now let the horizontal line a'-b' be drawn at a height such that the two shaded areas, A and B, are exactly equal. A little thought will make it clear that the desired area under the curve is the same as the area under the line a'-b', between the same limits, and the latter area is very easily determined. In other words, $\int_{x_1}^{x_2} y\,dx$ in this case is equal to $y'(x_2 - x_1)$ or $4(2.5 - .5) = 8$. Note particularly that a knowledge of the particular function represented by the curve was not required for the evaluation of the integral.

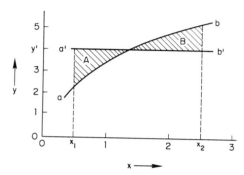

Fig. B.1 Illustrative example of graphical integration.

When the curvature of a curve is not great, the horizontal line to be used to determine the area under the curve can readily be drawn by inspection, with the unaided eye telling one when the height is such that the areas corresponding to A and B in Fig. B.1 are essentially equal. In many instances, however, it will be somewhat difficult to estimate equal areas using only a single horizontal line. In such cases the desired integral can be broken up into as many different parts as may be desirable, and the area of each part can then be determined separately.

An example of the complete technique is shown in Fig. B.2, which illustrates the determination of $\int_{-1}^{3} e^x\,dx$. The first step is to plot e^x vs. x. The range of x of interest is then broken into as many parts as may be desirable to enable the eye to judge the equality of the areas which result when the horizontal lines are drawn. In the example, four parts have been used, and it is noteworthy that the parts need not all be of the same width. Finally, the sum of the areas of the rectangles is determined and is equal to the value of the original integral.

The indicated answer of 19.8 compares quite favorably with the analytical, slide-rule answer of 19.7—and we can assure the student that the graphical result is completely honest and unfudged, although regular graph paper was used to facilitate interpolation in determining the various widths and heights. The clear implication is that graphical integration, if done carefully, affords a precision which is wholly suitable for engineering usage. It can therefore be used without reservation whenever analytical integration is impracticable for whatever reason.

The equal-area method of graphical integration illustrated in Fig. B.2 has another advantage which is worthy of mention: Suppose the figure

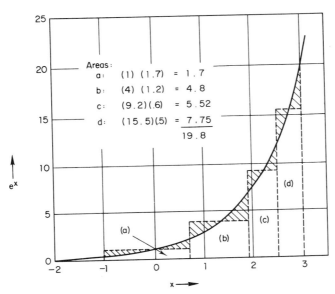

Fig. B.2 Graphical determination of $\int_{-1}^{3} e^x dx$.

represented a plot of applied force in pounds as a function of distance in feet from an arbitrary reference point, instead of a plot of e^x vs. x. In accordance with the rules of unit consistency, each area would have the units ft-lb$_f$, since it would be the product of a height in lb$_f$ and a width in ft. Thus the equal-area method of graphical integration automatically indicates the proper units of the answer, and no further conversion is necessary.

Graphical differentiation. A procedure completely analogous to the equal-area method of graphical integration may be used for graphical differentiation and will be an extremely useful technique in processing rate data. Suppose, for example, the distance traveled by an accelerating automobile has been measured as a function of time, and the speed of the car at any instant is to be determined. Hypothetical experimental data are given in the first two columns of Table B.1, and the steps leading to the graphical determination of the instantaneous rate as a function of either time or distance traveled are as follows:

The first step is to calculate Δx and $\Delta \theta$ between each set of datum points as shown in the third and fourth columns of Table B.1. The calculated values permit the determination of the quotient shown in the fifth column of the

TABLE B.1

DATA AND CALCULATIONS FOR GRAPHICAL DIFFERENTIATION

Distance Traveled, ft (x)	Elapsed Time, sec (θ)	Δx	$\Delta \theta$	$\dfrac{\Delta x}{\Delta \theta}$	Instantaneous Rate, ft/sec $(dx/d\theta)$
0	0				0
		100	25.3	3.96	
100	25.3				10.2
		100	7.6	13.15	
200	32.9				16.5
		200	9.3	21.5	
400	42.2				26.8
		400	11.3	35.4	
800	53.5				44.6

table, and it should be clear that the figures in this column denote the *average* speed over each corresponding interval of time. The average speeds may therefore be plotted as horizontal lines when $\Delta x/\Delta \theta$ is plotted against θ as has been done in Fig. B.3, lines rather than points being used because each average applies over a time *interval* and not to a *point* in time.

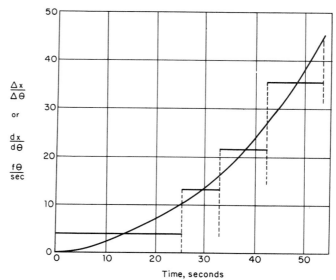

Fig. B.3 Illustrative example of graphical differentiation.

Now let us examine the significance of the rectangular area under any one of the horizontal lines: Since each area represents the product of $\Delta x/\Delta \theta$ times the corresponding $\Delta \theta$, it must be identically equal to Δx, the distance traveled during the time interval over which it applies. Similarly, were $dx/d\theta$ to be plotted vs. θ over the same time interval, the area under the curve would be equal to the integral of $(dx/d\theta)d\theta$ in accordance with the principles of graphical integration, but this simplifies to the integral of dx which in turn integrates to Δx. In other words, whatever curve represents the instantaneous rate, $dx/d\theta$, as a function of time must have an area under it which is exactly equal to the area of the corresponding average-rate rectangle.

The foregoing equality provides the basis for graphical differentiation: The instantaneous rate curve is constructed by trial-and-error, the test of validity of any particular curve being the extent to which it provides equal areas above and below each of the given horizontal line segments. The final curve obtained by such a procedure is shown in Fig. B.3, in which the dashed lines have been dropped down to facilitate the equal-area inspection. It is noteworthy that the curve passes through the origin, as it must if the car started from rest. Given initial conditions will often impose a similar restriction on the form of the instantaneous rate curve, and the significance of such conditions should never be overlooked.

The instantaneous rate at any time can now be read directly from the constructed curve, and values corresponding to each of the original time measurements are listed in the sixth column of Table B.1.

It should be emphasized that it would not be proper to plot $\Delta x/\Delta\theta$ vs. x in the event the instantaneous rate were desired as a function of distance traveled rather than as a function of time, for the rectangular area $\Delta x/\Delta\theta$ by Δx cannot be shown to be equal to the integral of $(dx/d\theta)dx$. It would be proper, however, to plot the *reciprocal* average rate, $\Delta\theta/\Delta x$, vs. x to obtain a curve of reciprocal instantaneous rate as a function of distance traveled. The alternative technique is to obtain the instantaneous rate as a function of time as illustrated above. The values tabulated in the sixth column of Table B.1 can then be plotted against the values of x in the first column if desired.

It may occur to the student that an alternative method of graphical differentiation would be to plot x vs. θ and merely measure the slope of the curve at various points for replotting against either x or θ. While such a procedure is technically correct, it is considerably less exact than the recommended procedure and can result in appreciable error if the original data are somewhat scattered. It should therefore be used only when time does not permit the more rigorous approach described herein.

The foregoing does not cover all aspects of graphical differentiation, but it will at least make the student aware of the existence of the technique as a complement to the more familiar procedure of graphical integration. As was noted at the outset, graphical differentiation is particularly advantageous in processing rate data, and, since rate is one of the fundamental aspects of change, the student can rest assured that he will have many opportunities to put the procedure to practical use in the not-too-distant future.

APPENDIX C

Physical Data for Selected Substances*

---

* For additional data see Perry's Handbook or indicated source reference.

APPENDIX C-1A

VAPOR PRESSURES UP TO 1 ATM*

Compound	Pressure, mm Hg — Temperature, °C									
	1	5	10	20	40	60	100	200	400	760
Acetone	-59.4	-40.5	-31.1	-20.8	-9.4	-2.0	+7.7	22.7	39.5	56.5
Acetylene	-142.9	-133.0	-128.2	-122.8	-116.7	-112.8	-107.9	-100.3	-92.0	-84.0
Ammonia	-109.1	-97.5	-91.9	-85.8	-79.2	-74.3	-68.4	-57.0	-45.4	-33.6
Benzene	-36.7	-19.6	-11.5	-2.6	+7.6	15.4	26.1	42.2	60.6	80.1
Carbon dioxide	-134.3	-124.4	-119.5	-114.4	-108.6	-104.8	-100.2	-93.0	-85.7	-78.2
Carbon monoxide	-222.0	-217.2	-215.0	-212.8	-210.0	-208.1	-205.7	-201.3	-196.3	-191.3
Chlorine	-118.0	-106.7	-101.6	-93.3	-84.5	-79.0	-71.7	-60.2	-47.3	-33.8
Ethane	-159.5	-148.5	-142.9	-136.7	-129.8	-125.4	-119.3	-110.2	-99.7	-88.6
Ethyl alcohol	-31.3	-12.0	-2.3	+8.0	19.0	26.0	34.9	48.4	63.5	78.4
Ethylene	-168.3	-158.3	-153.2	-147.6	-141.3	-137.3	-131.8	-123.4	-113.9	-103.7
Hydrogen	-263.3	-261.9	-261.3	-260.4	-259.6	-258.9	-257.9	-256.3	-254.5	-252.5
Hydrogen chloride	-150.8	-140.7	-135.6	-130.0	-123.8	-119.6	-114.0	-105.2	-95.3	-84.8
Hydrogen sulfide	-134.3	-122.4	-116.3	-109.7	-102.3	-97.9	-91.6	-82.3	-71.8	-60.4
Methane	-205.9	-199.0	-195.5	-191.8	-187.7	-185.1	-181.4	-175.5	-168.8	-161.5
Methyl alcohol	-44.0	-25.3	-16.2	-6.0	+5.0	12.1	21.2	34.8	49.9	64.7
Nitric oxide	-184.5	-180.6	-178.2	-175.3	-171.7	-168.9	-166.0	-162.3	-156.8	-151.7
Nitrogen	-226.1	-221.3	-219.1	-216.8	-214.0	-212.3	-209.7	-205.6	-200.9	-195.8
Oxygen	-219.1	-213.4	-210.6	-207.5	-204.1	-201.9	-198.8	-194.0	-188.8	-183.1
Propane	-128.9	-115.4	-108.5	-100.9	-92.4	-87.0	-79.6	-68.4	-55.6	-42.1
Propylene	-131.9	-120.7	-112.1	-104.7	-96.5	-91.3	-84.1	-73.3	-60.9	-47.7
Sulfur dioxide	-95.5	-83.0	-76.8	-69.7	-60.5	-54.6	-49.6	-35.4	-23.0	-10.0
Sulfur trioxide	-39.0	-23.7	-16.5	-9.1	-1.0	+4.0	10.5	20.5	32.6	44.8
Water	-17.3	+1.2	11.2	22.1	34.0	41.5	51.6	66.5	83.0	100.0

* Abstracted from Stull, D. R., Ind. Eng. Chem., 39, 517 (1947); copyrighted by the American Chemical Society and used by permission of the copyright owner.

Appendix C-1B

Vapor Pressures above 1 atm*

Compound	Pressure, atm								
	1	2	5	10	20	30	40	50	60
	Temperature, °C								
Acetone	56.5	78.6	113.0	144.5	181.0	205.0	214.5		
Acetylene	−84.0	−71.6	−50.2	−32.7	−10.0	+4.8	16.8	26.8	34.8
Ammonia	−33.6	−18.7	+4.7	25.7	50.1	66.1	78.9	89.3	98.3
Benzene	80.1	103.8	142.5	178.8	221.5	249.5	272.3	290.3	
Carbon dioxide	−78.2	−69.1	−56.7	−39.5	−18.9	−5.3	+5.9	14.9	22.4
Carbon monoxide	−191.3	−183.5	−170.7	−161.0	−149.7	−141.9			
Chlorine	−33.8	−16.9	+10.3	35.6	65.0	84.8	101.6	115.2	127.1
Ethane	−88.6	−75.0	−52.8	−32.0	−6.4	+10.0	23.6		
Ethyl alcohol	78.4	97.5	126.0	151.8	183.0	203.0	218.0	230.0	242.0
Ethylene	−103.7	−90.8	−71.1	−52.8	−29.1	−14.2	−1.5	+8.9	
Hydrogen	−252.5	−250.2	−246.0	−241.8					
Hydrogen chloride	−84.8	−71.4	−50.5	−31.7	−8.8	+5.9	17.8	27.9	36.2
Hydrogen sulfide	−60.4	−45.9	−22.3	−0.4	+25.5	41.9	55.8	66.7	76.3
Methane	−161.5	−152.3	−138.3	−124.8	−108.5	−96.3	−86.3		
Methyl alcohol	64.7	84.0	112.5	138.0	167.8	186.5	203.5	214.0	224.0
Nitrogen	−195.8	−189.2	−179.1	−169.8	−157.6	−148.3			
Oxygen	−183.1	−176.0	−164.5	−153.2	−140.0	−130.7	−124.1		
Propane	−42.1	−25.6	+1.4	26.9	58.1	78.7	94.8		
Propylene	−47.7	−31.4	−4.8	+19.8	49.5	70.0	85.0		
Sulfur dioxide	−10.0	+6.3	32.1	55.5	83.8	102.6	118.0	130.2	141.7
Sulfur trioxide	44.8	60.0	82.5	104.0	138.0	157.8	175.0	187.8	198.0
Water	100.0	120.1	152.4	180.5	213.1	234.6	251.1	264.7	276.5

* Abstracted from Stull, D. R., Ind. Eng. Chem., *39*, 517 (1947); copyrighted by the American Chemical Society and used by permission of the copyright owner.

Appendix C-2

Heat Capacities of Gases at Constant Pressure*

$C_p = a + (b \times 10^{-3})T + (c \times 10^{-6})T^2$, where T is in degrees Kelvin and C_p is the heat capacity in the ideal-gas state, $BTU/(lb\text{-}mol)(F°)$ or $cal/(gm\text{-}mol)(C°)$.

Compound	Formula	a	b	c
Acetone	CH_3COCH_3	5.371	49.227	−15.182
Acetylene	C_2H_2	7.331	12.622	−3.889
Ammonia	NH_3	6.086	8.812	−1.506
Benzene	C_6H_6	−0.409	77.621	−26.429
Carbon dioxide	CO_2	6.214	10.396	−3.545
Carbon monoxide	CO	6.420	1.665	−0.196
Chlorine	Cl_2	7.576	2.424	−0.965
Ethane	C_2H_6	2.247	38.201	−11.049
Ethyl alcohol	C_2H_5OH	6.990	39.741	−11.926
Ethylene	C_2H_4	2.830	28.601	−8.726
Hydrogen	H_2	6.947	−0.200	0.481
Hydrogen chloride	HCl	6.732	0.433	0.370
Hydrogen sulfide	H_2S	6.662	5.134	−0.854
Methane	CH_4	3.381	18.044	−4.300
Methyl alcohol	CH_3OH	4.394	24.274	−6.855
Nitric oxide	NO	7.020	−0.370	2.546
Nitrogen	N_2	6.524	1.250	−0.001
Oxygen	O_2	6.148	3.102	−0.923
Propane	C_3H_8	2.410	57.195	−17.533
Propylene	C_3H_6	3.253	45.116	−13.740
Sulfur dioxide	SO_2	7.116	9.512	−3.511
Sulfur trioxide	SO_3	6.077	23.537	−0.687
Water vapor	H_2O	7.256	2.298	0.283

* Abstracted from Smith, J. M., and Van Ness, H. C., *Introduction to Chemical Engineering Thermodynamics* (New York: McGraw-Hill Book Company, Inc., 1959); by permission.

APPENDIX C-3A

STANDARD HEATS OF FORMATION*

ΔH_f is the heat in kilocalories which would be absorbed were one gram-mol of the indicated compound to be formed from its constituent elements at a constant temperature of 25°C, reactants and product to be pure (unmixed) substances at a pressure of one atmosphere.

Compound	Formula	State	ΔH_f kcal/gm-mol
Acetaldehyde	CH_3CHO	gas	−39.72
Acetic acid	CH_3COOH	liquid	−116.2
Acetone	CH_3COCH_3	liquid	−59.32
Acetylene	C_2H_2	gas	54.194
Ammonia	NH_3	gas	−10.96
Benzene	C_6H_6	gas	19.82
Carbon dioxide	CO_2	gas	−94.052
Carbon disulfide	CS_2	gas	28.11
Carbon monoxide	CO	gas	−26.416
Ethane	C_2H_6	gas	−20.236
Ethyl alcohol	C_2H_5OH	gas	−52.23
Ethylene	C_2H_4	gas	12.496
Ethylene oxide	C_2H_4O	gas	−16.1
Ethylene glycol	$C_2H_6O_2$	gas	−92.53
Formaldehyde	CH_2O	gas	−28.29
Hydrogen chloride	HCl	gas	−22.063
Hydrogen cyanide	HCN	gas	31.1
Hydrogen sulfide	H_2S	gas	−4.77
Methane	CH_4	gas	−17.889
Methyl alcohol	CH_3OH	gas	−48.08
Nitric acid	HNO_3	liquid	−41.35
Nitric oxide	NO	gas	21.600
Nitrogen dioxide	NO_2	gas	7.96
Nitrous oxide	N_2O	gas	19.55
Phenol	C_6H_5OH	liquid	−37.80
Propane	C_3H_8	gas	−24.820
Propylene	C_3H_6	gas	4.879
Sulfur dioxide	SO_2	gas	−70.94
Sulfuric acid	H_2SO_4	liquid	−193.69
Sulfur trioxide	SO_3	gas	−94.39
Toluene	$C_6H_5CH_3$	liquid	2.867
Urea	NH_2CONH_2	liquid	−77.55
Water	H_2O	liquid	−68.317
”	”	gas	−57.798

* Abstracted from Perry, J. H. (ed.), *Chemical Engineers' Handbook* (New York: McGraw-Hill Book Company, Inc., 1950), 3rd ed; by permission.

Appendix C-3b

Standard Heats of Combustion*

ΔH_c is the heat in kilocalories which would be absorbed were one gram-mol of the indicated compound to react with oxygen at a constant temperature of 25°C and a constant pressure of one atmosphere to form $CO_2(g)$, $H_2O(l)$, $SO_2(g)$, and free N_2 to the extent that these products are pertinent.

Compound	Formula	State	ΔH_c kcal/gm-mol
Acetic anhydride	$C_6H_4O_3$	liquid	−426.00
Aniline	$C_6H_5NH_2$	liquid	−812.
Benzene	C_6H_6	liquid	−780.98
Camphor	$C_{10}H_{16}O$	solid	−1411.
Carbon disulfide	CS_2	liquid	−256.97
Carbonyl sulfide	COS	gas	−132.21
Cyanogen	C_2N_2	gas	−261.70
Cyclopentane	C_5H_{10}	liquid	−786.54
Dimethyl sulfide	C_2H_6S	liquid	−450.42
Ethyl alcohol	C_2H_5OH	liquid	−326.70
Ethyl mercaptan	C_2H_6S	liquid	−448.0
Ethylene glycol	$C_2H_6O_2$	liquid	−284.48
Formic acid	$CHOOH$	liquid	−64.57
Glycerol	$C_3H_8O_3$	liquid	−396.27
Methyl alcohol	CH_3OH	liquid	−173.65
Methyl mercaptan	CH_4S	gas	−298.68
Naphthalene	$C_{10}H_8$	solid	−1231.6
Nitrobenzene	$C_6H_5NO_2$	liquid	−739.
Phenol	C_6H_5OH	gas	−747.55
Phthalic anhydride	$C_8H_4O_3$	solid	−781.4
Trinitrotoluene	$C_7H_5N_3O_6$	solid	−821.
Urea	NH_2CONH_2	solid	−151.05

* Abstracted from O. A. Hougen, K. M. Watson, and R. A. Ragatz, *Chemical Process Principles* (New York: John Wiley & Sons, Inc., 1954) Part I; by permission.

Appendix C-4a

Vapor-Liquid Equilibrium Data, Ethanol-Water System at 1 Atmosphere*

Equilibrium Temperature °C	Mol Fraction Ethanol	
	In Liquid (x)	In Equilibrium Vapor (y)
100.0	0.0000	0.0000
95.7	0.0190	0.1700
	0.0400	0.2870
90.0	0.0600	0.3560
86.4	0.1000	0.4360
	0.1500	0.4960
83.3	0.2000	0.5285
81.8	0.3000	0.5725
80.7	0.4000	0.6125
79.8	0.5000	0.6520
79.1	0.6000	0.6965
78.6	0.7000	0.7525
78.3	0.8000	0.8175
78.2	0.8943	0.8943
78.4	1.0000	1.0000

* Abstracted from the data of Lewis and Carey, Ind. Eng. Chem., *24*, 882 (1932); copyrighted by the American Chemical Society and used by permission of the copyright owner.

Appendix C-4в

Vapor-Liquid Equilibrium Data, CO_2-Triethanolamine (0.5 Normal) System at 25°C and 1 Atmosphere*

Mol Ratio, CO_2 to CO_2-free Gas, in Vapor Phase	Mol Ratio, CO_2 to Triethanolamine, in Liquid Phase
0.0000	0.0000
0.0057	0.1000
0.0147	0.2000
0.0229	0.2500
0.0354	0.3000
0.0519	0.3500
0.0735	0.4000
0.0998	0.4500
0.1328	0.5000

* Prepared from the data of Mason and Dodge, Trans. Am. Inst. Chem. Engrs., *32*, 27 (1936).

Appendix C-5

Critical Constants for Some Typical Materials†

Material	P_c, atm	T_c, °K
Acetone	46.6	509
Acetylene	61.6	309
Ammonia	111.3	406
Benzene	48.6	562
Carbon dioxide	72.9	304
Carbon monoxide	34.5	133
Chlorine	76.1	417
Ethane	48.2	306
Ethyl alcohol	63.0	516
Ethylene	50.0	282
Hydrogen	12.8	33.3
Hydrogen chloride	81.5	325
Hydrogen sulfide	88.9	374
Methane	45.8	191
Methyl alcohol	78.5	513
Nitric oxide	64	180
Nitrogen	33.5	126
Oxygen	50.1	155
Propane	42.0	370
Propylene	45.6	365
Sulfur dioxide	77.8	431
Sulfur trioxide	83.8	491
Water	218	647

† Abstracted from K. A. Kobe and R. E. Lynn, Jr., Chem. Rev., *52*, 117 (1953); by permission of the American Chemical Society. Additional values may also be obtained from Perry's Handbook.

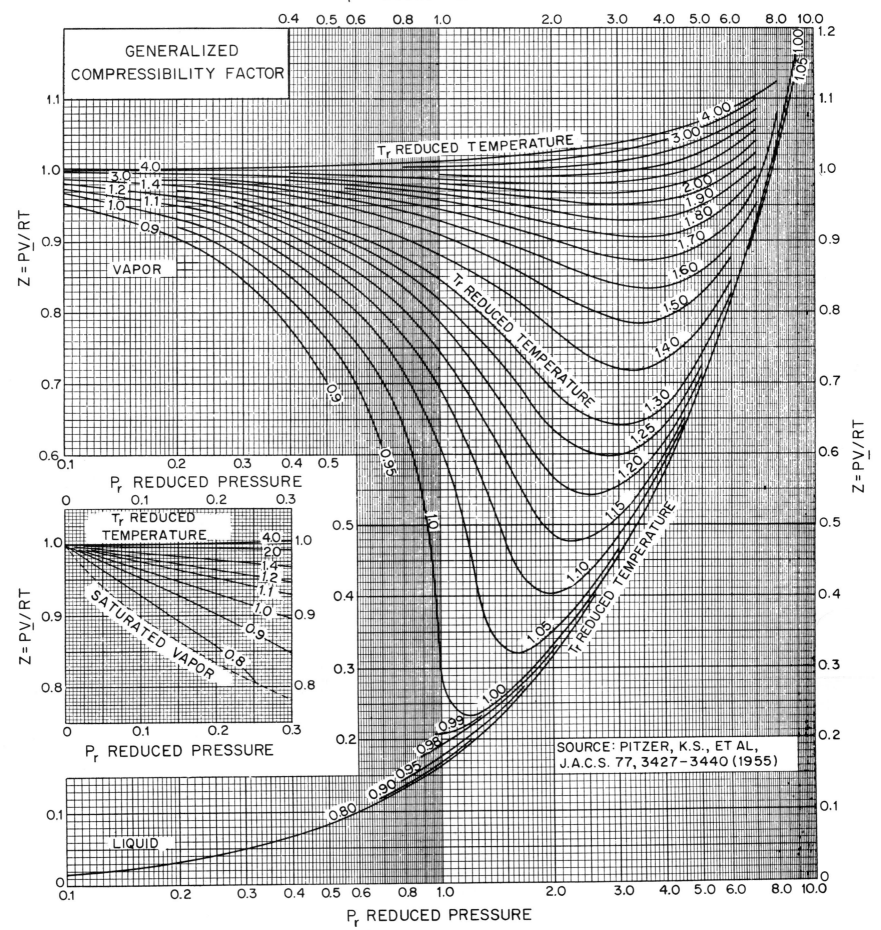

Fig. C.6 Generalized compressibility factor plot.

Edmister, W. C., *Petroleum Refiner*, 37, No. 4, April 1958, copyright 1958, Gulf Publishing Co.; by permission.

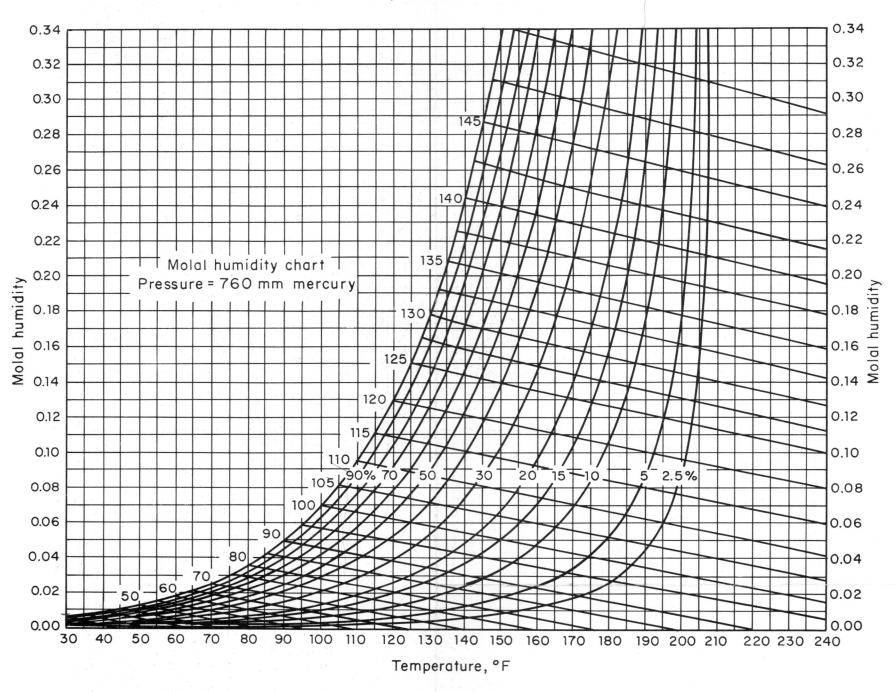

Fig. C.7 Psychrometric chart for the air-water system at atmospheric pressure. (Reprinted with permission from O. A. Hougen and J. M. Watson, *Industrial Chemical Calculations* (New York: John Wiley & Sons, Inc., 1936.).)

Appendix C-8

Thermodynamic Properties of Steam*

Table 1. Saturated Steam

Temp. Fahr. t	Absolute Pressure Lb. per Sq. In. p	Absolute Pressure In. Hg. 32 F.	Specific Volume Sat. Liquid v_f	Specific Volume Evap. v_{fg}	Specific Volume Sat. Vapor v_g	Enthalpy Sat. Liquid h_f	Enthalpy Evap. h_{fg}	Enthalpy Sat. Vapor h_g	Entropy Sat. Liquid s_f	Entropy Evap. s_{fg}	Entropy Sat. Vapor s_g	Temp. Fahr. t
32	0.0886	0.1806	0.01602	3305.7	3305.7	0	1075.1	1075.1	0	2.1865	2.1865	32
34	0.0961	0.1957	0.01602	3060.4	3060.4	2.01	1074.0	1076.0	0.0041	2.1755	2.1796	34
36	0.1041	0.2120	0.01602	2836.6	2836.6	4.03	1072.9	1076.9	0.0082	2.1645	2.1727	36
38	0.1126	0.2292	0.01602	2632.2	2632.2	6.04	1071.7	1077.7	0.0122	2.1533	2.1655	38
40	0.1217	0.2478	0.01602	2445.1	2445.1	8.05	1070.5	1078.6	0.0162	2.1423	2.1585	40
42	0.1315	0.2677	0.01602	2271.8	2271.8	10.06	1069.3	1079.4	0.0203	2.1314	2.1517	42
44	0.1420	0.2891	0.01602	2112.2	2112.2	12.06	1068.2	1080.3	0.0242	2.1207	2.1449	44
46	0.1532	0.3119	0.01602	1965.5	1965.5	14.07	1067.1	1081.2	0.0282	2.1102	2.1384	46
48	0.1652	0.3364	0.01602	1829.9	1829.9	16.07	1065.9	1082.0	0.0322	2.0995	2.1317	48
50	0.1780	0.3624	0.01602	1704.9	1704.9	18.07	1064.8	1082.9	0.0361	2.0891	2.1252	50
52	0.1918	0.3905	0.01603	1588.4	1588.4	20.07	1063.6	1083.7	0.0400	2.0786	2.1186	52
54	0.2063	0.4200	0.01603	1482.4	1482.4	22.07	1062.5	1084.6	0.0439	2.0684	2.1123	54
56	0.2219	0.4518	0.01603	1383.5	1383.5	24.07	1061.4	1085.5	0.0478	2.0582	2.1060	56
58	0.2384	0.4854	0.01603	1292.7	1292.7	26.07	1060.2	1086.3	0.0517	2.0479	2.0996	58
60	0.2561	0.5214	0.01603	1208.1	1208.1	28.07	1059.1	1087.2	0.0555	2.0379	2.0934	60
62	0.2749	0.5597	0.01604	1129.7	1129.7	30.06	1057.9	1088.0	0.0594	2.0278	2.0872	62
64	0.2949	0.6004	0.01604	1057.1	1057.1	32.06	1056.8	1088.9	0.0632	2.0180	2.0812	64
66	0.3162	0.6438	0.01604	989.6	989.6	34.06	1055.7	1089.8	0.0670	2.0082	2.0752	66
68	0.3388	0.6898	0.01605	927.0	927.0	36.05	1054.5	1090.6	0.0708	1.9983	2.0691	68

* Reproduced by permission from *Steam Tables: Properties of Saturated and Superheated Steam*, Combustion Engineering, Inc., New York (1940).

Table 1. Saturated Steam —Continued

Temp. Fahr. t	Absolute Pressure Lb. per Sq. In. p	Absolute Pressure In. Hg. 32 F.	Specific Volume Sat. Liquid v_f	Specific Volume Evap. v_{fg}	Specific Volume Sat. Vapor v_g	Enthalpy Sat. Liquid h_f	Enthalpy Evap. h_{fg}	Enthalpy Sat. Vapor h_g	Entropy Sat. Liquid s_f	Entropy Evap. s_{fg}	Entropy Sat. Vapor s_g	Temp. Fahr. t
70	0.3628	0.7387	0.01605	868.9	868.9	38.05	1053.4	1091.5	0.0745	1.9887	2.0632	70
72	0.3883	0.7906	0.01606	814.9	814.9	40.04	1052.3	1092.3	0.0783	1.9792	2.0575	72
74	0.4153	0.8456	0.01606	764.7	764.7	42.04	1051.2	1093.2	0.0820	1.9697	2.0517	74
76	0.4440	0.9040	0.01607	718.0	718.0	44.03	1050.1	1094.1	0.0858	1.9603	2.0461	76
78	0.4744	0.9659	0.01607	674.4	674.4	46.03	1048.9	1094.9	0.0895	1.9508	2.0403	78
80	0.5067	1.032	0.01607	633.7	633.7	48.02	1047.8	1095.8	0.0932	1.9415	2.0347	80
82	0.5409	1.101	0.01608	595.8	595.8	50.02	1046.6	1096.6	0.0969	1.9321	2.0290	82
84	0.5772	1.175	0.01608	560.4	560.4	52.01	1045.5	1097.5	0.1006	1.9230	2.0236	84
86	0.6153	1.253	0.01609	527.6	527.6	54.01	1044.4	1098.4	0.1042	1.9139	2.0181	86
88	0.6555	1.335	0.01609	497.0	497.0	56.00	1043.2	1099.2	0.1079	1.9047	2.0126	88
90	0.6980	1.421	0.01610	468.4	468.4	58.00	1042.1	1100.1	0.1115	1.8958	2.0073	90
92	0.7429	1.513	0.01611	441.7	441.7	59.99	1040.9	1100.9	0.1151	1.8867	2.0018	92
94	0.7902	1.609	0.01611	416.7	416.7	61.98	1039.8	1101.8	0.1187	1.8779	1.9966	94
96	0.8403	1.711	0.01612	393.2	393.2	63.98	1038.7	1102.7	0.1223	1.8692	1.9915	96
98	0.8930	1.818	0.01613	371.3	371.3	65.98	1037.5	1103.5	0.1259	1.8604	1.9863	98
100	0.9487	1.932	0.01613	350.8	350.8	67.97	1036.4	1104.4	0.1295	1.8517	1.9812	100
102	1.0072	2.051	0.01614	331.5	331.5	69.96	1035.2	1105.2	0.1330	1.8430	1.9760	102
104	1.0689	2.176	0.01614	313.5	313.5	71.96	1034.1	1106.1	0.1366	1.8345	1.9711	104
106	1.1338	2.308	0.01615	296.5	296.5	73.95	1033.0	1107.0	0.1401	1.8261	1.9662	106
108	1.2020	2.447	0.01616	280.7	280.7	75.94	1032.0	1107.9	0.1436	1.8179	1.9615	108
110	1.274	2.594	0.01617	265.7	265.7	77.94	1030.9	1108.8	0.1471	1.8096	1.9567	110
112	1.350	2.749	0.01617	251.6	251.6	79.93	1029.7	1109.6	0.1506	1.8012	1.9518	112
114	1.429	2.909	0.01618	238.5	238.5	81.93	1028.6	1110.5	0.1541	1.7930	1.9471	114
116	1.512	3.078	0.01619	226.2	226.2	83.92	1027.5	1111.4	0.1576	1.7848	1.9424	116
118	1.600	3.258	0.01620	214.5	214.5	85.92	1026.4	1112.3	0.1610	1.7767	1.9377	118

120	1.692	3.445	0.01620	203.45	203.47	87.91	1025.3	1113.2	0.1645	1.7687	1.9332	120
122	1.788	3.640	0.01621	193.16	193.18	89.91	1024.1	1114.0	0.1679	1.7606	1.9285	122
124	1.889	3.846	0.01622	183.44	183.46	91.90	1023.0	1114.9	0.1714	1.7526	1.9240	124
126	1.995	4.062	0.01623	174.26	174.28	93.90	1021.8	1115.7	0.1748	1.7446	1.9194	126
128	2.105	4.286	0.01624	165.70	165.72	95.90	1020.7	1116.6	0.1782	1.7368	1.9150	128
130	2.221	4.522	0.01625	157.55	157.57	97.89	1019.5	1117.4	0.1816	1.7289	1.9105	130
132	2.343	4.770	0.01626	149.83	149.85	99.89	1018.3	1118.2	0.1849	1.7210	1.9059	132
134	2.470	5.029	0.01626	142.59	142.61	101.89	1017.2	1119.1	0.1883	1.7134	1.9017	134
136	2.603	5.300	0.01627	135.73	135.75	103.88	1016.0	1119.9	0.1917	1.7056	1.8973	136
138	2.742	5.583	0.01628	129.26	129.28	105.88	1014.9	1120.8	0.1950	1.6980	1.8930	138
140	2.887	5.878	0.01629	123.16	123.18	107.88	1013.7	1121.6	0.1984	1.6904	1.8888	140
142	3.039	6.187	0.01630	117.37	117.39	109.88	1012.5	1122.4	0.2017	1.6828	1.8845	142
144	3.198	6.511	0.01631	111.88	111.90	111.88	1011.3	1123.2	0.2050	1.6752	1.8802	144
146	3.363	6.847	0.01632	106.72	106.74	113.88	1010.2	1124.1	0.2083	1.6678	1.8761	146
148	3.536	7.199	0.01633	101.82	101.84	115.87	1009.0	1124.9	0.2116	1.6604	1.8720	148
150	3.716	7.566	0.01634	97.18	97.20	117.87	1007.8	1125.7	0.2149	1.6530	1.8679	150
152	3.904	7.948	0.01635	92.79	92.81	119.87	1006.7	1126.6	0.2181	1.6458	1.8639	152
154	4.100	8.348	0.01636	88.62	88.64	121.87	1005.5	1127.4	0.2214	1.6384	1.8598	154
156	4.305	8.765	0.01637	84.66	84.68	123.87	1004.4	1128.3	0.2247	1.6313	1.8560	156
158	4.518	9.199	0.01638	80.90	80.92	125.87	1003.2	1129.1	0.2279	1.6241	1.8520	158
160	4.739	9.649	0.01639	77.37	77.39	127.87	1002.0	1129.9	0.2311	1.6169	1.8480	160
162	4.970	10.12	0.01640	74.00	74.02	129.88	1000.8	1130.7	0.2343	1.6098	1.8441	162
164	5.210	10.61	0.01642	70.79	70.81	131.88	999.7	1131.6	0.2376	1.6029	1.8405	164
166	5.460	11.12	0.01643	67.76	67.78	133.88	998.5	1132.4	0.2408	1.5958	1.8366	166
168	5.720	11.65	0.01644	64.87	64.89	135.88	997.3	1133.2	0.2439	1.5888	1.8327	168
170	5.990	12.20	0.01645	62.12	62.14	137.89	996.1	1134.0	0.2471	1.5819	1.8290	170
172	6.272	12.77	0.01646	59.50	59.52	139.89	995.0	1134.9	0.2503	1.5751	1.8254	172
174	6.565	13.37	0.01647	57.01	57.03	141.89	993.8	1135.7	0.2535	1.5683	1.8218	174
176	6.869	13.99	0.01648	54.64	54.66	143.90	992.6	1136.5	0.2566	1.5615	1.8181	176
178	7.184	14.63	0.01650	52.39	52.41	145.90	991.4	1137.3	0.2598	1.5547	1.8145	178

TABLE 1. SATURATED STEAM—*Continued*

Temp. Fahr. t	Absolute Pressure Lb. per Sq. In. p	Pressure In. Hg. 32 F.	Specific Volume Sat. Liquid vf	Evap. vfg	Sat. Vapor vg	Enthalpy Sat. Liquid hf	Evap. hfg	Sat. Vapor hg	Entropy Sat. Liquid sf	Evap. sfg	Sat. Vapor sg	Temp. Fahr. t
180	7.510	15.29	0.01651	50.26	50.28	147.91	990.2	1138.1	0.2629	1.5479	1.8108	180
182	7.849	15.98	0.01652	48.22	48.24	149.92	989.0	1138.9	0.2661	1.5412	1.8073	182
184	8.201	16.70	0.01653	46.28	46.30	151.92	987.8	1139.7	0.2692	1.5346	1.8038	184
186	8.566	17.44	0.01654	44.43	44.45	153.93	986.6	1140.5	0.2723	1.5280	1.8003	186
188	8.944	18.21	0.01656	42.67	42.69	155.94	985.3	1141.3	0.2754	1.5213	1.7967	188
190	9.336	19.01	0.01657	40.99	41.01	157.95	984.1	1142.1	0.2785	1.5147	1.7932	190
192	9.744	19.84	0.01658	39.38	39.40	159.95	982.8	1142.8	0.2816	1.5081	1.7897	192
194	10.168	20.70	0.01659	37.84	37.86	161.96	981.5	1143.5	0.2847	1.5015	1.7862	194
196	10.605	21.59	0.01661	36.38	36.40	163.97	980.3	1144.3	0.2877	1.4951	1.7828	196
198	11.057	22.51	0.01662	34.98	35.00	165.98	979.0	1145.0	0.2908	1.4885	1.7793	198
200	11.525	23.46	0.01663	33.65	33.67	167.99	977.8	1145.8	0.2938	1.4822	1.7760	200
202	12.010	24.45	0.01665	32.37	32.39	170.01	976.6	1146.6	0.2969	1.4759	1.7728	202
204	12.512	25.47	0.01666	31.15	31.17	172.02	975.3	1147.3	0.2999	1.4695	1.7694	204
206	13.031	26.53	0.01667	29.99	30.01	174.03	974.1	1148.1	0.3029	1.4633	1.7662	206
208	13.568	27.62	0.01669	28.88	28.90	176.04	972.8	1148.8	0.3059	1.4570	1.7629	208
210	14.123	28.75	0.01670	27.81	27.83	178.06	971.5	1149.6	0.3090	1.4507	1.7597	210
212	14.696	29.92	0.01672	26.81	26.83	180.07	970.3	1150.4	0.3120	1.4446	1.7566	212
215	15.591		0.01674	25.35	25.37	183.10	968.3	1151.4	0.3165	1.4352	1.7517	215
220	17.188		0.01677	23.14	23.16	188.14	965.2	1153.3	0.3239	1.4201	1.7440	220
225	18.915		0.01681	21.15	21.17	193.18	961.9	1155.1	0.3313	1.4049	1.7362	225
230	20.78		0.01684	19.371	19.388	198.22	958.7	1156.9	0.3386	1.3900	1.7286	230
235	22.80		0.01688	17.761	17.778	203.28	955.3	1158.6	0.3459	1.3751	1.7210	235
240	24.97		0.01692	16.307	16.324	208.34	952.1	1160.4	0.3531	1.3607	1.7138	240
245	27.31		0.01696	15.010	15.027	213.41	948.7	1162.1	0.3604	1.3462	1.7066	245
250	29.82		0.01700	13.824	13.841	218.48	945.3	1163.8	0.3675	1.3320	1.6995	250
255	32.53		0.01704	12.735	12.752	223.56	942.0	1165.6	0.3747	1.3181	1.6928	255
260	35.43		0.01708	11.754	11.771	228.65	938.6	1167.3	0.3817	1.3042	1.6859	260
265	38.54		0.01713	10.861	10.878	233.74	935.3	1169.0	0.3888	1.2906	1.6794	265
270	41.85		0.01717	10.053	10.070	238.84	931.8	1170.6	0.3958	1.2770	1.6728	270
275	45.40		0.01721	9.313	9.330	243.94	928.2	1172.1	0.4027	1.2634	1.6661	275

280	1.6596	1.2500	0.4096	1173.7	924.6	249.06	8.651	8.634	0.01726	49.20	**280**
285	1.6533	1.2368	0.4165	1175.2	921.0	254.18	8.032	8.015	0.01731	53.25	**285**
290	1.6471	1.2237	0.4234	1176.7	917.4	259.31	7.465	7.448	0.01735	57.55	**290**
295	1.6409	1.2107	0.4302	1178.2	913.7	264.45	6.948	6.931	0.01740	62.13	**295**
300	1.6350	1.1980	0.4370	1179.7	910.1	269.60	6.471	6.454	0.01745	67.01	**300**
305	1.6289	1.1852	0.4437	1181.1	906.3	274.76	6.032	6.014	0.01750	72.18	**305**
310	1.6232	1.1727	0.4505	1182.5	902.6	279.92	5.628	5.610	0.01755	77.68	**310**
315	1.6158	1.1587	0.4571	1183.9	898.8	285.10	5.257	5.239	0.01760	83.50	**315**
320	1.6116	1.1479	0.4637	1185.3	895.0	290.29	4.915	4.897	0.01765	89.65	**320**
325	1.6059	1.1356	0.4703	1186.6	891.1	295.49	4.601	4.583	0.01771	96.16	**325**
330	1.6003	1.1234	0.4769	1187.8	887.1	300.69	4.310	4.292	0.01776	103.03	**330**
335	1.5949	1.1114	0.4835	1189.1	883.2	305.91	4.039	4.021	0.01782	110.31	**335**
340	1.5894	1.0994	0.4900	1190.3	879.2	311.14	3.789	3.771	0.01788	117.99	**340**
345	1.5841	1.0875	0.4966	1191.5	875.1	316.38	3.557	3.539	0.01793	126.10	**345**
350	1.5787	1.0757	0.5030	1192.6	871.0	321.64	3.342	3.324	0.01799	134.62	**350**
355	1.5734	1.0640	0.5094	1193.7	866.8	326.91	3.144	3.126	0.01805	143.58	**355**
360	1.5681	1.0522	0.5159	1194.7	862.5	332.19	2.958	2.940	0.01811	153.01	**360**
365	1.5629	1.0406	0.5223	1195.7	858.2	337.48	2.786	2.768	0.01817	162.93	**365**
370	1.5577	1.0291	0.5286	1196.6	853.8	342.79	2.625	2.607	0.01823	173.33	**370**
375	1.5526	1.0176	0.5350	1197.5	849.4	348.11	2.476	2.458	0.01830	184.23	**375**
380	1.5475	1.0062	0.5413	1198.4	844.9	353.45	2.336	2.318	0.01836	195.70	**380**
385	1.5425	0.9949	0.5476	1199.2	840.4	358.80	2.207	2.189	0.01843	207.71	**385**
390	1.5375	0.9835	0.5540	1199.9	835.7	364.17	2.083	2.064	0.01850	220.29	**390**
395	1.5325	0.9723	0.5602	1200.6	831.0	369.56	1.9698	1.9512	0.01857	233.47	**395**
400	1.5274	0.9610	0.5664	1201.2	826.2	374.97	1.8632	1.8446	0.01864	247.25	**400**
405	1.5226	0.9499	0.5727	1201.8	821.4	380.40	1.7632	1.7445	0.01871	261.67	**405**
410	1.5179	0.9390	0.5789	1202.4	816.6	385.83	1.6696	1.6508	0.01878	276.72	**410**
415	1.5131	0.9280	0.5851	1203.0	811.7	391.30	1.5819	1.5630	0.01886	292.44	**415**
420	1.5082	0.9170	0.5912	1203.5	806.7	396.78	1.4995	1.4806	0.01894	308.82	**420**
425	1.5035	0.9061	0.5974	1203.9	801.6	402.28	1.4221	1.4031	0.01902	325.91	**425**
430	1.4989	0.8953	0.6036	1204.3	796.5	407.80	1.3494	1.3303	0.01910	343.71	**430**
435	1.4940	0.8843	0.6097	1204.6	791.2	413.35	1.2809	1.2617	0.01918	362.27	**435**
440	1.4894	0.8735	0.6159	1204.8	785.9	418.91	1.2166	1.1973	0.01926	381.59	**440**
445	1.4846	0.8626	0.6220	1204.9	780.4	424.49	1.1560	1.1367	0.01934	401.70	**445**
450	1.4799	0.8518	0.6281	1205.0	774.9	430.11	1.0990	1.0796	0.01943	422.61	**450**

TABLE 1. Saturated Steam—Concluded

Temp. Fahr. t	Abs. Press. Lb./Sq. In. p	Specific Volume			Enthalpy			Entropy			Temp. Fahr. t
		Sat. Liquid v_f	Evap. v_{fg}	Sat. Vapor v_g	Sat. Liquid h_f	Evap. h_{fg}	Sat. Vapor h_g	Sat. Liquid s_f	Evap. s_{fg}	Sat. Vapor s_g	
455	444.35	0.0195	1.0256	1.0451	435.74	769.3	1205.0	0.6342	0.8410	1.4752	455
460	466.97	0.0196	0.9745	0.9941	441.42	763.6	1205.0	0.6403	0.8303	1.4706	460
465	490.43	0.0197	0.9262	0.9459	447.10	757.8	1204.9	0.6463	0.8195	1.4658	465
470	514.70	0.0198	0.8808	0.9006	452.84	751.9	1204.7	0.6524	0.8088	1.4612	470
475	539.90	0.0199	0.8379	0.8578	458.59	745.9	1204.5	0.6585	0.7980	1.4565	475
480	566.12	0.0200	0.7972	0.8172	464.37	739.8	1204.2	0.6646	0.7873	1.4519	480
485	593.28	0.0201	0.7585	0.7786	470.18	733.6	1203.8	0.6706	0.7766	1.4472	485
490	621.44	0.0202	0.7219	0.7421	476.01	727.3	1203.3	0.6767	0.7658	1.4425	490
495	650.59	0.0203	0.6872	0.7075	481.90	720.8	1202.7	0.6827	0.7550	1.4377	495
500	680.80	0.0204	0.6544	0.6748	487.80	714.2	1202.0	0.6888	0.7442	1.4330	500
505	712.19	0.0206	0.6230	0.6436	493.8	707.5	1201.3	0.6949	0.7334	1.4283	505
510	744.55	0.0207	0.5932	0.6139	499.8	700.6	1200.4	0.7009	0.7225	1.4234	510
515	777.96	0.0208	0.5651	0.5859	505.8	693.6	1199.4	0.7070	0.7116	1.4186	515
520	812.68	0.0209	0.5382	0.5591	511.9	686.5	1198.4	0.7132	0.7007	1.4139	520
525	848.37	0.0210	0.5128	0.5338	518.0	679.2	1197.2	0.7192	0.6898	1.4090	525
530	885.20	0.0212	0.4885	0.5097	524.2	671.9	1196.1	0.7253	0.6789	1.4042	530
535	923.45	0.0213	0.4654	0.4867	530.4	664.4	1194.8	0.7314	0.6679	1.3993	535
540	962.80	0.0214	0.4433	0.4647	536.6	656.7	1193.3	0.7375	0.6569	1.3944	540
545	1003.6	0.0216	0.4222	0.4438	542.9	648.9	1191.8	0.7436	0.6459	1.3895	545
550	1045.6	0.0218	0.4021	0.4239	549.3	640.9	1190.2	0.7498	0.6347	1.3845	550
555	1088.8	0.0219	0.3830	0.4049	555.7	632.6	1188.3	0.7559	0.6234	1.3793	555
560	1133.4	0.0221	0.3648	0.3869	562.2	624.1	1186.3	0.7622	0.6120	1.3742	560
565	1179.3	0.0222	0.3472	0.3694	568.8	615.4	1184.2	0.7684	0.6006	1.3690	565
570	1226.7	0.0224	0.3304	0.3528	575.4	606.5	1181.9	0.7737	0.5890	1.3627	570

Temp									Temp
575	0.0226	0.3143	0.3369	582.1	597.4	1179.5	0.7810	0.5774	1.3584	575
580	0.0228	0.2989	0.3217	588.9	588.1	1177.0	0.7872	0.5656	1.3528	580
585	0.0230	0.2840	0.3070	595.7	578.6	1174.3	0.7936	0.5538	1.3474	585
590	0.0232	0.2699	0.2931	602.6	568.8	1171.4	0.8000	0.5419	1.3419	590
595	0.0234	0.2563	0.2797	609.7	558.7	1168.4	0.8065	0.5297	1.3362	595
600	0.0236	0.2432	0.2668	616.8	548.4	1165.2	0.8130	0.5175	1.3305	600
605	0.0239	0.2306	0.2545	624.1	537.7	1161.8	0.8196	0.5050	1.3246	605
610	0.0241	0.2185	0.2426	631.5	526.6	1158.1	0.8263	0.4923	1.3186	610
615	0.0244	0.2068	0.2312	638.9	515.3	1154.2	0.8330	0.4795	1.3125	615
620	0.0247	0.1955	0.2202	646.5	503.7	1150.2	0.8398	0.4665	1.3063	620
625	0.0250	0.1845	0.2095	654.3	491.5	1145.8	0.8467	0.4531	1.2998	625
630	0.0253	0.1740	0.1993	662.2	478.8	1141.0	0.8537	0.4394	1.2931	630
635	0.0256	0.1638	0.1894	670.4	465.5	1135.9	0.8609	0.4252	1.2861	635
640	0.0260	0.1539	0.1799	678.7	452.0	1130.7	0.8681	0.4110	1.2791	640
645	0.0264	0.1441	0.1705	687.3	437.6	1124.9	0.8756	0.3961	1.2717	645
650	0.0268	0.1348	0.1616	696.0	422.7	1118.7	0.8832	0.3809	1.2641	650
655	0.0273	0.1256	0.1529	705.2	407.0	1112.2	0.8910	0.3651	1.2561	655
660	0.0278	0.1167	0.1445	714.4	390.5	1104.9	0.8991	0.3488	1.2479	660
665	0.0283	0.1079	0.1362	724.5	372.1	1096.6	0.9074	0.3308	1.2382	665
670	0.0290	0.0991	0.1281	734.6	353.3	1087.9	0.9161	0.3127	1.2288	670
675	0.0297	0.0904	0.1201	745.5	332.8	1078.3	0.9253	0.2933	1.2186	675
680	0.0305	0.0810	0.1115	757.2	310.0	1067.2	0.9352	0.2720	1.2072	680
685	0.0316	0.0716	0.1032	770.1	284.5	1054.6	0.9459	0.2485	1.1944	685
690	0.0328	0.0617	0.0945	784.2	254.9	1039.1	0.9579	0.2217	1.1796	690
695	0.0345	0.0511	0.0856	801.3	219.1	1020.4	0.9720	0.1897	1.1617	695
700	0.0369	0.0389	0.0758	823.9	171.7	995.6	0.9904	0.1481	1.1385	700
705	0.0440	0.0157	0.0597	870.2	77.6	947.8	1.0305	0.0661	1.0966	705
705.34*	0.0541	0	0.0541	910.3	0	910.3	1.0645	0	1.0645	705.34*

Temp		Temp
575	1275.7	575
580	1326.1	580
585	1378.1	585
590	1431.5	590
595	1486.5	595
600	1543.2	600
605	1601.5	605
610	1661.6	610
615	1723.4	615
620	1787.0	620
625	1852.4	625
630	1919.8	630
635	1989.0	635
640	2060.3	640
645	2133.5	645
650	2208.8	650
655	2286.4	655
660	2366.2	660
665	2448.0	665
670	2532.4	670
675	2619.2	675
680	2708.4	680
685	2800.4	685
690	2895.0	690
695	2992.7	695
700	3094.1	700
705	3199.1	705
705.34*	3206.2	705.34*

* Critical temperature

Table 2. Superheated Steam

Abs. Press. Lb./Sq. In. (Sat. Temp.)		Sat. Water	Sat. Steam	200°	250°	300°	350°	400°	450°	500°	600°	700°	800°	900°	1000°	1100°	1200°
1 (101.76)	Sh			98.24	148.24	198.24	248.24	298.24	348.24	398.24	498.24	598.24	698.24	798.24	898.24	998.24	1098.24
	v	0.0161	333.79	392.5	422.5	452.1	482.1	511.7	541.8	571.3	630.9	690.6	750.2	809.8	869.4	929.1	988.7
	h	69.72	1105.2	1149.2	1171.9	1194.4	1217.3	1240.2	1263.5	1286.7	1333.3	1382.1	1431.0	1480.8	1531.4	1583.0	1635.4
	s	0.1326	1.9769	2.0491	2.0822	2.1128	2.1420	2.1694	2.1957	2.2206	2.2673	2.3107	2.3512	2.3892	2.4251	2.4592	2.4918
5 (162.25)	Sh			37.75	87.75	137.75	187.75	237.75	287.75	337.75	437.75	537.75	637.75	737.75	837.75	937.75	1037.75
	v	0.0164	73.600	78.17	84.24	90.21	96.26	102.19	108.23	114.16	126.11	138.05	149.99	161.91	173.83	185.80	197.72
	h	130.13	1130.8	1148.3	1171.1	1193.6	1216.6	1239.8	1263.0	1286.1	1333.5	1381.8	1430.8	1480.6	1531.3	1582.9	1635.3
	s	0.2347	1.8437	1.8710	1.9043	1.9349	1.9642	1.9920	2.0182	2.0429	2.0898	2.1333	2.1738	2.2118	2.2478	2.2820	2.3146
10 (193.21)	Sh			6.79	56.79	106.79	156.79	206.79	256.79	306.79	406.79	506.79	606.79	706.79	806.79	906.79	1006.79
	v	0.0166	38.462	38.88	41.96	44.98	48.02	51.01	54.04	57.00	63.01	68.99	74.96	80.92	86.89	92.88	98.85
	h	161.17	1143.3	1146.7	1170.2	1192.8	1216.0	1239.3	1262.5	1285.8	1333.3	1381.6	1430.6	1480.5	1531.2	1582.8	1635.2
	s	0.2834	1.7876	1.7928	1.8271	1.8579	1.8875	1.9154	1.9416	1.9665	2.0135	2.0570	2.0975	2.1356	2.1716	2.2058	2.2384
14.696 (212.00)	Sh				38.00	88.00	138.00	188.00	238.00	288.00	388.00	488.00	588.00	688.00	788.00	888.00	988.00
	v	0.0167	26.828		28.44	30.52	32.61	34.65	36.73	38.75	42.83	46.91	50.97	55.03	59.09	63.19	67.25
	h	180.07	1150.4		1169.2	1192.0	1215.4	1238.9	1262.1	1285.4	1333.0	1381.4	1430.5	1480.4	1531.1	1582.7	1635.1
	s	0.3120	1.7566		1.7838	1.8148	1.8446	1.8727	1.8989	1.9238	1.9709	2.0145	2.0551	2.0932	2.1292	2.1634	2.1960
15 (213.03)	Sh				36.97	86.97	136.97	186.97	236.97	286.97	386.97	486.97	586.97	686.97	786.97	886.97	986.97
	v	0.0167	26.320		27.86	29.90	31.94	33.95	35.98	37.97	41.98	45.97	49.95	53.93	57.91	61.91	65.89
	h	181.11	1150.7		1169.2	1192.0	1215.4	1238.9	1262.1	1285.4	1333.0	1381.4	1430.5	1480.4	1531.1	1582.7	1635.1
	s	0.3135	1.7548		1.7816	1.8126	1.8424	1.8705	1.8967	1.9216	1.9687	2.0123	2.0529	2.0910	2.1270	2.1612	2.1938
20 (227.96)	Sh				22.04	72.04	122.04	172.04	222.04	272.04	372.04	472.04	572.04	672.04	772.04	872.04	972.04
	v	0.0168	20.110		20.81	22.36	23.91	25.43	26.95	28.45	31.46	34.46	37.44	40.43	43.42	46.43	49.41
	h	196.16	1156.1		1168.0	1191.1	1214.8	1238.4	1261.6	1285.0	1332.7	1381.2	1430.3	1480.2	1531.0	1582.6	1635.1
	s	0.3356	1.7315		1.7485	1.7799	1.8101	1.8384	1.8646	1.8896	1.9368	1.9805	2.0211	2.0592	2.0952	2.1294	2.1620
25 (240.07)	Sh				9.93	59.93	109.93	159.93	209.93	259.93	359.93	459.93	559.93	659.93	759.93	859.93	959.93
	v	0.0169	16.321		16.58	17.84	19.08	20.30	21.53	22.73	25.15	27.55	29.94	32.33	34.73	37.14	39.52
	h	208.41	1160.4		1166.3	1190.2	1214.1	1237.9	1261.1	1284.6	1332.4	1381.0	1430.1	1480.0	1530.9	1582.5	1635.0
	s	0.3532	1.7137		1.7221	1.7570	1.7875	1.8160	1.8422	1.8673	1.9146	1.9584	1.9990	2.0371	2.0732	2.1074	2.1400
30 (250.34)	Sh					49.66	99.66	149.66	199.66	249.66	349.66	449.66	549.66	649.66	749.66	849.66	949.66
	v	0.0170	13.763			14.82	15.87	16.89	17.91	18.92	20.94	22.94	24.94	26.93	28.93	30.94	32.93
	h	218.83	1164.0			1189.2	1213.4	1237.4	1260.6	1284.2	1332.1	1380.8	1429.9	1479.9	1530.8	1582.4	1634.9
	s	0.3680	1.6992			1.7335	1.7643	1.7930	1.8192	1.8444	1.8918	1.9357	1.9763	2.0145	2.0506	2.0848	2.1174

Superheated Steam Table

Sh = superheat, deg. F.
v = specific volume, cu. ft. per lb.
h = enthalpy, B.t.u. per lb.
s = entropy, B.t.u. per deg. F. per lb.

35 (259.28) — Sat.: v 0.0171 / 11.907, h 227.92 / 1167.0, s 0.3807 / 1.6869

Sh	40.72	90.72	140.72	190.72	240.72	340.72	440.72	540.72	640.72	740.72	840.72	940.72
v	12.66	13.57	14.45	15.33	16.20	17.94	19.66	21.36	23.08	24.79	26.52	28.22
h	1188.2	1212.7	1236.9	1260.1	1283.8	1331.9	1380.6	1429.8	1479.8	1530.7	1582.3	1634.8
s	1.7156	1.7468	1.7758	1.8020	1.8274	1.8750	1.9189	1.9596	1.9978	2.0339	2.0681	2.1007

40 (267.24) — Sat.: v 0.0172 / 10.506, h 236.02 / 1169.7, s 0.3919 / 1.6763

Sh	32.76	82.76	132.76	182.76	232.76	332.76	432.76	532.76	632.76	732.76	832.76	932.76
v	11.04	11.84	12.62	13.40	14.16	15.68	17.19	18.69	20.18	21.68	23.20	24.69
h	1187.1	1211.9	1236.4	1259.6	1283.4	1331.6	1380.4	1429.6	1479.6	1530.6	1582.2	1634.8
s	1.6997	1.7313	1.7606	1.7868	1.8123	1.8600	1.9040	1.9447	1.9829	2.0191	2.0533	2.0860

45 (274.45) — Sat.: v 0.0172 / 9.408, h 243.38 / 1172.0, s 0.4019 / 1.6668

Sh	25.55	75.55	125.55	175.55	225.55	325.55	425.55	525.55	625.55	725.55	825.55	925.55
v	9.785	10.50	11.20	11.89	12.57	13.93	15.27	16.60	17.94	19.27	20.62	21.95
h	1185.9	1211.1	1235.8	1259.1	1283.0	1331.3	1380.1	1429.4	1479.4	1530.5	1582.1	1634.7
s	1.6854	1.7175	1.7471	1.7734	1.7990	1.8468	1.8908	1.9315	1.9697	2.0059	2.0401	2.0728

50 (281.01) — Sat.: v 0.0173 / 8.522, h 250.09 / 1174.0, s 0.4110 / 1.6583

Sh	18.99	68.99	118.99	168.99	218.99	318.99	418.99	518.99	618.99	718.99	818.99	918.99
v	8.777	9.430	10.06	10.69	11.30	12.53	13.74	14.93	16.14	17.34	18.55	19.75
h	1184.6	1210.3	1235.2	1258.6	1282.6	1331.0	1379.9	1429.3	1479.3	1530.4	1582.0	1634.6
s	1.6724	1.7051	1.7349	1.7613	1.7870	1.8349	1.8790	1.9198	1.9580	1.9942	2.0284	2.0611

55 (287.07) — Sat.: v 0.0173 / 7.792, h 256.30 / 1175.8, s 0.4193 / 1.6506

Sh	12.93	62.93	112.93	162.93	212.93	312.93	412.93	512.93	612.93	712.93	812.93	912.93
v	7.950	8.553	9.130	9.703	10.26	11.38	12.48	13.57	14.67	15.76	16.86	17.95
h	1183.2	1209.4	1234.6	1258.2	1282.2	1330.7	1379.7	1429.1	1479.2	1530.3	1581.9	1634.5
s	1.6604	1.6938	1.7240	1.7507	1.7764	1.8244	1.8685	1.9093	1.9475	1.9837	2.0179	2.0512

60 (292.71) — Sat.: v 0.0174 / 7.179, h 262.10 / 1177.5, s 0.4271 / 1.6437

Sh	7.29	57.29	107.29	157.29	207.29	307.29	407.29	507.29	607.29	707.29	807.29	907.29
v	7.260	7.821	8.353	8.882	9.398	10.42	11.44	12.44	13.44	14.44	15.45	16.45
h	1181.8	1208.5	1234.0	1257.7	1281.8	1330.4	1379.5	1428.9	1479.0	1530.2	1581.8	1634.4
s	1.6494	1.6834	1.7139	1.7407	1.7665	1.8146	1.8588	1.8996	1.9378	1.9741	2.0083	2.0410

65 (297.97) — Sat.: v 0.0174 / 6.654, h 267.51 / 1179.1, s 0.4342 / 1.6374

Sh	2.03	52.03	102.03	152.03	202.03	302.03	402.03	502.03	602.03	702.03	802.03	902.03
v	6.674	7.202	7.696	8.187	8.665	9.614	10.55	11.48	12.40	13.33	14.26	15.19
h	1180.4	1207.6	1233.4	1257.2	1281.4	1330.1	1379.3	1428.8	1478.9	1530.1	1581.7	1634.4
s	1.6391	1.6738	1.7047	1.7316	1.7575	1.8057	1.8500	1.8909	1.9291	1.9654	1.9996	2.0323

70 (302.92) — Sat.: v 0.0175 / 6.210, h 272.61 / 1180.5, s 0.4409 / 1.6314

Sh	47.08	97.08	147.08	197.08	297.08	397.08	497.08	597.08	697.08	797.08	897.08
v	6.671	7.132	7.592	8.036	8.920	9.791	10.65	11.51	12.37	13.24	14.10
h	1206.7	1232.8	1256.7	1281.0	1329.9	1379.0	1428.6	1478.7	1530.0	1581.6	1634.3
s	1.6647	1.6960	1.7230	1.7490	1.7974	1.8416	1.8826	1.9208	1.9572	1.9914	2.0241

75 (307.60) — Sat.: v 0.0175 / 5.820, h 277.44 / 1181.9, s 0.4472 / 1.6260

Sh	42.40	92.40	142.40	192.40	292.40	392.40	492.40	592.40	692.40	792.40	892.40
v	6.210	6.644	7.076	7.492	8.319	9.133	9.938	10.74	11.54	12.36	13.16
h	1205.8	1232.2	1256.2	1280.6	1329.6	1378.8	1428.4	1478.6	1529.8	1581.5	1634.2
s	1.6563	1.6879	1.7150	1.7411	1.7896	1.8339	1.8749	1.9132	1.9495	1.9837	2.0164

TABLE 2. SUPERHEATED STEAM—Continued

Abs. Press Lb./Sq. In. (Sat. Temp.)		Sat. Water	Sat. Steam	Temperature—Degrees Fahrenheit													
				340°	360°	380°	400°	420°	450°	500°	600°	700°	800°	900°	1000°	1100°	1200°
80 (312.03)	Sh			27.97	47.97	67.97	87.97	107.97	137.97	187.97	287.97	387.97	487.97	587.97	687.97	787.97	887.97
	v	0.0176	5.476	5.720	5.889	6.055	6.217	6.384	6.623	7.015	7.793	8.558	9.313	10.07	10.82	11.58	12.33
	h	282.02	1183.1	1200.0	1211.0	1221.2	1231.5	1240.3	1255.7	1280.2	1329.3	1378.5	1428.2	1478.4	1529.7	1581-4	1634.1
	s	0.4532	1.6209	1.6424	1.6560	1.6683	1.6804	1.6905	1.7077	1.7339	1.7825	1.8268	1.8679	1.9062	1.9426	1.9768	2.0095
85 (316.25)	Sh			23.75	43.75	63.75	83.75	103.75	133.75	183.75	283.75	383.75	483.75	583.75	683.75	783.75	883.75
	v	0.0176	5.169	5.368	5.528	5.685	5.839	5.995	6.226	6.594	7.329	8.050	8.762	9.472	10.18	10.90	11.61
	h	286.40	1184.3	1198.5	1210.0	1220.5	1230.7	1239.7	1255.1	1279.7	1329.0	1378.3	1428.0	1478.2	1529.6	1581.3	1634.0
	s	0.4587	1.6159	1.6339	1.6481	1.6608	1.6728	1.6831	1.7003	1.7266	1.7754	1.8198	1.8609	1.8992	1.9357	1.9699	2.0026
90 (320.27)	Sh			19.73	39.73	59.73	79.73	99.73	129.73	179.73	279.73	379.73	479.73	579.73	679.73	779.73	879.73
	v	0.0177	4.898	5.055	5.208	5.357	5.504	5.653	5.869	6.220	6.916	7.599	8.272	8.943	9.626	10.29	10.96
	h	290.57	1185.4	1197.3	1209.0	1219.8	1230.0	1239.1	1254.5	1279.3	1328.7	1378.1	1427.9	1478.1	1529.5	1581.2	1634.0
	s	0.4641	1.6113	1.6264	1.6408	1.6538	1.6658	1.6763	1.6935	1.7200	1.7689	1.8134	1.8546	1.8929	1.9294	1.9636	1.9964
95 (324.13)	Sh			15.87	35.87	55.87	75.87	95.87	125.87	175.87	275.87	375.87	475.87	575.87	675.87	775.87	875.87
	v	0.0177	4.653	4.773	4.921	5.063	5.205	5.346	5.552	5.886	6.547	7.195	7.834	8.481	9.111	9.751	10.38
	h	294.58	1186.4	1196.0	1208.0	1219.0	1229.3	1238.6	1254.0	1278.9	1328.4	1377.8	1427.7	1478.0	1529.4	1581.1	1633.9
	s	0.4692	1.6070	1.6191	1.6339	1.6472	1.6593	1.6700	1.6872	1.7138	1.7628	1.8073	1.8485	1.8869	1.9234	1.9576	1.9904
100 (327.83)	Sh			12.17	32.17	52.17	72.17	92.17	122.17	172.17	272.17	372.17	472.17	572.17	672.17	772.17	872.17
	v	0.0177	4.433	4.520	4.663	4.801	4.936	5.070	5.266	5.589	6.217	6.836	7.448	8.055	8.659	9.262	9.862
	h	298.43	1187.3	1194.9	1207.0	1218.3	1228.4	1238.6	1253.7	1278.6	1327.9	1377.5	1427.5	1478.0	1529.2	1581.0	1633.7
	s	0.4741	1.6028	1.6124	1.6273	1.6409	1.6528	1.6645	1.6814	1.7080	1.7568	1.8015	1.8428	1.8814	1.9177	1.9520	1.9847
105 (331.38)	Sh			8.62	28.62	48.62	68.62	88.62	118.62	168.62	268.62	368.62	468.62	568.62	668.62	768.62	868.62
	v	0.0177	4.232	4.292	4.429	4.562	4.691	4.820	5.007	5.316	5.916	6.507	7.090	7.670	8.245	8.819	9.391
	h	302.13	1188.2	1193.5	1205.9	1217.2	1227.6	1237.5	1252.9	1278.0	1327.6	1377.4	1427.3	1477.7	1529.2	1580.9	1633.7
	s	0.4787	1.5988	1.6055	1.6208	1.6344	1.6466	1.6580	1.6752	1.7020	1.7511	1.7960	1.8372	1.8757	1.9122	1.9464	1.9791
110 (334.79)	Sh			5.21	25.21	45.21	65.21	85.21	115.21	165.21	265.21	365.21	465.21	565.21	665.21	765.21	865.21
	v	0.0178	4.050	4.084	4.217	4.345	4.469	4.592	4.773	5.069	5.643	6.208	6.765	7.319	7.869	8.417	8.963
	h	305.69	1189.0	1192.2	1204.9	1216.4	1226.9	1236.9	1252.4	1277.5	1327.4	1377.1	1427.1	1477.5	1529.1	1580.8	1633.6
	s	0.4832	1.5950	1.5990	1.6147	1.6286	1.6410	1.6525	1.6698	1.6966	1.7460	1.7908	1.8321	1.8706	1.9072	1.9414	1.9742
115 (338.08)	Sh				21.92	41.92	61.92	81.92	111.92	161.92	261.92	361.92	461.92	561.92	661.92	761.92	861.92
	v	0.0179	3.882		4.022	4.146	4.266	4.384	4.558	4.843	5.393	5.935	6.469	6.999	7.525	8.049	8.572
	h	309.13	1189.8		1203.8	1215.6	1226.3	1236.3	1251.9	1277.1	1327.1	1376.9	1427.0	1477.4	1528.9	1580.7	1633.6
	s	0.4875	1.5915		1.6088	1.6230	1.6355	1.6471	1.6645	1.6915	1.7410	1.7859	1.8273	1.8658	1.9023	1.9366	1.9695

120 (341.26) — Sat.: v = 0.0179 / 3.728, h = 312.46 / 1190.6, s = 0.4916 / 1.5879

Sh	18.74	38.74	58.74	78.74	108.74	158.74	258.74	358.74	458.74	558.74	658.74	758.74	858.74
v	3.845	3.963	4.079	4.194	4.361	4.635	5.165	5.685	6.197	6.705	7.210	7.713	8.215
h	1202.7	1214.7	1225.4	1235.7	1251.4	1276.7	1326.8	1376.7	1426.8	1477.2	1528.8	1580.6	1633.5
s	1.6028	1.6173	1.6299	1.6417	1.6592	1.6863	1.7359	1.7809	1.8223	1.8608	1.8974	1.9317	1.9646

125 (344.34) — Sat.: v = 0.0179 / 3.586, h = 315.69 / 1191.3, s = 0.4956 / 1.5846

Sh	15.66	35.66	55.66	75.66	105.66	155.66	255.66	355.66	455.66	555.66	655.66	755.66	855.66
v	3.680	3.796	3.908	4.019	4.181	4.445	4.954	5.454	5.947	6.435	6.920	7.403	7.885
h	1201.6	1213.7	1224.5	1235.0	1250.8	1276.3	1326.5	1376.4	1426.6	1477.1	1528.7	1580.5	1633.4
s	1.5973	1.6119	1.6246	1.6367	1.6544	1.6817	1.7314	1.7764	1.8179	1.8565	1.8931	1.9274	1.9603

130 (347.31) — Sat.: v = 0.0180 / 3.455, h = 318.81 / 1192.0, s = 0.4995 / 1.5815

Sh	12.69	32.69	52.69	72.69	102.69	152.69	252.69	352.69	452.69	552.69	652.69	752.69	852.69
v	3.528	3.641	3.750	3.857	4.013	4.268	4.760	5.242	5.716	6.186	6.653	7.117	7.581
h	1200.4	1212.7	1223.6	1234.3	1250.3	1275.8	1326.1	1376.1	1426.4	1476.9	1528.6	1580.4	1633.3
s	1.5918	1.6066	1.6194	1.6317	1.6496	1.6769	1.7267	1.7718	1.8134	1.8520	1.8887	1.9230	1.9559

135 (350.21) — Sat.: v = 0.0180 / 3.333, h = 321.86 / 1192.7, s = 0.5032 / 1.5784

Sh	9.79	29.79	49.79	69.79	99.79	149.79	249.79	349.79	449.79	549.79	649.79	749.79	849.79
v	3.388	3.497	3.603	3.707	3.859	4.105	4.580	5.045	5.502	5.955	6.405	6.853	7.303
h	1199.2	1211.7	1222.7	1233.6	1249.7	1275.4	1325.8	1375.9	1426.2	1476.8	1528.5	1580.3	1633.2
s	1.5864	1.6015	1.6144	1.6269	1.6449	1.6724	1.7223	1.7674	1.8090	1.8476	1.8843	1.9186	1.9515

140 (353.03) — Sat.: v = 0.0180 / 3.220, h = 324.83 / 1193.3, s = 0.5069 / 1.5755

Sh	6.97	26.97	46.97	66.97	96.97	146.97	246.97	346.97	446.97	546.97	646.97	746.97	846.97
v	3.258	3.364	3.467	3.567	3.715	3.954	4.413	4.862	5.303	5.741	6.175	6.607	7.037
h	1198.0	1210.6	1221.8	1232.9	1249.1	1275.0	1325.5	1375.7	1426.0	1476.6	1528.4	1580.2	1633.2
s	1.5813	1.5965	1.6097	1.6225	1.6406	1.6683	1.7183	1.7635	1.8051	1.8437	1.8804	1.9147	1.9476

145 (355.76) — Sat.: v = 0.0181 / 3.114, h = 327.71 / 1193.9, s = 0.5104 / 1.5726

Sh	4.24	24.24	44.24	64.24	94.24	144.24	244.24	344.24	444.24	544.24	644.24	744.24	844.24
v	3.136	3.240	3.340	3.438	3.581	3.812	4.257	4.692	5.119	5.541	5.961	6.378	6.794
h	1196.7	1209.5	1220.8	1232.2	1248.5	1274.5	1325.1	1375.4	1425.8	1476.5	1528.3	1580.1	1633.1
s	1.5760	1.5914	1.6048	1.6178	1.6360	1.6638	1.7139	1.7592	1.8009	1.8396	1.8763	1.9106	1.9435

150 (358.43) — Sat.: v = 0.0181 / 3.016, h = 330.53 / 1194.4, s = 0.5138 / 1.5698

Sh	21.57	41.57	61.57	91.57	141.57	241.57	341.57	441.57	541.57	641.57	741.57	841.57
v	3.124	3.221	3.317	3.456	3.681	4.112	4.533	4.946	5.355	5.761	6.164	6.567
h	1208.4	1220.0	1231.4	1248.0	1274.1	1324.9	1375.1	1425.6	1476.3	1528.1	1580.0	1633.0
s	1.5865	1.6002	1.6133	1.6319	1.6598	1.7101	1.7553	1.7970	1.8357	1.8724	1.9068	1.9397

155 (361.02) — Sat.: v = 0.0181 / 2.921, h = 333.27 / 1195.0, s = 0.5172 / 1.5671

Sh	18.98	38.98	58.98	88.98	138.98	238.98	338.98	438.98	538.98	638.98	738.98	838.98
v	3.015	3.110	3.203	3.340	3.558	3.976	4.384	4.785	5.181	5.574	5.964	6.354
h	1207.2	1219.1	1230.7	1247.5	1273.6	1324.5	1374.9	1425.4	1476.2	1528.0	1579.9	1632.9
s	1.5818	1.5958	1.6091	1.6279	1.6558	1.7062	1.7516	1.7933	1.8321	1.8688	1.9032	1.9361

160 (363.55) — Sat.: v = 0.0182 / 2.834, h = 335.95 / 1195.5, s = 0.5204 / 1.5646

Sh	16.45	36.45	56.45	86.45	136.45	236.45	336.45	436.45	536.45	636.45	736.45	836.45
v	2.913	3.006	3.097	3.230	3.443	3.849	4.245	4.633	5.018	5.398	5.777	6.155
h	1206.0	1218.3	1230.0	1246.9	1273.2	1324.1	1374.7	1425.2	1476.0	1527.9	1579.8	1632.8
s	1.5772	1.5917	1.6052	1.6241	1.6522	1.7026	1.7482	1.7899	1.8287	1.8655	1.8999	1.9328

Sh = superheat, deg. F.   h = enthalpy, B.t.u. per lb.

v = specific volume, cu. ft. per lb.   s = entropy, B.t.u. per deg. F. per lb.

TABLE 2, SUPERHEATED STEAM—*Continued*

Abs. Press. Lb./Sq. In. (Sat. Temp.)		Sat. Water	Sat. Steam	Temperature—Degrees Fahrenheit													
				400°	420°	440°	460°	480°	500°	550°	600°	700°	800°	900°	1000°	1100°	1200°
165 (366.01)	Sh			33.99	53.99	73.99	93.99	113.99	133.99	183.99	233.99	333.99	433.99	533.99	633.99	733.99	833.99
	v	0.0182	2.752	2.909	2.997	3.084	3.170	3.251	3.334	3.533	3.729	4.114	4.491	4.864	5.234	5.601	5.967
	h	338.55	1195.9	1217.4	1229.3	1241.1	1251.8	1262.4	1272.8	1298.5	1323.8	1374.5	1425.0	1475.9	1527.8	1579.7	1632.7
	s	0.5236	1.5619	1.5874	1.6011	1.6144	1.6262	1.6376	1.6486	1.6747	1.6991	1.7448	1.7865	1.8254	1.8622	1.8966	1.9295
170 (368.42)	Sh			31.58	51.58	71.58	91.58	111.58	131.58	181.58	231.58	331.58	431.58	531.58	631.58	731.58	831.58
	v	0.0182	2.674	2.816	2.903	2.988	3.071	3.151	3.232	3.426	3.617	3.991	4.357	4.720	5.079	5.436	5.791
	h	341.11	1196.3	1216.5	1228.4	1240.5	1251.3	1261.8	1272.3	1298.2	1323.5	1374.2	1424.9	1475.7	1527.6	1579.6	1632.7
	s	0.5266	1.5593	1.5832	1.5969	1.6105	1.6224	1.6337	1.6448	1.6711	1.6955	1.7412	1.7831	1.8219	1.8587	1.8931	1.9261
175 (370.77)	Sh			29.23	49.23	69.23	89.23	109.23	129.23	179.23	229.23	329.23	429.23	529.23	629.23	729.23	829.23
	v	0.0182	2.601	2.730	2.814	2.897	2.979	3.057	3.136	3.325	3.510	3.875	4.231	4.584	4.932	5.279	5.625
	h	343.61	1196.7	1215.6	1227.6	1239.9	1250.8	1261.3	1271.9	1297.8	1323.2	1374.0	1424.7	1475.6	1527.5	1579.5	1632.6
	s	0.5296	1.5569	1.5793	1.5931	1.6069	1.6189	1.6302	1.6414	1.6677	1.6922	1.7380	1.7799	1.8185	1.8553	1.8897	1.9227
180 (373.08)	Sh			26.92	46.92	66.92	86.92	106.92	126.92	176.92	226.92	326.92	426.92	526.92	626.92	726.92	826.92
	v	0.0183	2.532	2.648	2.731	2.812	2.892	2.968	3.045	3.229	3.410	3.765	4.112	4.455	4.794	5.132	5.468
	h	346.07	1197.2	1214.6	1226.8	1239.2	1250.2	1260.8	1271.5	1297.4	1322.8	1373.7	1424.5	1475.5	1527.4	1579.4	1632.5
	s	0.5325	1.5545	1.5751	1.5891	1.6030	1.6151	1.6265	1.6378	1.6641	1.6886	1.7345	1.7765	1.8154	1.8522	1.8866	1.9196
185 (375.34)	Sh			24.66	44.66	64.66	84.66	104.66	124.66	174.66	224.66	324.66	424.66	524.66	624.66	724.66	824.66
	v	0.0183	2.466	2.570	2.651	2.731	2.809	2.884	2.958	3.139	3.315	3.661	3.999	4.333	4.664	4.992	5.319
	h	348.47	1197.6	1213.7	1226.0	1238.4	1249.6	1260.3	1271.0	1297.0	1322.4	1373.4	1424.3	1475.3	1527.3	1579.3	1632.4
	s	0.5354	1.5522	1.5712	1.5853	1.5992	1.6115	1.6230	1.6343	1.6611	1.6853	1.7312	1.7733	1.8122	1.8491	1.8835	1.9165
190 (377.55)	Sh			22.45	42.45	62.45	82.45	102.45	122.45	172.45	222.45	322.45	422.45	522.45	622.45	722.45	822.45
	v	0.0183	2.404	2.496	2.576	2.654	2.731	2.804	2.877	3.053	3.225	3.563	3.893	4.218	4.540	4.860	5.179
	h	350.83	1198.0	1212.7	1225.1	1237.7	1249.0	1259.8	1270.5	1296.6	1322.1	1373.1	1424.1	1475.2	1527.1	1579.2	1632.3
	s	0.5382	1.5501	1.5674	1.5817	1.5959	1.6083	1.6199	1.6312	1.6577	1.6823	1.7282	1.7703	1.8093	1.8461	1.8806	1.9136
195 (379.70)	Sh			20.30	40.30	60.30	80.30	100.30	120.30	170.30	220.30	320.30	420.30	520.30	620.30	720.30	820.30
	v	0.0184	2.344	2.426	2.505	2.581	2.656	2.728	2.799	2.972	3.140	3.470	3.791	4.109	4.423	4.735	5.046
	h	353.13	1198.4	1211.7	1224.2	1237.0	1248.3	1259.3	1270.0	1296.2	1321.8	1372.9	1423.9	1475.0	1527.0	1579.1	1632.2
	s	0.5409	1.5479	1.5636	1.5780	1.5924	1.6048	1.6166	1.6279	1.6545	1.6792	1.7252	1.7673	1.8063	1.8432	1.8777	1.9107
200 (381.82)	Sh			18.18	38.18	58.18	78.18	98.18	118.18	168.18	218.18	318.18	418.18	518.18	618.18	718.18	818.18
	v	0.0184	2.288	2.360	2.437	2.512	2.585	2.656	2.726	2.895	3.059	3.381	3.697	4.005	4.311	4.616	4.919
	h	355.40	1198.7	1210.8	1223.7	1236.3	1247.9	1258.7	1269.4	1295.6	1321.4	1372.5	1423.9	1474.9	1526.6	1579.0	1632.1
	s	0.5436	1.5457	1.5599	1.5748	1.5889	1.6017	1.6133	1.6245	1.6511	1.6761	1.7221	1.7646	1.8035	1.8402	1.8749	1.9079

Superheated steam properties. Each pressure block lists four rows — Sh (superheat), v, h, s. Sat. liq. columns give vf, hf, sf; Sat. vap. columns give vg, hg, sg.

205 (383.89)

	Sat. liq.	Sat. vap.														
Sh	—	—	16.11	36.11	56.11	76.11	96.11	116.11	166.11	216.11	316.11	416.11	516.11	616.11	716.11	816.11
v	0.0184	2.235	2.297	2.372	2.446	2.518	2.587	2.656	2.821	2.982	3.297	3.604	3.906	4.205	4.502	4.798
h	357.61	1199.0	1209.7	1222.5	1235.4	1247.1	1258.2	1269.0	1295.4	1321.0	1372.4	1423.5	1474.7	1526.8	1578.9	1632.1
s	0.5462	1.5436	1.5562	1.5709	1.5854	1.5983	1.6102	1.6216	1.6484	1.6731	1.7194	1.7616	1.8007	1.8377	1.8722	1.9052

210 (385.93)

	Sat. liq.	Sat. vap.														
Sh	—	—	14.07	34.07	54.07	74.07	94.07	114.07	164.07	214.07	314.07	414.07	514.07	614.07	714.07	814.07
v	0.0184	2.183	2.237	2.311	2.384	2.454	2.522	2.589	2.751	2.909	3.216	3.516	3.812	4.104	4.395	4.683
h	359.80	1199.6	1208.8	1221.8	1234.7	1246.5	1257.7	1268.5	1295.0	1320.7	1372.1	1423.3	1474.6	1526.6	1578.8	1632.0
s	0.5488	1.5417	1.5527	1.5676	1.5821	1.5951	1.6071	1.6185	1.6454	1.6702	1.7165	1.7588	1.7980	1.8349	1.8695	1.9025

215 (387.93)

	Sat. liq.	Sat. vap.														
Sh	—	—	12.07	32.07	52.07	72.07	92.07	112.07	162.07	212.07	312.07	412.07	512.07	612.07	712.07	812.07
v	0.0185	2.134	2.179	2.252	2.324	2.393	2.460	2.526	2.685	2.839	3.140	3.433	3.722	4.008	4.292	4.574
h	361.95	1199.6	1207.8	1221.0	1234.0	1245.9	1257.2	1268.0	1294.6	1320.4	1371.9	1423.1	1474.4	1526.5	1578.7	1631.9
s	0.5513	1.5395	1.5491	1.5643	1.5789	1.5920	1.6042	1.6156	1.6426	1.6675	1.7139	1.7562	1.7954	1.8324	1.8670	1.9000

220 (389.89)

	Sat. liq.	Sat. vap.														
Sh	—	—	10.11	30.11	50.11	70.11	90.11	110.11	160.11	210.11	310.11	410.11	510.11	610.11	710.11	810.11
v	0.0185	2.086	2.124	2.196	2.267	2.335	2.400	2.465	2.621	2.772	3.067	3.354	3.637	3.916	4.193	4.469
h	364.05	1199.9	1206.8	1220.1	1233.2	1245.2	1256.7	1267.5	1294.1	1320.0	1371.6	1422.9	1474.2	1526.4	1578.6	1631.8
s	0.5538	1.5376	1.5457	1.5610	1.5757	1.5889	1.6013	1.6127	1.6397	1.6647	1.7112	1.7536	1.7928	1.8298	1.8644	1.8974

225 (391.81)

	Sat. liq.	Sat. vap.														
Sh	—	—	8.19	28.19	48.19	68.19	88.19	108.19	158.19	208.19	308.19	408.19	508.19	608.19	708.19	808.19
v	0.0185	2.042	2.072	2.142	2.212	2.279	2.344	2.407	2.560	2.708	2.997	3.278	3.555	3.828	4.100	4.369
h	366.11	1200.0	1205.8	1219.2	1232.3	1244.5	1256.2	1267.1	1293.7	1319.6	1371.4	1422.7	1474.1	1526.3	1578.5	1631.7
s	0.5562	1.5358	1.5423	1.5577	1.5724	1.5858	1.5984	1.6099	1.6370	1.6619	1.7086	1.7510	1.7902	1.8272	1.8618	1.8948

230 (393.70)

	Sat. liq.	Sat. vap.														
Sh	—	—	6.30	26.30	46.30	66.30	86.30	106.30	156.30	206.30	306.30	406.30	506.30	606.30	706.30	806.30
v	0.0186	1.9989	2.021	2.091	2.160	2.226	2.289	2.352	2.502	2.647	2.930	3.205	3.477	3.744	4.010	4.274
h	368.16	1200.4	1204.9	1218.3	1231.6	1243.8	1255.6	1266.7	1293.3	1319.3	1371.1	1422.5	1474.0	1526.2	1578.4	1631.6
s	0.5585	1.5337	1.5390	1.5544	1.5693	1.5827	1.5954	1.6071	1.6341	1.6592	1.7059	1.7484	1.7877	1.8247	1.8593	1.8923

235 (395.56)

	Sat. liq.	Sat. vap.														
Sh	—	—	4.44	24.44	44.44	64.44	84.44	104.44	154.44	204.44	304.44	404.44	504.44	604.44	704.44	804.44
v	0.0186	1.9573	1.973	2.042	2.110	2.175	2.237	2.298	2.446	2.589	2.866	3.136	3.402	3.664	3.924	4.182
h	370.17	1200.7	1203.9	1217.5	1230.8	1243.2	1255.0	1266.2	1292.9	1319.0	1370.9	1422.3	1473.8	1526.0	1578.3	1631.5
s	0.5609	1.5320	1.5357	1.5513	1.5662	1.5798	1.5925	1.6043	1.6314	1.6566	1.7034	1.7459	1.7852	1.8222	1.8568	1.8899

240 (397.40)

	Sat. liq.	Sat. vap.														
Sh	—	—	2.60	22.60	42.60	62.60	82.60	102.60	152.60	202.60	302.60	402.60	502.60	602.60	702.60	802.60
v	0.0186	1.9176		1.995	2.062	2.126	2.187	2.247	2.392	2.532	2.805	3.069	3.330	3.586	3.841	4.095
h	372.16	1200.9		1216.6	1230.0	1242.5	1254.4	1265.7	1292.5	1318.6	1370.5	1422.1	1473.6	1525.9	1578.2	1631.5
s	0.5632	1.5301		1.5482	1.5633	1.5770	1.5898	1.6017	1.6289	1.6541	1.7009	1.7435	1.7828	1.8199	1.8545	1.8876

245 (399.20)

	Sat. liq.	Sat. vap.														
Sh	—	—	0.80	20.80	40.80	60.80	80.80	100.80	150.80	200.80	300.80	400.80	500.80	600.80	700.80	800.80
v	0.0186	1.8797		1.950	2.015	2.078	2.139	2.198	2.341	2.479	2.746	3.006	3.261	3.513	3.762	4.011
h	374.11	1201.1		1215.6	1229.1	1241.8	1253.8	1265.2	1292.0	1318.3	1370.3	1421.9	1473.5	1525.8	1578.1	1631.4
s	0.5654	1.5283		1.5450	1.5602	1.5742	1.5871	1.5991	1.6263	1.6517	1.6985	1.7411	1.7805	1.8176	1.8522	1.8853

Sh = superheat, deg. F.
v = specific volume, cu. ft. per lb.

h = enthalpy, B.t.u. per lb.
s = entropy, B.t.u. per deg. F. per lb.

TABLE 2. SUPERHEATED STEAM—Continued

Abs. Press. Lb./Sq.In. (Sat. Temp.)		Sat. Water	Sat. Steam	420°	440°	460°	480°	500°	520°	550°	600°	700°	800°	900°	1000°	1100°	1200°
250 (400.97)	Sh	0.0187		19.03	39.03	59.03	79.03	99.03	119.03	149.03	199.03	299.03	399.03	499.03	599.03	699.03	799.03
	v		1.8431	1.9065	1.9711	2.0334	2.0932	2.1515	2.2085	2.2920	2.4272	2.6897	2.9444	3.1949	3.4416	3.6867	3.9299
	h	376.04	1201.4	1214.6	1228.3	1241.0	1253.2	1264.7	1274.5	1291.6	1317.9	1370.0	1421.7	1473.3	1525.6	1578.0	1631.3
	s	0.5677	1.5267	1.5419	1.5573	1.5713	1.5844	1.5965	1.6066	1.6238	1.6492	1.6961	1.7388	1.7782	1.8153	1.8500	1.8831
255 (402.71)	Sh	0.0187		17.29	37.29	57.29	77.29	97.29	117.29	147.29	197.29	297.29	397.29	497.29	597.29	697.29	797.29
	v		1.8079	1.8686	1.9286	1.9899	2.0489	2.1065	2.1626	2.2447	2.3776	2.6354	2.8855	3.1313	3.3733	3.6138	3.8524
	h	377.91	1201.6	1213.7	1227.5	1240.3	1252.6	1264.2	1274.2	1291.2	1317.5	1369.8	1421.5	1473.2	1525.5	1577.9	1631.2
	s	0.5698	1.5249	1.5388	1.5543	1.5684	1.5816	1.5938	1.6041	1.6212	1.6466	1.6937	1.7364	1.7759	1.8130	1.8477	1.8808
260 (404.43)	Sh	0.0187		15.57	35.57	55.57	75.57	95.57	115.57	145.57	195.57	295.57	395.57	495.57	595.57	695.57	795.57
	v		1.7742	1.8246	1.8876	1.9482	2.0063	2.0631	2.1185	2.1991	2.3299	2.5833	2.8289	3.0701	3.3077	3.5437	3.7778
	h	379.78	1201.8	1212.8	1226.6	1239.5	1252.0	1263.6	1273.8	1290.8	1317.1	1369.5	1421.3	1473.0	1525.4	1577.8	1631.1
	s	0.5720	1.5233	1.5359	1.5514	1.5656	1.5790	1.5912	1.6017	1.6188	1.6442	1.6914	1.7342	1.7737	1.8109	1.8456	1.8787
265 (406.12)	Sh	0.0187		13.88	33.88	53.88	73.88	93.88	113.88	143.88	193.88	293.88	393.88	493.88	593.88	693.88	793.88
	v		1.7416	1.7858	1.8481	1.9080	1.9654	2.0213	2.0759	2.1554	2.2840	2.5331	2.7744	3.0114	3.2446	3.4761	3.7061
	h	381.62	1202.0	1211.9	1225.7	1238.7	1251.2	1263.0	1273.4	1290.4	1316.8	1369.3	1421.1	1472.9	1525.3	1577.7	1631.1
	s	0.5741	1.5217	1.5330	1.5485	1.5628	1.5762	1.5886	1.5993	1.6164	1.6419	1.6892	1.7320	1.7715	1.8087	1.8434	1.8765
270 (407.79)	Sh	0.0188		12.21	32.21	52.21	72.21	92.21	112.21	142.21	192.21	292.21	392.21	492.21	592.21	692.21	792.21
	v		1.7101	1.7486	1.8101	1.8692	1.9259	1.9810	2.0350	2.1131	2.2399	2.4847	2.7219	2.9548	3.1838	3.4112	3.6370
	h	383.43	1202.2	1211.0	1224.9	1238.0	1250.6	1262.5	1273.0	1290.0	1316.4	1369.0	1420.9	1472.7	1525.1	1577.6	1631.0
	s	0.5761	1.5200	1.5301	1.5457	1.5601	1.5736	1.5861	1.5969	1.6140	1.6395	1.6869	1.7298	1.7693	1.8065	1.8413	1.8744
275 (409.44)	Sh	0.0188		10.56	30.56	50.56	70.56	90.56	110.56	140.56	190.56	290.56	390.56	490.56	590.56	690.56	790.56
	v		1.6798	1.7127	1.7735	1.8318	1.8879	1.9422	1.9956	2.0725	2.1973	2.4382	2.6714	2.9002	3.1253	3.3486	3.5704
	h	385.22	1202.3	1210.0	1224.1	1237.3	1250.0	1262.0	1272.6	1289.5	1316.1	1368.7	1420.7	1472.6	1525.0	1577.5	1630.9
	s	0.5782	1.5183	1.5271	1.5429	1.5574	1.5711	1.5837	1.5946	1.6116	1.6373	1.6847	1.7277	1.7673	1.8045	1.8393	1.8724
280 (411.06)	Sh	0.0188		8.94	28.94	48.94	68.94	88.94	108.94	138.94	188.94	288.94	388.94	488.94	588.94	688.94	788.94
	v		1.6504	1.6780	1.7381	1.7957	1.8512	1.9048	1.9575	2.0334	2.1562	2.3932	2.6226	2.8475	3.0688	3.2883	3.5062
	h	386.99	1202.5	1209.0	1223.2	1236.5	1249.4	1261.5	1272.2	1289.1	1315.7	1368.5	1420.5	1472.4	1524.9	1577.4	1630.8
	s	0.5802	1.5167	1.5241	1.5401	1.5547	1.5686	1.5813	1.5923	1.6093	1.6350	1.6826	1.7256	1.7652	1.8024	1.8372	1.8703
285 (412.66)	Sh	0.0188		7.34	27.34	47.34	67.34	87.34	107.34	137.34	187.34	287.34	387.34	487.34	587.34	687.34	787.34
	v		1.6232	1.6446	1.7040	1.7610	1.8157	1.8687	1.9207	1.9955	2.1165	2.3499	2.5756	2.7968	3.0143	3.2300	3.4443
	h	388.74	1202.7	1208.0	1222.3	1235.6	1248.5	1260.9	1271.8	1288.6	1315.4	1368.2	1420.3	1472.2	1524.7	1577.3	1630.7
	s	0.5822	1.5153	1.5214	1.5375	1.5521	1.5662	1.5790	1.5902	1.6071	1.6330	1.6806	1.7237	1.7633	1.8005	1.8353	1.8684

290 psia (Sat. temp. 414.24 °F)

	Sat. water	Sat. steam	5.76	25.76	45.76	65.76	85.76	105.76	135.76	185.76	285.76	385.76	485.76	585.76	685.76	785.76
v	0.0189	1.5947	1.6122	1.6710	1.7273	1.7815	1.8338	1.8853	1.9590	2.0783	2.3080	2.5302	2.7478	2.9616	3.1738	3.3844
h	390.47	1202.9	1207.0	1221.4	1234.8	1248.0	1260.4	1271.4	1288.2	1315.0	1367.9	1420.1	1472.1	1524.6	1577.2	1630.6
s	0.5841	1.5137	1.5184	1.5346	1.5493	1.5635	1.5766	1.5879	1.6048	1.6307	1.6784	1.7195	1.7612	1.7984	1.8332	1.8663

295 psia (Sat. temp. 415.80 °F)

	Sat. water	Sat. steam	4.20	24.20	44.20	64.20	84.20	104.20	134.20	184.20	284.20	384.20	484.20	584.20	684.20	784.20
v	0.0189	1.5684	1.5809	1.6391	1.6948	1.7484	1.8001	1.8510	1.9236	2.0413	2.2677	2.4863	2.7004	2.9108	3.1195	3.3267
h	392.17	1203.0	1206.1	1220.5	1234.0	1247.4	1259.8	1271.0	1287.8	1314.7	1367.6	1419.9	1472.0	1524.5	1577.1	1630.5
s	0.5861	1.5122	1.5157	1.5319	1.5467	1.5611	1.5742	1.5857	1.6026	1.6286	1.6763	1.7175	1.7593	1.7965	1.8313	1.8644

300 psia (Sat. temp. 417.33 °F)

	Sat. water	Sat. steam	2.67	22.67	42.67	62.67	82.67	102.67	132.67	182.67	282.67	382.67	482.67	582.67	682.67	782.67
v	0.0189	1.5426	1.5506	1.6082	1.6634	1.7164	1.7677	1.8172	1.8896	2.0056	2.2286	2.4447	2.6547	2.8634	3.0670	3.2707
h	393.85	1203.2	1205.2	1219.5	1233.4	1246.6	1259.2	1270.5	1287.4	1314.4	1367.4	1419.7	1471.8	1524.4	1577.0	1630.4
s	0.5879	1.5107	1.5130	1.5291	1.5443	1.5585	1.5718	1.5834	1.6004	1.6265	1.6742	1.7175	1.7572	1.7945	1.8294	1.8625

310 psia (Sat. temp. 420.35 °F)

	Sat. water	Sat. steam	19.65	39.65	59.65	79.65	99.65	129.65	179.65	279.65	379.65	479.65	579.65	679.65	779.65
v	0.0189	1.4938	1.5495	1.6036	1.6555	1.7054	1.7546	1.8246	1.9375	2.1541	2.3631	2.5675	2.7682	2.9671	3.1645
h	397.16	1203.5	1217.8	1231.5	1245.3	1258.0	1269.6	1286.4	1313.5	1366.9	1419.3	1471.5	1524.1	1576.8	1630.3
s	0.5917	1.5079	1.5240	1.5391	1.5539	1.5673	1.5793	1.5962	1.6224	1.6705	1.7138	1.7536	1.7909	1.8258	1.8590

320 psia (Sat. temp. 423.29 °F)

	Sat. water	Sat. steam	16.71	36.71	56.71	76.71	96.71	126.71	176.71	276.71	376.71	476.71	576.71	676.71	776.71
v	0.0190	1.4479	1.4943	1.5473	1.5982	1.6472	1.6954	1.7637	1.8737	2.0844	2.2874	2.4857	2.6804	2.8735	3.0648
h	400.40	1203.8	1216.0	1229.9	1244.0	1256.8	1268.6	1285.6	1312.8	1366.3	1418.9	1471.2	1523.8	1576.6	1630.1
s	0.5953	1.5052	1.5189	1.5342	1.5494	1.5629	1.5751	1.5922	1.6186	1.6667	1.7102	1.7501	1.7874	1.8224	1.8556

330 psia (Sat. temp. 426.16 °F)

	Sat. water	Sat. steam	13.84	33.84	53.84	73.84	93.84	123.84	173.84	273.84	373.84	473.84	573.84	673.84	773.84
v	0.0190	1.4048	1.4424	1.4944	1.5445	1.5925	1.6397	1.7064	1.8138	2.0189	2.2163	2.4090	2.5981	2.7855	2.9712
h	403.56	1204.0	1214.1	1228.2	1242.5	1255.5	1267.6	1284.7	1312.1	1365.8	1418.4	1470.8	1523.6	1576.4	1630.0
s	0.5988	1.5023	1.5136	1.5291	1.5445	1.5582	1.5707	1.5879	1.6144	1.6628	1.7063	1.7463	1.7837	1.8187	1.8520

340 psia (Sat. temp. 428.96 °F)

	Sat. water	Sat. steam	11.04	31.04	51.04	71.04	91.04	121.04	171.04	271.04	371.04	471.04	571.04	671.04	771.04
v	0.0191	1.3640	1.3935	1.4446	1.4936	1.5409	1.5872	1.6525	1.7573	1.9572	2.1493	2.3368	2.5206	2.7027	2.8831
h	406.65	1204.2	1212.2	1226.5	1241.0	1254.2	1266.6	1283.8	1311.4	1365.2	1418.0	1470.5	1523.3	1576.2	1629.8
s	0.6023	1.4997	1.5086	1.5243	1.5399	1.5538	1.5666	1.5839	1.6106	1.6591	1.7027	1.7428	1.7802	1.8152	1.8485

350 psia (Sat. temp. 431.71 °F)

	Sat. water	Sat. steam	8.29	28.29	48.29	68.29	88.29	118.29	168.29	268.29	368.29	468.29	568.29	668.29	768.29
v	0.0191	1.3255	1.3472	1.3976	1.4460	1.4923	1.5377	1.6016	1.7041	1.8991	2.0863	2.2687	2.4475	2.6246	2.8000
h	409.70	1204.4	1210.3	1224.8	1239.5	1252.9	1265.5	1282.9	1310.6	1364.7	1417.6	1470.2	1523.0	1576.0	1629.6
s	0.6057	1.4972	1.5038	1.5197	1.5355	1.5496	1.5626	1.5801	1.6069	1.6556	1.6993	1.7395	1.7769	1.8120	1.8453

360 psia (Sat. temp. 434.39 °F)

	Sat. water	Sat. steam	5.61	25.61	45.61	65.61	85.61	115.61	165.61	265.61	365.61	465.61	565.61	665.61	765.61
v	0.0192	1.2889	1.3035	1.3532	1.4008	1.4463	1.4909	1.5536	1.6538	1.8441	2.0266	2.2044	2.3784	2.5506	2.7213
h	412.67	1204.5	1208.5	1223.1	1238.0	1251.5	1264.5	1282.0	1309.9	1364.1	1417.2	1469.9	1522.8	1575.8	1629.4
s	0.6090	1.4946	1.4991	1.5151	1.5311	1.5453	1.5587	1.5763	1.6033	1.6521	1.6960	1.7362	1.7737	1.8088	1.8421

Sh = superheat, deg. F.
v = specific volume, cu. ft. per lb.
h = enthalpy, B.t.u. per lb.
s = entropy, B.t.u. per deg. F. per lb.

TABLE 2. SUPERHEATED STEAM—Continued

Abs. Press. Lb./Sq. In. (Sat. Temp.)		Sat. Water	Sat. Steam	460°	480°	500°	520°	540°	560°	580°	600°	700°	800°	900°	1000°	1100°	1200°
370 (437.01)	Sh			22.99	42.99	62.99	82.99	102.99	122.99	142.99	162.99	262.99	362.99	462.99	562.99	662.99	762.99
	v	0.0192	1.2545	1.3111	1.3579	1.4028	1.4466	1.4881	1.5286	1.5675	1.6063	1.7921	1.9703	2.1435	2.3131	2.4809	2.6471
	h	415.58	1204.6	1221.4	1236.5	1250.2	1263.4	1275.2	1286.7	1298.3	1309.1	1363.6	1416.8	1469.6	1522.5	1575.6	1629.2
	s	0.6122	1.4921	1.5106	1.5268	1.5412	1.5548	1.5667	1.5781	1.5897	1.5997	1.6488	1.6928	1.7331	1.7706	1.8058	1.8391
380 (439.59)	Sh			20.41	40.41	60.41	80.41	100.41	120.41	140.41	160.41	260.41	360.41	460.41	560.41	660.41	760.41
	v	0.0193	1.2217	1.2711	1.3173	1.3614	1.4045	1.4452	1.4850	1.5232	1.5612	1.7428	1.9168	2.0859	2.2512	2.4148	2.5768
	h	418.45	1204.7	1219.8	1235.0	1248.8	1262.3	1274.2	1286.0	1297.5	1308.4	1363.0	1416.4	1469.2	1522.2	1575.4	1629.1
	s	0.6154	1.4897	1.5063	1.5226	1.5371	1.5510	1.5630	1.5747	1.5859	1.5963	1.6465	1.6896	1.7299	1.7675	1.8027	1.8361
390 (442.11)	Sh			17.89	37.89	57.89	77.89	97.89	117.89	137.89	157.89	257.89	357.89	457.89	557.89	657.89	757.89
	v	0.0193	1.1904	1.2332	1.2788	1.3222	1.3647	1.4046	1.4436	1.4812	1.5184	1.6961	1.8661	2.0311	2.1925	2.3521	2.5101
	h	421.27	1204.8	1218.0	1233.4	1247.4	1261.2	1273.2	1285.1	1296.7	1307.7	1362.5	1416.0	1468.8	1522.0	1575.2	1628.9
	s	0.6184	1.4872	1.5017	1.5183	1.5330	1.5472	1.5593	1.5711	1.5824	1.5929	1.6423	1.6865	1.7269	1.7646	1.7998	1.8332
400 (444.58)	Sh			15.42	35.42	55.42	75.42	95.42	115.42	135.42	155.42	255.42	355.42	455.42	555.42	655.42	755.42
	v	0.0193	1.1609	1.1972	1.2422	1.2849	1.3269	1.3660	1.4042	1.4413	1.4777	1.6522	1.8179	1.9796	2.1367	2.2926	2.4475
	h	424.02	1204.9	1216.5	1231.6	1245.9	1259.9	1272.4	1284.3	1295.8	1307.0	1362.1	1415.5	1468.6	1521.4	1574.8	1628.8
	s	0.6215	1.4850	1.4977	1.5140	1.5290	1.5434	1.5561	1.5678	1.5790	1.5897	1.6393	1.6835	1.7240	1.7615	1.7968	1.8304
410 (447.00)	Sh			13.00	33.00	53.00	73.00	93.00	113.00	133.00	153.00	253.00	353.00	453.00	553.00	653.00	753.00
	v	0.0194	1.1327	1.1628	1.2071	1.2494	1.2906	1.3291	1.3669	1.4033	1.4390	1.6095	1.7722	1.9297	2.0837	2.2359	2.3864
	h	426.74	1205.0	1214.6	1230.2	1244.5	1258.8	1271.2	1283.5	1295.1	1306.2	1361.4	1415.1	1468.3	1521.4	1574.8	1628.6
	s	0.6244	1.4828	1.4933	1.5101	1.5252	1.5399	1.5524	1.5646	1.5759	1.5865	1.6362	1.6806	1.7212	1.7589	1.7943	1.8277
420 (449.38)	Sh			10.62	30.62	50.62	70.62	90.62	110.62	130.62	150.62	250.62	350.62	450.62	550.62	650.62	750.62
	v	0.0194	1.1058	1.1300	1.1738	1.2156	1.2561	1.2942	1.3312	1.3671	1.4021	1.5693	1.7285	1.8826	2.0332	2.1819	2.3290
	h	429.42	1205.0	1213.0	1228.6	1243.1	1257.5	1270.2	1282.6	1294.3	1305.4	1360.8	1414.6	1468.0	1521.2	1574.6	1628.4
	s	0.6273	1.4805	1.4892	1.5060	1.5213	1.5361	1.5489	1.5612	1.5726	1.5832	1.6331	1.6776	1.7184	1.7561	1.7915	1.8249
430 (451.72)	Sh			8.28	28.28	48.28	68.28	88.28	108.28	128.28	148.28	248.28	348.28	448.28	548.28	648.28	748.28
	v	0.0195	1.0800	1.0986	1.1419	1.1834	1.2233	1.2607	1.2972	1.3326	1.3670	1.5309	1.6869	1.8377	1.9850	2.1305	2.2742
	h	432.05	1205.0	1211.2	1227.0	1241.7	1256.3	1269.1	1281.8	1293.5	1304.6	1360.3	1414.2	1467.6	1520.9	1574.4	1628.2
	s	0.6302	1.4782	1.4850	1.5020	1.5175	1.5326	1.5455	1.5581	1.5695	1.5801	1.6303	1.6748	1.7156	1.7534	1.7888	1.8222
440 (454.01)	Sh			5.99	25.99	45.99	65.99	85.99	105.99	125.99	145.99	245.99	345.99	445.99	545.99	645.99	745.99
	v	0.0195	1.0554	1.0688	1.1116	1.1524	1.1918	1.2288	1.2648	1.2996	1.3334	1.4943	1.6472	1.7949	1.9390	2.0814	2.2220
	h	434.63	1205.0	1209.6	1225.3	1240.2	1255.0	1268.0	1280.9	1292.6	1303.9	1359.7	1413.8	1467.3	1520.6	1574.1	1628.0
	s	0.6330	1.4762	1.4812	1.4981	1.5138	1.5291	1.5422	1.5550	1.5664	1.5772	1.6275	1.6722	1.7130	1.7508	1.7862	1.8197

Superheated steam (pressures 450–530 psia). The lowest row of each block gives the saturated‑liquid ("sat. liq.") and saturated‑vapor ("sat. vap.") values; remaining columns are at the total temperatures shown (°F). The Sh row gives the superheat for each pressure.

psia (sat. temp.)		sat. liq.	sat. vap.	460°	480°	500°	520°	540°	560°	580°	600°	700°	800°	900°	1000°	1100°	1200°
450 (456.27)	Sh			3.73	23.73	43.73	63.73	83.73	103.73	123.73	143.73	243.73	343.73	443.73	543.73	643.73	743.73
	v	0.0195	1.0318	1.0401	1.0624	1.1230	1.1617	1.1982	1.2337	1.2681	1.3013	1.4593	1.6092	1.7539	1.8951	2.0345	2.1720
	h	437.18	1205.0	1207.9	1223.7	1238.6	1253.8	1266.9	1280.0	1291.8	1303.1	1359.1	1413.4	1467.0	1520.3	1573.9	1627.8
	s	0.6357	1.4739	1.4771	1.4941	1.5099	1.5255	1.5387	1.5517	1.5632	1.5740	1.6245	1.6694	1.7103	1.7481	1.7836	1.8171
460 (458.48)	Sh				21.52	41.52	61.52	81.52	101.52	121.52	141.52	241.52	341.52	441.52	541.52	641.52	741.52
	v	0.0196	1.0092		1.0545	1.0946	1.1329	1.1690	1.2039	1.2379	1.2706	1.4258	1.5729	1.7147	1.8530	1.9896	2.1243
	h	439.69	1205.0		1222.0	1237.2	1252.5	1265.8	1279.0	1291.0	1302.3	1358.6	1413.0	1466.6	1520.0	1573.7	1627.7
	s	0.6384	1.4719		1.4902	1.5062	1.5220	1.5354	1.5485	1.5602	1.5710	1.6217	1.6667	1.7076	1.7455	1.7811	1.8146
470 (460.66)	Sh				19.34	39.34	59.34	79.34	99.34	119.34	139.34	239.34	339.34	439.34	539.34	639.34	739.34
	v	0.0196	0.9875		1.0278	1.0676	1.1053	1.1410	1.1755	1.2091	1.2412	1.3937	1.5381	1.6772	1.8127	1.9466	2.0785
	h	442.17	1205.0		1220.2	1235.7	1251.2	1264.7	1278.0	1290.0	1301.5	1358.0	1412.5	1466.3	1519.8	1573.5	1627.5
	s	0.6411	1.4699		1.4862	1.5025	1.5185	1.5321	1.5453	1.5570	1.5680	1.6189	1.6639	1.7050	1.7429	1.7785	1.8120
480 (462.80)	Sh				17.20	37.20	57.20	77.20	97.20	117.20	137.20	237.20	337.20	437.20	537.20	637.20	737.20
	v	0.0197	0.9668		1.0021	1.0416	1.0789	1.1141	1.1482	1.1813	1.2131	1.3630	1.5049	1.6413	1.7742	1.9054	2.0347
	h	444.60	1205.0		1218.6	1234.2	1249.9	1263.5	1277.0	1289.1	1300.8	1357.5	1412.1	1466.0	1519.5	1573.3	1627.3
	s	0.6436	1.4679		1.4825	1.4989	1.5151	1.5288	1.5422	1.5539	1.5650	1.6161	1.6612	1.7023	1.7402	1.7758	1.8093
490 (464.91)	Sh				15.09	35.09	55.09	75.09	95.09	115.09	135.09	235.09	335.09	435.09	535.09	635.09	735.09
	v	0.0197	0.9466		0.9774	1.0166	1.0535	1.0884	1.1220	1.1548	1.1860	1.3335	1.4729	1.6067	1.7371	1.8659	1.9927
	h	447.00	1204.9		1217.0	1232.7	1248.4	1262.3	1276.0	1288.3	1300.0	1356.9	1411.7	1465.6	1519.2	1573.1	1627.1
	s	0.6462	1.4659		1.4789	1.4954	1.5116	1.5256	1.5392	1.5511	1.5622	1.6135	1.6588	1.6999	1.7379	1.7736	1.8071
500 (467.00)	Sh				13.00	33.00	53.00	73.00	93.00	113.00	133.00	233.00	333.00	433.00	533.00	633.00	733.00
	v	0.0197	0.9274		0.9538	0.9926	1.0290	1.0636	1.0969	1.1292	1.1600	1.3051	1.4417	1.5735	1.7016	1.8280	1.9532
	h	449.40	1204.9		1215.3	1231.4	1246.6	1261.1	1275.0	1287.3	1299.3	1356.3	1411.2	1465.1	1518.8	1572.9	1626.9
	s	0.6488	1.4641		1.4752	1.4922	1.5079	1.5225	1.5363	1.5482	1.5596	1.6110	1.6564	1.6975	1.7356	1.7714	1.8052
510 (469.05)	Sh				10.95	30.95	50.95	70.95	90.95	110.95	130.95	230.95	330.95	430.95	530.95	630.95	730.95
	v	0.0198	0.9090		0.9310	0.9695	1.0056	1.0397	1.0727	1.1046	1.1350	1.2780	1.4127	1.5418	1.6675	1.7915	1.9135
	h	451.75	1204.8		1213.5	1229.6	1245.6	1259.9	1274.0	1286.6	1298.4	1355.7	1410.9	1465.0	1518.7	1572.6	1626.8
	s	0.6513	1.4621		1.4714	1.4883	1.5048	1.5192	1.5332	1.5454	1.5566	1.6082	1.6538	1.6951	1.7332	1.7689	1.8026
520 (471.07)	Sh				8.93	28.93	48.93	68.93	88.93	108.93	128.93	228.93	328.93	428.93	528.93	628.93	728.93
	v	0.0198	0.8912		0.9091	0.9472	0.9829	1.0169	1.0494	1.0810	1.1110	1.2519	1.3844	1.5113	1.6347	1.7565	1.8763
	h	454.07	1204.7		1211.8	1228.1	1244.2	1258.6	1272.9	1285.6	1297.6	1355.1	1410.4	1464.6	1518.4	1572.4	1626.6
	s	0.6537	1.4601		1.4677	1.4849	1.5015	1.5160	1.5302	1.5425	1.5539	1.6057	1.6514	1.6928	1.7310	1.7668	1.8005
530 (473.05)	Sh				6.95	26.95	46.95	66.95	86.95	106.95	126.95	226.95	326.95	426.95	526.95	626.95	726.95
	v	0.0199	0.8741		0.8879	0.9258	0.9612	0.9948	1.0269	1.0582	1.0878	1.2267	1.3571	1.4818	1.6031	1.7228	1.8402
	h	456.35	1204.6		1210.0	1226.5	1242.8	1257.3	1271.8	1284.8	1296.8	1354.6	1410.0	1464.3	1518.1	1572.2	1626.4
	s	0.6562	1.4584		1.4642	1.4816	1.4984	1.5130	1.5274	1.5400	1.5514	1.6035	1.6493	1.6908	1.7290	1.7648	1.7985

Sh = superheat, deg. F.
v = specific volume, cu. ft. per lb.
h = enthalpy, B.t.u. per lb.
s = entropy, B.t.u. per deg. F. per lb.

TABLE 2. SUPERHEATED STEAM—*Concluded*

Abs. Press. Lb./Sq. In. (Sat. Temp.)		Sat. Water	Sat. Steam	Temperature—Degrees Fahrenheit													
				500°	520°	540°	560°	580°	600°	650°	700°	750°	800°	900°	1000°	1100°	1200°
540 (475.02)	Sh			24.98	44.98	64.98	84.98	104.98	124.98	174.98	224.98	274.98	324.98	424.98	524.98	624.98	724.98
	v	0.0199	0.8576	0.9051	0.9401	0.9736	1.0054	1.0363	1.0665	1.1356	1.2025	1.2671	1.3309	1.4535	1.5727	1.6903	1.8056
	h	458.62	1204.5	1225.0	1241.4	1256.1	1270.7	1283.8	1296.0	1325.6	1354.0	1382.1	1409.6	1463.9	1517.8	1572.0	1626.2
	s	0.6585	1.4565	1.4781	1.4950	1.5098	1.5243	1.5370	1.5486	1.5759	1.6009	1.6246	1.6469	1.6884	1.7266	1.7625	1.7962
550 (476.94)	Sh			23.06	43.06	63.06	83.06	103.06	123.06	173.06	223.06	273.06	323.06	423.06	523.06	623.06	723.06
	v	0.0199	0.8416	0.8851	0.9198	0.9530	0.9846	1.0151	1.0441	1.1132	1.1791	1.2428	1.3055	1.4262	1.5434	1.6590	1.7724
	h	460.83	1204.4	1223.4	1240.0	1254.8	1269.6	1282.9	1295.2	1324.9	1353.5	1381.6	1409.2	1463.6	1517.5	1571.7	1626.0
	s	0.6609	1.4548	1.4748	1.4919	1.5068	1.5215	1.5344	1.5461	1.5735	1.5987	1.6224	1.6447	1.6862	1.7244	1.7603	1.7940
560 (478.85)	Sh			21.15	41.15	61.15	81.15	101.15	121.15	171.15	221.15	271.15	321.15	421.15	521.15	621.15	721.15
	v	0.0200	0.8263	0.8658	0.9003	0.9332	0.9644	0.9947	1.0233	1.0917	1.1566	1.2193	1.2810	1.3998	1.5151	1.6289	1.7403
	h	463.04	1204.3	1221.8	1238.5	1253.5	1268.5	1282.0	1294.4	1324.2	1352.9	1381.1	1408.7	1463.2	1517.2	1571.5	1625.8
	s	0.6632	1.4530	1.4714	1.4886	1.5038	1.5187	1.5318	1.5436	1.5711	1.5964	1.6202	1.6425	1.6841	1.7224	1.7584	1.7921
570 (480.73)	Sh			19.27	39.27	59.27	79.27	99.27	119.27	169.27	219.27	269.27	319.27	419.27	519.27	619.27	719.27
	v	0.0200	0.8114	0.8472	0.8814	0.9141	0.9450	0.9749	1.0033	1.0708	1.1348	1.1966	1.2575	1.3744	1.4879	1.5998	1.7093
	h	465.22	1204.1	1220.2	1236.9	1252.2	1267.3	1281.0	1293.5	1323.5	1352.3	1380.6	1408.3	1462.9	1517.0	1571.3	1625.6
	s	0.6655	1.4512	1.4681	1.4853	1.5008	1.5156	1.5291	1.5410	1.5686	1.5940	1.6179	1.6403	1.6820	1.7204	1.7564	1.7901
580 (482.58)	Sh			17.42	37.42	57.42	77.42	97.42	117.42	167.42	217.42	267.42	317.42	417.42	517.42	617.42	717.42
	v	0.0201	0.7968	0.8291	0.8631	0.8956	0.9263	0.9558	0.9839	1.0506	1.1137	1.1747	1.2347	1.3498	1.4616	1.5714	1.6794
	h	467.37	1204.0	1218.6	1235.5	1250.9	1266.1	1280.0	1292.6	1322.8	1351.6	1380.0	1407.8	1462.5	1516.7	1571.0	1625.4
	s	0.6677	1.4494	1.4648	1.4822	1.4978	1.5128	1.5264	1.5384	1.5662	1.5916	1.6156	1.6381	1.6799	1.7183	1.7543	1.7881
590 (484.41)	Sh			15.59	35.59	55.59	75.59	95.59	115.59	165.59	215.59	265.59	315.59	415.59	515.59	615.59	715.59
	v	0.0201	0.7831	0.8116	0.8455	0.8778	0.9082	0.9373	0.9653	1.0310	1.0934	1.1535	1.2128	1.3262	1.4360	1.5442	1.6505
	h	469.50	1203.8	1217.0	1234.0	1249.6	1265.0	1278.9	1291.8	1322.1	1351.1	1379.5	1407.4	1462.2	1516.4	1570.8	1625.3
	s	0.6699	1.4477	1.4616	1.4791	1.4949	1.5101	1.5236	1.5359	1.5638	1.5894	1.6134	1.6360	1.6778	1.7162	1.7522	1.7861
600 (486.21)	Sh			13.79	33.79	53.79	73.79	93.79	113.79	163.79	213.79	263.79	313.79	413.79	513.79	613.79	713.79
	v	0.0201	0.7695	0.7945	0.8284	0.8605	0.8907	0.9194	0.9471	1.0123	1.0738	1.1332	1.1915	1.3032	1.4115	1.5179	1.6224
	h	471.59	1203.6	1215.6	1232.5	1248.3	1263.7	1278.1	1290.9	1321.4	1350.5	1379.0	1407.0	1461.8	1516.0	1570.5	1625.0
	s	0.6721	1.4460	1.4586	1.4760	1.4920	1.5072	1.5212	1.5334	1.5615	1.5871	1.6112	1.6339	1.6757	1.7141	1.7502	1.7841
610 (487.99)	Sh			12.01	32.01	52.01	72.01	92.01	112.01	162.01	212.01	262.01	312.01	412.01	512.01	612.01	712.01
	v	0.0202	0.7565	0.7781	0.8120	0.8436	0.8736	0.9022	0.9296	0.9942	1.0548	1.1135	1.1708	1.2809	1.3878	1.4928	1.5964
	h	473.67	1203.5	1213.8	1230.9	1246.9	1262.5	1276.8	1290.0	1320.6	1350.0	1378.5	1406.5	1461.5	1515.8	1570.3	1624.9
	s	0.6743	1.4444	1.4552	1.4728	1.4890	1.5044	1.5183	1.5309	1.5591	1.5850	1.6091	1.6318	1.6738	1.7123	1.7484	1.7823

Sh = superheat, deg. F.
v = specific volume, cu. ft. per lb.
h = enthalpy, B.t.u. per lb.
s = entropy, B.t.u. per deg. F. per lb.

Pressure 620 (sat. temp. 489.75) — sat. liquid: v = 0.0202, h = 475.72, s = 0.6764

Sh	0	10.25	30.25	50.25	70.25	90.25	110.25	160.25	210.25	260.25	310.25	410.25	510.25	610.25	710.25
v	0.7438	0.7622	0.7960	0.8275	0.8572	0.8856	0.9127	0.9765	1.0364	1.0943	1.1505	1.2596	1.3648	1.4677	1.5707
h	1203.3	1212.2	1229.5	1245.5	1261.3	1275.8	1289.1	1319.9	1349.3	1377.4	1406.1	1461.2	1515.5	1570.1	1624.7
s	1.4427	1.4520	1.4698	1.4860	1.5016	1.5157	1.5284	1.5568	1.5827	1.6068	1.6296	1.6717	1.7102	1.7464	1.7803

Pressure 630 (sat. temp. 491.49) — sat. liquid: v = 0.0202, h = 477.75, s = 0.6785

Sh	0	8.51	28.51	48.51	68.51	88.51	108.51	158.51	208.51	258.51	308.51	408.51	508.51	608.51	708.51
v	0.7316	0.7466	0.7802	0.8117	0.8413	0.8694	0.8963	0.9595	1.0187	1.0757	1.1312	1.2387	1.3423	1.4445	1.5449
h	1203.1	1210.6	1227.8	1244.1	1260.1	1274.7	1288.3	1319.2	1348.7	1377.7	1405.7	1460.8	1515.2	1569.9	1624.5
s	1.4410	1.4488	1.4665	1.4830	1.4988	1.5130	1.5260	1.5545	1.5805	1.6047	1.6276	1.6697	1.7083	1.7445	1.7784

Pressure 640 (sat. temp. 493.21) — sat. liquid: v = 0.0203, h = 479.79, s = 0.6806

Sh	0	6.79	26.79	46.79	66.79	86.79	106.79	156.79	206.79	256.79	306.79	406.79	506.79	606.79	706.79
v	0.7197	0.7317	0.7651	0.7963	0.8258	0.8537	0.8804	0.9429	1.0015	1.0578	1.1124	1.2187	1.3210	1.4213	1.5193
h	1202.9	1209.0	1226.3	1242.7	1258.9	1273.6	1287.4	1318.5	1348.2	1376.8	1405.2	1460.5	1515.0	1569.7	1624.3
s	1.4394	1.4458	1.4636	1.4802	1.4962	1.5105	1.5236	1.5523	1.5785	1.6026	1.6256	1.6678	1.7065	1.7427	1.7766

Pressure 650 (sat. temp. 494.90) — sat. liquid: v = 0.0203, h = 481.73, s = 0.6826

Sh	0	5.10	25.10	45.10	65.10	85.10	105.10	155.10	205.10	255.10	305.10	405.10	505.10	605.10	705.10
v	0.7082	0.7171	0.7504	0.7816	0.8107	0.8384	0.8648	0.9269	0.9846	1.0404	1.0944	1.1988	1.2999	1.3987	1.4958
h	1202.7	1207.3	1224.8	1241.3	1257.6	1272.5	1286.5	1317.8	1347.6	1376.3	1404.7	1460.1	1514.7	1569.4	1624.1
s	1.4379	1.4427	1.4607	1.4774	1.4935	1.5080	1.5213	1.5501	1.5764	1.6006	1.6236	1.6659	1.7046	1.7408	1.7748

Pressure 660 (sat. temp. 496.58) — sat. liquid: v = 0.0204, h = 483.77, s = 0.6847

Sh	0	3.42	23.42	43.42	63.42	83.42	103.42	153.42	203.42	253.42	303.42	403.42	503.42	603.42	703.42
v	0.6969	0.7031	0.7361	0.7672	0.7962	0.8237	0.8499	0.9113	0.9686	1.0234	1.0769	1.1803	1.2797	1.3774	1.4727
h	1202.5	1205.7	1223.2	1240.0	1256.4	1271.4	1285.5	1317.1	1347.0	1375.8	1404.3	1459.7	1514.4	1569.2	1624.0
s	1.4363	1.4367	1.4549	1.4746	1.4908	1.5054	1.5188	1.5479	1.5742	1.5985	1.6216	1.6639	1.7027	1.7390	1.7730

Pressure 670 (sat. temp. 498.23) — sat. liquid: v = 0.0204, h = 485.61, s = 0.6867

Sh	0	1.77	21.77	41.77	61.77	81.77	101.77	151.77	201.77	251.77	301.77	401.77	501.77	601.77	701.77
v	0.6861	0.6892	0.7224	0.7531	0.7820	0.8093	0.8354	0.8963	0.9527	1.0072	1.0599	1.1617	1.2600	1.3560	1.4503
h	1202.3	1204.0	1221.7	1238.7	1255.1	1270.2	1284.5	1316.3	1346.3	1375.3	1403.9	1459.4	1514.1	1569.0	1623.8
s	1.4349	1.4367	1.4549	1.4721	1.4883	1.5030	1.5166	1.5459	1.5723	1.5968	1.6200	1.6624	1.7012	1.7376	1.7716

Pressure 680 (sat. temp. 499.87) — sat. liquid: v = 0.0204, h = 487.64, s = 0.6886

Sh	0.13	20.13	40.13	60.13	80.13	100.13	150.13	200.13	250.13	300.13	400.13	500.13	600.13	700.13
v	0.6757	0.7089	0.7397	0.7683	0.7954	0.8212	0.8814	0.9375	0.9912	1.0432	1.1440	1.2408	1.3357	1.4283
h	1202.1	1220.2	1237.3	1253.9	1269.1	1283.6	1315.6	1345.8	1374.7	1403.4	1459.0	1513.8	1568.7	1623.6
s	1.4332	1.4519	1.4692	1.4856	1.5004	1.5142	1.5437	1.5703	1.5947	1.6179	1.6603	1.6992	1.7356	1.7697

Pressure 690 (sat. temp. 501.49) — sat. liquid: v = 0.0205, h = 489.56, s = 0.6906

Sh	0	18.51	38.51	58.51	78.51	98.51	148.51	198.51	248.51	298.51	398.51	498.51	598.51	698.51
v	0.6652	0.6956	0.7263	0.7549	0.7818	0.8075	0.8673	0.9225	0.9758	1.0272	1.1267	1.2223	1.3162	1.4075
h	1201.8	1218.5	1235.8	1252.5	1268.0	1282.7	1314.9	1345.1	1374.2	1402.8	1458.7	1513.6	1568.5	1623.4
s	1.4316	1.4488	1.4663	1.4828	1.4978	1.5118	1.5415	1.5681	1.5927	1.6159	1.6586	1.6975	1.7339	1.7680

Pressure 700 (sat. temp. 503.09) — sat. liquid: v = 0.0205, h = 491.49, s = 0.6925

Sh	0	16.91	36.91	56.91	76.91	96.91	146.91	196.91	246.91	296.91	396.91	496.91	596.91	696.91
v	0.6552	0.6830	0.7133	0.7419	0.7687	0.7941	0.8534	0.9084	0.9608	1.0117	1.1096	1.2043	1.2965	1.3870
h	1201.6	1217.1	1234.7	1251.3	1266.8	1281.9	1314.3	1344.6	1373.7	1402.5	1458.2	1513.4	1568.2	1623.3
s	1.4301	1.4461	1.4638	1.4803	1.4953	1.5097	1.5396	1.5663	1.5908	1.6141	1.6567	1.6958	1.7321	1.7663

INDEX

LIST OF SYMBOLS

Pertinent dimensions are indicated by the bold-face letters enclosed in parentheses.

A	area ($\mathbf{L^2}$); Helmholtz work function ($\mathbf{E}$); a constant.
a	acceleration ($\mathbf{L}/\boldsymbol{\theta}^2$); activity (dimensionless); surface area per unit volume ($\mathbf{L^{-1}}$); van der Waals constant ($\mathbf{FL^4/M^2}$); heat capacity correlating constant ($\mathbf{E/MT}$).
A_p	projected area ($\mathbf{L^2}$).
B	bottoms product, quantity ($\mathbf{M}$) or rate ($\mathbf{M}/\boldsymbol{\theta}$); vapor pressure correlating constant ($\mathbf{T}$).
b	van der Waals constant ($\mathbf{L^3/M}$); heat capacity correlating constant ($\mathbf{E/MT^2}$).
C	heat capacity ($\mathbf{E/MT}$); concentration ($\mathbf{M/L^3}$).
C_D	drag coefficient, $= 2g_cF_D/u_o{}^2\rho A_p$ (dimensionless).
c	velocity of light ($\mathbf{L}/\boldsymbol{\theta}$); heat capacity correlating constant ($\mathbf{E/MT^3}$).
D	diameter ($\mathbf{L}$); distillate product, quantity ($\mathbf{M}$) or rate ($\mathbf{M}/\boldsymbol{\theta}$).
D_m	molecular diffusivity ($\mathbf{L^2}/\boldsymbol{\theta}$).
d	differential operator, denoting an infinitesimal change (dimensionless).
E	energy ($\mathbf{E}$).
$\mathbf{E}$	dimension of energy ($= \mathbf{FL}$).
E_c	energy created by a nuclear process ($\mathbf{E}$).
E_m	Murphree efficiency (dimensionless).
E_o	overall efficiency (dimensionless).
e	base of natural logarithms, $= 2.718$ (dimensionless).
F	force ($\mathbf{F}$); feed quantity ($\mathbf{M}$) or rate ($\mathbf{M}/\boldsymbol{\theta}$).
$\mathbf{F}$	dimension of force ($= \mathbf{ML}/\boldsymbol{\theta}^2$).
F_D	drag force ($\mathbf{F}$).
f	fugacity ($\mathbf{F/L^2}$); friction factor (dimensionless).
$\bar{f}$	fugacity of a component in a mixture ($\mathbf{F/L^2}$).
G	Gibbs free energy function ($\mathbf{E}$); mass velocity ($\mathbf{M/L^2}\boldsymbol{\theta}$).
$\bar{G}$	chemical potential or partial molal free energy, $= (\partial G/\partial M_j)_{T,P,M_A,M_B,\cdots}$ ($\mathbf{E/M}$).
g	gravitational acceleration, $= 32.17$ ft/sec^2 at sea level.
g_c	gravitational constant, $= 32.17$ (lb$_m$)(ft)/(lb$_f$)(sec)^2.
H	enthalpy, $= U + PV$ ($\mathbf{E}$); humidity (dimensionless).
H'	Henry's Law constant ($\mathbf{F/L^2}$).
HTU	height of a transfer unit ($\mathbf{L}$).
h	convective heat transfer coefficient ($\mathbf{E/L^2}\boldsymbol{\theta}\mathbf{T}$).
h_r	radiation heat transfer coefficient ($\mathbf{E/L^2}\boldsymbol{\theta}\mathbf{T}$).
K	generalized rate coefficient (dimensions vary); overall mass transfer coefficient (dimensions vary); vapor-liquid equilibrium constant, $= y^*/x$ (dimensionless).
K_a	chemical equilibrium constant in terms of activities (dimensionless).
K_f	chemical equilibrium constant in terms of fugacities (dimensionless).
K_p	chemical equilibrium constant in terms of partial pressures (dimensionless).
K_N	chemical equilibrium constant in terms of mol quantities (dimensionless).
KE	kinetic energy ($\mathbf{E}$).
k	local mass transfer coefficient (dimensions vary); chemical reaction rate coefficient (dimensions vary); thermal conductivity ($\mathbf{E}/\boldsymbol{\theta}\mathbf{TL}$).
k_f, k_r	chemical reaction rate coefficients for forward and reverse reaction, respectively (dimensions vary).
L	length ($\mathbf{L}$); liquid or raffinate quantity ($\mathbf{M}$) or rate ($\mathbf{M}/\boldsymbol{\theta}$).
$\mathbf{L}$	dimension of length (primary dimension).
lb$_m$	pound mass ($\mathbf{M}$).
lb$_f$	pound force ($\mathbf{F}$).
lw	lost work ($\mathbf{E}$).

M	mass ($\mathbf{M}$).
$\mathbf{M}$	dimension of mass (primary dimension).
M_c	mass converted to energy by a nuclear process ($\mathbf{M}$).
MW	molecular weight (dimensionless).
m	mass per unit time ($\mathbf{M}/\boldsymbol{\theta}$); slope of equilibrium curve (dimensionless).
N	number of mols, $= M/\text{MW}$ (dimensionless).
N_c	number of components (dimensionless).
N_f	number of degrees of freedom (dimensionless).
N_p	number of phases (dimensionless).
N_{TU}	number of transfer units (dimensionless).
n	mols per unit time ($\mathbf{M}/\boldsymbol{\theta}$); equilibrium stage number (dimensionless).
P	pressure ($\mathbf{F}/\mathbf{L}^2$).
P_c	critical pressure ($\mathbf{F}/\mathbf{L}^2$).
P_r	reduced pressure, $= P/P_c$ (dimensionless).
PE	potential energy ($\mathbf{E}$).
p	partial pressure ($\mathbf{F}/\mathbf{L}^2$).
p^*	vapor pressure ($\mathbf{F}/\mathbf{L}^2$).
Q	heat absorbed by a system ($\mathbf{E}$).
q	heat absorbed per unit time ($\mathbf{E}/\boldsymbol{\theta}$); quality, or mass fraction vapor in a vapor-liquid mixture (dimensionless).
R	gas law constant (dimensions vary); generalized resistance (dimensions vary).
S	entropy ($\mathbf{E}/\mathbf{T}$); cross-sectional area ($\mathbf{L}^2$); space velocity (dimensions vary).
$\$$	dollar sign—a very important engineering symbol.
s	distance ($\mathbf{L}$).
T	absolute temperature, degrees Rankine or Kelvin ($\mathbf{T}$).
$\mathbf{T}$	dimension of temperature (primary dimension).
T_c	critical temperature ($\mathbf{T}$).
T_r	reduced temperature, $= T/T_c$ (dimensionless).
t	temperature in degrees Fahrenheit or Centigrade ($\mathbf{T}$).
U	internal energy ($\mathbf{E}$); overall heat transfer coefficient ($\mathbf{E}/\mathbf{L}^2\boldsymbol{\theta}\mathbf{T}$).
u	linear velocity ($\mathbf{L}/\boldsymbol{\theta}$).
u_o	superficial or free-stream velocity ($\mathbf{L}/\boldsymbol{\theta}$).
V	volume ($\mathbf{L}^3$); vapor or extract quantity ($\mathbf{M}$) or rate ($\mathbf{M}/\boldsymbol{\theta}$).
v	volume per unit time ($\mathbf{L}^3/\boldsymbol{\theta}$).
W	work done by a system ($\mathbf{E}$).
X	mol or mass ratio in liquid phase (dimensionless).
x	mol or mass fraction in liquid phase (dimensionless).
Y	mol or mass ratio in vapor phase (dimensionless).
y	mol or mass fraction in vapor phase (dimensionless).
Z	compressibility factor, $= P\underline{V}/RT$ (dimensionless).
z	elevation ($\mathbf{L}$).
α	relative volatility (dimensionless).
Γ	generalized property or quantity (dimensions vary).
γ	change of Γ per unit time (dimensions vary); activity coefficient (dimensionless).
Δ	difference symbol denoting a finite change: final minus initial or outlet minus inlet (dimensionless).
δ	modifier denoting an infinitesimal quantity (dimensionless).
θ	time ($\boldsymbol{\theta}$).
$\boldsymbol{\theta}$	dimension of time (primary dimension).
Λ	generalized extensive factor characterizing the extent of a system (dimensions vary).
μ	viscosity ($\mathbf{M}/\mathbf{L}\boldsymbol{\theta}$).
π	generalized potential or driving force (dimensions vary).
ρ	density ($\mathbf{M}/\mathbf{L}^3$); ρ_f, fluid density; ρ_s, solid density.
Σ	summation symbol (dimensionless).

τ_s	shear stress ($\mathbf{F}/\mathbf{L}^2$).

Superscripts

*	denotes equilibrium relationship.
°	standard state; ideal-gas state
—	denotes a partial molal or partial poundal property:
	$\overline{\Gamma}_j = (\partial\Gamma/\partial M_j)_{T,P,M_A,M_B,\ldots}$; (see footnote in Sec. 7.3).
′, ″	denote symbols which have been modified as to definitions or units.

Subscripts

$A, B, \ldots j$	refer to individual components in a multi-component mixture.
c	refers to a condensible component in an otherwise non-condensible gas mixture.
db	dry-bulb.
f	refers to saturated liquid.
fg	refers to change when saturated liquid is converted to saturated vapor.
G	gas-phase units.
g	refers to saturated vapor.
h	high.
i	in or inlet.
L	liquid, or liquid-phase units.
l	low.
M	mixture.
m	mean.
o	out or outlet; reference state or boundary value.
R	reversible.
s	system.
sc	pseudo-critical.
V	vapor.
wb	wet-bulb.
$1,2$	refer to initial and final conditions, respectively.
$1,2,\ldots i,n$	refer to a particular equilibrium stage in a multi-stage operation.
—	denotes an extensive property converted to a per-unit-mass or per-mol basis.

The use as a subscript of any symbol representing a property indicates that property is held constant.

ABBREVIATIONS

The following abbreviations are used somewhat informally in chemical engineering. Capital and lower-case letters are used interchangeably in many cases, and periods may be inserted by some users. Common, standard abbreviations such as ft for foot or feet have been omitted.

°API   (American Petroleum Institute); refers to a specific gravity scale used in the petroleum industry. See Perry's Handbook for conversion to conventional units.

°Be   (Baume); refers to a specific gravity scale used to denote the strength of acids. See Perry's Handbook for conversion to conventional units.

Bhp   brake horsepower

BPD   barrels per day

BPSD   barrels per stream day; also BSD

BTU   British thermal unit

CFM   cubic feet per minute; also CFS (second), CFH (hour), CFD (day), and CFSD (stream day)

Chu   Centigrade heat unit (equivalent to 1.8 BTU)

cps   cycles per second

csa   cross-sectional area

fps   feet per second

gpm   gallons per minute; also gph (hour)

HETP   height equivalent to a theoretical plate

HETS   height equivalent to a theoretical stage

hp   horsepower

HTU   height of a transfer unit

ID   inside diameter

KVA   kilovolt-amperes

kw   kilowatt

kwh   kilowatt-hour

LHF   latent heat of fusion

LHV   latent heat of vaporization

LMTD   logarithmic-mean temperature difference

M   thousand (used as a prefix)

MM   million (used as a prefix)

mph   miles per hour; less frequently, mols per hour

MW   molecular weight

OD   outside diameter

pcu   pound-Centigrade unit (equivalent to 1.8 BTU)

ppb   parts per billion

ppm   parts per million

psi   pounds per square inch

psia   pounds per square inch absolute

psig   pounds per square inch gage

RH   relative humidity

rpm   revolutions per minute; also rps (second)

SCF   standard cubic feet

SCFM   standard cubic feet per minute (see CFM)

SD   stream day

SG   specific gravity; also sp gr

STP   standard temperature and pressure

°Tw   (Twaddell); refers to a specific gravity scale used primarily in England. See Perry's Handbook for conversion to conventional units.

INTERNATIONAL ATOMIC WEIGHTS
(More common elements only)

Element	Symbol	Atomic Weight
Aluminum	Al	26.98
*Bromine	Br	79.92
Calcium	Ca	40.08
Carbon	C	12.00
*Chlorine	Cl	35.46
Copper	Cu	63.54
*Fluorine	F	19.00
*Hydrogen	H	1.008
*Iodine	I	126.91
Iron	Fe	55.85
Lead	Pb	207.2
Magnesium	Mg	24.32
Manganese	Mn	54.94
Mercury	Hg	200.6
Nickel	Ni	58.71
*Nitrogen	N	14.01
*Oxygen	O	16.00
Phosphorus	P	30.98
Potassium	K	39.10
Silicon	Si	28.09
Sodium	Na	22.99
Sulfur	S	32.07
Tin	Sn	118.70
Zinc	Zn	65.38

*Diatomic gas. Multiply atomic weight by 2 to obtain molecular weight.

CONVERSION FACTORS AND NUMERICAL CONSTANTS

Length: $2.54 \frac{cm}{in.}$ $\quad 10^4 \frac{micron}{cm}$ $\quad 30.48 \frac{cm}{ft}$

Area: $6.45 \frac{cm^2}{in.^2}$ $\quad 929 \frac{cm^2}{ft^2}$

Volume: $7.48 \frac{gal}{ft^3}$ $\quad 28.32 \frac{liter}{ft^3}$ $\quad 42 \frac{gal}{bbl}$

$231 \frac{in.^3}{gal}$ $\quad 1728 \frac{in.^3}{ft^3}$

Mass: $453.6 \frac{gm}{lb}$ $\quad 7000 \frac{grain}{lb}$

$32.17 \frac{lb_m}{slug}$ $\quad 2.205 \frac{lb}{kg}$

Force: $32.17 \frac{poundal}{lb_f}$ $\quad 13,822 \frac{dyne}{poundal}$

Temperature: $1.8 \frac{F°}{C°}$ $\quad 1.8 \frac{R°}{K°}$

$1.8 \frac{°R}{°K}$

Absolute zero: $0°R \sim 0°K \sim -459.7°F \sim -273.2°C$

Energy: $252 \dfrac{cal}{BTU}$ $778 \dfrac{ft\text{-}lb_f}{BTU}$

                       $1.8 \dfrac{BTU}{Chu}$ $1.8 \dfrac{BTU}{pcu}$

Specific energy: $1.8 \dfrac{BTU/lb}{cal/gm}$

Density: $62.4 \dfrac{lb/ft^3}{gm/cm^3}$ $8.34 \dfrac{lb}{gal}$ (water only)

                       $62.4 \dfrac{lb}{ft^3}$ (water only)

Specific volume of gases at 32°F (0°C) and 1 atmosphere:

                       $359 \dfrac{ft^3}{lb\text{-}mol}$ $22.4 \dfrac{liter}{gm\text{-}mol}$

Gravitational acceleration at sea level:

                       $32.17 \dfrac{ft}{sec^2}$ $980.5 \dfrac{cm}{sec^2}$

Gravitational constant: $32.17 \dfrac{lb_m\text{-}ft}{lb_f\text{-}sec^2}$

Pressure: $760 \dfrac{mm\ Hg}{atm}$ $14.7 \dfrac{lb_f/in.^2}{atm}$

                       $29.92 \dfrac{in.\ Hg}{atm}$ $33.93 \dfrac{ft\ water}{atm}$

Power: $550 \dfrac{ft\text{-}lb_f/sec}{hp}$ $746 \dfrac{watt}{hp}$

                       $2545 \dfrac{BTU/hr}{hp}$ $3413 \dfrac{BTU/hr}{kw}$

Gas law constant, R: $10.73 \dfrac{(psia)(ft^3)}{(lb\text{-}mol)(°R)}$

                       $0.73 \dfrac{(atm)(ft^3)}{(lb\text{-}mol)(°R)}$ $82.06 \dfrac{(atm)(cm^3)}{(gm\text{-}mol)(°K)}$

                       $1.987 \dfrac{BTU}{(lb\text{-}mol)(°R)}$ $1.987 \dfrac{cal}{(gm\text{-}mol)(°K)}$

Composition of dry air: 79 per cent N_2, 21 per cent O_2 (carbon dioxide, argon, and other minor constituents included with nitrogen)